HYMAN'S

GUIDE TO THE BEST BUYERS

**How and Where to Easily Sell
Collectibles, Antiques & Other Treasures**

Dr. Tony Hyman

Nationally recognized authority on
buying and selling collectibles by mail

D0375820

Treasure Hunt Publications
Shell Beach, California 93448

This Directory was published by
Treasure Hunt Publications
PO Box 3028
Shell Beach, CA 93448

It can be purchased through many sources. Questions about delivery, various offers or packages must be directed to the company from whom you purchased it.

See pages 618 to 619 for special ©2005 address update.

Printed in the United States of America

ISBN: 0-937111-11-2

Congratulations. This book has everything you need to get accurate info about millions of antiques and collectibles. That information should enable you to sell any collectible items you might own for fair prices.

This book was written for amateurs but is also used by pros. Even if you don't know or care about antiques or collectibles you can cash in on the high prices paid today without leaving the comforts of your own home.

You can write, phone or e-mail experts like those on *Antiques Road Show* without standing in long lines! E-mail addresses are included for most of the buyers, making for faster response.

This book is a powerful and valuable tool. Like any tool, you get the best results when you use it the way it was intended. **Read the first 20 pages** (the ones with Roman numbers) and follow the tried and true methods used by me and hundreds of thousands of others who are ready to testify how effective the information in this book can be.

Read the first 20 pages, follow directions, use the index and you too can easily put money into your pocket by getting rid of unwanted old things into the hands of people who want them.

Trash or Treasure is based on two principles:

1. It pays to deal with experts. When you want something done right, do business with experienced, knowledgeable, helpful people. As a general rule, the more expert and the more experienced, the better.

2. It pays to deal with honest people. There are many greedy dishonest corner-cutters in the world, but there are also plenty of decent, honest, hardworking people who try to treat you fairly. You'll meet many of my personal favorite collectors and dealers in here.

Instead of blindly setting your own prices for things, I believe you should ask honest experts to evaluate what you have, then based on that information, decide whether or not to sell. By letting experts in Trash or Treasure set the value, I've had less hassle and more profit than when attempting to research on my own or sell locally.

This book is filled throughout with valuable tips and strategies learned during my 50+ years as a successful buyer and seller of collectibles. Reading them will help you be successful too.

Tony Hyman
Shell Beach, CA 93448

IV

Table of Contents

HOW TO SUCCEED iii-xx
FAST way to fair prices, ask an expert, using the index, finding & contacting a buyer, describing items, condition, Sell-A-Gram, ask for an offer, how you know it's fair, shipping, ten common questions, updates, special offer

FURNITURE 2-15
How to Sell Furniture & Rugs, furniture, rugs, lamps, clocks

HOUSEHOLD 16-41
Miscellaneous household items, fans, glasses, canes, pencils, pens, kitchen items, cookbooks, tea & cookies, kitchen ceramics & glass, cast iron cookware, other cast iron, tableware, spoons

CHINA 42-52
How to Sell China, crystal

POTTERY & GLASS 53-69
How to Sell Pottery & Glass, art & utilitarian pottery, European pottery, glass, paperweights

WEARABLES 70-94
Clothing, sewing, textiles, How to Sell jewelry, jewelry, watches, keys, knives, razors, perfume, compacts, make-up, purses

DOLLS 95-105
How to Sell Dolls, antique dolls, teddy bears, modern dolls, Barbie Cabbage Patch, Annalee

SPECIAL INSERTS
HOW TO SELL ESTATES 251
WHEN BUYERS DON'T 337+
APPRAISAL TYPES 539
JEWELRY BONUS 564

TOYS & GAMES 106-130
How to Sell Toys, banks, cap guns, soldiers, games, puzzles, marbles trains, motors & engines, plastic model kits, toy vehicles, gas & electric cars, pedal cars

POP CULTURE 131-160
How to Sell Miscellaneous Pop Culture, G.I. Joe, other action figures, science fiction, space, food packages, pop cowboys, superheroes, comic characters, radio characters, TV characters, literary characters, lunch boxes, character glasses, nodder dolls, gum cards

COMICS 161-166
How to Sell Comic Books, Sunday comics, original art

ENTERTAINMENT 167-188
How to Sell Entertainment memorabilia, movies, actors, Worlds' Fairs, magic, theater, theme parks, other amusements

RADIOS & TV'S 189-195
How to Sell Radios, hi-fi's, transistor radios, TV sets

MUSIC 196-225
How to Sell Strings, brass, other instruments, mechanical music, sheet music, phonograph records, juke boxes, coin operated music, singers, rock and roll

SPORTS 226-250
How to Sell Baseball, misc sports, football, Olympics, golf, boxing, tennis, auto racing, horse racing, wrestling, pool, hunting, fishing, duck decoys, riding, traps

V

SELLING ESTATES   251-252

VICES   253-284
How to Sell cards, chips, slot machines, lottery, wine, liquor, beer, steins, cigarettes, lighters, tobacco cards, tobacco cans, cigar items, pipes, tobacco jars, matches, match safes, erotica, pin-ups

HISTORICAL   285-336
Politics, Indians, cowboys, weird, morbid, Black history, Scouting, religious items, holidays, miscellaneous figures, famous people, animals, horses, cats, dogs, wet pets

WHEN BUYERS DON'T   337+

TRANSPORTATION   338-366
How to sell cars & car ephemera, license plates, busses, trolleys, taxis, motorcycles, bicycles, ships, boats, planes, space, trains

WORKPLACE   367-436
Government services, fire dept., doctors, drug stores, bottles, law enforcement, business cards, office machines, calculators, computers, scientific instruments, phones, insulators, telegraph, printing, architecture, tools, electric devices, packaging, advertising, soft drink, soda fountains, fast food, farms, dairy, mining, gas & oil, rocks, trees, barbershop

WEAPONS & WAR   437-459
How to Sell Guns, shooting clubs, war souvenirs, swords

MONEY & TOKENS   460-473
How to Sell Antiquities, coins, errors, elongates, counterfeits, credit cards, stocks, bonds, fiscal paper, tokens, medals

STAMPS   474-477
How to sell stamps, revenues

ART   478-503
How to sell paintings, prints, wood blocks, Wallace Nutting, folk art, Orientalia, sculpture, figurines, & limited editions

PAPER EPHEMERA   504-529
How to Sell Paper Miscellany, paper dolls, maps, road maps, autographs, Types of Postcards, postcards, posters, photographs

CAMERAS   530-533
How to Sell Cameras, View-Master & 3-D equipment

SOUVENIRS   534-550
How to Sell Souvenirs of the Northeast, South, Midwest, West, and foreign countries

MAGAZINES   551-557
How to Sell Magazines, pulps

NEWSPAPERS   558-560
How to Sell Newspapers

BOOKS   561-578
How to Sell Books, books, illustrated, fiction, children's

INDEX OF BUYERS   579-591
Alphabetical list of all buyers

INDEX OF THINGS   592-616
More than 2,200 categories of things you can sell

HOW TO SELL ESTATES   251
WHEN BUYERS DON'T   337+
APPRAISAL TYPES   539
JEWELRY BONUS   564
SELL-A-GRAM   617
SEND ONE TO A FRIEND   619

HOW TO USE THIS BOOK

The FAST way to get fair prices

The letters **F-A-S-T** stand for **Find something** that might be valuable, **Ask an expert, Send the item, Take the money.** That's my shorthand way of making it easy for you to remember an important strategy for getting information, assistance, and cash.

THE VALUE PYRAMID

Value isn't found in Price Guide or books.
No giant grocery-checker sits in Heaven stamping an absolute value on goods. Every situation is different, but ultimately it's buyers and sellers alone who determine what something is "worth." Money talks.
The more that someone wants a particular item, the higher the price that person is willing to pay.
Doesn't it make sense to sell something to the person who wants it the most?

Find something that might be valuable

Most Americans already have valuable things among their possessions. That's because so many things made in the 1940's, '50s, '60s and '70s have become collectible.

The key to finding things

The key to finding things is knowing what to look for. Valuables are all around you. People discard items worth thousands of dollars because they don't recognize their new collector value. You live in a time when $5 toys made in the 1960's bring $1,000 from some buyers. So do fishing lures, children's marbles, and plastic 40's jewelry. **It's time to be careful.** There can be a lot of money at stake every time you clean house. **The best way to protect yourself is to read and use this book.**

On page 591 is a list of everything valuable

In the back of this book you'll find a list of all the things you own that are collectible today. Starting on 591 is a 25 page double column list of 2,000 categories worth money to you.

Use that list to find a buyer

Most of you reading this book already have found something you'd like to know the value of. Since value is determined by a buyer and seller, **your next step is to find a buyer**. A real buyer is someone willing to hand you money in exchange for whatever you have. No other person is a buyer. Advice from anyone else is suspect. Whether it's one thing or a household, the *Trash or Treasure* "Things You Can Sell" Index is an important key to learning whether any item has value. **The Index tells you where to find the people who know and the people who buy.**

The "Things You Can Sell" Index is easy to use and saves you days of research in libraries and hundreds of price guides. **Read the tips on page VIII to increase your odds of success.**

Ask a buyer what your stuff is worth

A primary purpose of this book is to put you in touch with one or more buyers to help you determine the desirability and value of what you have.

Over the past 50 years I've bought from, sold to, and asked questions of thousands of people in every state and province. My address book is filled with authors, newsletter editors, club presidents and other officers, auctioneers, and prominent collectors.

These are people with whom I personally do business. They are the buyers and experts I turn to when I need help answering a question on radio, TV or for my newspaper column. More than 100 of these buyers were featured on my CBS TV Saturday Early Show"What's It Worth?" segment during the years I was on camera. These are people I sell to confidently, quickly, easily, discretely and profitably.

Since I personally use the information in *Trash or Treasure* for interviews and referrals in my column and on my radio show, every effort has been made to be accurate and comprehensive. If you know a prominent buyer who is not included, I either have not met them yet or they didn't choose to open themselves to contact by large numbers of amateur sellers.

One expert bragged he became an expert so he could take advantage of people's ignorance. I don't knowingly do business with people like that. You shouldn't find him or his ilk in here.

USING THE INDEX

This index makes it easy to locate a discrete, reliable, expert buyer faster, with fewer mistakes, fewer dead-ends, and better resulting prices than any other list anywhere.

Turn to page 591 and look at the "Things You Can Sell" index. This index is a detailed list of more than 2,200 types of items buyers are seeking. Many entries are obvious, like dolls and coins, but did you know that toasters and dog collars were also worth money?

Take a moment to read all the boldface items in the index. Readers often discover they are richer than they thought when they take a minute to read this list carefully. The bold items are the ones I get asked about most often. Everything listed in the index can be sold.

Increase your chances of making money by looking under several categories. For example, an art glass cigar box with a label depicting Lincoln playing poker in a railroad car would be desirable to buyers of art glass, cigar boxes, labels, advertising, card playing, Lincoln, gambling and railroads. A buyer may be under any of those categories. Circle possibilities as you go.

If you can't find your item in the index on the first try, it might be rewarding to look it up in a different way.

Any item you own might be sold because of

- What it is (perfume bottle, knife, clothing, art, etc.);
- Who made it (John Deere, Maytag, Planters, etc.);
- Where it was made (Salem bottles, NY guns, etc.);
- What it is made of (ivory, glass, china, silver, etc.);
- Where it was sold (Disneyland, Walgreens, etc.);
- What it is shaped like (dog, cat, reptile, etc.);
- Who painted it (Vargas, Norman Rockwell, etc.);
- Who owned it (gangsters, celebrities, etc.);
- Who signed it (ball players, Presidents, artists, etc.).

Creativity in using the index to find a buyer can pay off big. Buyers in one category might pay two or three times more than buyers in another.

How to find a buyer in this book

Where do you find a buyer and or expert? Remember that 25 page list of things you can sell found in the back of this book? Every item in that list is followed by one or more page numbers. Turn to those pages, and you'll find from one to a half dozen entries, each of which introduces you to a buyer.

Each buyer's entry begins with bold type telling you the main category of things that person wants. Read the entire entry because it may contain info about other things the person wants, how to describe what you have, what the buyer pays, what books are available and what the buyer doesn't want. The more entries you read, the more likely you are to learn about things you own, but did not know had collector value.

Entries are grouped so that buyers with similar wants are on the same or nearby pages. You may find three or four people interested in something you have. By reading each entry, you should have a fair idea of whether or not your item fits what that buyer wants. When in doubt, ask.

Buyers listed in *Trash or Treasure* are a mix of collectors, universities, museums, auctioneers, and specialty dealers. They have been selected for experience, knowledge, willingness to give information to amateur sellers, and their commitment to pay fair prices. No one paid a fee to be included in this book.

Contacting a buyer

The majority of buyers prefer you to state clearly in your first letter what you have and its condition. They want you to set a price or to request an offer. Buyers want sellers, not pen pals.

Before you contact a buyer, read their entry carefully. If an entry reads "No tribbles," you will not be able to sell your tribble to that buyer. Don't waste your time asking. If an entry reads "Tribbles considered," it means that tribbles are not a specialty, but if your tribble is particularly scarce and in fine condition, the buyer may make an offer. Don't offer anything but the best.

If you believe you own something a buyer might want, it is easy to ask him or her by mail or by phone. Each entry in *Trash or Treasure* gives you the buyer's name and address and, in most cases, their phone number. E-mail addresses are included for more than half the people. You'll find most buyers to be "just plain folks," friendly, and easy to talk to.

Most buyers provide their phone number. Phone calls are fast, easy, and let you get the most information to the buyer with the least effort. The telephone gives the buyer an opportunity to ask questions, so have your item in front of you when you call, if possible, and be prepared to discuss details, including size, color, maker, distinguishing characteristics, and damage. An expert can often tell what you have based on a few simple questions.

A few buyers indicate specific hours during which they'd like you to call. Respect their wishes and you'll get off to a good start. If no hours are suggested, call during normal business hours for the time zone in which they live. If you don't reach them, try between 7 and 8 p.m. their time. Folks in California do not appreciate 6 a.m. calls from eager Easterners.

When leaving a message on an answering machine, be brief yet specific about what you have. Say your name and phone number *slowly* so it can be understood and written down when your message is played. Repeat your phone number. You may have to call back as many buyers don't return blind calls.

Many items can't be adequately described over a phone. The advantage of contacting a potential buyer by mail is that you can send pictures or Xerox™ copies. Buyers are much more likely to pay well for things they can see.

E-mail is increasingly popular with buyers and sellers. If you scan and send photos electronically, attach your photo as a simple jpeg image at relatively low resolution. Many buyers can't open Zipped or other compressed or modified images.

THE BUYER PYRAMID
THE HIGHER YOU GO...THE MORE MONEY YOU MAKE

COLLECTOR

SPECIALTY DEALER

ANTIQUE SHOP

FLEA MARKET

PICKER

YOUR YARD SALE

WHO PAYS THE MOST?

The typical collectible changes hands 7-9 times as it moves up the pyramid from the original owner to the final collector. Each person who handles it raises the price. If the collector at the top of the pyramid pays 100% of value, what do others pay?

Collectors tend to pay 50% to 100% of retail value. They pay the highest percentage for rare and expensive items, often more than others consider "fair market value."

Specialty dealers pay from 30% to 75% of an item's retail value. How much they pay depends on how anxious he/she is to add your item to inventory, and how quickly your item is likely to resell. The more expensive the item, the higher percentage of retail you should get.

Auction houses exist at all levels of skill and clientele. The price you get at auction will depend upon the quality of your item, its history, what is being auctioned with it, when and where the auction is held, and, most important of all, who will be attracted to bid in the auction. **Most sales at auctions are to dealers,** who will raise, double, or triple the auction price when they sell to their customers. Prices range from a typical 15% to 60%. Only rare goods under perfect conditions in important auctions will sell for 75% - 100% of value, or more. Remember to deduct the auction house charges, typically 15% to 25% of the bid.

Ebay, like any auction, presents a risk, perhaps even greater since you are dealing with strangers, quite different from dealing with experts in this book. I personally buy more items on ebay than any other way because there are far more bargains than record prices.

Antique Shop owners come in all sizes, shapes, specialties and skill levels, but generally pay from 5% to 30% of retail to survive. Higher prices are paid only for fast moving quality goods. Shop owners make many mistakes because their experience is usually limited to a few fields. When they buy outside their specialty, you may be paid only 1% to 5% for a rare item.

Mall dealers' profits are low, so the prices they pay must be low too. They do best when they pay under 5% and seldom pay you more than 20%.

Flea market dealers generally pay in the same range as pickers, from 1% to 15%. Their knowledge and markets are limited. They try to buy estates, paying as little as 1%.

Pickers who buy from yard sales pay from 1% to 20% of dollar value, often less. Picking can be very profitable.

Yard sale buyers pay well for children's clothes, but few other items fare as well. Items worth $300 to $10,000 may get 5¢ to 10¢ for each $10 of value.

**Specialty dealers and collectors pay the most
and make deals with the least fuss.
That's why I sell to them.**

Use a Sell-A-Gram when writing

Sell-a-Grams make contacting a possible buyer as easy as filling in the blanks. This handy form letter (see opposite page) gives you easy to follow guidelines so you're never in doubt as to what you should say and what information you should provide. Buyers give special attention to Sell-a-Grams. Some buyers normally charge for services they will provide free only to my readers or listeners. If you don't use a Sell-a-Gram, whether you write or call, identify yourself as a reader of *Trash or Treasure*.

To get the most from a Sell-A-Gram, blow it up to a full size 8 1/2" x 11" page on a copy machine. Use that page as a master. You have my permission to make as many copies of this © form as you need for your personal use. Copy the Sell-A-Gram onto yellow paper as it's an attention getting color.

Ask for an offer

When I sell something, I almost never set the price. I ask the buyer to set a fair price. Fifty-one years experience taught me that I make more money easier by dealing with experts qualified to decide what I have and what fair value is. **If you deal with reputable people, you'll get a fair offer.** That is the heart of my FAST system.

One reader asked buyer Mickie Zekley for $200 for her oboe rather than asking him to set the price. Since she set the price, he could have legally and ethically paid it. But he instantly recognized it as a valuable instrument and paid her $7,000 instead. Jim Bohenstengel was offered a Christmas ornament for $30 yet paid $300. That's why I deal with them. That's why I sell to experts I know and not to strangers on the internet.

S.A.S.E.

When you ask someone for information or an offer, take a long business size #10 envelope, address it to yourself, put a stamp in the corner, and fold it into thirds. **This is called a Self-Addressed Stamped Envelope or SASE. Include one with every request.** Use a long envelope because many buyers have brochures, wants lists, and other informative material they'll send you free. Buyers are under no obligation to answer mail without an SASE.

SELL-A-GRAM from one of Tony Hyman's readers

TO: _____

FROM: _____

Phone: (_____) _____

I have the following item:

Remember to include the (1) shape, (2) colors, (3) dimensions, and (4) all names, dates, and marks.

It's condition is:

List all chips, creases, cracks, dents, scratches, rips, tears, holes, stains, fading, and foxing. Note any missing pages, parts, or paint. Describe any repairs that have been done.

CHECK ONE

☐ The item is for sale for $_____ plus shipping.

☐ The item is for sale. I am an amateur seller and would like you to make an offer.

☐ The item may be for sale if the price is sufficient. Would you like to make an offer?

☐ The item is not for sale, but I am willing to pay a fee to learn its value.

To assist you to evaluate the item, I am enclosing a:
☐ Sample ☐ Photocopy ☐ Photo ☐ Tracing ☐ Sketch ☐ Rubbing ☐ Nothing

This is to certify that, to the best of my knowledge, the item is genuine and as described. Buyer has a 5 day examination period during which the item may be returned for any reason.

Signature: _____ Date: _____

☐ Answer Requested (SASE enclosed). ☐ No answer needed.

BUYER'S RESPONSE:

How do you know the offer is fair?

Although many buyers prefer you to set a price you want, nearly all have agreed to share their knowledge to make certain you receive fair value. One buyer expressed the sentiments of many when he said, "I am not interested in doing free appraisals but I will help any amateur genuinely uncertain about what price to ask." **If you are an amateur, ask for help.** Since I am an amateur in most fields, I ask buyers to price my items. If you are a dealer, most buyers expect you to price your goods.

Buyers whose listing reads "no offers" mean exactly that. You must tell them in the first letter what price you want. Buyers who refuse to make offers are inevitably people who have bad experience dealing with other readers.

If you describe your item well and it is something the buyer wants, you will receive an offer, often in the form of a check. Because they are making an offer based on your description, and many amateurs who use *Trash or Treasure* do not describe things well, **buyers may have to see your item before making a firm offer or sending final payment.** This is not unusual. Condition is always important.

If a buyer decides that your item is not of interest, don't waste time arguing. If you're talking on the phone, ask if the buyer can recommend another collector or dealer who might be interested. If your item is in good condition, but not wanted by specialists, you can safely sell it at a yard sale, donate it to a charity, or sell to a local antique dealer.

You ultimately decide whether to accept an offer or not. When I sell things about which I know little, I try to deal with people with reputations for integrity who will make that offer a fair one. Experience has taught me that dealing with experts is usually quicker, easier, and more profitable than selling at yard sales, flea markets or to local dealers and auctioneers.

Experts and people with experience can recognize what you have, and, if they are listed in here, have pledged to treat you fairly. Twenty years of putting buyers and sellers together has shown that it is more likely a reader will cheat one of my buyers than the other way around.

Since 1980 I've asked readers to report any bad experience with someone I recommend. Over a million transactions, less than sixty complaints and six people dropped is an outstanding record!

CONDITION, CONDITION, CONDITION

It is vital that you examine and accurately describe the condition of your item. Some items lose 40-50% of their value with their first scratch or dent. Stains, tears, wear, fading, foxing, thin spots, fraying, nicks, handwriting and brittleness all affect value. Describing toys, it's important to estimate the % of remaining paint.

Low or medium quality items in only fair condition almost never have buyers at any price. Neither dealers nor collectors want to tie up cash in poor goods. Chips and cracks in most china, pottery and glass make values drop to almost nothing. Children's books, calendars, valentines, sheet music and magazines are among paper collectibles which become nearly valueless if not in excellent condition.

On the other hand, some less-than-perfect paper will sell. "Rock & roll concert posters and handbills found in the drawers of aging hippies are rare enough to be a cash windfall in any condition," reports one expert.

Mechanical items will sell with parts missing. Radios, jukeboxes, slot machines, etc., can be restored, although buyers warn **you should never try restoring or cleaning anything you want to sell.** Cleaning silver, brass, tools, coins, and many other items can cut the value by 50% or more.

Whatever your item's condition, if you don't describe it accurately, the buyer will return it, costing you and the buyer money and wasted effort.

Amateur sellers are notorious for overestimating the quality of condition. As a result, many dealers and collectors will ask to see the item before they make a final offer. This is particularly true of buyers of paper goods like postcards, trade cards, match covers, sheet music, and stamps. Paper dealers want to see what you have, because very small variations in condition mean substantial difference in price. For example, paper money worth $50 in very fine condition might be worth only $5 in circulated condition. Postcards with creases, or match covers with their strikers removed, are worth little or nothing. Four creases on the cover of an $80,000 comic book turn it into a $15,000 comic book.

Send the item

If you have accepted a buyer's offer, or a potential buyer has requested you to send the item for inspection, you will need to ship your item. **Shipping is easier than you think.** In the case of large items like furniture and juke boxes, the buyer will probably arrange to have all shipping done for you.

When packing smaller items you sell, always use sturdy boxes. **You can get quite an assortment of boxes in various sizes FREE at your post office.** You can also buy boxes at most post offices , stationery stores, and packing companies, but heavy duty boxes can often be obtained free from book stores. Don't ship anything, even shoes, in shoe boxes.

If you are shipping a breakable item, double boxing is the preferred method. Pack your item carefully in the smallest box that leaves an inch or two of protection around your item. Write the name and address of the recipient on that box, then pack it inside a larger box, with two or three inches of padding.

When packing breakables, never let two items touch. Wrap each item separately in styrofoam sheets, bubble wrap, or clean paper. **Never leave lids on cookie jars, sugar bowls, and the like.** They are likely to chip or break if you do.

Never pack your item in direct contact with newspaper. Newsprint smears and can damage clothing and ruin items like porous china. Wrap breakables in tissue, paper towel or plain unprinted paper, then use newspaper wads to fill the carton.

Flat items should be shipped between two or more sheets of cardboard approximately one inch bigger on all sides than what you are sending. Put the grain of the two pieces at right angles. That makes your package less likely to bend. Four pieces is even better. When shipping posters, maps, and large paper items that are to be shipped rolled, use square plastic rain gutter downspout available at any hardware store. It can be cut to exact length needed and is much stronger than any cardboard tube.

Ship by First Class or Priority mail (almost always the best choice) or by private carrier. Do not use Parcel Post. The difference in price between Parcel Post and first class is small. If your package weighs under two pounds, you can send it anywhere in America for less than four dollars.

When an item is worth more than $300, I ship it Registered Mail, because registered items receive special security handling.

Registered Mail can also be insured for up to $25,000 and must be signed for by the addressee. All this for one fee from $5 to $10 (which will be paid by the buyer). You should consider using Registered Mail for anything valuable that is one-of-a-kind or cannot be replaced. I prefer the Post Office to UPS, Fed-Ex, etc.

If using Registered Mail, there are a few special rules. You must use a clean box with no damage or printed advertising. The address and return address must be written directly on the box, not on an applied label. Each seam of the box must be covered with brown paper tape. No plastic tape is allowed.

Insure what you ship. Insurance on a First Class package is about $5. Insurance on Registered Mail costs less, because of the strict security under which Registered Mail is handled.

After you ship your item, a buyer has a three to five day inspection period and may return it for a refund. You must return the full amount of their check, although most buyers are willing to pay postage both ways, unless you misrepresented what you were offering. The most common reason for an item to be returned is its condition was not as good as you described.

If a buyer moves, dies or has a new phone

If you discover that a buyer has moved, died or has a new phone number, please tell me. We live in a very mobile society, changes do occur, and busy folks sometimes forget to notify us, especially about area code changes. **"That number is no longer in service" usually means a new area code.** Ask the operator.

When you tell me about any changes, I'll send you a free update sheet listing all changes in the current edition reported by other readers . This offer is good as long as this edition is in print. You can get an update sheet any time by sending a SASE and two one dollar bills (no small checks, please).

Ten most asked questions

My FAST system has worked so well for buyers and sellers that I have been invited to appear on TV shows with Oprah, Donahue, Vicki! and 2,200 other radio and TV shows to teach it. Hundreds of letters pour in each week as a result of my weekly segment on the CBS-TV Saturday A.M news, my monthly advice column and the weekly "Trash or Treasure" call-in radio show heard on 100 stations nationally. Each year, I answer thousands of questions about the disposition of antiques and collectibles. People everywhere share the same concerns.

1 "Why bother? Why not simply give it away?"

A fine idea. But it's smart to know what you are giving away and what its cash value is. Items worth $5,000 turn up in charity shops far more often than you realize. When toys less than 30 years old can be sold for 300 times what you paid for them, I urge you to be cautious about what you give away. Instead of donating an item, why not sell it properly, and donate part or all of the proceeds? You'll be giving your church or charity a lot more, and getting a healthy tax break as well.

2 "Why not sell at a yard sale?"

Great idea, as long as you sell things appropriate to a yard sale: children's clothing, modern kitchen items, and newer household do-dads. Beware of selling anything fifteen or more years old at a yard sale.

The problem with selling at a yard sale is that you must set the price, and most people reading this are not qualified to do that. Do you know what lace is $100 an inch? Which kid's marbles are $1,000? Which Vietnam Army patches are $250? Which postcards and photos have value? Which briar pipe is $300? Most people don't. That's why antique dealers shop at your yard sales. One properly sold collectible could make more money than all the rest of your yard sale.

3 "Why not sell to a local dealer?"

Sell to a local dealer only after you have made certain you don't own an item wanted by one of the specialty dealers or collectors.

The problem with selling to anyone other than an expert is that the buyer may not know exactly what your item is. One dealer in a thousand might recognize the rarest Indian stone spear point; fewer yet would pay you the $6,000 you'd get by dealing with someone who knows and appreciates Indian stone. Dealing with an expert will require a phone call, a letter, and perhaps a photocopy or photo. Selling your spear point to the dealer around the corner will take about the same amount of time, but the difference in price will be substantial.

4 "Will I get cheated?"

What is to keep a buyer from cheating you and saying your $5,000 watch is worth $5? Honesty, for one thing; reputation for another. This book contains the people I personally do business with. Experience has taught me I seldom go wrong dealing with authors, club presidents, newsletter editors, and people like that. The world of collectibles is a small one. Word gets around fast, and dishonest buyers seldom stay in business long. "Why would I risk a reputation it took me thirty years to build, just to cheat some old lady out of $500? It doesn't make sense," explains one veteran pro.

Some people believe a conflict of interest exists when the same person evaluates and sets the price. To some extent, that may be. But when you deal with people who have reputations for knowledge and integrity, you're likely to get fair prices and be many dollars ahead of selling at a yard sale, flea market, local auction or on the internet.

Dishonesty, misunderstandings, and disagreements are possible in any human interactivity. I don't worry about that because I've known some of these people personally for 20 years. I've featured them in books, newspapers, radio and television since 1980. Millions of transactions have taken place between readers and these buyers. I've received less than sixty letters of complaint, resulting in six people being removed. Buyers who fail to treat my readers and listeners honestly are dropped from the very next printing.

5 "If I wait, won't the value go up?"

Maybe. Maybe not. Many items sell for less today than they did a few years ago. Just as the value of gold or the stock market goes up and down constantly, so does the value of antiques and collectibles. Avon, Jim Beam bottles, Cabbage Patch dolls, electric trains and Levis are just a few examples of items selling for much less than they once did.

Items sold during the inflation of 1987-89 are frequently resold now at 50% to 75% of what they cost then, and in a few hobbies only the very best items are selling at all. It's true that in the past prices have tended to rise, but ebay has driven most prices down, in many cases severely. Sell to experts now, before they buy it cheaper on ebay.

6 "Can I make money as a picker?"

People in their 60s and 70s tell me they're having fun and making money the *Trash or Treasure* way. They report adding income by reselling things they buy from yard sales and flea markets run by people who have not read *Trash or Treasure*. If you would like to become a successful part time seller of collectibles with a minimum of effort, *Trash or Treasure* is the single most important book you can own.

7 "I wrote to a buyer. Why didn't I get an answer?"

If you offer something rare or desirable for sale, you'll get an answer from any collector or dealer.

If you don't get a response to your inquiry from one of the people in *Trash or Treasure*, it may mean that your item was not collectible, or you didn't include a self-addressed stamped envelope, or the buyer has not had time to respond. Perhaps you wrote the wrong person, or offered something the buyer specifically said was not wanted. It's also possible your letter got lost in the mail or that the buyer is out of town or sick. Remember, you're writing to real people. Like you, they have families, work long hours, and sometimes travel. You may not have gotten an answer because the person to whom you wrote has moved and mail was forwarded slowly, or not at all. **If you discover that a phone has been disconnected, try writing, requesting the letter be forwarded.**

8 "Why aren't there pictures and prices in this book?"

In the last 150 years more than a billion different items have been manufactured. A book which pictures them all would be 47 miles thick, an obvious impossibility. For me to include a few hundred pictures in this book would help no one and make it more expensive to bring you this valuable reference book.

Pictures are essential only in price guides used by amateurs curious about the "worth" of their item and by novice antiques and flea market dealers. You get accurate prices from expert buyers, not books. *Trash or Treasure* explains how and to whom you sell the items pictured in other books. It introduces you to the people who write price guides instead of other amateurs who read them.

Not one of the seven most valuable things known to have been sold by my readers was pictured or listed in any price guide, yet they got as much as $200,000 for what they had. Photos seldom exist of the most valuable items.

9 "How often do you update *Trash or Treasure*?"

We never stop. The first address or phone change usually arrives about the time a new edition rolls off the press. By January of 2003 expect 20 or so changes, by Fall of 2003 there may be 50 or more. By the time an edition of our *Guide* has been out for two years, 15% to 20% of the addresses, area codes or emails will have changed.

You can write us for a current list of changes at any time. Include a Stamped Envelope and two one dollar bills to: Buyer Update, PO Box 3028, Pismo Beach, CA 93448. Please, no checks. If an update sheet has been issued, we'll be happy to send you one.

10 "How do we get you on TV, radio and the Web?"

Every Saturday morning for three years, I was seen on the CBS-TV Saturday Early Show hosting a feature called "What's It Worth?" By the time you receive this book, that feature will have ended, in part thanks to new network handling procedures involving packages which makes it no longer safe to ship valuable collectibles into the studio. You can see previous segments by visiting <cbsnews.com> archives on the Web. It is especially effective when viewed through aol.

Special money-saving bonus question

11 "Can I save money when I buy another copy of *Trash or Treasure* as gifts for friends?"

Sure can. One is $29.95 (save $5) and two are $54.90 (save $15). The best deal of all is three for $69.85. That's right! You get a giant discount and your friends and relatives will receive *The World's Most Accurate Price Guide* and a pad of Sell-A-Grams as well. Neither of those two important bonuses are available in stores.

Yes, I'd like to order additional copies of Trash or Treasure

Regularly $34.95 (29.95 + $5 s/h). With this Coupon:

❑ **One for $29.95** postpaid (save $5)
❑ **Two for $54.90** postpaid (save $15)
❑ **Three for $69.85** postpaid (save $35...like getting one free)
California residents add 8.25% sales tax

Send to_____

_____

_____

Treasure Hunt Offer, Box 3000, Pismo Beach, CA 93448

TONY'S TIPS ON SELLING FURNITURE, RUGS AND LAMPS

If you own "furniture store" bedroom or dining room suites made after 1920 they probably have little collector value. Sell factory furniture from this period through classified ads in a local newspaper. Read the next few pages to see what you can sell. Many pieces have been reproduced or copied, so a good clear photo is essential.

Some ordinary looking furniture can have value. Be especially careful with hand carved items, mission oak, and designer furniture from the 1930-1960 period. Before contacting a possible buyer, examine the legs and underside looking for signatures, maker's marks, or labels. They can make a big difference in selling price.

Damaged rugs lose some value, but very old Oriental rugs should be evaluated by an expert, no matter what their condition. The finest Oriental rugs are not thickly piled, but are rather thin so don't think your carpet has no value just because the threads aren't long and lush. One reader found a $2,000 carpet (3'x5') used as a mud rug outside a mountain cabin. All you need to avoid expensive mistakes is a good photo and the buyers in Trash or Treasure.

If sending a photo is not possible, you may phone the buyer and discuss your item. Always call with the item in front of you. Be prepared to answer questions about colors, size, type of wood, labels, etc. It is very difficult to sell rugs, lamps, or furniture without a photo, however.

Make certain when selling large or heavy items that you and the buyer agree who has responsibility for packing and shipping. This cost is normally born by the buyer, but sellers make the arrangements. If this will be difficult for you, ask the buyer to help. Generally, you should request the buyer to have large items picked up as part of the sale. This is particularly important if you are elderly, have difficulty getting around, or if you live outside a big city.

FURNITURE

★ **Entire estates which include furniture and accessories from the American colonial** period, art, or important collections of toys, dolls, guns, decoys, miniature lamps, art glass, advertising, or other specialties. Your estate or collection must have a value in excess of $50,000 to be handled by this important firm. Julia has no interest in minor collectibles, limited edition plates, or common items.

     James D. Julia Auctioneers
     PO Box 830
     Fairfield, ME 04937
  (207) 453-7904   fax (207) 453-2502   <jjulia@juliaauctions.com>

◆ **Heavily carved or decorated American furniture** made between 1820-80 including fancy Empire, Gothic revival, rococo, American Renaissance, etc., especially furniture made by Belter, Roux, or Meeks. Also gas chandeliers and Argand Astral lamps. This prestigious dealer does not make offers so research is in order since many of these pieces can be very valuable. Send her a photo of the furniture plus a copy of every label or maker's mark you can find. She will help an amateur "if they are really selling and not fishing for free appraisals."

     Joan Bogart
     PO Box 265
     Rockville Centre, NY 11571
  (516) 764-5712   fax (516) 764-0529   <joanbogart@yahoo.com>

★ **Furniture and accessories from the Arts & Crafts or Mission period.** Buys oak furniture, light fixtures, and metalwork by L. & J.G. Stickley, Gustav Stickley, Roycroft, Limberts, Lifetime, Charles Stickley, Rohlfs, Stickley Brothers, and Dirk Van Erp, especially unusual pieces, custom made pieces, and items inlaid with silver, pewter or copper. Also textiles, various publications, and catalogs from these firms. "If you have any doubts, please call. I will be glad to help."

     Robert Berman
     Le Poulaille
     441 South Jackson Street
     Media, PA 19063
  (610) 566-1516   cel (610) 659-3789   fax (610)566-3319
         <ber441@aol.com>

TONY'S TIP: Do not refinish oak furniture you plan to resell. Collectors want that dark original finish found on most Mission pieces. An original finish is worth more than anything you or your local refinisher will do.

◆ **Furniture that is square in appearance**, made of oak, and characterized by square spindles, cut out designs, and/or inset tiles. Wants chairs with adjustable backs, benches, beds, couches, dressers, desks, library tables, book stands, cabinets, sideboards, etc. Examine the piece carefully for woodburned maker's marks or paper labels. A photo is strongly suggested. Does not want refinished pieces. Call if in doubt.

Gary Struncius
PO Box 1374
Lakewood, NJ 08701
(800) 272-2529   <gstrun@aol.com>

◆ **Arts & Crafts or "Mission" style furniture** but only signed pieces by Gustav Stickley, L. & J.G. Stickley, Roycroft, Limbert and other important makers. "I don't want furniture by generic makers." A Gustav Stickley inlaid armchair with rush seat and in its original black finish can bring as much as $10,000. Send a photo and include the dimensions, and a drawing of the mark. Marks on furniture can be on legs, underneath, on the back, and elsewhere so look carefully for labels or woodburned names. This well known expert in the Arts & Crafts period has agreed to make offers to amateur sellers who learn about him through this book if they are serious about selling what they own, but states clearly that he "does not wish readers to price fish or to involve him in bidding wars with other buyers." If you need an appraisal for estate or insurance purposes, the fee is $10 per item.

David Rago
117 South Main Street
Lambertville, NJ 08530
(609) 397-1802   fax (609) 397-5543   <perraggal@ragoarts.com>

◆ **Furniture and accessories from the Arts & Crafts or "Mission" period.** Buys oak furniture, lamps, light fixtures, and hammered copper metalwork by L. & J.G. Stickley, Gustav Stickley, Roycroft, Limberts, Lifetime, Charles Stickley, Rohlfs, Stickley Brothers, Jarvie, Albert Berry, Onondaga Metal Shop, Karl Kipp, Harry Dixon and Dirk Van Erp, especially Morris chairs, case pieces (like dressers), bedroom and living room furniture, and benches. Smaller items include **desk sets, bookends, lamps, vases, trays,** and **candle holders**. Prices can be high, as lamps often bring $2,000 up. Photo is helpful as part of your description. Note the maker and any repairs or damage. Note whether the original finish is still there. "I expect sellers to give me a minimum acceptable price. If their item is worth a great deal more, I'll let them know." Bruce wrote *The America Arts & Crafts Movement in Western NY, 1900-1920*, available for $16 postpaid.

Bruce Austin
RIT College of Liberal Arts
Rochester, NY 14623
(716) 475-2879   (716) 387-9820 eves   <baagll@rit.edu>

◆ **Roycroft furniture and accessories.** Buys and sells lamps, waste baskets, clocks, frames, art, pottery, china, glassware, and all books and paper ephemera associated with the Roycroft company or its founder, Elbert Hubbard. When you write, make certain to state honestly whether the item is for sale or whether you are seeking identification and appraisal. Please give the source of the item for sale and include any stories or history you know about the piece(s).

> Tom and Rosaline Knopke
> House of Roycroft
> 1430 East Brookdale Place
> Fullerton, CA 92631
> (714) 526-1749

◆ **Designer furniture and accessories, 1920 to 1960.** They seek Art Deco and Mid century American and European design in chairs, tables, couches, lamps, and small high class decorative items. They DO NOT WANT reproductions, items made in vintage styles, country furnishings, primitives, or ordinary department store furniture. They buy better quality pieces, and pay fair prices for them. Give a detailed description. Dealers must set the price wanted, but beginners or estate handlers may ask for offers if the item is really for sale and they're not price fishing.

> Dennis Clark & Lisa Bosey
> Off The Wall Antiques
> 7325 Melrose Ave.
> Los Angeles, CA 90046
> (323) 930-1185   fax (323) 930-1595   <weirdstuff@earthlink.net>

◆ **Designer furniture from the 1940's** through the present by Herman Miller, Knoll, Eames, Nelson, Gilbert Rohde, Frank Lloyd Wright, Heywood Wakefield, Noguchi, Thonet, and other national and international designers. Also interested in unusual plastic and fiberglass designer furniture. Most pieces are signed on the bottom. Primarily interested in bent plywood chairs and fiberglass arm chairs with no upholstery made by Herman Miller.

> Jay Novak, Modernica
> 7366 Beverly Boulevard
> Los Angeles, CA 90036
> (213) 933-0383   (323) 933-0383   fax (213) 683-1312
> <rey@modernica.net>   <http://www.modernica.net>

◆ **Blond furniture by Heywood Wakefield** from the 1930's through 1960's. Please send a photo along with information about any markings or labels. Describe condition accurately. Also interested in buying catalogs of Wakefield furniture.

> Don Colclough
> 732 North Cuyler Avenue
> Oak Park, IL 60302
> (800) 775-5078 days   (708) 848-7496   <mrmodern@aol.com>

★ **Twig furniture.** "I'm interested in any type of rustic or Adirondack furniture. This includes pieces by Old Hickory and Twig Furniture. The wilder the style, the more I will want it. As always the better the condition, the more I will pay. If you have any doubts, call."

Robert Berman
Le Poulaille
441 South Jackson Street
Media, PA 19063
(610) 566-1516   cel (610) 659-3789   fax (610)566-3319
<ber441@aol.com>

★ **Adirondack and other rustic twig furniture.** "Please let me hear from you if you have large quantities of rustic furniture to sell or if you have individual pieces of excellent quality. I can handle any size deal and am experienced at both buying and brokering the contents of any rustic camp. summer home, motel or hotel that contains fine rustic furniture and accessories."

Barry Friedman
PO Box 55492
Valencia, CA 91385
(661) 255-2365   <barryf@thevine.net>

◆ **Furniture made with or decorated with steer horns** is sought by this long time scholar of the genre. "I'll buy chairs, tables, hat racks, etc., made from cattle or buffalo horn. I prefer pieces that have the appearance of being artfully or creatively constructed with as many horns as possible, and made between 1880 and 1920. I have no interest in contemporary horn furniture. The fabric on most horn furniture is in poor condition, so we are mostly concerned with the condition of the horns themselves so make sure you check for cracks and bug damage. These pieces can be fairly valuable, so it is worth your time to take pictures from the front, back and sides. Give the dimensions of the furniture you have. I also want furniture which is decorated with inlaid horn, particularly fine examples which can be worth thousands of dollars."

Alan Rogers
1012 NE Shady Lane Drive
Kansas City, MO 64118
(816) 436-9008   <kcstockyards@aol.com>

◆ **Unusual "fantasy" chairs and other furniture** made between 1880 and 1980. Please call or send photos along with asking price.

Charles Martignette
PO Box 293
Hallandale, FL 33008
(954) 454-3474

◆ **High quality rugs and tapestries.** Oriental, Chinese, European, American Indian, and large hooked rugs are of interest if of sufficient quality and condition. Buys Art Deco, Art Nouveau, and Arts & Crafts rugs and textiles as well. Worldwide interest in fine tapestries, textiles, embroideries, and weavings. A good clear color photo is important. Make certain to mention wear or stains. Appraisals and offers are made only after actually seeing your rug. Claims "highest prices paid" for Oriental rugs of all types: "antique, semi-antique, used, or just plain old, regardless of size or condition."

> David Tiftickjian, Jr.
> 260 Delaware Avenue
> Buffalo, NY 14202
> (716) 852-0556   (716) 634-8835   <tifrugs@aol.com>
> <www.tifrugs.com>

◆ **Oriental rugs** made by hand before 1950 in any size or condition. A good sharp photo plus the dimensions is essential for this dealer/appraiser with 24 years experience to make an offer. Aaron's buys, sells, cleans and repairs antique Oriental rugs.

> Robert Anderson, Aaron's Oriental Rug Gallery
> 1217 Broadway
> Fort Wayne, IN 46802
> (219) 422-5184   <iloverugs2@aol.com>

★ **Grenfell hooked mats and rugs.** "I'll buy any tightly hooked mat, rug, or purse labeled "Grenfell Labrador Industries" as long as it is in excellent condition. These always depict Northern scenes like polar bears, hunters, Eskimos, etc. Please send dimensions and a photo with your first letter. Dealers are expected to price their goods, but amateurs may request an offer."

> Barry Friedman
> PO Box 55492
> Valencia, CA 91385
> (661) 255-2365   <barryf@thevine.net>

◆ **Rugs with advertising logos** or cartoon characters. Pre 1960.

> Charles Martignette
> PO Box 293
> Hallandale, FL 33008
> (954) 454-3474

TONY'S TIP ABOUT OLD RUGS: Old Oriental rugs should be evaluated by an expert, no matter what their condition. The finest Oriental rugs are not thickly piled, but are rather thin so don't think your carpet has no value just because the pile isn't deep.

LAMPS

◆ **Oil and other fluid lamps and parts** are wanted. This 25 year veteran collector/dealer looks for **student lamps**, embossed table lamps, **Aladdin** colored oil lamps, and all types of parts for lighting including oil and whale oil burners, mercury reflectors, oil tanks, shade rings (6", 7" and 10"), flame spreaders, old unusued round wicks, and shades from student lamps if opal or colored. He DOES NOT WANT pressed or mold blown plain clear oil lamps, common pressed glass lamps, reproduction lamps or parts, electric parts, or Aladdin electric lamps. Please give the maker if known, the condition, and indicate whether the item has been electrified. He prefers you to set the price wanted, but will make "ball park estimates." Lamp must be inspected before payment.

> Richard Dudley
> A-Bit-of-Antiquity
> 1412 Forest Lane
> Woodbridge, VA 22191
> (703) 491-2878

◆ **Gas lighting.** "I want burners removed from 19th century gas lamps which used gas from city gas mains. I also want protective wire globes which were installed around open-flame gas burners, spark coils and manuals and catalogs for gas lighting. Please, no parts from liquid fuel gasoline, propane or kerosene lamps."

> Lindsay Lambert
> 41 Bellwood Avenue
> Ottawa, ON Canada K1S 1S6
> (613) 730-7797

◆ **Frosted or etched glass lamp shades** (1840-1900) made for gas chandeliers or for Astral Argand or Sinumbra lamps. The size of the opening is 2 5/8" or 4" for gas shades, 6" for the Astrals and 9" or 10" for the Sinumbra. "I DO NOT WANT reproductions, modern shades, or simple gas chandeliers. I only want ornate items, preferably in sets."

> Joan Bogart
> PO Box 265
> Rockville Centre, NY 11571
> (516) 764-5712   fax (516) 764-0529   <joanbogart@yahoo.com>

◆ **Catalogs from lamp and lighting fixture companies** published before 1935 showing lamps with leaded or scenic glass shades, especially if company was based in Milwaukee. Does not want department store catalogs with lighting sections. Xerox© the cover and send a page count and an indication of how many color illustrations are included.

> Merlin Merline
> PO Box 16265
> Milwaukee, WI 53216
> (414) 871-6261

◆ **Lamps and lamp parts of all types** from all periods. Buys a wide range of wall, floor, and table lamps from the Betty lamps of the 1700's right through to the 1950's. Will buy kerosene, whale oil, electric, Aladdin, organ, marriage, student, desk, and other lamps. Also interested in Tiffany and other high quality leaded and painted lamps. This major Western dealer can be very helpful to amateurs with just about any type of lamp to sell. Especially wants Aladdin lamps and parts including galleries, chimney cleaners, bug screens, flame spreaders, wick cleaners, wick raisers, finials, and anything else made by Aladdin. Also buys parts from other lamp makers. If you have lamps or parts for sale, please note whether they are brass or nickel plated and give all numbers and wording. A photo is very helpful if asking for an offer.

Richard Melcher
PO Box 1812
Wenatchee, WA 98807
(509) 662-0386

◆ **Lamps and light fixtures** from the early 1800's to the early 1940's are wanted by this veteran lighting restoration dealer. He buys old iron, brass, or tin electric, gas or kerosene fixtures, wall sconces, chandeliers, colored glass shades from fixtures, and damaged fixtures suitable for scavenging parts. He will buy inside or outside lighting fixtures (including street lights) and has particular interest in those from commercial buildings as well as homes. He notes that large fixtures can be disassembled and shipped at his expense. Note all cracks or chips in glass. He does not want reproduction shades or in any fluorescent fixtures, but is strongly interested in old catalogs from manufacturers or retailers which depict large numbers of lighting fixtures from before 1920.

Robert Daly's Historic Lighting Restoration Sales & Service
10341 Jewell Lake Court
Fenton, MI 48430
(810) 629-4934   <Ldaly1@aol.com>

Lamp collectors want to know whether your lamp is original and complete, and if there is anything wrong with it. You should mention if it shows any signs of repair or of being a marriage of parts from different lamps. Describe the quality of the finish on the base and whether the glass shows any cracks or chips. A signature on the base or shade usually makes a lamp worth more. Look carefully, as signatures can be hard to locate on some valuable lamps.

◆ **Reverse painted, leaded glass, or art glass lamps** including table lamps, boudoir lamps, and floor lamps. "I am interested in buying shades, bases or parts for lamps of these types. I have a special interest in Moe-Bridges, Classique Studios, or Phoenix Light Co. I am also interested in catalogs from lamp and lighting fixture manufacturers (not retailers) before 1935." Does not want oil lamps, hurricane lamps, Gone With the Wind lamps, etc. No lamps after 1920's. Give all names and numbers found anywhere on the lamp or shade, and all dimensions. Please set the price you want for your lamp and include a photo.

    Merlin Merline
    PO Box 16265
    Milwaukee, WI 53216
        (414) 871-6261

TONY'S TIP: Many leaded lamps have been reproduced. These reproductions sell new for around $250 and are worth only $20 to $100 in local markets. If you have original leaded or painted lamps from before 1930, however, the value can top a thousand dollars, so don't be hesitant to ask an expert for assistance.

★ **Tiffany and other high quality glass lamps.** "I believe we are the only auction firm in North America that conducts specialty auctions for rare lamps only." Collections, large or small, of Tiffany, Handel, Jefferson, Pairpoint, and other quality lamps, lamp bases, and lamp shades from both large and small oil and electric lamps will be considered by this record setting auctioneer. Photos are a must. Telephone if you have a large group of lamps to sell.

    James D. Julia Auctioneers
    PO Box 830
    Fairfield, ME 04937
  (207) 453-7904   fax (207) 453-2502   <jjulia@juliaauctions.com>

◆ **Tiffany lamps,** lamp parts, chandeliers, windows, art glass, and enamel pieces in addition to other maker's high quality glass lighting fixtures. Please include photos and your phone number. Lots more info is available at <http://www.carlheck.com>.

    Carl Heck
    PO Box 8416
    Aspen, CO 81612
  (970) 925-8011 voice/fax   <webmaster@carlheck.com>

TONY'S TIP: Broken lamps and lamp parts before 1930 almost always can be worth some cash to you.

★ **Lamps and light fixtures from the "Mission" or Arts & Crafts period.** Anything signed by L. & J.G. Stickley, Gustav Stickley, Roycroft, Limberts, Lifetime, Charles Stickley, Rohlfs, Stickley Brothers, and Dirk Van Erp, especially unusual pieces, custom made pieces, and items inlaid with silver, pewter or copper. Also catalogs from these firms. "If you have any doubts, please call. I will be glad to help."

> Robert Berman,   Le Poulaille
> 441 South Jackson Street
> Media, PA 19063
> (610) 566-1516   cel (610) 659-3789   fax (610)566-3319
> <ber441@aol.com>

◆ **Emeralite lamps,** 1909 to 1940's, wall, desk, table, and floor models. Buys green-shaded, acid etched or painted models. These are found with brass, metal, marble or glass bases.

> Bruce Bleier
> 73 Riverdale Road
> Valley Stream, NY 11581
> (516) 791-4353   fax (516) 792-0519   <emeralite@aol.com>

◆ **Student lamps,** lamp shades, and lamp burners, 1870-1890, are wanted, especially lamps made by Manhattan Brass Co. A double Griffin can be worth $10,000 in fine condition and a single up to $450. "Make certain your lamp has an oil or kerosene tank that lifts out of the lamp, as many reproductions do not." Note if your lamp has been electrified, as well as any other damage which may have occurred.

> Jerry and Marsha Ritch
> 6407 Transit Road
> East Amherst, NY 14051   (716) 741-9580
> <jerry.ritch@bms.com> <www.eastamherstantiques.com>

◆ **Bellova lamps,** 1920's and 1930's. Boudoir, table, and floor models but frequently found with green-shaded, acid etched or painted shades. These are found with brass, metal, marble or glass bases. Bellova lamps are frequently signed on the base and shade. May be marked with a dime size 4 leaf clover in a circle. May be marked czechoslovakia.

> Bruce Bleier
> 73 Riverdale Road
> Valley Stream, NY 11581
> (516) 791-4353   fax (516) 792-0519   <emeralite@aol.com>

◆ **Miniature oil lamps** made of metal, art glass, or milk glass. Give the size, and indicate all names and numbers you can find on the lamp. A photo is appreciated.

> Carl Cotting
> 1441 Crowell Road
> Vienna, VA 22182
>   (703) 759-5646

★ **Motion lamps that are heat driven.** Seeks all heat driven lamps, not motorized ones, especially lamps made by Econolite, Goodman, Scene-in-Action, and other smaller companies made from the 1930's through the 1960's. Not interested in lamps made in the last ten years, psychedelic lamps, reproductions or lamps that say "Bar is Open." Email is best. Include complete description of your lamp including maker and material. They wrote the new "Collectors Guide to Motion Lamps" available from them for $24 autographed.

  Sam and Anna Samuelian
  PO Box 504
  Edgmont, PA 19028
  (610) 566-7248   fax (610) 566-7285 days   <sms@bee.net>

◆ **Lamp shades of cloth or beaded silk** (1890-1930) if in near perfect condition. Send a photo, the dimensions, and your asking price.

  Charles Martignette
  PO Box 293
  Hallandale, FL 33008

CLOCKS

◆ **Electric Kit Cat, Owl, Poodle, Teddy Bear and Panda bear clocks** made by Allied or California Clock Co., whether working or not. "I even buy basket cases to get usable parts. I can't evaluate any clock over the phone. I ask owners to send the clock to me for evaluation, providing your name, address, phone number and e-mail address. I will give a firm quote within 24 hours. If my offer is accepted I will pay your postage. If my offer is rejected, I will ship your clock back at my expense." Complete undamaged (normal wear) clocks are worth at least $30, and some are worth up to $140, even if they don't run. Original box and paperwork add to value. "I do not buy battery operated clocks. Electric only." Give a "good general description" noting all damage, age if known, a list of missing or damaged parts, and the serial number if it's an Allied clock. Note whether the motor is quiet, noisy or doesn't work. His *Service Guide to Kit Cat Clocks* is available for $3.

  Gordon Ledford's Clock Repair Service
  506 Sun Valley Blvd.
  Hewitt, TX 76643
  (254) 399-9924 eves   <gledford@kitcatservice.com>

◆ **Cast iron clocks with eyes that blink.** To sell your clock, include a full and accurate description noting any defects. Measure it carefully and give the length and width. Include sharp color photos.

  Sy Schreckinger
  PO Box 104
  East Rockaway, NY 11518
    (516) 536-4154 any time

◆ **Old wall and shelf clocks.** This family business describes itself as "a clock adoption agency, looking for nice items in need of a good new home." They buy a wide range of 18th and 19th century shelf and wall clocks, but are especially interested in the following:

- **Victorian shelf and wall clocks.** Wants ornate ones, with busts, teardrops, cherubs or side mirrors;
- **Reverse painting on glass** pillar and scroll clocks about 36" high with free standing wooden pillars and curved scroll ("swan's neck") tops;
- **Steeple or beehive** shelf clocks, but only if the veneer is perfect, or nearly so. "These are plentiful with poor veneer. I want those in beautiful condition;"
- **American carved clocks.** "I'm a pushover for clocks with carved columns or splats, eagles or fruit baskets;"
- **Spring or weight driven clocks;**
- **Eli Terry clocks** or those by any of his sons;
- **Seth Thomas** clocks;
- **French, German and English clocks** from the 18th and 19th century. "Some excellent 20th century German clocks were made, but no matter how good the clock we don't buy 20th century," he cautions, so please don't ask;
- **Cuckoo clocks** if very old, very heavily carved, and in perfect condition. "I'm afraid I'll open a floodgate if I mention I'll buy cuckoos, because there are so many junk ones around. I only want those that are very early and very ornate." No souvenir clocks. Photo a must;
- **Black Forest trumpeter clocks.** These are like cuckoos, but instead of a bird, a man plays a tune on a trumpet. "These are valuable, and we'll travel to pick yours up if it's a nice one."

"We buy **clocks with walnut or cherry cases**. We buy clocks with wooden works only if in running condition," they say, "but there are a few exceptions, so it's worth inquiring. We DO NOT BUY any 20th century clocks, oak gingerbread kitchen clocks, electric clocks, or Mission (Arts and Crafts) clocks. We also do not buy plain ogee clocks (rectangular veneered clocks with fronts that look like picture frames). We almost never buy clocks that have undergone restoration or modification. We don't want to spend lots of time restoring the clocks. We prefer to buy them in nearly perfect condition."

Ken Markley
Old Timers
PO Box 392
Camp Hill, PA 17001
(717) 761-1908   fax (717) 761-7446   <anytime@prodigy.net>

TONY'S TIP ON DESCRIBING CLOCKS:
To describe a clock, answer as many of the following as you can:
- *What name is on the dial?*
- *What name is on the movement?*
- *How tall and wide is the case?*
- *What is the case made of?*
- *Is the case decorated?*
- *Is there a label inside the case?*
- *Is there a serial number?*
- *Is there anything unusual about its looks?*
- *How is it wound or activated?*
- *Do you have the key and weights?*
- *Is it presently running?*

◆ **American wall and mantle clocks** from the 1700's through the Arts & Crafts movement of the early 20th century. "I'll buy, sell, or trade a wide range of clocks, but my specialties are weight driven calendar and regulator clocks that hang on a wall. I also buy interesting, unusual, and better grades of shelf (mantle) and other wall clocks of the 1800's. Especially like clocks with multiple dials or faces in either plain or fancy cases." Some of the many names to look for include Simon-Willard, E.N. Welch, Howard, Ithaca, Waterbury, Seth Thomas, New Haven, and other early Connecticut makers. Bruce is well versed in clocks of all types so can be helpful to the amateur seller. "If I'm offered something I can't use, I try to refer folks to someone who might like to buy it. Early electric clocks don't interest me much, but I may be able to give readers some help in identifying or evaluating them." Bruce says, "For my own collection, I like to find ones that are a little out of the ordinary." Some interest in European clocks with porcelain dials, or with fine cases with gilt, inlay, or marble.
    Bruce Austin
    RIT College of Liberal Arts
    Rochester, NY 14623
  (716) 475-2879   (716) 387-9820 eves   <baagll@rit.edu>

◆ **Grandfather clocks both European and American.** "I prefer 100+ year old grandfather clocks made in the United States, especially in Pennsylvania, but will also consider fine grade European and English clocks. If you have something good in the way of an old tall case clock, we will be glad to hear from you."
    Ken Markley, Old Timers
    PO Box 392
    Camp Hill, PA 17001-0392
  (717) 761-1908   fax (717) 761-7446   <anytime@prodigy.net>

★ **Motion clocks with dancers, cowboys, or other moving characters** such as grandma rocking, girls on swings, etc. Especially wanted clocks by: Mastercrafters, Haddon, Spartus and United. Don't try to clean. Working or not. Describe condition. They also recondition motion clocks for $75-$100 each.

> Sam and Anna Samuelian
> PO Box 504
> Edgmont, PA 19028
> (610) 566-7248   fax (610) 566-7285 days   <sms@bee.net>

◆ **Howard Miller clocks** from the 1950's and 60's. These are usually metal or metal and wood and marked on the back (and sometimes the front). A photograph or sketch is helpful.

> Modernica
> 7366 Beverly Boulevard
> Los Angeles, CA 90036
> (213) 933-0383   (323) 933-0383   fax (213) 683-1312
> <rey@modernica.net>   <http://www.modernica.net>

◆ **Winking eye clock**s. "I'll buy any good specimens of these 19th century figural cast iron clocks which wink their eyes as the hands go around. Made in Connecticut during the 3rd quarter of the 19th century by Bradley and Hubbard, figures include dogs, owls, lions, elves, Topsy, a man on a barrel, and others. They bring $1,000 up in fine condition and paint, but I'll buy them in any condition, including broken, missing paint, or incomplete. Take photos from more than one angle or phone me with the item in front of you."

> Gregory "Dr. Z" Zemenick
> 1350 Kirts Blvd.   #160
> Troy, MI 48084
> (248) 244-9426   fax (248) 244-9495   <drzzeezz@aol.com>

TONY'S TIP: In most cases, buyers will want to inspect your timepiece before making a final offer. Always discuss exact shipping procedures with the buyer.

◆ **Alarm clocks,** 1880-1910. These battery driven "tin can" clocks usually have a bell on top, but he's looking for unusual varieties that strike the hour, have calendars, play music, or are in unusual shapes. Parker, Terry, Darche and Kroeber are among the important early brands. He does not want anything that plugs in, or any modern wind-up clocks like Big Ben, Little Ben and Ingersoll. Give the brand name and any other info you can find on the clock. Everyone must include a photo and price their items. Will not make offers.

> Steve Cunningham
> 3200 Ashland Drive
> Bedford, TX 76021
> (800) 991-0165   fax (800) 991-0166   <sacunningham@attbi.com>

MISCELLANEOUS ACCESSORIES

★ **Accessories from the Mission or Arts & Crafts period** including light fixtures and metalwork by L. & J.G. Stickley, Gustav Stickley, Roycroft, Limberts, Lifetime, Charles Stickley, Rohlfs, and Dirk Van Erp, especially unusual pieces, custom made pieces, and items inlaid with silver, pewter or copper. He is also interested in catalogs from these firms. "If you have any doubts about what you have, please call. I will be glad to help."

Robert Berman, Le Poulaille
441 South Jackson Street
Media, PA 19063
(610) 566-1516   cel (610) 659-3789   fax (610)566-3319
<ber441@aol.com>

◆ **Arts & Crafts period lamps and accessories** made by Van Erp, Roycroft, Limberts, Stickley, and others. Lamps are often copper and colored glass, as are cigarette boxes, bookends, ashtrays, humidors, desk sets, and other items. Better pieces are often inlaid with silver. Also buys simple unornamented furniture by these makers, which many people call "mission oak." Send a photo or call if you think you have one of these pieces, as some can be quite valuable.

David Rago
17 South Main Street
Lambertville, NJ 08530
(609) 397-1802   fax (609) 397-5543

◆ **Art Deco accessories.** "I'll buy Deco items to compliment my radio collection." Ed wants a wide range of distinctive Deco items, so give him a try for items like clocks, picture frames, and lamps. If you are the original owner, he'd appreciate the item's history. He prefers you to set your price but will make offers to amateurs intending to sell.

Ed Sage
PO Box 13025
Albuquerque, NM 87192
(505) 298-0840

TONY'S TIP: Always check accessories for maker's marks, as signed pieces are usually of better quality and more likely to be collected. You should look for quality of workmanship, fine materials, and good design. Deciding what is good design is difficult. I'm sure you've seen valuable things you thought were ugly. I know I have. Many of these items may not appeal to you personally, but that shouldn't keep you from profiting when you find them. Good luck!

★ **Bookends** made before 1940 that are three dimensional figures of men or women that are at least 4 inches high. Metal are preferred, but glass, wood and plaster will be considered, as will metal bookends with interesting designs that are not necessarily figural. Do not offer small bookends, singles, or newer items. Picture preferred, along with dimensions. Point out any cracks, flaws, or wear. "This is a new hobby for me, so you must price what you have so I can decide whether it appeals to me at your price. Don't contact me with things not for sale."

Susan Mast
413 Western Drive #1#C-270
Santa Cruz, CA 95060
(831) 423-9786 eves <sme@cruzio.com> <www.hawaiiana-shop.com>

◆ **Hammered copper and other Arts &Crafts period items** such as:
• Lamps with mica or glass shades;
• Vases and candlesticks by Roycroft, Van Erp, Jarvie and others working in the Arts & Crafts style;
• Silver by Kalo;
• Metal with applied or cut-out squares by Roycroft;
• Arts & Crafts jewelry.
Descriptions are difficult without a photo. Since some of these pieces are fairly valuable, it could be worth your time. Describe all maker's markings, damage, and give dimensions.

Gary Struncius
PO Box 1374
Lakewood, NJ 08701
(800) 272-2529   <gstrun@aol.com>

◆ **Roycroft accessories** such as bookends and other small items. A photo or Xerox™ is a good idea if requesting an offer.

Richard Blacher
209 Plymouth Colony/Alps Road
Branford, CT 06405
(203) 481-3321 eves   <dblacher@javanet.com>

◆ **Standing picture frames** made of wood, brass, silver plate, celluloid, copper, ivory and bronze, usually from 3" to 15" high. "Larger OK, smaller even better. Missing glass OK, too, but the frame itself must be in fine condition, made before 1930, preferably with the easel in back. Best frames are marked Gorham, Tiffany, Germany or Aspreys. Porcelain or ivory pictures in the frame add greatly to value, but ordinary portraits do not. Photocopies and good description will bring a cash offer.

Carol Payne, Carol's Gallery
14455 Big Basin Way
Saratoga, CA 95070
(408) 867-7055 11-5 Wednesday to Saturday

★ **Victorian era boxes** which held collars, cuffs, gloves, brush and mirror sets, shaving sets, neckties, etc. "The boxes we collect have a picture on the front or top that is covered with a thin layer of celluloid. Our favorite lithos are of women and children, and we do not buy those picturing French or Colonial attired folks. Boxes are usually covered with celluloid. Nothing will be considered that isn't in top condition, that has cracked celluloid, split seams, or missing hardware." Interior condition is not as critical. Color photo needed. Note all damage. Pays finder's fees. For more info, request their illustrated wants list.
> Mike and Sherry Miller
> 303 Holiday Avenue
> Tuscola, IL 61953
>> (217) 253-4991 <miller1@net66.com>

★ **Photo and autograph albums.** "The albums we collect have a lithograph on the cover that is coated with a thin layer of clear celluloid. Our favorite lithos are of women and children, and we do not buy those picturing people in French or Colonial dress. Albums that play music when opened are particularly desirable; we pay from $100 to $250 for nice ones. Nothing will be considered that isn't in top condition, that has cracked celluloid, split seams, or missing hardware. Interior condition is not as critical." Color photo needed. Note all damage. Wants list is available.
> Mike and Sherry Miller
> 303 Holiday Avenue
> Tuscola, IL 61953
>> (217) 253-4991 <miller@net66.com>

◆ **Gold bearing quartz items.** Masculine items made from or decorated with quartz containing gold veins are sought. Items include matchsafes, cane handles, watch fobs, watches, pocket knives, boxes, etc. Sandra doesn't have much interest in jewelry, "unless it's exceptional." A Xerox™ or photo is the best way to sell.
> Sandra Whitson
> PO Box 272
> Lititz, PA 17543
>> (717) 626-4978   fax (717) 626-7625

★ **Items made of banded agate.** Will purchase pens, button hooks, snuff boxes, and small decorative items made mostly of banded agate. If you want to sell, give dimensions and condition.
> Stanley Block
> PO Box 51
> Trumbull, CT 06611
>> (203) 261-0057 <blockschip@aol.com>

◆ **Indian motif sterling silver** items made for men by Unger Bros. Items she seeks include desk sets, clothes brushes, matchsafes, etc. Has only limited interest in women's items and jewelry by Unger, but will buy some items.

> Sandra Whitson
> PO Box 272
> Lititz, PA 17543
>   (717) 626-4978   fax (717) 626-7625

◆ **Peter Max designs on any household item** or article of clothing such as shoes, tights, pants, shirts, jackets, scarves, ties, jewelry, sheets, furniture, pillows, glassware, posters, clocks, ashtrays, dishes, bowls, and anything else. Condition is important. Items must be clean, with no wear, tears, stains or chips. Send a photo or Xerox@ along with an accurate description for her offer.

> Judy Polk Harding
> 4347 Farm House Lane
> Fairfax, VA 22032
>   (703) 503-7323   <thefivejs@aol.com>

◆ **Glass powder jars** with fancy metal depicting heads of women or angels. Also **brushes and mirrors** with flowers or the same type faces. Also **mirrors that stand on legs** and have a place for jars and brushes.

> Lisa Underwood
> PO Box 815
> Pinson, AL 35126
>   (205) 681-2065   <landhunder@msn.com>

◆ **Light bulbs** (1880-1905) with ball or other tips on the end of the glass bulb. Also wants bulbs with dimmers inside and those with figural filaments (Masonic emblems, Fraternal lodges, Worlds Fair, etc.) but not bulbs with flowers or peace signs for filaments. Also wants old catalogs from light bulb companies.

> Steve Cunningham
> 3200 Ashland Drive
> Bedford, TX 76021
> (800) 991-0165   fax (800) 991-0166   <sacunningham@attbi.com>

◆ **Figural light bulbs** and neon glow lights are wanted by this long time collector. Christmas figurals are preferred, but all types of novelty light bulbs, such as Playboy bunny, Abraham Lincoln and the Statue of Liberty will be considered. Also buys all types of advertising and display materials for figural bulbs. Send a description with a photo. Cindy wrote Neon Glow Lights and auctions Christmas collectibles.

> Cindy Chipps
> 4027 Brooks Hill Road
> Brooks, KY 40109
> (502) 955-9238   fax (502) 957-5027   <holauction@aol.com>

MISCELLANEOUS HOUSEHOLD ITEMS

◆ **Glascock stoves and other ephemera**. "We want cook stoves, heaters, ranges and other items (whether complete or not) produced by G.T. Glascock & Son[s] or Glascock Stove & Mfg. Co. of Greensboro, NC Also want all advertising, catalogs, and other items related to Glascock. I'd even like a photo of your stove if it's still in use!" There were many models, and stoves were produced under many names, such as Carolina, Charter, Carbon Banner, Blue Ridge, Victor, Tar Heel and many more. This company historian is interested in everything you have. Do not try to repair or repaint anything, please. Please send a photo, and anything you know about the piece's history and use.

> Nollie Neill, Jr.
> PO Box 38
> Ennice, NC 28623
> <saddlemtn@skybest.com>

◆ **Gas kitchen stoves** from before 1930 are preferred, but will consider all types of stoves, including heating type, as long as they are early models. Also want all related industry memorabilia such as catalogs and advertising signs. "The earlier the better." Photo, please.

> Paul Schoenharl
> Cincinnati Stove & Range Museum
> 1328 Aster place
> Cincinnati, OH 45224
> (513) 541-0450 days

◆ **Washing machines.** "I buy old and unusual washing machines, usually wooden, galvanized, or copper tubs with wringers, although some hand-operated varieties did not have wringers. What may look worse than junk may be quite restorable and indeed an exciting machine so you are encouraged to inquire. I usually do not buy machines with porcelain tubs. If you have something I want, I'll pick it up so send a good sharp photo and any information."

> Lee Maxwell
> 35901 WCR 31
> Eaton, CO 80615
> (970) 454-3856   <oldewash@aol.com>

◆ **Early Victorian terrariums and aquariums.** Please send a photo or description. Include your phone number.

> Mark Miller
> PO Box 52261
> Philadelphia, PA 19115
> (215) 464-3561 voice/fax   <70176.1153@compuserve.com>

★ **Pressing irons.** "I'll buy unusual pressing irons of all types including goffering irons, crimping irons, fluters, charcoal heated irons, slug irons, Pyrex glass irons, miniature irons of any material, irons with animals or other figures for handles, ruffle irons, hat irons, and flower irons used in making artificial flowers." He also buys advertising for irons by various companies and some smoothing boards. He does not want common cast iron sad irons or ordinary electrics. Dave is author of three excellent books on irons, and Pressing Iron Patents, available from him. Inquire about current prices.

> Dave Irons
> 223 Covered Bridge Road
> Northampton, PA 18067
>   (610) 262-9335   <dave@ironsantiques.com>

◆ **Miniature sad (flat) irons.** Wants irons smaller than 4 inches only. No electric irons, no matter how early.

> George Fougere
> 67 East Street
> North Grafton, MA 01536

★ **American sewing machines** from before 1875, especially rare early treadle machines with low serial numbers for which he will pay from $1,000-$10,000. Small hand operated machines in the shape of animals are of particular interest. Also photographs of sewing machines in use before 1890. Tell him the maker and the serial number as well as the condition. If there is no name, send a photograph. **Carter does not buy Singer, White, Wheeler & Wilson, Willcox & Gibbs,** or other machines with that turn-of-the-Century Singer look, nor does he buy treadle machines in oak cases, or any sewing machine with a chrome or nickel plated flywheel. "High serial numbers on your machine mean it's a common one and of no collector interest." His beautiful Encyclopedia of Early American Sewing Machines is available for $49.

> Carter Bays
> 143 Springlake Road
> Columbia, SC 29206
>   (800) 332-2297   <bays@sc.edu>

★ **Decorative wooden bowls by artists** such as Ed Moulthrop, James Prestini, David Ellsworth, Bob Stocksdale, Ron Kent, Barbara Hepworth, Michelle Holzapfel, Melvin Lindquist and other master wood turners. Pircutes and a complete description, please.

> Barry Friedman
> PO Box 55492
> Valencia, CA 91385
>   (661) 255-2365   <barryf@thevine.net>

22 HOUSEHOLD

◆ **Miscellaneous household items** including:
- **Glass** (not ceramic) **wall pocket vases** in any color;
- **Reamers,** especially figurals, fine china, and precious metals;
- Two-piece **china tea strainers** as long as they are complete;
- **Napkin doll ladies;**
- **Stringholders** made of china or chalkware, but not metal;
- **Children's cups** that are whimsical, with whistles or figures on the handle or writing on the cup like "Whistle for milk";
- Figural **egg timers;**
- Ceramic figural tea balls;
- **Laundry sprinkler bottles in the shape of people**.

They do not not damaged items. Please give the color, size, and a description of the material, figure, and any marks. A photo is a good idea and an SASE is a must. You're on your own as these folks insist that both amateurs and dealers set the price wanted. No offers.

Bobbie and Alan Bryson
1 St. Eleanora's Lane
Tuckahoe, NY 10707
(914) 779-1405 <napkindoll@aol.com>

◆ **Victoriana.** "I'll buy anything likely to have been in Sherlock Holmes' apartment in 1895. This includes but is not limited to the following items specifically mentioned in stories:
- Bull's eye **hand held oil lantern with focusing lens**, 1859-1900
- Dark lantern hand held lamp which has a sliding cover that blocks out the light without having to extinguish it.
- **Gasogene.** "These devices make soda water and consist of two glass globes, one sitting above the other, usually with metal mesh encasing both globes/"
- **Tantalus decanter stand**. "These are stands containing cut glass decanters which,, though apparently free, can not be removed until the bar which engages the stoppers is raised."
- **Wall gas lamps;**
- **Settee style couch, coal scuttle, floor safe**, etc.

"When in doubt, please contact me with information on any items you hope will interest me." His website has a long list of items wanted.

Rev. Sherlock Holmes
PO Box 3
Worcester, MA 01613
free (877) 306-4059 <antiques@sherlockholmes.com>
<www.sherlockholmes.com>

◆ **Wallpaper rolls and sample books, shelf liner and decorative decals,** but only if they date from before 1960.

Edie Rowe, Ye Olde Paper Shoppe
2838 Salamander Road SE
Jefferson, OR 97352
(541) 327-3265 <edierowe@proaxis.com>

★ **Gadgets.** "I'll buy interesting old small mechanical devices such as:
  • **Pocket typewriters** or sewing machines;
  • **Pocket size calculators;**
  • **Miniature cameras;**
  • Small **optical devices,** like sundials and instruments;
  • Trick, tool, gadget or special purpose knives;
  • Lighters, compacts, and other pocket items combined with other
    tools;
  • Things that fold, hide-away or look like things they aren't;
  • Personal check protectors and other small business devices;
  • Scientific instruments;
  • Combination pen-pencil-rulers;
  • **Adding machines.**
**I'm interested in everything that whirs, buzzes, clanks, or just looks
interesting."** Darryl is particularly fond of typewriters and adders, pay-
ing $1,500 for important pocket typewriters. A photo is generally a
good idea, and your description should include a detailed statement of
condition. Will respond promptly to all offers.
Darryl Rehr
2591 Military Avenue
Los Angeles, CA 90064
(310) 477-5229   fax (310) 268-8420   <dcrehr@earthlink.net>

◆ **Useful items** designed to be carried in your pocket. Buys "mechan-
ically interesting functional things, not just pretty items. The items I like
are usually made before 1930, so modern plastic stuff is of little inter-
est." His wants include:
  • **Mini books** (less than 4") on any topic;
  • Tool and gadget knives;
  • Trick or special purpose knives;
  • Folding cups, silverware and tools;
  • Vest pocket flashlights;
  • Hand warmers;
  • Lighters, compacts, other pocket items combined with tools;
  • Optical devises, sundials, etc.;
  • Scientific devices;
  • Calculators;
  • Things that look like a pocket watch but aren't;
  • Any device that says 'pocket' on it.
Please send a photocopy, a description of any damage or other prob-
lems, and copy any printing or symbols which appear on the item.
Bruce Axler
PO Box 1288 Ansonia Station
NY, NY 10023
        (212) 579-0348

◆ **Thermometers,** pre-1920, especially ornate Victorian desk or mantle types. "I buy just about every non advertising one I can locate," but outdoor and decorative models are particularly prized, as are those from Russia and Eastern Europe. "I have the largest antique thermometer collection in the world but am always looking for more." Not wanted: commercial, industrial, clinical, advertising or "cutesy" thermometers. No barometers or souvenir key chain thermometers. Send a photo, accompanied by information regarding the maker, any dates or numbers, condition and whether mercury or red liquid is in the bulb. "Many of the items go to the American Thermometer Museum in Baker, CA." Thermometer catalogs and other ephemera are sought.

> Warren Harris
> 6130 Rampart Drive
> Carmichael, CA 95608
>   (916) 654-2097 days   (916) 966-3490 eves
>   <jockobwca@aol.com>

◆ **Vacuum cleaners, toasters, heaters and other home appliances** before 1940 that are ornate or attrractive streamlined or deco design and in fine condition. The earlier and more unusual, the better. Send photo, dimensions, brand name and SASE.

> Rick Padrone
> 1005 E. Idlewild Ave.
> Tampa, FL 33604
> (800) 991-0165   fax (800) 991-0166   <ricpadron@webtv.net>

◆ **Vacuum cleaners** that are hand powered. "I'll travel anywhere, buy one or a collection, and will pay finder's fees for information leading to my obtaining a fine scarce item."

> Peter Frei
> PO Box 500
> Brimfield, MA 01010
> (800) 942-8968   (413) 245-4660   fax (413) 245-6079
>   <peterfrei@prodigy.net>

◆ **Leftovers and other stuff.** "If you have a box of odd items of no apparent interest, don't throw them out! I want to buy ALL your small leftovers. I guarantee only to reimburse your cheapest-rate not insured postage for anything small, old and unbroken you send me. I want it all. I pay low, better than nothing, wholesale prices. For my offer, please ship anything complete and undamaged that might have value. Call if in doubt." Calling is advised.

> Rich Hartzog
> PO Box 4143 CGX
> Rockford, IL 61110
>   (815) 226-0771   <hartzog@exonumia.com>

◆ **Strap type watch fobs** picturing machinery or advertising products. No lodge, American Legion, VFW or similar fobs. He'd like you to tell him how much wear it shows and the name of the stamper, usually found at the bottom. No fakes or modern fobs.
> Albert Goetz
> 1763 Poplar Ave.
> South Milwaukee, WI 53172
> (414) 762-4111

◆ **Hotwater and enema bottles**, rubber syringes, bulbs, pumps, irrigators, and other similar home devices that are in complete as-found condition, with clamps, tubes, instructions, box, etc. U.S. or foreign, complete in wooden box they bring $45-75. More unusual ones made of pewter, brass, or other materials are also sought. Does not want modern plastic items, or anything made after 1965. Does not want ice caps, throat bags, atomizers, and other home health devices that don't involve insertion. When describing, give maker, color, size, accessories, info on the box, and where you obtained it. Would also like any stories of personal experiences with these home remedy/treatment devices.
> Ms. Brunswick
> Box 9729
> Baltimore, MD 21286

◆ **Baby and child care manuals,** books, booklets, magazines, films and articles that contain illustrated information on using enemas as part of sick care and treatment, This 30+ year veteran researcher also wants diaries, hand written notes, and family reminisces in letter form revolving around this particular treatment.
> Ms. Brunswick
> Box 9729
> Baltimore, MD 21286

◆ **Flashlights.** Old flashlights, advertising, and catalogs are wanted, especially anything early marked Eveready.
> Bill Utley
> PO Box 4095
> Tustin, CA 92781
> (714) 730-1252   <flashlight1@cox.com>

★ **Flashlights.** Old unusual and ornate flashlights, and advertising and catalogs of flashlight companies are wanted. Schneider is author of numerous books, including one on flashlights.
> Stuart Schneider
> 820 Kindermack Road
> River Edge, NJ 07661
> (201) 599-4250   fax (201) 599-4251
> <stuart@wordcraft.net>

◆ **Fans with brass blades and cages.** Also wants loose brass blades and cages, name tags, motors, oscillating mechanisms, advertising for fans as well as fan and motor catalogs. Does not want fans with steel cages or steel blades, but will buy parts of non-working old fans. Give the size of the blade and cage, the information on the motor tag, and the condition. Dealers, price your goods. Amateurs may request offers.

> Steve Cunningham
> 3200 Ashland Drive
> Bedford, TX 76021
> (800) 991-0165   fax (800) 991-0166
> <sacunningham@attbi.com>

◆ **Desk, ceiling, or pedestal fans** that are antique or unusual. Wants brands like G.E., Westinghouse, Emerson, Peerless, Diehl and others, but especially those made before 1920 or with unusual mechanisms. These early fans are usually cast iron and brass. **Also wants literature, catalogs, ads** and other information about fans and the companies that made them. If you want to sell your fan, include the brand, nameplate information, dimensions of the blades, number of blades, and what the various parts are made of, if you can. When describing condition, indicate whether your fan operates. Michael is president of the American Fan Collectors Ass'n and editor of its bimonthly newsletter.

> Michael Breedlove
> Antique Fans of Kansas
> 1875 SE Highway 96
> Leon, KS 67074
> (800) 858-3267   (316) 742-9995   <inthewind97@yahoo.com>

◆ **Mechanical fans** of all types are wanted, including:
- Electric and battery fans before 1920;
- Water fans before 1900;
- Belt driven fans before 1920;
- Gyro ceiling fans from the 1920's;
- Bank teller fans from the 1920's;
- GE and Robbins & Myers Art Deco fans from 1930's;
- Photos of fans in use before 1910;
- Advertising signs, posters and banners for fans.

Prices paid range from $10 to $2,000, depending on the model and condition. Please don't inquire about newer fans. To describe a fan, tell him the the brand name and model number and how many blades it has. Then answer the following questions: Are the blades shaped like dogs' ears or pizza slices? Is the base round or footed? Are the blades brass or steel? Is the cage brass or steel? Is it complete? Does it work?

> Richard Padron
> 1005 East Idlewild Ave.
> Tampa, FL 33604
> (800) 320-FANS   (941) 688-6800   <ricpadron@webtv.net>

◆ **Hand fans,** specifically the "beautiful or unusual" including fans concealed in canes, fans that double as masks, fans that look like a bouquet when closed, advertising fans, celluloid fans, and those illustrated with hot air balloons. All periods from the 1700's to the 1950's. She does not buy feather fans, poor condition fans, plastic fans, ordinary cardboard-on-a-stick fans, or Chinese bone cut-out fans (actually very common). Describe the picture and design of your fan, tell what it's made of, and give it's size both open and closed. Indicate any damage or soil. An Email request brings you a newsletter about fan collecting.
Cynthia Fendel
5128 Spyglass Drive
Dallas, TX 75287
<handfanpro@aol.com> <www.handfanpro.com>

◆ **Opera glasses.** Give dimensions, material, and condition. I photo or a Xerox™ copy is helpful.
Vivian Temes
Bird in the Cage Antiques
110 King Street
Alexandria, VA 22314
(703)549-5114 <bird-in-the-cage-antiques@compuserve.com>

◆ **Canes and walking sticks.** Seeks "nicely carved" sticks made of ivory, bone or wood with figural handles. Also canes with all metal handles or knobs with unusual shapes or engravings. Container canes, gadget cans and other novelty canes EXCEPT glass ("I have enough of those"). No contemporary items, please. Will also consider interesting metal cane handles which have been removed from their original stick. Cracks and chips in porcelain are not acceptable. Please include condition and photo along with an SASE. Dealers price your goods, please.
Bruce Thalberg
23 Mountainview Drive
Weston, CT 06883
(203) 227-8175 <mightyfinejan@yahoo.com>

◆ **Canes.** Especially likes dual purpose, container, weapon, gadget, and fancy carved canes made with ivory, gold, or silver. "Any cane or walking stick that does something, or has something enclosed or attached to the shaft for purposes other than support, is of interest, as are well executed hand-carved canes." Describe the tip of the cane and indicate whether it gives any evidence of having been shortened. Is there a hole in the shaft? What materials are used in making the cane?
Arnold Scher
1637 Market Street
San Francisco, CA 94103
(415) 863-4344 fax (415) 863-4399 <beaverprop@aol.com>

◆ **Fountain pens** in fine condition are sought by the head of the Pen Collectors of America ($25/year to join). To help you sell your pens, Boris has provided the information below. Check condition carefully and don't forget an SASE.

Boris Rice
Pen Collectors of America
11319 Wickersham Lane
Houston, TX 77077
(281) 496-7152   fax (281) 496-2290   <boris_rice@compuserve.com>

◆ **Fountain pens,** quill pens, desk sets and inkwells. "I want better quality items in excellent condition only." Does not want pencils or ball point pens. Please send a Xerox™ of what you have, along with a description of color, any markings, and condition. Glen is publisher of *Pen World* magazine, available for $42/year and author of Collectible Fountain Pens, available for $25. He has other publications as well.

Glen Bowen
PO Box 6007 or 3946 Glade Valley
Kingwood, TX 77339
(281) 359-4363   fax (281) 359-4468   <gbowen@penworld.com>

TONY'S TIPS ON WHAT INFO PEN COLLECTORS WANT.
- *Brand name. Less than 12 brands are considered premium, but many others are also collected.*
- *All numbers you find on your pen on the end of the barrel, the clip, etc.*
- *Color is very important in determining value. Early pens are black, red, or swirled red and black.*
- *Length. Measure with the cap on. Pens longer than 5" sell for more than pens shorter than 5".*
- *What it says on the pen point. 14k points are cheap.*
- *Condition.*

TONY'S TIPS ON HOW TO TELL A PEN'S CONDITION.
Take off the cap and run your fingernail around the rim, feeling for hairline cracks. More than 50% of the value is gone if you find one. Inspect the two halves looking for fading. Make sure the clip, fill lever, and any gold banding is still there. Roll the barrel of the pen on a flat surface to see if it is warped.

Is it worth your time to do all this for a fountain pen? Someone who didn't contact one of my buyers gave their pen to a Hartford rummage sale where it sold for $55. The person who bought it resold it to one of the people in this book for $15,000.

◆ **Inkwells,** either U.S. or foreign, figural or traveling, whether made of pottery, glass, or wood. Especially would like one made by *Tiffany*. He DOES NOT WANT desk sets or fountain pens.
> Eli Hecht
> 19 Evelyn Lane
> Syosset, NY 11791

◆ **Inkwells.**
> Ken Clee
> PO Box 11412
> Philadelphia, PA 19111
> (215) 722-1979   <waxntoys@aol.com>

◆ **Pencil sharpeners,** but only figural hand-held sharpeners made of metal, celluloid, or Bakelite in Germany, Japan and the USA during the 1920's, 30's and 40's. Also wants metal souvenir type sold for last 20 years at tourist spots around the country. "I do not want plastic sharpeners or common die-cast antiqued sharpeners found at every flea market. Detailed description of condition is important. Dealers must set price wanted. Amateurs may request offers. I will gladly share my knowledge with beginning collectors."
> Bernice Kraker
> 9800 McMillan Avenue
> Silver Spring, MD 20910

◆ **Cast iron pencil sharpeners** and other indoor home or office iron devices are also wanted.
> Rick Padrone
> 1005 E. Idlewild Ave.
> Tampa, FL 33604
> (800) 991-0165   fax (800) 991-0166
> <ricpadron@webtv.net>

◆ **Louis Vuitton trunks and hard case luggage**, the older the better, especially in early cloth designs other than the typical LV pattern. "We'd pay $4,000 for a mint condition steamer trunk, but we do not want things in less than fine condition and we do not buy any soft sided luggage." Send a photo, dimensions and whatever you might know of the history of the item, if possible.
> Duane and Eunice Bietz
> Les Meilleurs
> 6461 SE Thorburn
> Portland, OR 97215
> fax (503) 233-1602   <heartbietz@aol.com>

KITCHEN TOOLS

◆ **Apple parers,** but only specific ones. He will pay from $200 to $500 for the following brands only: Bergner, Browne's Nonpareil, Buchi, Champion, Climax by Brokaw, Dandy, Eagle, Electric, Empire State, Eureka, Excelsion, GEM, Jersey, Little Giant, Mammoth, Maxam, Monarch, Nonpareil, Oriole, Oscillator, Parker, Peerless, Returntable, Rices, SS Hersey, Selick's, Star (Foster & Cotton), Standard, Thompson, Tripp Bros., Victor, Wiggins, and Yankee. **He does not buy other brands** or rusted or broken parers. Give the name and date, if marked, the material from which it's made, and the number of gears.

John Lambert
236 South Main
Mount Vernon, OH 43050
(740) 393-2508   fax (740) 392-8047   <zlambert@yahoo.com>

◆ **Butter molds** that are hand carved of wood, ivory or clay. Will consider all sizes and forms, especially those with carvings of people, animals, or things rather than abstract patterns. Does not want machine carved items or anything new. Give the shape and size, material, and make a Xerox™ of the design.

Carl Cotting
1441 Crowell Road
Vienna, VA 22182
(703) 759-5646

◆ **Hand can openers.**

Craig Dinner
PO Box 4399
Sunnyside, NY 11104
(718) 729-3850

◆ **Tin can openers.** Will consider wall, counter, or hand operated kinds, but he wants old ones (1810-1940), not modern openers. There are more than 1,200 patents for can openers! Give all information that is stamped on the opener.

Joe Young
PO Box 587
Elgin, IL 60121
(847) 695-0108   fax (847) 695-1679   <istamp2@msn.com>

◆ **Cocktail shakers** made before 1960, especially unusually shaped shakers (golf bags, lady's leg, lighthouse) and designer shaker sets.

Stephen Visakay
PO Box 1517
West Caldwell, NJ 07007
(914) 358-0024   <svisakay@aol.com>

★ **Egg beaters.** "I'll buy pre-1910 cast iron rotary crank egg beaters, the older the better, the more unusual the better." Also buys rotary cranks that came with jars, especially looking for the E-A-S-Y and Family brands. Does not want any beaters after 1910 or beaters with tin wheels. Descriptions should include the height and any markings. He is author of the interesting and recommended *The Eggbeater Chronicles* new expanded 2nd edition available from him for $45.

> Don Thornton
> PO Box 57
> Moss Beach, CA 94038   Days: (650) 728-7978
> (650) 563-9445   fax (650) 728-7980   <dt@thorntonhouse.com>

★ **Egg beaters,** cream whips and glass bottomed mixers are wanted. Old cast iron beaters and or beaters with unusual mechanical actions are most sought after. Please describe the condition, size, markings, etc. A clear photo, sketch or photocopy is extremely helpful. Will buy some undamaged parts, but the better the condition of the mixer, the better the price. Most are valued $5 to $100/ Please, no beaters with plastic or stainless steel. Also no electric mixers except early Horlicks.

> Reid Cooper
> 32942 Josheroo Court
> Temecula, CA 92592
> (909) 302-3348   fax (909) 506-3349   <rcoop4129@aol.com>

◆ **Toasters.** "I buy early electric toasters with unusual mechanisms and/or design, especially those made of porcelain in whole or in part and those with buttons or cranks that flip the toast. I do not want toasters in poor condition, or most pop-up types." Please give the make, model, color, and condition. Dealers, price your goods; amateurs may ask for offer. Will pay $600-$750 for a Pan-Electric porcelain toaster.

> Dan Lunzmann
> PO Box 482
> Auburn, NE 68305
> (402) 274-4555

★ **Toasters.** "I'll buy old or unusual electric toasters, porcelain models and ones with toast racks, as long as they are in good, non-corroded condition, with no pieces missing. Prices vary greatly. Mint condition and ones with original boxes bring the best prices, but toasters do not have to work to be desirable. Please call or write if you have specific questions." Give maker's name and model number. A sketch is helpful, but a photo is best. An accurate description of condition is essential. Toasters bring $15 up, with rare ones bringing you $1,000.

> Joe Lukach
> 7111 Deframe Court
> Arvada, CO 80004
> (303) 422-8970 eve   fax (303) 623-2262   <jlukach@smarchs.com>

◆ **Tunbridge Ware** is attractive woodware with geometric or mosaic designs, or with embedded pictures created with cut woods of different colors. She buys **boxes, candlestick holders, tea caddies**, etc. made in Tunbridge. These pieces are rarely marked. If in doubt, send a good photo or a photocopy of the patterned portion of the item.

> Lucille Malitz
> Lucid Antiques
> PO Box KH
> Scarsdale, NY 10583
>   (914) 636-7825   <lithophane@aol.com>

◆ **Hard and soft covered cookbooks**, especially soft cover advertising recipe books published by various food companies, such as *Jell-O, Rumford Baking Powder*, etc., especially fine condition ones from before 1900. Will pay $50 each for the 1930's *Jell-O* cookbooks based on the OZ books by Frank Baum. The founder of the Cook Book Collectors Club, and editor of its newsletter, does not want appliance company recipe books, diet books, or other modern health cookbooks such as heart and cholesterol related cookbooks. As with all books for sale, sellers should give complete bibliographic information. Sellers must price the books they offer.

> Col. Bob Allen
> Cookbook Collectors Club of America
> PO Box 56
> St. James, MO 65559
>   (573) 265-8296 anytime

◆ **Cookbooks, but ONLY hardcover from before 1920.** No others. "I buy for resale, so don't want books with stains, dirt, or missing pages and I really don't want all those scaps and notecards that people keep in their cookbooks." Please give the author, title and date. A Xerox™ of the front cover really helps. Mention whether the cover is loose and give the condition of the backstrap (the part you see when a book is on the shelf) and whether or not your book has a dust jacket.

> Jim Presgraves
> Bookworm & Silverfish
> PO Box 639
> Wytheville, VA 24382
>   (276) 686-5813   <bookworm@naxs.com>

TONY'S TIP ON SELLING BOOKS: Complete bibliographic information is a must when selling any book: title, author, publisher, place and date of publication, number of pages, and type and number of illustrations. Describe condition of pages, binding and covers.

◆ **Figural cookie jars** are wanted by Chicago's only shop devoted exclusively to kitchen counter novelties. Wants figural ceramic jars and jar tops, but nothing cracked or repaired. Jars that aren't figural aren't of interest. She also buys figural salt and pepper shakers. She declares a photo to be essential, plus wants you to describe all markings on the bottoms of jars or salt sets. Make certain to mention every chip! Prefers you to price what you want to sell. She charges $10 per jar to make appraisals for insurance or estate purposes.

  Mercedes DiRenzo
  Jazz'e Junque
  3831 North Lincoln Avenue
  Chicago, IL 60613
    (773) 463-7411   <jazzyjunk@aol.com>

◆ **Teapots, tea tins and tea related items.** Check out your teapot as values range from $1 TO $1,000+. Items not of interest include teapots made in Japan since WWII and tea sets with sugars, creamers and trays. Dealers set your price but amateurs may request offers. No damage. Photo showing the decoration is helpful. Or you may reference it to her book Teapots, A Collector's Guide which is only $16. SASE a must.

  Tina M. Carter
  882 South Mollison Avenue
  El Cajon, CA 92020
    (619) 440-5043   <premos2@aol.com>

◆ **Russian samovars** from before 1930. Please send picture with descriptive information and a statement of condition. He needs to know the size, shape, type of metal, markings, condition, and whether there are any additional matching pieces. He prefers you to price what you have. Wants written material on samovars, especially catalogs.

  Jerome Marks
  120 Corporate Woods #260
  Rochester, NY 14623
    (716) 475-0220 Mon-Fri 9-5   fax (716) 475-0208

TONY'S TIP ON "FIGURAL" ITEMS: When collectors or dealers say they want "figural" items that means they want your item if it is shaped like a person, an animal, or some other three dimensional object. A plain round cookie jar would not be wanted but one shaped like a frog or an orange might be.

◆ **Jadite green (a milky light green) or delphite blue (a similar blue) kitchen ware.** Wants bowls, reamers, canisters, **salt and peppers** and "anything else." A wide range of items, often in a variety of shapes, were made. Green pieces start at $4, with rare pieces reaching $100, whereas the blue is much more scarce with most pieces starting around $75. Tell what piece you have, its size, whether it is marked on the bottom (most weren't), and the condition, indicating any flakes or chips in the rim and base, and the condition of the painted decoration on canisters, salts, etc. There are other similar glass makers, and very little is marked, so it's best if Steve looks at a photo of what you have. "I feel badly for your readers," he says, "because most of what I'm offered isn't what I'm looking for, but I urge them to keep trying."

> Steve Kelley
> PO Box 695
> Desert Hot Springs, CA 92240
> (760) 329-3206   <kskelley@earthlink.net>

◆ **Older fruit (canning) jars** with unusual closures or in unusual colors other than aqua or clear. Colors wanted include amber, brown, deep green, and shades of cobalt blue. Is willing to pay up to $400 for a pint sized embossed *Cadiz* jar with a glass screw top. Also wants pre-1960 advertising, promotional brochures, letterheads, signs and paperweights from jar and bottle manufacturers, including wooden canning jar boxes or box ends, which generally bring $10-$30. Give the size and color, and report exactly what is embossed on the jar. Note all cracks, chips, dings, or unwashable stains.

> Tom and Deena Caniff
> 1223 Oak Grove Avenue
> Steubenville, OH 43952
> (614) 282-8918   <tomcaniff@aol.com>

◆ **Glass knives** are wanted in rare shapes and colors, and can bring $50 and up for good ones. It's worth having her check out your knife because it's difficult for amateurs to tell the rare from the common. Send a Xerox© copy of your knife along with a Self Addressed Stamped Envelope. Describe the color of the glass. List all chips.

> Adrienne Escoe
> 4448 Ironwood Avenue
> Seal Beach, CA 90740
> (562) 430-6479   <escoebliss@earthlink.net>

TONY'S TIP ABOUT DAMAGED GLASS: *Damage is very important to glass collectors. You must mention every chip, crack, scratch or worn design.*

SALT & PEPPER SHAKERS

◆ **Salt and pepper shakers.** "I buy novelty figural shakers. I specialize in Black Americana, Disney and other comic characters, Kewpies, advertising, and figural nodders which rock back and forth on a stationary base. I also like German porcelain and **shakers that are part of a condiment set** (on a tray with mustard jar, etc.), especially those with comic characters, baseball, nursery rhyme, dinosaurs, and outer space themes. Anthropomorphic sets (animals or inanimate objects dressed as people) are of particular interest. Value is determined by condition, desirability, quality and rarity. Topic and form are more important in determining value than age or country of origin. I don't buy non-figural glass or wooden sets, but I'll buy hundreds of shakers that aren't mentioned here. Please supply a description and or photos."

Judy Posner, winter   summer
PO Box 2194   RR #1 Box 273
Englewood, FL 34295   Effort, PA 18330
(941) 475-1725   (570) 629-6583
<judyandjef@aol.com>

◆ **Salt and pepper shakers.** "After 35 years, I'm looking only for fine condition novelty shakers, especially those featuring Negro stereotypes, but I also buy animals, people, and other types of objects. I'll buy your collection, no matter how large or small. Also want German-made **condiment sets with mustard jars.** About the only thing I don't want is reproductions or shakers made of wood. Please send a photo or video of your collection. I would like the seller to tell me the price they'd like for their collection." Larry is president of the Novelty Salt and Pepper Shakers Club ($20/year) and co-author of *Salt and Pepper Shakers: Over 1001 Shakers* (available from him for $22) as well as other books. Inquire as to what is currently available.

Larry "The Salt & Pepper Man" Carey
PO Box 329
Mechanicsburg, PA 17055
(717) 766-0868   <snpman@itech.net>

TONY'S TIP ON DAMAGED GLASS: Every scratch, chip, crack, fading, or worn spot makes an item less valuable. There is no such thing as "good for its age." It does not matter how old an item is. Damage is damage. A buyer needs to know what the damage is, where the damage is, and what is affected.

CAST IRON COOKWARE

★ **Cast iron muffin pans,** gem pans, popover pans, and maple sugar molds in unusual patterns and shapes. Also interested in old catalogs, etc., which list multi-sectioned baking or muffin pans. **Buys any cast iron item marked Griswold.** Will pay $500+ for Griswold #13, 50, and 2800 muffin pans. Publishes a bimonthly 8 page newsletter, Kettles 'n Cookware, for $20. Author of the excellent *The Book of Griswold and Wagner,* autographed copies of which are $33 postpaid.

    David "The Pan Man" Smith
    PO Box 247
    Perrysburg, NY 14129
        (716) 532-5154   <panman@panman.com>

◆ **Early kitchen items made of cast iron** or of wood which has been folk carved or decorated are wanted by this important dealer.

    Louis Picek
    PO Box 340
    West Branch, IA 52358
        (319) 643-2065   <msantiques@bigplanet.com>

★ **Iron pans and broilers in odd or decorative shapes,** including pans for muffins, popovers, rolls, and maple sugar molds. Roll pans shaped like hearts bring $100 and up, while those shaped like fruits and vegetables are worth $150. Pans made by GF Filley start at $75. Cast iron broilers look like strange frying pans with grid work, slots, and holes. Not interested in reproductions (they have rough surface and grind marks) or in tin pans of any type. Trace your pans or photocopy. Dave write the excellent *Book of Griswold and Wagner,* autographed copies of which are $33 postpaid.

    David "The Pan Man" Smith
    PO Box 247
    Perrysburg, NY 14129
        (716) 532-5154   <panman@panman.com>

TONY'S TIP ABOUT CAST IRON COOKWARE: Buyers do not want cast iron cookware that is pitted, badly burned, or rusty. If you wouldn't use it to cook, they don't want it to collect. Remember that lids can have value. These pans can be valuable so be certain to ask about any (except a basic "starter set") that you have.

◆ **Cast iron garden furniture, statuary, fencing, light posts, lawn sprinklers** and other outdoor items mdecorative items made of iron. Send photo, dimensions and statement of condition, noting worn paint, cracks, missing pieces, etc. **Cast iron pencil sharpeners** and other indoor or office iron devices are also wanted.

    Rick Padrone
    1005 E. Idlewild Ave.
    Tampa, FL 33604
          (800) 991-0165   fax (800) 991-0166
          <ricpadron@webtv.net>

◆ **All useful items made from cast iron in the shape of figures.** "I'll buy **doorstops, bottle openers, lawn sprinklers, paperweights, pencil holders, match holders, string holders, windmill weights, horse weights, shooting gallery targets,** and **firemarks.** I have no interest in buying modern reproductions and castings but I will buy some non figural cast iron cookware." Include your phone number and an SASE.

    Craig Dinner
    PO Box 4399
    Sunnyside, NY 11104
          (718) 729-3850

◆ **Cast iron doorstops and windmill weights** are sought by this prominent dealer. No reproductions or modern pieces.

    Louis Picek
    Main Street Antiques
    PO Box 340
    West Branch, IA 52358
          (319) 643-2065   <msantiques@bigplanet.com>

◆ **Cast iron lawn sprinklers, doorstops, windmill weights, shooting gallery targets, croquet wickets and other figural cast iron.** Does not want reproductions, damaged and repaired items, items with new paint or "small shooting gallery targets such as ducks and birds." Please include color photo, phone number, and price range you'd like.

    Richard Tucker
    Argyle Antiques
    PO Box 262
    Argyle, TX 76226
  (940) 464-3752   fax (940) 464-7293   <rtucker@jw.com>

TONY'S TIP: *Always include an SASE (a stamped envelope addressed to yourself). Long #10's are best.*

SILVERWARE & TABLE ITEMS

◆ **Sterling flatware and serving pieces** are wanted by the nation's largest buyer and seller of second hand sterling tableware. "If a customer sends a SASE and the name of their pattern and its maker, we will send a written offer." If you do not know the name of the pattern, make a picture on a copy machine and list how many pieces you have. "Most sterling is standard, so if you know the name of the pattern, we know exactly what you have. As a result, we do not need to see what you have before buying. Please note, we do not make offers on non-standard items. We don't offer on coin silver, souvenir items, old unmarked tea sets, and the like, although we will consider them for purchase if you send a photograph or photocopy and set the price you want. We only make offers on standard items." If an item is damaged, worn, or monogrammed, be certain to note that fact. MidweSterling also repairs and restores flatware.

> Head Buyer
> MidweSterling
> 4311 NE Vivion Road, Dept HY
> Kansas City, MO 64119
> (816) 454-1990   fax (816) 454-1605
> <buyer@silverwarehouse.com>

◆ **Sterling and silver plated flatware**, especially made by Holmes & Edwards, 1847 Rogers, and Community. Also all old grape patterns. Send the information on the back of your silver, and a photocopy if you don't know the name of the pattern. An SASE will get you a pattern guide. Particularly interested in more unusual pieces such as pie forks, punch ladles, ice tongs, sardine forks, etc. "We do not want monogrammed, damaged or worn silver except large serving pieces or very rare patterns." A 30 year veteran of buying through the mail.

> L.C. Fisher
> Silver Exchange
> PO Box 8027
> Huntsville, TX 77340
> (936) 295-7212

◆ **Modern European sterling** silver from French, Scandinavian, Italian, and U.K. companies like Christfofle, Buccellati, Puiforcat, Ricci, Jensen Cohr, Frigast, Bruckmann, etc. Buys and sells.

> Russ Burkett
> PO Box 4231
> Mission Viejo, CA 92690
> (949) 364-3844

◆ **Sterling silver flatware and serving pieces** as well as novelty items such as goblets, mint julep cups, and trays, especially in elaborate antique patterns. You should take photos of larger pieces, and make photocopies of flatware. Everything must be in fine condition, cautions this 25 year veteran dealer. Their *Silver Flatware: An Illustrated Guide to Pieces, Manufacturers and Care* is helpful in identifying what you have for sale. It is available from the authors for only $15 postpaid.

Helen & Duncan Cox
As You Like It Silver Shop
3033 Magazine Street
New Orleans, LA 70115
(800) 828-2311   fax (504) 897-6933   <ayliss@bellsouth.net>

◆ **Unusual condiment sets.** Combination **salt, pepper, and mustard sets** are wanted if they are unusual and figural. Wants pieces without chips or repairs, but will consider slightly damaged goods if the piece is extremely unusual. Especially likes German sets, and those with designs related to water. A picture is important.

Sylvia Tompkins
25-C Center Drive
Lancaster, PA 17601
(717) 569-9788   <stompkins@iopener.net>

◆ **Victorian figural silverplate napkin rings.** Wants old figural napkin rings. Describe your rings to her well, including all markings, and "I'll probably know what you have."

Sandra Whitson
PO Box 272
Lititz, PA 17543
(717) 626-4978   fax (717) 626-7625
<npknring@desupernet.net>

TONY'S TIP: Table items made of silver are similar to all other antiques and collectibles in that you should not attempt to clean, polish, or repair them prior to offering them for sale. Polishing silver can reduce, not enhance, value.

TONY'S TIP: A photocopy machine (Xerox®) is a seller's best friend when it comes to selling silverware and china. Both will copy very well.

◆ **Eggcups.** If you have a fine eggcup to sell, the *Eggcup Collectors Corner* may be your best source of information. Sample copies of this club newsletter cost only $5 and will give you insights into cups and their prices, plus a bibliography. When you order your sample, tell Joan why you want one and she'll pick an appropriate issue. Eggcup Collectors' Club members share information about buying and selling.

> Joan George, editor
> Eggcup Collectors Corner
> 67 Stevens Avenue
> Old Bridge, NJ 08857
> (908) 679-8924

◆ **Toast racks** (silver, pewter, copper or ceramic frames, often footed, with 4-8 wire racks to hold toast upright at the table). Values from $25 to $175 depending on fanciness and rarity. Good condition only. Please draw a picture of any maker's marks and give measurements.

> Carol Payne
> 14455 Big Basin Way
> Saratoga, CA 95070
> (408) 867-7055 11-5 Wednesday thru Saturday

◆ **Tea caddies** are boxes for holding loose tea at the table and are made of wood, silver, ceramic, tortoise shell, or other materials Values vary from $50 to $300 depending on rarity and quality. Photos helpful. Describe size, shape, decoration, and condition. Xerox™ the bottom to show marks if you can't draw accurately.

> Carol Payne
> 14455 Big Basin Way
> Saratoga, CA 95070
> (408) 867-7055 11-5 Wednesday thru Saturday

◆ **Toasters and other kitchen electric appliances** before 1940 that are ornate or attrractive streamlined or deco design and in fine condition. The earlier and more unusual, the better. Send photo, dimensions, brand name and SASE.

> Rick Padrone
> 1005 E. Idlewild Ave.
> Tampa, FL 33604
> (800) 991-0165   fax (800) 991-0166   <ricpadron@webtv.net>

TONY'S TIP: If you don't get a reply, it's because the buyer is busy, out of town, the wrong buyer for your item, moved sick, etc. There can be lots of reasons. Don't give up until you've tried mail, e-mail and phone. Some people have limited availability.

★ **Sterling silver souvenir spoons**, U.S. or foreign, particularly those made between 1890 and 1920. "Almost any spoon which is a turn-of-the-century quality souvenir will be considered for purchase or accepted on consignment for my auctions." Of most interest are spoons with:
 • Enameled bowls, especially Gorham;
 • Figural handles;
 • Special topics like Negroes, Indians, military, coins, music, historic sites, etc.;
 • Famous persons, especially on European spoons;
 • World's Fair themes before 1920.
"I only want old, pre-WWI souvenir spoons, not modern spoons which are typically sold in airports and tourist shops." Values range from a few dollars for some, $20-$30 for most, to more than $300 for top items like the Gorham spoon with their factory depicted in the bowl. Please make a photocopy of your spoon(s) and make a drawing or copy of the markings on the back. If you don't Xerox™ the spoon, please measure it and give the total length.
   Chris McGlothlin
   "The Original Spoon Auctioneer"
   780 Rock Springs Road
   Kingsport, TN 37664
      (423) 239-6776 <mcspoons@aol.com>

◆ **Sterling spoons with "cute" Negro figures.** Will pay up to $150 for enameled teaspoons and $100 for enameled demitasse spoons.
   Elijah Singley
   2301 Noble Avenue
   Springfield, IL 62704
      (217) 546-5143 eve <greenriver1899@yahoo.com>

*TONY'S TIP: Spoons are similar to all other antiques and collectibles in that **you should not** clean, polish, or repair them prior to offering them for sale.*

TONY'S TIPS ON HOW TO SELL CHINA

The first thing to do if you plan to sell china is to take a long hard look at what you have. Then ask yourself, "Would I want to buy this and use it?"

No one wants chipped, stained, or damaged items. Dishes less than 150 years old must be in **perfect** condition to find a buyer. Don't waste time offering items with chips and/or cracks, crazing, heavy knife scratches and pattern wear. Pay particular attention to gold trim. If the gold is worn to where you can see the china underneath, you must tell a buyer that. Don't be surprised if the value of your china drops by 60% to 80% if the gold is worn.

Your set does not have to be complete to sell. That's the big advantage to selling to matching services. Since their goal is to fill in someone else's china, your set doesn't have to be complete to have some value.

Serving pieces and items with lids are worth the most. Serving pieces, especially large pieces and those with lids (like soup tureens) are harder to find and as a result worth more than ordinary table settings. The more unusual the piece, the more likely it is to have a market. Cups and saucers are the most common pieces.

You can sell your china with a few simple steps. Begin by listing the pieces, and how many of each you have. Do not list damaged pieces. If you don't know the pattern name, don't despair.

A photocopy (Xerox™) machine is a seller's best friend. Send a photocopy of the front and back of a small plate and indicate the colors in your pattern and the color of the maker's mark on the back (as some companies use color codes). Photocopies usually give excellent detail, so will give an expert an accurate look at what you have. Many china companies have similar names. There are many Wedgwood and Haviland companies. The marks on the bottom tell experts what you have.

If possible, take a close up 35mm photograph. *If you are able to take sharp, close-up 35mm photographs, include a photo which shows the shape of a cup handle. If you can't take photos, a sketch which shows the shape of the handle and base of the cup compared to the bowl of the cup can be very useful.*

Keep your expectations of value reasonable. *Don't expect to be paid a fortune for old china just because it belonged to great granny. China patterns and makers fall in and out of favor. Recent trends toward informality mean you can't assume people are waiting to purchase your old china, silver, or glassware, no matter how lovely. If your set is reasonably complete, or not a popular pattern, consider giving it to a friend or relative who has admired it and would use it.*

Packing china is not difficult as long as two pieces never touch. *The buyer will provide packing instructions. If packed properly, china can be shipped around the world safely as long as two pieces of china don't touch while packed. Padding such as bubble pack, styrofoam sheets, or similar material must separate every packed piece. Lids will chip or break if they are left on sugar bowls or other covered dishes while they are being shipped.* *Never wrap china in newspaper as the ink can rub off onto the china and ruin its value.*

Remember these simple steps:

- *List how many of each type item (plates, saucers, cups, and other items) you have;*

- *Include a color photograph or a b/w photocopy which indicates the colors and patterns;*

- *Include a drawing or Xerox™ of all marks on the bottom of the china, remembering to indicate the color of the marks.*

- *Include a Self Addressed Stamped Envelope (SASE)*

CHINA

◆ **China, crystal, and flatware is sought for resale.** More than 65,000 different patterns from 1,200 American, European, and Japanese manufacturers will be purchased if in fine condition. Chips, cracks, stains, or serious knife marks are not acceptable. Pieces with some pattern or gold wear may be purchased if the pattern is rare or in high demand. Provide the maker's name, pattern name and/or number, and an accurate count of what and how many pieces are available. If you do not know the pattern or the manufacturer, make a Xerox™ of a small plate and describe the colors, or make a copy of a place setting of silverware along with any serving pieces you have, and include whatever is written on the back of your silver. A good sharp photo is always helpful, particularly with stemware. They have 3,200,000 pieces in stock and will try to fill your china, crystal, or silverware needs.

> Robert Page
> Replacements, Ltd.
> 1089 Knox Road or PO Box 26029
> Greensboro, NC 27420
> > (800) 737-5223   fax (336) 697-3100
> > <inquire@replacements.com>

Follow these simple steps:

- **List** how many of each type item (plates, saucers, cups, and other items) you have;

- **Include** a color photograph or a b/w photocopy which indicates the colors and patterns;

- **Include** a drawing or Xerox™ of all marks on the bottom of the china, remembering to indicate the color of the marks.

- **Include** a Self Addressed Stamped Envelope (SASE)

◆ **American and English china and earthenware** by the following makers: Booths, Castelton, Coallport, Franciscan, Flintridge, Gorham, Hammersley, Hohnson Brothers, Lenox, Minton, Pickard, Royal Albert, Royal Doulton, Royal Winton, Royal Worcester, Shelley, Spode, and Wedgwood. Dinnerware must be in like new condition.

> Jacquelynn Ives
> China Matching
> 219 North Milwaukee Street
> Milwaukee, WI 53202
> (414) 272-8880   fax (414) 272-0361   <jchinams860@cs.com>

◆ **Sets and pieces of obsolete dinner china.** Primarily interested in English china, but buys American, European and Japanese patterns. Buys Adams, Aynsley, Cauldon, Coalport, Crown Staffordshire, Denby, Denby/Langley, Foley, George Jones, Johnson Bros., Mason's, Minton, Midwinter, Paragon, Rosenthal, Spode, Royal Albert, Royal Crown Derby, Royal Doulton, Royal Worcester, Shelley, Wedgwood and others. European chinas wanted are MZ, Bernardaud & Co, Elite, Villary & Boch, M. Redon, Schumann, T&V and Vignaud, Theodore Haviland and Haviland & Company. US Franciscan and Japanese Noritake and Mikasa are also often of interest. **Some crystal is also wanted.** They do business worldwide and will make offers for items they can use. Items must be in excellent condition.   If you wish china or stemware appraised, there is a fee, which is refundable if and when they buy your dishes. Send a Xerox™ of the pattern and the markings on the underneath. Note the colors of the markings and all pattern elements. They do not buy giftware, figurines, or floral arrangements. Remember, no SASE to foreign countries.

    Old China Patterns Limited
    1560 Brimley Road
    Scarborough, ON M1P 3G9   CANADA
(800) 663-4533   (416) 299-8880   fax (416) 299-4721
<ocp@chinapatterns.com>   <http://www.chinapatterns.com>

◆ **Fine and popular dinnerware from all manufacturers**, English, American, German, Bavarian, and fine Japanese. Will consider china, crystal, flatware, giftware, Christmas ornaments and made-to-be-collected collectibles such as Hallmark ornaments and figures. Has 25 years experience as a dealer in dinnerwares around the world.

    Alice Korman
    Alice's Past & Present Replacements
    PO Box 465
    Merrick, NY 11566
        (516) 379-1352   fax (516) 379-7302

◆ *Fiesta* **dinnerware and serving pieces** by Homer Laughlin are wanted for auction. "We want one piece or 1,000, as long as it's not the modern Fiesta or badly damaged vintage Fiesta. Please send photos or a description of the size, color and condition of what you have" says the nation's largest auctioneer of Fiesta.

    Michael G. Strawser Auctions
    PO Box 332
    Wolcottville, IN 46795
        (219) 854-2859   <michael@strawserauctions.com>

◆ **Wedgwood commemorative transfer print china.** Earthenware or bone china plates, hollow ware, trivets, tiles, etc., that contain American scenes, views of historic places, children's topics, or scenes from literature. "We mainly want items of American interest, but will also buy some Canadian and Australian scenes." These pieces bear backstamps marked JOSIAH WEDGWOOD & SONS, WEDGWOOD ETRURIA or ETRURIA & BARLASTON. Calendar tiles are from 1879 to 1929. Those before 1890 are worth in excess of $200. Jugs such as the Washington Light Infantry depicting the Civil War are worth in excess of $400 each. "It's hard to tell what we don't want. People are better off to inquire by giving a good description or sending a photo or Xerox™ of the item and its marks. Some items will have to be seen before we can make an offer."

Benton and Beverly Rosen
Mansion House
9 Kenilworth Way
Pawtucket, RI 02860
(401) 722-2927 winter   (508) 759-4303 summer

◆ **Haviland china for resale.** Buys sets or single unusual pieces. Especially wants jardinieres, claret jugs, unusual tea or toast sets, free form salads, syrup jugs, spoon trays, tea caddies, lemonade sets, and other unusual pieces. No individual saucers. If your Limoge china isn't marked Haviland, she doesn't want it. Pieces must be in mint condition with no wear or scratches. To sell your dishes, give the pattern name on the back-stamp, a photocopy of the pattern, and note the colors. Holly has 22,000 pieces in stock and has a computerized search service to help customers find other dishes.

Holly Kreig, Auld Lang Syne
6321 Delta Court
Magalia, CA 95954
(800) 709-8060   <hollyshit@aol.com>

◆ **Royal Doulton, Royal Worcester,** and **Fitz and Floyd fine china** and **crystal by Fostoria, Gorham, Lenox, Royal Doulton** and selected patterns of **Mikasa and Noritake** are purchased for stock. Buys whole or partial sets. Some Spode, Wedgwood and Willeroy and Boch will be "purchased if I have a ready customer." She cannot use worn, damaged, or repaired pieces. "If an item is in fine condition, but I do not wish to buy it, I will try to refer the seller to someone else who may." Give the maker and pattern name and number. Send a Xerox™ if convenient for you. Connie has inherited the family business from her mom, Freda Bell, a lady whom we have recommended for years.

Connie Stolz
China Match & Crystal Match
72 Longacre Road
Rochester, NY 14621
(585) 338-3781   <chinamat@frontiernet.net>

◆ **Series Ware by Royal Doulton** includes hundreds of shapes and patterns of pitchers, mugs, plates and other useful but highly decorated items. This popular transfer ware with a hand-painted look includes a wide variety of themes such as motoring, golfing, fishing, and coaching. Value depends on the rarity and desirability of the form and the image. There have been four books written on Doulton Series Ware, so you can get information at your local public library. If your item is for sale, call Ed, who has edited price guides to Royal Doulton. Also buys Royal Doulton figurines, figural bottles and red animals (see his listings in this book under Animals, Whiskey, and Figurines for more info). **He is not interested in buying dinnerware**, and does not do pattern matching.

Ed Pascoe, Pascoe & Co.
575 SW 22nd Avenue
Miami, FL 33135
(800) 872-0195 (305) 643-2550 fax (305) 643-2123
<ed@pascoeandcompany.com>

◆ **Grandmother's Ware - Chelsea - Applied Sprigware**... Whatever you call it, this mid 1800's English china, ironstone, stoneware and porcelain is sought by this veteran collector-dealer who is currently writing a book on this white ware with applied blue/lavender sprigs (grape, thistles, etc) accompanied by other design elements. She wants mugs, tureens, toilet sets, vases, and more. "I do not buy common items with chips on rims, major cracks, or bad stains (hairline cracks make most items worth less than $10) but will buy very rare items in less than perfect condition." She does not want common cups and saucers with simple sprigs. Tell her the type of item, size, pattern, and maker's mark. Photo if possible. Xerox™ copy of the pattern is a good idea. "I am trying to document as many makers and motifs as possible, and would love to hear from other collectors."

Stephanie Schnatz
17 Tallow Court
Baltimore, MD 21244
(410) 944-0819 <chelsealady@hotmail.com>

◆ **Dishes with dark blue decoration made in England or the U.S**. before 1900. Especially wants pieces with impressed marks such as clews, adams, or hall. Teapots, sugars, creamers, cups and saucers are particularly wanted, Staffordshire, flow blue, Spode, Wedgwood and historical patterns are all desirable, although items marked E.WEDGWOOD are not the Wedgwood and are a lot less valuable. Xerox™ flat pieces, photograph others. Send photo, description of condition and accurate drawing of marks found on the bottom if you'd like an offer.

Carol Payne's Gallery
14455 Big Basin Way
Saratoga, CA 95070
(408) 867-7055 11-5 Wednesday thru Saturday

◆ **Noritake china in "Azalea" or "Tree in the Meadow"** patterns in any quantity from single pieces to entire sets, as long are there are no chips, cracks, or worn gold or paint. Azalea pieces are backstamped "#19322." Tree in the Meadow pieces must have blue water in the foreground and a tree in the rear of the house. Serving pieces, children's sets, and salesmen's samples are the most desirable and will bring from $100 to $1,000. Does not want "Azalea" pattern with a blue backstamp that reads "Nippon." Include the dimensions of your pieces.

> Ken Kipp or Gloria Munsell
> PO Box 116
> Allenwood, PA 17810
>   (570) 538-1440   <allenwoodantique@aol.com>

◆ **Nippon and Noritake china.** "We're seeking large vases, urns, portrait pieces, dolls, chocolate and tea sets, jugs, wall plaques, smoke sets, humidors, and anything else that's quality and perfect. We'll buy Coralene, Moriage, blown-outs, rectangulars, pieces with silver overlay, you name it! We're also in the market for Noritake with Art Deco decorations of men and women. Call or write if you have any."

> Mark Griffin and Earl Smith
> 1417 Steele Street
> Fort Myers, FL 33901
>   (800) 726-1489   <nippononly@aol.com>

◆ **Chintz china** with an all-over floral design made in England. All except damaged items or items in the "Winter Summertime" pattern.

> Russell Mascieri
> 9 North Sunset Drive
> Voorhees, NJ 08043
> (856) 354-2154   fax (609) 953-7768   <rmascieri@aol.com>

◆ **Sets or pieces of German, Bavarian, Czechoslovakian, and Austrian china** in fine condition. Companies stocked include Johann Haviland, Bavarian, Heinrich, Fronconia, Meissen, Rosenthal Thomas, Royal Heidelberg, Krautheim, and many more. China need not be old, just discontinued. Also buys a few French patterns, but no Haviland, Japanese china, or English china. "We buy no china with cracks, crazing, chips, or with the color in a pattern worn off, although we will accept pieces with a slight amount of gold wear. Please send a colored photocopy of a 6" or 8" plate. Copy the front for the design and the back so we can see the hallmark. We also need a color photo of a plate and a cup in silhouette to see the shape of the cup handle and base. We will quote a fair price for any items we can use. If we cannot use what you have, we will try to tell you how to sell it in your locality."

> Joan Nackman
> 56 Meadowbrook
> Ballwin, MO 63011
>   (636) 227-3444

◆ **Phoenix bird china,** both English and Japanese, is wanted. As an advanced collector, she is interested only in serving pieces and unusual shapes not normally found in a dinner set. She does not want cups, saucers, small sauce dishes, bread & butter plates, or 7 1/4" salad plates. Please give condition, noting any hairline cracks. Give the diameter of plates or bowls, and describe any markings on the bottom. She wants you to set the price, so you might want to buy her books on Phoenix, available at $16 each.
    Joan Oates
    685 South Washington
    Constantine, MI 49042
        (616) 435-8353   <koates@remc12.k12.mi.us>

◆ **Flying phoenix china.**
    Carl Cotting
    1441 Crowell Road
    Vienna, VA 22182
        (703) 759-5646

◆ **Clarus Ware** plates, bowls, vases and other china. "We also buy old pieces of Pope Gosser China Ware and want any vase, bowl, plate, or other china signed AST VAN HISE."
    C.W. and Hilda Roderick
    27858 TR 31
    Warsaw, OH 43844
        (740) 824-3083

★ **Clarice Cliff Bizarre Ware.** This English hand painted pottery is decorated with fanciful, geometric, and floral themes. Most pieces are marked, often with the name of the artist, but usually clarice cliff or bizarre. Does not want transfer patterns, only painted ones such as Crocus, Fantasque, Delecia, Caprice, Ravel, and many others. A photo or photocopy is very important as the company made so many patterns, it's almost impossible to know which you have without seeing it.
    Darryl Rehr
    2591 Military Avenue
    Los Angeles, CA 90064
  (310) 477-5229   fax (310) 268-8420   <dcrehr@earthlink.net>

◆ **Warwick china, especially portrait items**. Include a photo with your complete description, and he'll return it. Promises to answer every letter regarding the work of this fine American china maker. Prefers you to set the price wanted, but "amateurs should still write."
    Jeff Mauck
    1900 Warwood Avenue
    Wheeling WV 26003
        (304) 277-2356   <svwarwood@aol.com>

◆ **Autumn Leaf (Jewel Tea) china** and other items marked with Jewel Tea's red, orange, and brown leaf pattern. There are 300+ different pieces of Autumn Leaf china; it takes an expert to tell the difference between a $10 piece and a $100 piece. Common cups, saucers, plates, and mixing bowls are only a dollar or two, but items like candle holders, teapots, bud vases, and butter dishes can bring $40 to $500 each with a few worth more than $1,500. Silverplated and stainless steel Jewel Tea tableware is also highly collectible, bringing $10/$15 per item, with some as much as $100. Other Autumn Leaf products, including canisters, bean pots, and linens are also worth an inquiry. "If your item is in good condition, but it's not something I want to buy, I've got a dozen friends whom I can route you to." Send an SASE. Dimensions are a good idea. Annual membership in the National Autumn Leaf Collector's Club includes a 40+ page newsletter and is only $20.

> Tom Whipple
> National Autumn Leaf Collector's Club
> 62200 East 236 Road
> Wyandotte, OK 74370
> (918) 786-7632 <twhipple@rectec.net>

◆ **Buffalo Pottery or Buffalo china.** "I'll buy almost any marked piece made in that factory," he says.

> Seymour Altman
> 39 Spice Bush
> Williamsville, NY 14221
> (716) 688-6925

◆ **Coors pottery and porcelain,** including dinnerware, art pottery, older ashtrays, Colorado State Fair memorabilia, spittoons, malted milk containers, advertising (including paper), etc. "I also buy other Coors Malted Milk and dairy items such as labels, boxes, back bar containers, milk bottles, and all advertising related to them." Does not want small vases, common mugs with lions on them, newer bar ashtrays, Coors Beer ads, or anything newer than 1950. "You may call for an offer on Coors pottery. I cannot answer questions about brewery items, but if you have something very old, I may be able to recommend a buyer."

> Jo Ellen Winther
> 8449 West 75th Way
> Arvada, CO 80005
> (800) 872-2345 days (303) 421-2371 eves fax (303) 431-5350
> <repofam@aol.com>

◆ **Chintz china.** Describe the piece and the pattern as best you can, including dimensions. A photo is very helpful. How is the item marked? No reproductions or modern wanted.

> Vivian Temes
> Bird in the Cage Antiques
> 110 King Street
> Alexandria, VA 22314
> (703)549-5114   <bird-in-the-cage-antiques@compuserve.com>

◆ **Children's dishes.** "Any china used by children to eat or drink" is sought, "but I prefer American items, and I prefer those made by Roseville (both unmarked and those marked r on the bottom), S.E.G., Paul Revere or Dedham. No damaged pieces.

> Steve Kelley
> PO Box 695
> Desert Hot Springs, CA 92240
>   (760) 329-3206   <kskelley@earthlink.net>

◆ **Oyster plates.** Nothing damaged, please.

> Sheldon Katz
> 18 Cliffside Drive
> Port Jefferson, NY 11777
>   (631) 928-1800

◆ **Old pictorial souvenir chin**a with views of various towns, streets, and places of interest before 1930. "I prefer cups, vases, unusual shapes, and three dimensional figures, but some plates are OK. I am especially interested in pictorial china with New England views, but all old U.S. pictorial souvenir china will be considered. I don't want 1950's and 60's church plates." Indicate what the scene is, where the item was made, and whether there are any cracks or chips. Gary publishes Antique Pictorial Souvenirs Buyer's Guide.

> Gary Leveille
> 5 Brook Land
> Great Barrington, MA 01230
>   (413) 528-5490   <garyleve@aol.com>

TONY'S TIP: Packing china for shipment is not as hard as you think, but does require some care. Never allow two pieces to touch. Ask your buyer for specific packing instructions.

◆ **College plates** depicting scenes or seals of universities and colleges. Prefers those made by Wedgwood, Spode and Lamberton. Items must be in perfect condition without cracks or chips, even if they have been professionally restored. They prefer you to set the price you want, but will make offers.

> Pat or Bill Klein
> PO Box 262
> East Berlin, CT 06023
>> (860) 828-6528 days (860) 828-3973 eves
>> <pklein262@yahoo.com>

◆ **Calendar plates.** This relatively new collector/dealer wants all calendar plates, 1875 to 1949, especially those that were advertising giveaways. He does not buy those that are damaged, chipped or worn, however. Give the date, condition and the scene depicted on the plate. He offers $150 for a 1900 Wedgwood plate and $2,000 for a 1909 by Deldare. He publishes a quarterly newsletter, *The Calendar*.

> Alan Gumtow
> Odd Things
> 710 North Lake Shore Drive
> Tower Lakes, IL 60010
>> (847) 526-5319 voice/fax <agumtow@aol.com>

◆ **Presidential and patriotic English urns, vases and mugs** with American historical motifs, pictures of political figures, battles, or famous events. May be any type of china by any maker. A delft teapot advocating "No stamp act" would bring around $8,000.

> Rex Stark
> Americana
> PO Box 1029
> Gardner, MA 01440
> (978) 630-3237 fax (978) 630-2388 <rexstark@yahoo.com

◆ **Advertising china made by Royal Doulton.** All types including ashtrays, jugs, mugs, bottles, ginger beers, display signs. Old and rare pieces do not have to be in perfect condition to be considered for purchase, but you must indicate any flaws in your description. Make sure to mention the item, the product being advertised, size, color, condition, and any markings.

> Diane Alexander
> 20834 San Simeon Way #70-C
> North Miami Beach, FL 33179
>> (305) 770-4422 <tobyreet@mindspring.com>

TONY'S TIPS ON SELLING POTTERY AND GLASS

Pottery, porcelain, china, bisque, parian, and stoneware are names which confuse amateur sellers. **Fortunately, to sell the Trash or Treasure way, you need to know only the simplest basics about pottery.**

All these names describe ceramics or earthenware made from one form or another of clay. The different names signify the quality and colors of the raw materials and the processes by which they are fired and decorated. You don't need to know too much more than that, because I'm going to steer you to people who care about those distinctions and can make them for you. If you want to explore the topic and learn more about these distinctions, head for your local public library. Many books are available, including books that will help you identify marks you find on the bottom of your pieces.

Pottery ranges in value from a few pennies to thousands of dollars. *Collectors often pay well for items once thought ordinary, so take caution when disposing of pottery items of all types. Valuable pottery is not always easy for the untrained eye (that's you) to detect.*

The output of a few commercial 20th century factories such as Rookwood, Roseville, Cowan, Fulper, and Weller are popular, while the work of other makers is ignored by collectors. Some one-person operations, like that of eccentric George "The Mad Potter of Biloxi" Ohr, created unusual pottery in great demand today.

Stoneware crocks were made in unimaginative shapes, but their folksy decorations (usually in blue on a gray crock) make them desirable. Prices can reach $20,000 or more, although most sell for less than $300 A reader reports being told by his local antique dealer his crock was worth about $50. He turned to Trash or Treasure and found crock expert Dick Hume who paid $4,800 for the same crock. You'll meet Dick in a few pages.

Determining the value of earthenware is not easy. *The quality of the clay and the delicacy of the painting do not guarantee collector interest and high prices. Popularity and scarcity do. Some really ugly stuff brings big bucks!*

TIPS ON SELLING POTTERY AND GLASS (CON'T)

Much of what is true for pottery is true for glass. The work of some companies and periods is hotly sought after, while other older and more rare glass goes relatively ignored.

Glass, like clay, is manufactured into many forms and colors, some worth tens of thousands of dollars, others only worth recycling! Advice in selling glass is essential since it is difficult for the amateur to tell the good from the bad, the common from that worth $100 or more.

Because color has so much to do with value of both glass and earthenware, a photo is almost essential to sell anything. An otherwise identical piece of glass or pottery can be worth 50 times as much in one color as in another. If you can't send a photo, "at the very least," advises Majolica buyer Denise Sater, "accurately describe the color, give the dimensions, patterns, and marks, along with a statement of condition."

When purchasing earthenware or glass, buyers seldom want chipped, stained, or damaged items, although a few very large and/or rare "bruised" pieces may find a market at a small percentage of the price of a perfect one.

Always inspect glass and pottery carefully for damage. Look along all rims, including the base, lid and inside lip. Check the top and bottom for cracks. The best way to do this is to run your fingernail along the top and other edges. Your fingernail will find cracks your eye will miss.

Pottery and glass can be shipped safely. Buyers will give you specific instructions telling you how they want their newly purchased items packed. If you double box your breakables you'll usually be safe.

Trash or Treasure pottery buyers are all valuable sources of information capable of putting money in your pocket. A number of the buyers you'll meet in the next few pages have written books, price guides, and catalogs. Others edit newsletters or are officers in clubs.

I recommend them.

POTTERY (ceramics and earthenware)

★ **American art pottery of all types.** Buys pottery from Fulper, Paul Revere, Rookwood, Grueby, Dedham, TECO, Tiffany, Clewell, Marblehead, Saturday Evening Girls, Newcomb College, George Ohr, Van Briggle, Cowan, Grand Feu, Losanti, New Orleans Art Pottery, Robineau, and other quality American art pottery. Also buys good quality European pottery such as Martin Bros, Moorcroft, and others. Especially likes large and unusual pieces, and has been known to consider damaged pieces if they are important. "If you have any doubts, phone me and I will be glad to be of assistance."

Robert Berman
Le Poulaille
441 South Jackson Street
Media, PA 19063
(610) 566-1516 cel (610) 659-3789 fax (610)566-3319
<ber441@aol.com>

◆ **Rookwood and other art pottery** is wanted by the world's largest dealer in Rookwood, who also buys other American and European art pottery, both production and artist-signed pieces. Brand names they will buy include Grueby, Teco, Van Briggle, Newcomb, Marblehead, Weller, UND, Roseville, Fulper, Overbeck, and Cowan among American companies. European pottery makers of interest include Moorcroft, Massier, Amphora, Gustavsberg, Bock, Freres, Deck, Lachenal, Haviland, Robj, Longwy, Delaherche, Picasso, Zsolnay, Lauger, Rorstrand, Clarice Cliff and Ruskin. Pieces made between 1890 and 1950 are generally the most desirable. Quality Rookwood pieces will be considered even if damaged, although their value is reduced. "If you have any questions about the value of your art pottery, Rookwood or other, please write or call for information at no charge." When writing, include a photo and describe all markings found on the bottom. Please give the dimensions of each piece, and mention any damage no matter how tiny. This well-known dealer has bought, sold, and auctioned high quality pottery for more than 20years, and offers beautiful illustrated catalogs of past and future auctions at prices ranging from $20 to $50.

Riley Humler
Cincinnati Art Galleries
225 East 6th Street
Cincinnati, OH 45202
(513) 381-2128 (513) 381-7527 <info@cincinnatiartgalleries.com>

TONY'S TIPS: Because color has so much to do with value of both glass and earthenware, a photo is almost essential to sell anything other than a stock item from a well-known factory

◆ **Hand decorated art pottery,** American or European, is sought, but David emphasizes that his interest as a dealer is exclusively in "hand decorated" pottery, such as that by Newcomb College, Grueby, George Ohr, Robineau, Overbeck, and Marblehead. Artist signed Rookwood is also of interest, but "we are not looking to buy factory production Rookwood or Roseville." He needs to know the maker, condition, size, shape, decoration, and markings on the bottom, so including a photo is a good idea. This well known expert in the Arts & Crafts period has agreed to make offers to amateur sellers who learn about him through this book if they are serious about selling what they own, but states clearly that he "does not wish readers to price fish or to involve him in bidding wars with other buyers." If you need an appraisal for estate or insurance purposes, the fee is $10/ item. Dave writes a monthly column on pottery, and publishes *Arts and Crafts Quarterly*, an attractive and informative magazine available by subscription for $25/year. His book on Fulper may be purchased from him for $35. Other books, catalogs, and materials on art pottery are available. SASE for more information.

David Rago
117 South Main Street
Lambertville, NJ 08530
(609) 397-1802   fax (609) 397-5543   <perraggal@ragoarts.com>

◆ **Van Briggle and other American art pottery.** A variety of fine pottery will be considered, including Rookwood that is artist signed, North Dakota School of Mines pottery "with good color contrast," Hylong, Newcomb, decorated Marblehead, and the like. But his primary interest is in pre-1913 Van Briggle pottery, the man who created it, and the company that produced it. Wants company records and catalogs, as well as paintings and pots signed by Van Briggle. Will even accept damaged pre-1913 pieces "if priced accordingly." Is not interested in undated Van Briggle or in ND School of Mines that is plain. Describe the size, shape, colors, glaze quality, bottom markings, and condition. Scott is a former president of the American Art Pottery Association and author of *The Collector's Guide to Van Briggle*, available from him for $35 and a *Van Briggle Price Guide* for $6.50. He does appraisals for a fee, and expects you to price your own goods.

Scott Nelson
PO Box 6081
Santa Fe, NM 87502
(505) 424-8584   <scottvqf@aol.com>

◆ **John Bell pottery** made in the 19th century in Waynesboro, especially fancy pieces, which can bring $1,000 or more.

Ken Broyles
PO Box 42
Waynesboro, PA 17268
(717) 762-3068   <kenaudrey@desupernet.net>

◆ **Stangl pottery.** "We especially want the following dinnerware patterns: Blueberry, Bittersweet, Chicory, Colonial #1388, Country Garden, Country Life, Fruit, Fruit and Flowers, Garden Flower, Garland, Grape, Holly, Jeweled Christmas Tree, Lyric, Magnolia, Mediterranean, Newport, Ranger, Rooster, Thistle, Blue & Yellow Tulip, Wild Rose and Town and Country spatterware. We don't want brown stains, chips, or cracks, but minor flaws are acceptable. We'll buy any pieces of Kiddieware, even 'as is', especially Wizard of Oz and Flying Saucer. Stangl artware, vases, and lamps are desired, as are perfect condition Stangl birds and animals, animal planters, and piggy banks. We also buy specialty pottery by Stangl such as flower pots, flower ashtrays, political pitchers and mugs, cigarette boxes, etc., as well as any advertising or promotional pieces for this pottery company.

Bob and Nancy Perzel, Popkorn Antiques
PO Box 1057
Flemington, NJ 08822
(908) 782-9631   <popkorn@blast.net>

◆ **Fulper art pottery,** especially bullet vases, cabinet vases, candles, figural flower frogs, bookends, door stops, wall pockets, porcelain figural perfume lamps, powder jars and more. Also wants catalogs and advertising from the Fulper pottery. Send photos, along with all marks.

Bob and Nancy Perzel, Popkorn Antiques
PO Box 1057
Flemington, NJ 08822
(908) 782-9631   <popkorn@blast.net>

◆ **TECO, Weller and other American art pottery.** "TECO pottery is my favorite. I'll buy geometric and organic vases with square or built in handles. Sculptural leaves and plant forms, usually in matte finish with green tones, but also brown, yellow, gray, etc. This is often highlighted in a black/gray gunmetal color. I am also a strong buyer of Weller vases with raised figures, lizards, snakes, nudes, etc. Weller also comes in strong geometrics. Colors are rose, pink, blue, gray, yellow, brown and matte green, often mixed, often veined with gunmetal. Normally signed. I buy a great deal of Weller, including many of their other lines." He also buys a wide range of other art pottery including Grueby, Saturday Evening Girls, Newcomb College, University of North Dakota, Jervis, American Art Clay, Fulper, George Ohr, Arequipa, California Faience, Chelsea Keramic, Clewell, Clifton (large vases only) and many more. Strongly advise you take a picture since the form and color of pottery determines value. When you send your photo, write down carefully all the marks on the bottom.

Gary Struncius
PO Box 1374
Lakewood, NJ 08701
(800) 272-2529   <gstrun@aol.com>

◆ **Pottery by Hull, McCoy, Weller, Roseville, Watt, Red Wing and Shawnee.** She buys vases, wall pockets, pitchers, candlesticks, bookends, bowls, and most other forms. She does not buy items with chips, cracks or repairs. She does not buy items that are not marked with the name of a maker. Please send a photo along with any numbers or words on the bottom of your item.

> Sharon Vohs
> PO Box 3413
> Chandler, AZ 85244
> (480) 792-0360   <antiqueaz1@aol.com>

◆ **Shawnee pottery.** Although once an active buyer, Pam now acts as a consultant, relying on her decades of experience as an author, editor and dealer to help those with Shawnee questions. "I have a national network of collectors, and can often refer sellers to potential buyers if they have important pieces. My contacts are not interested in more common planters and shakers." Your descriptions must note all chips and hairline cracks. Indentify the color of any and all marks on the bottom. SASE is a MUST.

> Pamela Curran
> PO Box 713
> New Smyrna Beach, FL 32170
> <gpcurran@msn.com>

◆ **Roseville pottery** in many patterns in both their Rozane and production lines. Does not want "brown florals." Photo urged.

> Gary Struncius
> PO Box 1374
> Lakewood, NJ 08701
> (800) 272-2529   <gstrun@aol.com>

◆ **Roseville pottery,** especially in Sunflower, Pinecone and Jonquil patterns. No cracks or chips. Please send photo and dimensions plus any markings you find on the bottom.

> Leda Andrews
> 2110 Staples Avenue
> Key West, FL 33040
> (305) 296-4195   fax (305) 293-0904   <in1era@aol.com>

◆ **Roseville and other children's dishes.** "Any china used by children to eat or drink" is sought, "but I prefer American items, and I prefer those made by Roseville (both unmarked and those marked R on the bottom), S.E.G., Paul Revere or Dedham." No damaged pieces.

> Steve Kelley
> PO Box 695
> Desert Hot Springs, CA 92240
> (760) 329-3206   <kskelley@earthlink.net>

◆ **Miniature American art pottery** less than four inches high made by Niloak, Camark, Redwing, Muncie, Rookwood and others.These are frequently unmarked except for USA or Made in USA. These amall vases were sometimes used as toothpick holders and can be found in a variety of sizes and shapes. He DOES NOT WANT any items marked as being from Japan or China.

> Jim Kegebein
> 6831 Colton Blvd.
> Oakland, CA 94611
> <njak@aol.com>

◆ **Ceramic flower frogs and candelabra depicting ladies dancing** or posing in the Art Deco style. "I'm especially interested in those made by the Ohio company called Cowan, but also buy European makers." He especially seeks Cowan frogs number 708, 717, 803, 804, 805, 812, and 853 as well as the figural dancing candelabra #752. These can bring from $150 to $600, depending on the figure, colors, and condition. To sell your frog, note all the markings you can find.

> William Sommer
> 9 West 10th Street
> New York, NY 10011
> (212) 260-0999   <wgs2@columbia.edu>

◆ **Cowan pottery flower vases and frogs** decorated with women (especially in colors other than white), bookends ($250+), vases (up to $500 depending on the artist, design and skill of execution). Black sculptures trimmed in gold can go even higher. Pieces are usually marked but cowan can be hard to read under the glaze, so he advises you to look closely. Many Cowan artists including Thelma Frazier Winter, Waylande Gregory, and Viktor Schreckengest continued to make pottery and ceramic sculpture on their own after Cowan closed in 1931. These are also wanted by this Cowan researcher who notes, "bowls and candlesticks are of little interest unless they have an unusual design, such as those shaped like women." He requests you give the height of your piece along with a photo. The color of the glaze is so important in valuation, it's impossible to give values without a clear sharp photo. Examine the piece carefully for chips, repairs, or hairline cracks as well as worn patches or scratches in the finish. mark is author of *Introducing Roseville Potter, Bassett's Roseville Prices, Understanding Roseville* and *Cowan Pottery and the Cleveland School.* Autographed copies are available by mail. Visit his website for info. He also buys **European art pottery in Art Nouveau, Art Deco and Arts & Crafts style.**

> Mark Bassett
> PO Box 771233
> Lakewood, OH 44107
> (216) 221- 6025   <mark@markbasset.com>
> <www.markbasset.com>

◆ **California ceramics by Madison or Florence.** Sharon requests you send a description (including all info on the bottom) along with a photo whenever possible if you have figural ceramics made by Madison Ceramic Art Studio or Florence Ceramics.

      Sharon Vohs
      PO Box 3413
      Chandler, AZ 85244
            (480) 792-0360   <antiqueaz1@aol.com>

◆ **Buffalo Pottery.** "I'll buy almost any marked piece."
      Seymour "Si" Altman
      39 Spice Bush
      Williamsville, NY 14221
      (716) 688-6925

◆ **Head vases.** These are small vases shaped like human heads, mostly made during the 1940's, 50's and 60's. She wants ladies (the most common), children, clowns, Indians, Orientals, and whatever. Please send a photo along with any numbers on the bottom of your item. "Please, no damaged vases."

      Sharon Vohs
      PO Box 3413
      Chandler, AZ 85244
            (480) 792-0360   <antiqueaz1@aol.com>

★ **Redware plates, bowls, and other pieces.** "We buy decorated redware from the Midwest and from the Northeastern and Southern United States. Multi-colors are the more desirable pieces, as are those decorated with animals or people, or with verses written on them. We'll pay $1,000 or more for the best pieces." Please take photos or make a sketch of any markings on the bottom and take a photo or make a sketch of the pattern, indicating what part of the pattern is what color. Make certain you note if there are any cracks or chips or other damage.

      Richard Hume
      1300 North Stream Parkway
      Point Pleasant, NJ 08742
            (732) 899-8707   <mazy911@aol.com>

◆ **Ariquipa pottery.** Please send a sharp clear photograph along with your description. Dimensions and bottom marks should be included. All cracks, chips or other defects must be noted.

      Geri Rosato
      150 East Coronado Road #54
      PhoenixAZ 85004
      (602) 258-6202

★ **Decorated stoneware crocks and jugs.** Especially likes pottery with clear markings from NY, NJ, OH, PA, and New England. "I'll pay top dollar for unusual forms decorated with people, animals, ships, trees, houses, strong blue florals, etc. Dated pieces are particularly desirable. I pay from $100 to as much as $10,000 for the right items." He emphasizes that he is interested only in stoneware that is blue decorated, not brown or white. **Also buys inkwells, flasks, and unusual small items made of blue decorated stoneware.** Needs to know the size of the piece in quarts or gallons if marked, in inches if not. Take a photo or make a good sketch of the decoration because the more unusual the decoration, the more he pays. Mention the darkness of the blue. He will help amateur sellers determine what they have. "If you are interested in joining a stoneware collectors club, call me."

Richard Hume
PO Box 281
Bay Head, NJ 08742
(732) 899-8707   <libertyforever76@hotmail.com>

◆ **Decorated stoneware** of all types and forms by all makers before 1920. Damage may be acceptable on rare pieces. Send a color photo along with your description, showing all decoration and all damage. Dealers please price your goods.

Mike Waters
PO Box 2097
Westerville, OH 43086
(800) 894-8095   <marblemike@veriomail.com>

◆ **Spongeware, stoneware, and redware pottery and crockery.** Note all markings on the sides and bottoms, please, if you'd like this important dealer to evaluate what you have. These are often incised with the name of the maker or user, and their city and town, as well as the size of the container. Minor damage and cracks are acceptable in very rare pieces, but you must note all damage, no matter how small. The decoration is the key to value, so photos are essential.

Louis Picek
Main Street Antiques and Art
PO Box 340
West Branch, IA 52358
(319) 643-2065   <msantiques@bigplanet.com>

TONY'S TIP: Remember these simple steps:

• **Include** a color photograph or a b/w photocopy which indicates the colors and patterns;
• **Include** a drawing or Xerox™ of all marks on the bottom
• **Include** a Self Addressed Stamped Envelope (SASE)

EUROPEAN POTTERY & CERAMICS

◆ **Majolica of all types** by George Jones, Holdcroft, Wedgwood, Minton, Etruscan and others are wanted for auction. Describe size, color and condition, plus any marks or signatures on the bottom.
>   Michael G. Strawser Auctions
>   PO Box 332
>   Wolcottville, IN 46795
>   (219) 854-2859   <michael@strawserauctions.com>

◆ **European ceramic flower frogs and candelabra** depicting ladies dancing or posing in the Art Deco style. These can bring from $50 to $500, depending on the figure, colors, and condition. To sell your frog, note all the markings you can find.
>   William Sommer
>   9 West 10th Street
>   New York, NY 10011
>   (212) 260-0999   <wgs2@columbia.edu>

◆ **Art pottery of Eastern Europe,** especially pottery made in Art Nouveau or Secession style by Zsolnay in Pecs (Hungary), Fischer in Budapest, E. Whaliss in Vienna and Amphora in Turn Teplitz (Czechoslovakia) between 1890 and 1920. The names of these makers are incised into the bottom of the items, the values of which can range from $50 to more than $1,000. "Though we do buy rare examples that are damaged, the value is diminished." They do not buy Zsolnay made after 1940. Please send a photo, the size, and markings on the bottom.
>   Federico Santi, The Zsolnay Store
>   PO Box 641
>   Newport, RI 02840
> (401) 841-5060   fax (401) 848-0953   <santi39@mail.idt.net>

◆ **European pottery and porcelain** of the following types:
  - French quimper from the 19th century especially vases and jardiniere which can be worth $1,000 or more;
  - Italian colorful pottery;
  - Gold banded dinnerware, vases, serving pieces, with or without other colors;
  - English Staffordshire blue and white historical pieces;
  - Italian porcelain by Richard Ginori.

"I am not interested in common dinnerware or anything with chips, cracks, hairlines, or restorations. Please send a photo, and include a photo or drawing of the markings on the back/bottom." Dealers should price their goods; amateurs may ask for offers.
>   Rita Armstrong
>   393 Main Street
>   Los Altos, CA 94022
>   (650) 941-9682   <www.mariasantiques.com>

◆ **Italian pottery (Majolica)** of all types: flower pots, vases, dinnerware, bottles, lamps, tiles, dishes, figurines, pockets, etc. "The pieces are all hand-painted in bright colors, often on a white background. There are hundreds of types of decoration: fruit, flowers, people, mythical and religious themes, architecture, etc, but always in bright reds, blues, yellows, greens, and rose (usually all of the above!). Many are reproductions of pieces created during the Renaissance, others are more modern and look like souvenirs. I am interested in all types marked "Made in Italy" on the bottom. Sometimes the markings also identify the region where they were made, such as Gubbio, Deruta, Assisi, etc." A photo is "very helpful," but at the very least, give the dimensions, patterns, colors, and marks, along with a statement of condition. The price you'd like is "helpful" but not required.

> Denise Sater
> 16 Strawberry Lane
> Lititz, PA 17543
>   (717) 625-4310   <dsater7650@aol.com>

◆ **Quimper** ("kam-pair"), a form of antique French peasant pottery, is sought, especially older large examples such as candlesticks, chargers, jardinieres, and figures. New pieces are not wanted. Send a clear photo, the dimensions, and a statement of condition. It is important to describe the markings on the bottom (most pieces are marked), including the color. Among other books, the Bagdades wrote *English and Continental Pottery and Porcelain: An Illustrated Price Guide* and a similar guide to American pottery and porcelain, each available for $22.95. Send an SASE for more information about books written by these popular columnists.

> Susan and Al Bagdade
> The Country Peasants
> 1325 North State Parkway
> Chicago, IL 60610
> (312) 397-1321   fax (847) 392-5848   <adbsdb@aol.com>

◆ **Mexican tourist pottery.** Wants colorful old inexpensive Mexican pottery sold to tourists (1920 to 1960): animal figures, vases, dinnerware and huge decorative platters painted with designs of people, animals, cacti and houses in bright earthy colors. Special interest in pottery with black background and exceptionally large pieces with finer than average brush work. Pottery should be in good condition with no major cracks. Send photo with asking price. Please include SASE.

> Kier Linn
> 2591 Military Avenue
> Los Angeles, CA 90064
>   (310) 477-5229   <dcrehr@earthlink.net>

GLASS

★ **Antique and 20th century art glass.** This well known auctioneer conducts cataloged auctions of art glass, so can handle collections and fine individual pieces of Daum Nancy, **Steuben,** Galle, **Tiffany** and other art glass, as well as collections and fine pieces of Wedgwood and other fine porcelain.

James D. Julia Auctioneers
PO Box 830
Fairfield, ME 04937
(207) 453-7904   fax (207) 453-2502   <jjulia@juliaauctions.com>

◆ **Art glass from Victorian and Art Nouveau periods** including English and French cameo glass by Galle and others, **Tiffany** flower forms and other glass, Burmese, Royal Flemish, Crown Milano, lava glass, Loetz silver overlays, **Steuben** acid cut back, Rose Findlay onyx, Aurene, Wheeling Peachblow, Quezal, Holly amber, and reverse painted table lamps by Handel and Pairpoint lamps with puffy shades. She will answer all mail that includes a photo, dimensions and SASE. As with all glass, condition is crucial. Call for confidential consultation.

Karen Singleton
Cincinnati Art Galleries
225 East 6th Street
Cincinnati, OH 45202
(513) 381-2128   (513) 381-7527   <info@cincinnatiartgalleries.com>

◆ **Black glass** has been her passion for 30 years, so "I am not interested in common pieces made by L.E.Smith I am looking for truly unusual figurines, animals, Victorian pieces, creamers, and glass made by Fenton that is white or pink with black glass edging around the top ruffles. There is little known about black glass (which often looks a very deep violet when held to bright light) so I can't tell you exactly what I want...just unusual pieces." She does say she isn't interested in the octagonal black dinner sets made in France and sold in discount stores today, nor does she want dishes and plain vases. Because there are so many different pieces, a picture and dimensions are a must, as it's the only way she can identify what you have. She is the author of *Collector's Guide to Black Glass,* available from her for $20 postpaid.

Marlena Toohey
PO Box 553
Marietta, OH 45753
(800) 533-3433   (740) 373-6146   <info@glasscollectingbooks.com>

TONY'S TIP: When a listee says he or she is not interested in a particular item, please do not waste his or her time and yours by offering what they do not want.

◆ **Ruby glass.** This 30 year veteran collector is looking for the more rare and unusual items made in this distinctive deep red glass, such as candle sticks and other pieces with leaf pattern made by Cambridge. She does not want "common Anchor Hocking glass (look for an anchor in a circle on the bottom) or nondescript foreign made glass." Please send her a picture of what you have (glass is very difficult to describe). You may be able to find it in her book *Ruby Glass of the 20th Century*, available from her for $25 postpaid.

Naomi Over
8909 Sharon Lane
Arvada, CO 80002
(303) 424-5922

◆ **Victorian glassware.** "We pay cash for collections, estates, or single pieces of the following:
* Decorated glass;
* Cobalt blue glass;
* Ruby-stained glass;
* Cranberry glass;
* Blown opalescent glass;
* Fancy art glass.

Buys all types of Victorian glass including pitchers and tumblers, salt shakers and sugar shakers, syrup jugs, and milk glass vases in silver-plated holders. He does not buy depression glass, bottles, clear glass (without color), or anything that is chipped, cracked or damaged. Please give a detailed description and tell how you came to own it. A picture is important. "Dealers should price their goods; amateurs ready to sell may ask for offers."

Scott Roland
Glimmer Glass Antiques
PO Box 262
Schenevus, NY 12155
(607) 638-5428

◆ **Coin glass dated 1892.** "I'll buy glass bowls, lamps, and other items with clear or frosted glass coins attached or inset. Coins should be dated 1892. It's important to give exact height and diameter. If I don't want your piece of coin glass, I'll try to suggest another collector who is looking for it." Tim pays $500 and up for lamps, and will send you a price list of what he pays for all pieces. Watch for reproductions (most of them have a ribbon above the eagle's head on the reverse side of the coin). Tim wrote *US Coin Glass: A Century of Mystery* which pictures nearly all known coin glass, available from him for $20.

Tim Timmerman
11655 SW Allen Blvd. #31
Beaverton, OR 97005
(503) 646-8300   <timt@wa-net.com>

◆ **Many kinds of glassware and china** are sought by one of the country's larger auction firms specializing in post-Victorian glass. He buys outright or accepts on consignment for auction:
  • **Carnival glass**, especially pitcher sets, tumblers, whimsies, opalescent pieces, and common items in rare patterns and colors. Contact him with one item or a collection since there are many valuable pieces that *only* an expert will recognize;
  • **Victorian pattern glass**;
  • **Cameo glass** vases, plates,urns, and other glass items made by the Phoenix Glass Co.;
  • **RS Prussia** china with scenes, portraits, or pearlized florals;
  • **Noritake china** with geometric designs;
  • **Nippon china** humidors and large high relief "blown out" vases depicting birds, animals, or figures;
  • **Mandarin red glassware** by Fenton Glass Company.
Include your phone number if the piece is for sale. Tom has a reputation for being slow to respond, but helpful with amateur sellers. Phone him midweek if you think you have something good.

  Tom Burns, Burns Auction Service
  109 East Steuben Street
  Bath, NY 14810
      (607) 776-7942

◆ **Carnival glass** is wanted "in any amount and any color." Prefers dealers to price, but warns that some of the standard price guides are highly overpriced. This 25 year veteran collector is willing to help amateurs "who are actually selling, not just calling everyone fishing for free appraisals and the highest price."

  Dick Hatscher
  142 Walnut Hill Road
  Bethel, CT 06801
      (203) 743-1468   <hatscher@worldnet.att.net>

◆ **Carnival glass.** "I'll buy one piece or a collection, in any colors." Prefers you to set the price.

  W. J. Warren
  38 Mosher Drive
  Tonawanda, NY 14150
      (716) 692-2886   <wwa38@aol.com>

◆ **Carnival glass.** Describe the piece and the pattern as best you can, including color and dimensions. A photo of larger pieces or a Xerox™ copy of plates is very helpful. No reproductions or modern wanted.

  Vivian Temes, Bird in the Cage Antiques
  110 King Street
  Alexandria, VA 22314
  (703)549-5114   <bird-in-the-cage-antiques@compuserve.com>

★ **Steuben crystal** is wanted by a long time collector. Please describe your piece, noting any damage. Photo is very helpful.

Robert Block
PO Box 2321
Shelton, CT 06484
(203) 924-2802 voice/fax   <blockschip@aol.com>

◆ **Steuben crystal** is wanted: animals, birds, mushrooms, caterpillars, dinosaurs, and all major table accessories, ornamental designs and exhibition pieces. Specializes exclusively in buying and selling classic Steuben crystal. Send a photo and other information.

Jeffrey Purtell
PO Box 28
Amherst, NH 03031
(800) 973-4331   fax (603) 673-1525
<jfpurtell@steubenpurtell.com>

TONY'S TIP: A few pieces of the colored glass dinnerware of 1910-1940, called "depression glass." are surprisingly valuable. Covered butter dishes bring $100 - $400 each. **Expert advice is essential,** because pieces with no value in one color or pattern can be worth $100 in another.

◆ **Depression glass** in various colors and patterns. A Xerox© copy is very helpful if you don't know the pattern. Do not count pieces that have chips. A photo helps if your item is colored. "I'll pay fair prices for any depression glass I can resell in my shop."

Nadine Pankow
8825 West 98th Street
Palos Hills, IL 60465
(708) 599-9107   <nadineglas@aol.com>

◆ **Fostoria glass and memorabilia** are wanted by the founder of the Fostoria Glass Society in Southern California. "I'll buy dealer signs, dealer catalogs from before 1940, postcards, displays, trade cards, calendars, magazine ads (1924 to 1931 only), and any other Fostoria Glass Company item in mint condition." His glass wants are more restricted as he only buys frosted or clear Victoria (pattern #183) and rare pieces of pattern #2412 called Colony. He is not interested in common Colony glassware or other Fostoria patterns, but finding a Victoria oil lamp is high on his list. "All items must be in mint condition or don't bother."

Gary Schneider
18864 J & J Lane
Yorba Linda, CA 92886
(714) 777-8823

◆ **Elegant glassware** by Cambridge, Fostoria, Heisey, Imperial, Morgantown or Paden City. Give the maker and pattern if you know it. If not, send good sharp photos of each of the styles you are offering. Sets preferred. Do not count any chipped or cracked pieces. Dealers price your goods. Amateur sellers may ask for an offer.

> Mike Waters
> PO Box 2097
> Westerville, OH 43086
> (800) 894-8095   <marblemike@veriomail.com>

◆ **Crystal stemware.** Buys English, American, Japanese and European manufacturers, but is only interested in named and numbered patterns. Indicate the maker and pattern, and how many of each item you have. Do not count anything damaged.

> Old China Patterns Limited
> 1560 Brimley Road
> Scarborough, ON M1P 3G9   CANADA
> (800) 663-4533   (416) 299-8880   fax (416) 299-4721
> <ocp@chinapatterns.com>   <http://www.chinapatterns.com>

◆ **Glass toothpick holders** in mint condition. She seeks numerous patterns. Make a photocopy or photo of your holder if you don't know the name of its pattern, and describe the color as best you can. There are many reproduction holders, so she may have to examine yours before making a final offer. Will also consider interesting holders made of metal or china. Judy is founder of the National Toothpick Holder Collectors Society and has published their newsletter for 23 years.

> Judy Knauer
> 1224 Spring Valley Lane
> West Chester, PA 19380
> (610) 431-3477   <winkjk@netaxs.com>

◆ **Early American pressed glass in Willow Oak pattern** in amber, blue, or Vaseline colors.

> Audrey Buffington
> PO Box 386
> South Thomaston, ME 04858
> (207) 594-2683

◆ **Baccarat crystal.** Send photo and complete description including the location of any and all marks. No chips or cracks are acceptable.

> Rita Armstrong
> 393 Main Street
> Los Altos, CA 94022
> (650) 941-9682 voice/fax   <www.mariasantiques.com>

Other buyers of fine crystal stemware see 44-45

◆ **Colored cut glass** from the 19th century. A sharp photo along with the dimensions are important. Note any and all chips or defects. "I'm looking for high quality, perfect condition works of cut glass art."
Ken Clee
PO Box 11412
Philadelphia, PA 19111
(215) 722-1979   <waxntoys@aol.com>

◆ **Antique glass paperweights,** 1845-1900. "I will buy fine French (Pantin, Baccarat, Clichy, St. Louis), American (Boston Glass Co., Sandwich Glass Co., New England Glass Co., Gillinoer, Mt. Washington), English (Bacchus, Whitefriars), Russian and Bohemian paper-weights. I am especially looking for Pantin paperweights from the late 1870's for which I will pay from $2,000 to $35,000. I also seek early Clichy bouquet on a moss background which can be worth as much as $40,000. I don't want paperweights with blobs of colored glass or with large bubbles in the design." A close up color photo of your weight is important and should be accompanied by a good description, including the diameter. This well known author and collector does not send out a wants list because, he explains, "I will purchase all top quality weights." Paul's book *The Jokelson Collection of Antique Cameo Incrustation* is available with price guide for $60.
Paul Dunlop
The Dunlop Collection
PO Box 6269
Statesville, NC 28687
(800) 227-1996   In NC: (704) 871-2626   fax (704) 871-2329

◆ **Paperweights.** "I pay the highest prices for both antique and modern art glass paperweights of all types," says this 25 year veteran Please send him a photo with your name and phone number. Call for information about the International Paperweight Society and full-color magazine. Selman is a major auctioneer of valuable art glass weights and the author of numerous books on paperweights, available through him.
Larry Selman
123 Locust Street
Santa Cruz, CA 95060
(800) 538-0766   fax (831) 427-0111   <lselman@got.net>

◆ **Antique glass paperweights** and other items including **art glass, glass pens, and whimsies**. "I'm looking for the old and rare." Make certain to note all damage, no matter how small or send close up pix. Semi-annual paperweight auctions are conducted. Write for info.
Stanley Block
PO Box 51
Trumbull, CT 06611
(203) 261-3223   <blockschip@aol.com>

CLOTHING

◆ **Vintage clothing and hats.** "I buy and sell mint condition men's, women's, children's and fancy baby clothing dating from the 1890's through the 1940's, especially flapper dresses, stylish women's suits and jackets, 1940's rayon dresses, evening suits and dresses. Both day wear and evening wear are desirable.
  • Stylish **hats** from the early 1930's or before with full lining;
  • Old **draperies,** and old **bolts of material**;
  • Early **bridal clothing and headpieces**;
  • Accessories such as **shoes,** hats, belts, etc.;
  • **Jewelry, compacts**, etc.;
  • **Handbags** and **parasols;**
  • **Lace**.
Individual prices run from $10 to $75, with only "absolutely incredible" items bringing more. "I do not want things that are ripped, faded, have underarm stains, too small for today's wearers (with tiny neck or arm holes), worn out, or that have poor craftsmanship. Nor do I want anything from the 1950's or 60's except designer clothes. **I do not buy fur.** If you want to sell clothing, you must tell me the period, give the size and color, indicate whether it has a zipper or buttons, identify the material if possible, and list any defects." Note whether hats have lining. Amateur sellers may request an offer, which will be made after seeing the item. Dealers must price their goods. Photo a good idea. Call her about shipping on approval to make it easy on everyone.
    Pahaka September
    19 Fox Hill
    Upper Saddle River, NJ 07458
    (201) 327-1464 after 6 p.m.   <pahakasept@aol.com>

◆ **Clothing from before 1940 for resale.** Also buys shoes, belts, hats, purses and accessories. Everything must be clean, complete, and undamaged. Describe the item, size, color and maker. Dealers price your goods; amateurs may request an offer from this 30 year veteran.
    Fay Knicely, Antique Apparel
    PO Box 1
    Acworth, NH 03601
        (603)-835-2295   <fay@sover.net>

◆ **Vintage clothes made before 1950** such as beaded sweaters and beaded purses and bags, evening gowns, prom dresses, men's tuxedos and hats, etc. Also buys parasols and piano shawls. No damaged or stained items as items are purchased for resale in her 2,000 sq.ft. shop. Price your goods when possible.
    Vivian Temes, Bird In the Cage Antiques
    110 King Street
    Alexandria, VA 22314
    (703) 549-5114   <bird_in_the_cage_antiques@compuserve.com>

★ *Levis, Lee,* and *Wrangler* **jeans and jackets** for resale. "I'll buy all pre-1970 *Levi Strauss* jeans and jackets and some older *Wrangler* and *Lee* jeans and jackets." The *Levis* he wants all have a small red tag on the front pocket (jackets left, pants right) which spells out *l-E-v-i-s.* Jackets before 1949 bring $300 and up even if heavily worn. Jackets, with two front pockets bring $25 to $500. Does not want *Levis* with tags of any color other than red. Describe condition carefully noting stains, holes, wear, the condition of the leather ID tag. The serial number on the back pocket leather ID tag is helpful. Also buys **advertising signs and figures** from *Levi, Wrangler* and *Lee* products. Also silk or rayon **Hawaiian shirts** made before 1960.

> David Bailey, Aloha
> 517 Kapahulu
> Honolulu, HI   96815
>   (808) 734-7628   <baileysantiques@webtv.net>

★ **Vintage Hawaiian shirts,** 1930-1955. The label, size, coloration, and pattern are important, as is the material, so include all that when you write. Shirts can be made of cotton, rayon, or silk. A silk shirt with a fish pattern (his personal favorite) could bring as high as $500. Most are considerably less, but well worth your time. "I'm willing to answer questions and provide information to people who are not sure if their shirts are old enough." A photograph or photocopy is helpful.

> Evan Olins
> Hula Heaven
> 75-5744 Alii Drive
> Kailua-Kona, HI 96740
> (808) 329-4122   (808) 329-7885   <hulaheaven@aol.com>

◆ **Men's and women's clothing and accessories,** 1900-1940. Seeks designer clothing by Fortuny, Poiret, Vionnet, Redfern, Worth, Schiaparelli, Gallenga, Chanel, Dior, Adrian, Balenciaga, Rudi Gernreich, Hermes, Gucci, Pucci, McCardell, Ricci, Cardin, Courreges, etc. Especially likes "anything whimsical" and would like to know about any **ethnic clothing and textiles** you might have.. Wants average sizes in good condition. If the items have been altered where th;ey cannot be returned to their original state, she's not interested.

> Doris Raymond
> The Way We Wore
> 1094 Revere Avenue   #A-29
> San Francisco, CA 94124
>   (415) 822-1800 voice/fax   cel (415) 505-9443
>   <drwww@ncal.verio.com>

TONY'S TIP: Clothing buyers do not want items that are torn, or stained by paint or grease. Check your items carefully and describe condition accurately.

◆ **Men's clothingand accessories from 1880-1895**, original or reproduction, in specific sizes, such as top hats, watch chains and other items
worn by an English gentleman of that time. Contact him for a list of
sizes for each item." His website has a long list of items wanted.

> Rev. Sherlock Holmes
> PO Box 3
> Worcester, MA 01613
> free (877) 306-4059   <antiques@sherlockholmes.com>
> <www.sherlockholmes.com>

◆ **Men's old clothes,** with an emphasis on sport, casual and work
clothing from 1920 through the 1960's. Items wanted are:
  - *Levi's* jeans and jackets (age, size, and condition determine the
    value...from $100-$3,000);
  - **Military khakis;**
  - **Flight jackets** and **Military tour jackets;**
  - **Decorated sweat shirts** with interesting designs and logos;
  - **Hawaiian shirts** ($50-$200);
  - **Bowling shirts** ($50-$200);

"We DO NOT WANT women's jeans, newer jeans with problems, polyester jeans, colored jeans, or jeans with chemical treatment (like acid
wash or stone wash)." Please give specific information about the size,
color, any defects. To get the best offer, make sure to include a good
color photo, especially on expensive items with colors or designs.

> Dan Kelley's Experienced Denim
> PO Box 239
> Fayetteville, AR 72702
> (479) 444-7541   fax (501) 521-8331   <exd@edenim.com>

◆ **Leather mini skirts, micro skirts and hot pants** from the 1960's.
"I buy leather only. No suede or vinyl, please." Describe the condition,
any tears, stains, dirt, smells. Give the label and size, too, please.

> Steve Hannan
> 141 East Central Street
> Natick, MA 01760

◆ **Women's rubber undergarments** including girdles, panty girdles,
garter belts, sanitary garments, corsets, corselettes and all-in-ones. They
can be U.S. or foreign made, perforated or solid, gum rubber or sheet
rubber, and in any color. The more unusual the better. Original boxes are
a plus, as is any original counter advertising for the product.   does not
want cracked, melted or hopelessly stuck together items or those that
have hardened. Your description should include what it is, the size,
color, and condition. "The price you'd like helps."

> Ms. Brunswick
> PO Box 9729
> Baltimore, MD 21286

◆ **Women's rubber boots,** both rain and fashion type, especially those from 1940 to 1970 in odd colors, decorated, thigh highs, Cuban heels and other less ordinary boots. Wants U.S. or foreign made in any color except black, but will consider black ones if unusual. Original boxes are a plus as is any counter or display material. does not want vinyl or plastic "unless they're high white or other dramatic colors." Your description should include what it looks like, size, color, and condition. Photo helpful, as is the price wanted (usually $20-$50).

> Ms. Brunswick
> PO Box 9729
> Baltimore, MD 21286

◆ **Hand painted neckties.** "Most are 1940's vintage wide ties in silk or rayon blend with various scenes or abstracts. Especially wants nudes, lusty women, and hula dancers (worth up to $100 each), but also cowboy and fishing themes (which can bring to $75). Does not want narrow ties. Include maker's name and a Xerox™. Condition critical.

> Don Colclough
> 732 North Cuyler Avenue
> Oak Park, IL 60302
> (800) 775-5078   <mrmodern@aol.com>

◆ **Clothing buttons made of glass, brass, or wood.** Also wants pearl, porcelain, irory, vegetable ivory, Bakelite, lucite, rhinestone and moonglow buttons. Any buttons that are figural or pictorial featuring religion, mythology, cupids, fairies, fables, and other attractive interesting items. Uniform and other embossed buttons, especially military and work buttons such as from railroad or transit uniforms. They must be clean and in good condition. "I will pay you according to subject, size, material and condition with some buttons bringing $25 to $100 each. I will buy one or a collection. I DO NOT WANT shirt buttons or other modern ordinary plastic buttons.

> JoAnne Polk
> PO Box 133
> Coggon, IA 52218
> (319) 435-2213   <thepolkfolk@aol.com>

◆ **Buttons,** especially U.S. military, Confederate, military school, and uniform buttons with state seals. He also buys "high quality clothing buttons of porcelain, satsuma, or with pictures." He does not want WWI or WWII buttons or "simple clothing buttons made of plastic or bone." Please describe the design, and note anything stamped on the back. This former director of the National Button Society prefers that you ship for inspection prior to final offer.

> Warren Tice
> 8 Orchard Terrace
> Essex Junction, VT 05452
> (802) 878-3835 voice/ fax   <wtice@vbimail.champlain.edu>

LACE & NEEDLEWORK

★ **Handmade lace from 1500-1900.** "The best thing is to photocopy as much of the piece as possible. From a photocopy I can often tell whether a full appraisal is warranted or if it is a piece I might like to buy. Even small pieces are worth your attention. A great deal of valuable lace is lost each year because people don't take time to inquire." She does not want machine made lace or ordinary crochet and tatting. She prefers sellers to set the price, but will assist genuine amateurs to identify what they have "if it's for sale." Produces an interesting newsletter for lace fanciers for $10 a year. Elizabeth is author of the excellent *Guide to Lace and Linens*, available at bookstores or directly from her.
> Elizabeth Kurella, Lace Merchant
> PO Box 244
> Whiting, IN 46394
> (219) 659-1124   <ekurella@home.com>

◆ **Lace, trimmings, embroidery and stitchery.** Wants assortments of pre-1920 rosettes, fabric or ribbon trims for clothing or hats, tatted items that are more than 5" in size (including doilies), white on white stitchery, red stitchery on white, beaded clothing and accessories, and clothing (including pantaloons, skirts, and dresses) with decorative handiwork. Also buys quilt tops, crazy quilts, and other handmade cloth items. Send a good photograph or photocopy of what you wish to sell. "Items can be partially damaged if I use them to make other things. Please, no hankies or crochet items." Include SASE for response.
> Linda Gibbs, Heirloom Keepsakes
> 10380 Miranda Ave.
> Buena Park, CA 90620
> (714) 827-6488

◆ **Samplers and vintage needlework and linens.** "I'll consider rugs, coverlets, needlepoint and other fine quality handiwork." Send a photo or photocopy, along with dimensions and a clear description of damage or wear. Include an SASE.
> Denise Hamilton
> 899 Latta Brook Road
> Elmira, NY 14901

◆ **Old material, cloth scraps, patterned flour and feed sacks,** and other material useful for old style quilting. Also buys **quilting and patchwork patterns, books and tools** before 1950. Send a sample or make a Xerox™ of what you have to offer.
> Judy Speezak
> 425 5th Avenue
> Brooklyn, NY 11215
> (718) 369-3513   <speesakquilt@earthlink.net>

★ **Blankets with Indian or cowboy patterns.** "I buy commercially made wool blankets by Beacon, Buell, Candelario, Capps, Esmond, Hamilton, Oregon City, Pendleton, American Indian Blanket Mills, Provo Woolen Mills, Knight Woolen Mills, and Racine (Badger State). Don't worry if your blanket has lost its label; if old, it's still worth money to me. I also buy Indian material patterned bathrobes, jackets, pillows, couch covers, etc. I prefer all material to be priced, but will make offers to people who are not dealers. I answer calls and letters promptly." A photograph or photocopy is a must, and you are requested to list all flaws, holes, etc., in your first letter. Because blankets are often washed improperly, shrunk, and therefore undesirable, you should include accurate dimensions.

Barry Friedman
PO Box 55492
Valencia, CA 91385
(661) 255-2365   <barryf@thevine.net>

◆ **Old plain or patterned cotton yardage** in fine condition so the material can be used for quilting. Wants bolts, squares, scraps in good clean condition. Also old **quilting books, patterns** and related items. She DOES NOT WANT materials other than cotton. No knits or polyester. Prices paid are based on design, age, size and condition.

Judy Speezak
425 5th Avenue
Brooklyn, NY 11215
(718) 369-3513   <speezakquilt@earthlink.net>

◆ **Chenille bedspreads, rugs and house robes.** These come in a variety of designs. They can can be solid colors or a mix of colors in interesting designs. She especially wants animals, bright florals, Art Deco geometrics, birds, cowboys and other characters as well as various themes designed for infants. Chenille is made of soft tufted cords of silk, cotton or worsted and was very popular in the 1950's (sold by Ward's among others). Condition must be excellent with no tears, stains or visible wear.

Judy Polk Harding
4347 Farm House Lane
Fairfax, VA 22032
(703) 503-7323   <thefivejs@aol.com>

◆ **Lace, linnen, embroidery and fine material of all types.** Please make a photocopy of part of what you have and include an envelope addressed to yourself with a 33¢ stamp on it. "I'm buying for resale so condition must be perfect. No tears or stains." Mention this book.

Kaaren Harstad Nowlin
1351 Bullard Lane
Tustin, CA 92780
(714) 838-1890

TONY'S TIPS ON SELLING JEWELRY

You must get all jewelry into the hands of someone trained and experienced in old jewelry.
If you try to evaluate it yourself, you could make costly mistakes. Diamonds and other precious and semi-precious stones are often mistaken for glass in old jewelry.
You cannot rely upon local jewelers *and diamond merchants for accurate appraisals of antique jewelry.*

19th century gemstones were cut differently than is popular today. *A reader showed me a two and a half carat diamond ring he bought at a yard sale for 25¢. I hope he wasn't shopping at your house!*

Jewelry buyers want to know:

(1) *The basic material from which your item is made, such as silver, gold, brass, plastic, etc.*
(2) *All names, numbers, and markings. The right mark can put hundreds of extra dollars in your pocket.*
(3) *Shape, color, and number of any stones.*
(4) *Dimensions are helpful; values can be influenced by size. Photocopying is a good way to describe hatpins, brooches, bracelets and other jewelry.*

Be prepared to ship your jewelry with a five day return privilege. *Buyers want to inspect jewelry before buying. If they do pay first, you must give the money back if the buyer isn't happy for any reason with what you send.*

When mailing items worth more than $500, send them Registered Mail. *Ask your Post Office as some minor restrictions apply.* **Do not use FedEx or Airborne** *as your jewelry items can not be adequately insured.*

A certified gemologist and costume jewelry expert said, "Few dealers know who the important makers of costume jewelry are. If they sell good pieces at junk prices, that means they paid junk prices for them. The original owner lost money. Sellers should always go to jewelry experts."

JEWELRY

★ **Antique and collectible jewelry** from the 1700's to 1940's "with a preference for precious metals but I do deal in some costume jewelry." Her special interests include:
- **Victorian jewelry;**
- **Enameled pieces;**
- **Hair jewelry;**
- Old cut **diamonds;**
- **Unusual jewelry;**
- High grade **wrist and pocket watches.**

Send her a description of the item, including its size. A photo of both the front and back is highly advisable. Dealers must price their goods. Amateurs may ask for an appraisal or an offer. Appraisals are for a fee. "If I do an appraisal, I will not make an offer to buy. If I make an offer, I will not appraise." Ms. Bell is a Graduate Gemologist and certified to evaluate fine gems and jewelry. She has been in antique jewelry for 30 years and wrote*How To Be Jewelry Detective* ($22 postpaid), *Q & A About Old Jewelry 1840-1950* ($28pp), and *Encyclopedia of Hairwork Jewelry* ($28) and an instructional video on jewelry and her bimonthly newsletter. She appraises for Antiques Roadshow and is available to share her knowledge of jewelry at various gatherings for a fee.

C. Jeanenne Bell, Jewelry Box Antiques
7325 Quivira Road #238
Shawnee, KS 66216
(913) 962-8533   fax (913) 962-4418   <cjbell@msn.com>
<http://www.jewelryboxantiques.com>

★ **Old and antique jewelry,** especially:
- **Karat gold pieces,** particularly signed pieces with Art Nouveau and Art Deco designs (1890-1915);
- **Sterling** silver items signed by Unger Brothers or Kerr, mostly Art Nouveau brooches featuring female faces;
- **Designer costume jewelry** signed by Trifari, Mariam Haskell, Hattie Carnegie, Coro, Eisenberg Original and others;
- **Georg Jensen** jewelry, tablewear or serving pieces;
- **Mexican silver** jewelry, signed or unsigned;
- **Enameled jewelry** even if chipped or damaged;
- **Diamonds;**
- **Bakelite bracelets, bangles and brooches.**

Describe your items completely, or make a photocopy. If you know the item's ownership history, please give it. Note all markings.

Arnold Reamer, Timepiece Antiques
PO Box 26416
Baltimore, MD 21207
(410) 486-8412   (410) 944-6414   cel (410) 336-1002
fax (410) 265-7877   <arnoldreamer@webtv.net>

◆ **Costume and other jewelry** is sought, but only particular kinds:
- All **signed designer pieces** by B.David, Boucher, Ciner, Cini, Coro sterling, DeRosa, Dior, Eisenberg, Gerrys, J.J., Joseff, Ledo, Matisse, Mazer, Pennino, Pinnetta, Renoir or Reja;
- **Rhinestone jewelry** with red or purple stones in any size or style, especially large and gaudy pieces;
- **Czech jewelry** (especially bracelets, brooches and necklaces with drop pendants); pieces tend to be large, intensely colored, and have brass filigree often marked Czech or Czechoslovakia;
- **Hair jewelry and wreaths.** During the mid 1800's, human hair was braided or interlaced into rings, bracelets, necklaces, lockets, watch fobs or large wreaths;
- **Mood rings** from the 1970's that change color while you wear them. Must be in working condition;
- **Hand hammered aluminum bracelets,** pendants, brooches, key chains and money clips;
- **Aluminum souvenir jewelry** marked as being a souvenir of a particular place;
- **Copper jewelry** marked "Matisse," "Renoir" or Rebaje, many of which have an enamel overlay;
- **Holiday pins** with a Christmas, Halloween, Easter or other holiday theme or character;
- **Animal and insect pins,** especially those with Lucite bellies;
- Pins depicting humans or animals;
- **Charms and charm bracelets** made of gold, sterling, silver plate, plastic or Mexican silver in a variety of themes: novelties, awards, animals, people, animated characters, souvenirs, and realistic objects, especially those with wheels that turn or other moving parts;
- **Cuff links** pre-1940 made of gold or silver, plain or ornate, especially with precious or semi-precious stones; single cuff links welcome;
- **Men's watch chains and fobs** in a variety of themes;
- **Award pins** designed to be worn on a lapel or shirt-front, made of 14k, 10k, sterling or gold filled only, with or without a pearl or other stone; all types (years of service, attendance, activities) issued by any group, fraternal organization, church, school or service organization;
- **Broken pieces of good jewelry;**
- **Ladies'** non-working 14k **wrist watches** priced for craft use.

"I'll buy one piece or a showcase full," she says. Please send a photo or photocopy, along with a description and the history if known. Dealers must price their goods, but amateur sellers may request an offer.

Judy Polk Harding
4347 Farm House Lane
Fairfax, VA 22032
(703) 503-7323   <thefivejs@aol.com>

◆ **Bakelite jewelry and household items,** including bracelets, pins, necklaces, old purses, buttons, clocks, belt buckles, kitchen items, hat pins and other items made with this early plastic. "I need a picture of your item(s) sent to me for inspection."

Sharon Vohs
PO Box 3413
Chandler, AZ 85225
(480) 792-0360   <antiqueaz1@aol.com>

◆ **Bakelite bangles and pins** are wanted by this veteran collector and author of Bakelite books. He wants only heavily carved, transparent or other high end pieces, especially designs by Shultz. He DOES NOT WANT plain bangles, hinged bangles, earrings, belt buckles, or clips. Send a .jpg image along with your contact information.

Parry Karima
fax (718) 668-2933   <info@plasticfantastic.com>
<http://www.plasticfantastic.com>

◆ **Bakelite jewelry and boxes.** She wants older Bakelite in bright colors, especially whimsical pieces in bright reds and yellows. "I love figurals, animals, people, flowers and "fun" pins, especially in sets with bangles and other pieces. I also buy modern pieces made by contemporary artists from old Bakelite, including those by Ester & Ron Shultz, Penny & Dan Lains, Judy Clarke, Karen & Howard Kronimus, and Jackie Weeks." She notes that later modern pieces are usually signed but some of these artists' early work is not. You are encouraged to ask. In addition to jewelry, she also collects **Bakelite boxes.** She DOES NOT WANT belt buckles, reproductions, common items, or junk.

Barbara Wood
4946 Post Oak Timber
Houston, TX 77056
(713) 850-9749 eve   (713) 520-9755 day   <hotx12@aol.com>

TONY'S TIP: To tell if you have Bakelite-Catalin or a newer plastic, feel it. A slightly oily feel is characteristic of the older plastics. So is its weight as it's heavier than modern plastics. Look for seams as Bakelite-Catalin jewelry does not have them. Touch new plastic with a red hot needle and it will melt or give off a puff of smoke. Bakelite can't be hurt with a hot needle (it's so tough it's even hard to drill). **Always test in inconspicuous places.**

SEE PAGES 564 AND 565 FOR MORE JEWELRY BUYERS AND INFORMATION ABOUT OLD JEWELRY

★ **Cuff links, tie bars, money clips** and button covers are sought by the President of the National Cuff Link Society. He pays from 50¢ to $10 a pair depending on age, condition and whether they are in their original box. He also wants ads, display boxes and point of sale advertising and promotional items. You can join the Society for $30 a year and receive their quarterly magazine.

> Gene Klompus
> National Cuff Link Society
> PO Box 5970
> Vernon Hills, IL 60061
> (847) 816-0035 voice/fax
> <genek@cufflink.com>

◆ **Old jewelry before 1930,** garnets, black jets, **cameos, rings,** lockets, **charms,** filigree beads, glass beads, and glass buttons. Craftsmanship and detail ("ornate and unusual") is more important than whether it's made of gold or not. Lockets, hearts, stars, flowers and other keepsake jewelry is wanted in gold or silver. "I look for all unusual items of clothing, jewelry, and accessories." Photocopy is suggested. Jewelry may be broken and need repair. SASE a must.

> Linda Gibbs
> 10380 Miranda Avenue
> Buena Park, CA 90620
> (714) 827-6488

◆ **Mexican sterling jewelry.** Wants "strange or unusual eye-catching pieces, especially very heavy ones from the 1920's to 1940's. "A photo or photocopy will tell me a lot" but you should also list anything marked on the piece. This 40 year veteran prefers you to indicate a price range, but will make offers.

> Marilyn Baseman
> Birdcage Antiques
> PO Box 1166
> Sheffield, MA 01258
> (413)229-2294   <abca@bca.net>

◆ **Old Taxco (Mexico) jewelry,** flatware and hollowware, especially pieces by William Spratling, Hector Aguilar, Fred Davis, Hubert Harmon, Antonio, Mat'l, and other known artists. These pieces are decorated with a variety of stones, including onyx, garnet and amethyst and are almost always marked by the maker. A good sharp photo is essential. Please copy the mark if you can't take a photo of it. Also buys old **Navaho jewelry made before 1940.**

> Daniel Brown
> PO Box 149
> Davenport, CA 95017
> (800) 492-6786   <green-garnet@sbcglobal.net>

◆ **Gold, platinum and diamondd watches and jewelry.** Give the karat of the gold, percent of platinum and its gram or pennyweight. Include certificate of appraisal if you have one.
> Howard Leong, Golden Image Jewelers
> 2219 East Thousand Oaks Blvd., #101
> Thousand Oaks, CA 91362
> (805) 446-2733   fax (805) 870-0041   <platmans@aol.com>

◆ **Photo keepsake jewelry** with real photos mounted in pendants, lockets, brooches, etc., from the 1800's. He does not want photo jewelry if the original photo has been removed. Prices are determined individually based on the esthetic value of the piece [how attractive it is...ed.]. If possible, a color picture in closeup, both front and back is helpful. Indicate any inscriptions or markings as well as any damage." If you want your photos back, please include an SASE. Dealers price your goods. Amateur sellers may ask for help.
> Ed Clark, Texas Photo Center
> 215 West Camp Wisdom #6
> Duncanville, TX 75116
> (800) 327-1654   (972) 780-5735   fax (972) 780-0937
> <edclark@texasphoto.com>

◆ **Woodburned glove and jewelry boxes** are purchased for resale, as are jewelry boxes made of cast iron, particularly those that are silk lined. Please give a thorough description. SASE a must.
> Linda Gibbs
> 10380 Miranda Avenue
> Buena Park, CA 90620
> (714) 827-6488

◆ **B & D barrettes** made of inexpensive colorful plastic in the early 1980's by the Buch and Deichmann company in Denmark. "They are only worth a few dollars each, but please let me know if you have any for sale." A Xerox™ is an effective way to tell her.
> Holly Lyall
> 34 Meadowbank Road
> Winnipeg, MB   R3Y 1N8 CANADA
> <triton@ilos.net>

◆ **Costume jewelry,** especially designer pieces by Miriam Haskell, but will consider any glass beads, rhinestoness, gold filled, plastic, gold and silver, class rings, Mexican silver, and Indian jewelry. NOT interested in newer jewelry made in Asia. "Some pieces must be seen in person before I can make a final offer."
> Patsy Comer
> 7249 Reseda Blvd.
> Reseda, CA 91335
> (818) 345-1631   fax (818) 345-1914   <patsycomer@yahoo.com>

TONY'S TIPS ON SELLING WATCHES

Watches have been made by the hundreds of millions for a century! A great variety of watches exist and a great variety of collectors seek them. Values can range from a dollar or two to prices over $100,000.

Whenever a great deal of money is at stake, it is smart to get expert advice.

Be cautious about selling old watches locally. *Your local jeweler is probably not qualified to evaluate and price old watches even though he sells new ones. You may put five or ten times as much money in your pocket when you deal with watch buyers who keep up with the world-wide market for used watches.*

If you wish to sell your watch, be prepared to tell a potential buyer the following information:

- *What is the case made of?*
- *What is the size of the case?*
- *Is the case decorated or engraved?*
- *What name is on the dial?*
- *What name is on the movement?*
- *Does it say how many jewels?*
- *Is there a serial number?*
- *How is it wound?   Do you have the key?*
- *Is it running?*
- *Is there anything unusual about the case or watch?*

Watch buyers will want to inspect your timepiece before making a final offer. *Send watches via Registered US Mail, insured. This is usually a safe way to ship, and requires the recipient to sign for the package.*

Always discuss exact shipping procedures with the buyer. Shipping via the U.S. Post Office can be fast, safe and reliable if you ship via Registered Mail.

WATCHES

★ **Wrist and pocket watches,** both men's and women's, in gold, silver, or gold fill. Pocket watches may be in other metals if they date before 1940. Doesn't matter whether running or not. Describe all markings and give dimensions.
Arnold Reamer, Timepiece Antiques
PO Box 26416
Baltimore, MD 21207
(410) 944-6414   (410) 486-8412   fax (410) 265-7877
<arnoldreamer@webtv.net>

◆ **Pocket watches and high grade wristwatches.** Especially seeking *Patek Philippe, Howard, Illinois, Hamilton, Rolex* and signed railroad dials and RR movements. Also buys keywinds, watches that chime, Civil War watches, enameled watches, calendar watches, moonphases, historical watches, gold cases, novelty character watches, sports related watches, unusual American and European watches and chronographs. "I always buy any American made pocket watch 21 jewels or higher." Pays finders fees for leads to purchase of collections, estates, and good accumulations. He does NOT buy *Timex* or inexpensive watches made after 1965, nor does he buy any lady's watches. Please describe your watch as per Dr. Hyman's instructions at the beginning of this section, and include an SASE along with a Xerox™ of the watch front and back if possible. Watches do not need to run. 33 years of experience.
Mike Jobe
PO Box 13028 TH
Shawnee Mission, KS 66282
(800) 235-2866   <mitime@hotmail.com>

◆ **High quality and collectible watches** by *Patek Phillipe, Rolex, Cartier, Tiffany, Audemars* and types of watches like chronographs, repeaters, alarm, doctor's watches, two time zone, and rectangular faces made between 1870 and 1960. Also advertising items relating to watches. Irv deals in watches from rare to common. Buys parts, cases, boxes, movements, dials, and bands from all *Rolex, Patek* or *Cartier* watches. If you are thinking of auctioning watches or antique gold jewelry, Irv says, "We will buy any piece that interests us at 95% of anticipated net sellers hammer proceeds." Irv promises: "Fair prices, next day payment, postage refunded, and free appraisals," adding "I will come to you if what you have is very valuable or if you have many good pieces." Describe metal, shape, details, all names and numbers, as indicated on previous page. Irv offers a priced wants list.
Irv Temes, Temes and Co.
338 North Charles Street
Baltimore, MD 21201
(800) 722-5274   (410) 347-7600   fax (410) 685-3299
<itemes@aol.com>

◆ *Hamilton* **men's electric wristwatches** watches and mechanical watches with unusual case styles. An electric watch repairman, he also wants dealer's stock, parts, movements, advertising materials, catalogs, store displays and anything else related to the Hamilton Watch Co. No Hamilton Electronic watches. Only American made pre-1970 watches, especially in their original boxes and with original literature. Rene's comprehensive book on the history of Hamilton electric watches is $30 and a must for anyone considering collecting them.

> Rene Rondeau
> PO Box 391
> Corte Madera, CA 94976
> (415) 924-6534   <rene@rondeau.net>

◆ **Watches and clocks with cartoon characters** or products on the face. Any items mint in their original box are particularly desirable. Tell whether face is round or rectangular, any wording on the face or back, defects (including scratches), the condition of the box (if any), and whether it is working. Be careful not to overwind your watch while trying to see if it works. Many of these had less than great movements and can be easily damaged. Free appraisals for amateur sellers. Maggie both buys and sells these pop-culture watches, so if there's a particular image you seek, give her a call.

> Maggie Kenyon
> One Christopher Street   #14G
> New York, NY 10014
> (212) 675-3213   <mlkx@aol.com>

★ **LED calculator watches from the early 70's.** These lit up, usually in red, when you pressed a button. He most wants a Hewlett-Packard HP-01 combination watch/calculator in gold or stainless steel, especially if complete with original stylus and is willing to pay substantially if you have one. List make and model and indicate if it works. Please indicate type and condition of the band.

> Guy Ball
> PO Box 345
> Tustin, CA 92781
> fax   (714) 730-6140   <mrcalc@USA.net>

◆ **Ladies 14k wristwatches** that no longer work. "Any maker, any year, any style, with or without a band...I'm buying for craft use not as jewelry. Please send a Xerox™ and your asking price.

> Judy Polk Harding
> 4347 Farm House Lane
> Fairfax, VA 22032
> (703) 503-7323   <thefivejs@aol.com>

LOCKS, KEYS & SCALES

◆ **Antique and unusual padlocks.** "We'll buy padlocks of all kinds and types, those that are oddly shaped, made of cast iron or brass, figural, locks marked "Wells Fargo," locks by *Winchester,* locks marked with the initials of a railroad, miniature, and many others." If you want so sell your lock, a photocopy will help them know what you have. Indicate whether your lock has a key with it. Also has great interest in locks and keys used by escape artists in their act.

> Joe and Pam Tanner
> Wheeler-Tanner Escapes
> 6442 Canyon Creek Way
> Elk Grove, CA 95758
> (916) 684-4006 voice/fax   <jnpwlrtnr@aol.com>

◆ **Padlocks and keys** are wanted, especially American locks marked with patent dates or the name of the maker. Some English and other European locks are of interest as well. Locks can be worth hundreds of dollars apiece, so it's worth your while to inquire, although he has no interest in modern locks made after 1930. A good rule of thumb is "the older and more unusual the better." A Xerox™ of the lock and the key along side it is a good idea. Note all dates, words, or symbols found on the lock, and indicate whether you have the key or not as "a lock without a key is acceptable, but definitely worth a lot less" for obvious reasons. Bob is secretary of the West Coast Lock Collectors, whose quarterly newsletter may be ordered through him for $15/year.

> Bob Heilmann
> Ace Lock & Key
> 1427 Lincoln Boulevard
> Santa Monica, CA 90401
> (310) 454 7295 eves   <locksmann@aol.com>

◆ **Antique scales** of any type, in any condition and quantity, are sought by this 20 year veteran collector/dealer who also buys toy scales, signs depicting old scales, advertising for scales, scale company catalogs, postcards showing scales, scale parts, and "anything else" related to scales. Provide the brand name, model, serial number and condition. Note whether the scale is complete and seems to work.

> Bill and Jan Berning
> 135 West Main Street
> Genoa, IL 60135
> (815) 784-3134   <iweighu@yahoo.com>

KNIVES

◆ **Pocket, hunting, and military knives.** A few **good brands to look for:** *New York, Canastota, Remington, Wabash, Winchester, Honk Falls, Napanoch, Henry Sears, Shapleigh, Union Cut, Keen Kutter, Bingham, American, Bridge, Capitol, Case, Cattaraugus, Phoenix, James Price, Platts, Press Button, Wallkill, Walden, Van Camp, Union Razon, Standard, Zenith, Northfield, Crandall,* and others. "I love large bone-handled knives made in the U.S." **If your knife is one of the following brands, it is not of interest:** *Ambassador, Atco, Camco, Colonial, Executive, Frontier, Hit, Ideal, Klien, Richards, U.S.A., Pakistan,* and *Sabre.* For an evaluation of your knife and an offer, photocopy knives with the blade(s) open, write down everything found on the blades and handles, identify the handle material and include an SASE.

> Charles Stapp
> 7037 Haynes Road
> Georgetown, IN 47122
> (812) 923-3483   fax (812) 982-3890   <dennyjoyce@aol.com>

◆ **Knives of all types,** but especially pocket knives, Bowie knives, hunting knives, commemorative knives, and custom knives. "We are primarily interested in older and higher grade items, but we do have a market for the junk as well. We will purchase entire collections without cherry-picking. If it's a knife, we're interested."
• Handmade knives by Wm. Scagel ($1,000-$5,000)
• Handmade knives by RW Loveless ($800-$2,500)
• Antique Bowie knives ($200-$25,000)
• Older *Randall* knives ($200-$1,000)
• Old American made pocket knives ($20-$500)
They also buy pre 1940 advertising related to knives. Photos or Xerox© copies are needed. Give a brief description and include your phone number.

> Tom Clark
> Blue Ridge Knives
> 166 Adwolfe Road
> Marion, VA 24354
> (276) 783-6143   fax (276) 783-9298   <brk@netva.com>

◆ **Knives less than 1" long** are wanted, especially multi-bladed knives with mother-of-pearl, sterling, stag or horn handles. To sell your knife, give as much information as possible, including number of blades, maker, condition, etc. Old knives only. No new items or reproductions. Says he also "buys and trades swords and razors."

> Jim Kegebein
> 6831 Colton Blvd.
> Oakland, CA 94611
> (510) 339-1147   fax (510) 339-1146   <njak@aol.com>

◆ **Knives, tools and other items** by selected makers: *Keen Kutter, Winchester, Simmons, Shapleigh, Norvell-Shapleigh*, and various combinations thereof. "They made thousands of different things. Look at your tools carefully, as the names are often hard to read or find. I pay most for items in their original box. I don't want scissors or meat grinders that clamp on the table. I don't buy broken items, reproductions, heavily worn knives, or items that have been modified. If you call with an item made by one of these companies in front of you, I can usually evaluate it over the phone. Some items have been reproduced. When in doubt, call." **He also buys** catalogs, advertising, promotional items, signs, showcases, postcards, cookbooks, clocks, radios and other products marked with the name of one of those companies. Send photocopy (Xerox©) or tracing, the exact wording of the mark and any other numbers or words. Include an SASE and your evening phone number. Tom is currently president of the Winchester, Keen Kutter and Diamond Edge Collector's Club.

> Tom Basore
> 715 West 20th Ave.
> Hutchinson, KS 67502
>   (620) 665-3613 eves

◆ **Antique pocket knives of all kinds** in excellent to mint condition. "I will consider buying all kinds of knives as I buy for resale as well as for my own collection. I personally collect quill knives, whittler pattern knives and hobo (slot) knives. Value of knives depends on maker, age, rarity, condition, and desirability. A knife can range from $50 to $1,000 just on condition. I generally pay 40% to 60% of full market value when buying for resale. How much I pay for things for my own collection depends on how badly I want it. I will tell the seller what I think fair market value is, then explain my offer." He does not want broken blades, deep rust, or *Case* knives made after 1980. Tell this 25 year veteran knife buyer the number of blades, the maker's markings on the blades, the handle material, the size and the condition. SASE. Bob is the ex-veep of the Southern California Blades.

> Robert Berman
> Robert Berman Gallery
> 1807 Baton Rouge
> Henderson, NV 89052
> (702) 617-1551   fax (818) 349-3923   <rrberman@lvcm.com>

◆ **Antique pocket and hunting knives, custom knives, Scagel knives, and Loveless knives.** He DOES NOT WANT reproductions.

> Rhett Stidham
> Box 570
> Roseland, FL 32957
> (561) 589-0618   fax (561) 589-3162   <ystidham@gate.net>

STRAIGHT & SAFETY RAZORS

◆ **Straight razors with handles of sterling, rough bone, mother-of-pearl, or aluminum.** Celluloid or pressed horn razors with several characters are also wanted. Good razors generally bring from $50-$75, with some higher, some less. Please provide all information found on the blade or handle. **He does not want** plain handled razors from Solingen, Germany. Make photocopies with the blade(s) open. Indicate the material from which the handle is made.

> Charles Stapp
> 7037 Haynes Road
> Georgetown, IN 47122
> (812) 923-3483   Fax: (812) 282-3890   <dennyjoyce@aol.com>

◆ **Straight razors with fancy handles of gold or sterling silver.** Also razors with figural handles, multiple blades, fancy etching on the blade, or with fraternal emblems or advertising on the handle. Handles may be made of horn, mother-of-pearl, or multi-colored celluloid. Rare razors will be considered even if they are slightly damaged. Also razor and cutlery advertising and memorabilia, catalogs, trade cards, etc., including oversize displays.

> William Campesi
> PO Box 140
> Merrick, NY 11566
> (516) 546-9630

TONY'S TIP ABOUT RAZORS:
Value of straight razors lays almost all in the handle. When buyers ask for unusual handles, they really mean it!

Ordinary black handled straight razors have little if any value. Don't ask.

◆ **Safety razors and accessories.** This 20 year veteran collector wants to buy odd safety razors and advertising for razors including posters, magazine ads, and signs. He'd love to find oversize store display razors or oversize shaving mugs or brushes. Give all colors and metals and note "all writing on the items. A good clear photo is best," he says, but photocopies will suffice.

> Cary Basse
> 6927 Forbes Avenue
> Van Nuys, CA 91406
> (818) 781-4856

◆ **Safety razors, stropping machines, packs of blades, blade banks, and other early or unique shaving items,** "with highest prices paid for safety razors with unusual or oddly shaped blades." Phil wrote the huge and well documented *The Complete Gillette Collector's Handbook* available from him for $24.

Phillip Krumholz
PO Box 4050
Bartonville, IL 61607
(309) 697-1120   <barber@heart.net>

◆ **Safety razor shaving memorabilia,** 1880-1930, including safety razors, mechanical blade sharpeners, razor blade banks, advertising signs and buttons, counter and window displays, giveaways, catalogs, and miscellaneous paper associated with any of the above. Also wants figural shaving mugs in the shape of animals, people, or birds and shaving brushes with figural handles. Shaving mugs and barber bottles which appear to be covered with imitation bark are also of interest. **The following brands of safety razor are not wanted**: *Rolls, Durham, Valet* or *Gillette* (if the serial number is higher than 500,000). Blade sharpeners that are too common to have value are *Kriss Kross* and *Twinplex.* Blade banks given away by *Listerine* are also very common. Please provide as much detail as possible, including all names, letters, dates, colors, etc. A drawing is helpful. Author of *Razor Blade Banks, a Price Guide,* available from the author for $22 postpaid.

Lester Dequaine
155 Brewster Street
Bridgeport, CT 06605
(203) 335-6833   (203) 639-9778
<shaving-bshopmuseum@snet.net>

◆ **Razor blades and blade sharpeners.** "I'll buy U.S. or foreign blades, in singles, packages, or on cards as well as interesting advertising signs, posters, and displays related to razor blades." Describe your sharpener carefully, pointing out all damage, and noting any words or numbers on it.

Cary Basse
6927 Forbes Avenue
Van Nuys, CA 91406
(818) 781-4856

PERFUME

◆ **Perfume bottles.** Wants high quality commercial, miniature and other perfume bottles from 1700 to 1950. Especially wants elaborate 18th and 19th century scent bottles and 20th century bottles made by famous glassmakers like Lalique and Baccarat. She does not want anything made by *Avon*. Please indicate the size in inches, color of the glass and stopper, whether or not the original label and box are present, and if the bottle is signed (look very closely at both bottle and stopper with a magnifying glass as signatures and markings can be very small). If the stopper does not seem to match the base, it may be OK as many valuable bottles have unusual stoppers which seem mismatched. Photos or Xerox© copies of your bottle are helpful. Ms. Parris is a founding member of the Perfume & Scent Bottle Association and their membership chairperson. **Please contact her only if your bottle is old, in perfect condition, and for sale, or if you would like to join the club.** Self Addressed Stamped Envelope please.

Jeane Parris
Sugarplums, etc.
2022 East Charleston Boulevard
Las Vegas, NV 89104
(702) 385-6059 days   fax (702) 388-1202

★ **Perfume bottles, decanters and vases with sterling silver overlay.** Will purchase Lalique, DeVilbis atomizers, Gallé, Webb Czechoslvakian glass, or any fancy blown glass bottles with fancy stoppers. Please snd a photo along with a description of any marks. All items must be perfect with no cracks, chips or other damage. Give the dimensions and colors. "Our 40th year in Business."

Arnold Reamer, Timepiece Antiques
PO Box 26416
Baltimore, MD 21207
(410) 486-8412   (410) 944-6414   cel (410) 336-1002
fax (410) 265-7877   <arnoldreamer@webtv.net>

TONY'S TIP: Collectors seek many perfume bottles from the 1920's, 30's, and 40's. Since these bottles were designed and made by top European glass companies, they are frequently worth $100 and up. Record prices of over $10,000 have been paid, so advice is essential.
Look for pretty shapes, silver trim, atomizers, glass stoppers, and anything unusual, figural, or particularly decorative.

◆ **Perfume bottles.** "I collect, buy and sell perfume bottles, from 1900 to the 1960's, in good to mint condition. I'm looking for unusual bottles, ceramic bottles with metal crown stoppers, and unusual shapes as well as "testers" with daubers. A photo of your bottle would be appreciated, accompanied with a description. Please include an SASE if you want photos returned. I pay fair market prices, and will make offers when necessary, but prefer you to set the price wanted."
Sue Murphy
29668 Orinda Road
San Juan Capistrano, CA 92675
(949) 364-4333

◆ **Perfume bottles** made of blown or cut art glass, singles or matching sets. Wants fine beautiful bottles including those with atomizers. Some important makers include DeVilbis, Daum Nancy, Galle, Baccarat, Webb, Moser, Czechoslovakian, Lalique, and Steuben. Also English scents, bottles with sterling overlay, and figural perfume bottles. She does not make offers, nor does she buy *Avon* bottles.
Madeleine France
PO Box 15555
Plantation, FL 33318
(954) 921-0022   fax (954) 584-0014

◆ **DeVilbis atomizers,** with or without original bulb and cord. Describe the size, colors, and condition. A detailed sketch or close up photo is essential. Please, no commercial or medicinal atomizers as he wants only the pretty ones that were used for perfume.
Bruce Bleier
73 Riverdale Road
Valley Stream, NY 11581
(516) 791-4353   <emeralite@aol.com>

◆ **California Perfume Company (CPC) products** made between 1886 and 1920, especially *Natoma Rose* fragrances. He also wants CPC products marketed as *Goetting and Company, Savoi Et Cie, Marvel Electric Silver Cleaner,* and the *Easy Day Automatic Clothes Washer.* Please give a complete description of the item you have for sale, including its condition and whether or not it has its original box. Is there a label and/or a neck band? Are there cracks or chips? Photocopy is helpful. Be prepared to leave a message stating exactly what you have, its condition and the price you'd like for it. Dealers price your goods. Genuine amateurs may request help in setting prices. Dick does not want anything with *Avon* or *Perfection* on the label.
Dick Pardini
3107 North El Dorado Street, Dept TH
Stockton, CA 95204
(209) 466-5550 6am to 9am

COMPACTS, MAKEUP & PURSES

★ **Women's figural compacts.** "We buy compacts that are in the shape of an object like a padlock, Christmas ornament, miniature stuffed animal, etc. Compacts must be in very fine condition, with no scratches, dents, or worn finish. It is best if the original rouge, powder and mirror are intact, but the more unusual the compact, the more forgiving we are. We do not collect conventional round or square compacts even if they have an embossed, engraved or applied figure on the lid." A clear close-up photo is needed, or a good Xerox™ if possible. Your description should indicate the condition of the mirror, the puff, and the contents. "Small markings stamped into the metal on the inside are critical to mention." An illustrated wants list is available.

> Mike and Sherry Miller
> 303 Holiday Avenue
> Tuscola, IL 61953
> (217) 253-4991   <miller1@net66.com>

◆ **Women's sterling silver dresser sets, hair brushes, mirrors and other boudoir items.** The proprietor of this unusual shop for women does not make offers, so you'll have to price what you have.

> Madeleine France
> Past Pleasures for the 20th Century Woman
> PO Box 15555
> Plantation, FL 33318
> (954) 921-0022   fax (954) 584-0014

◆ **Women's powder compacts,** from before 1950. All types of good looking, fine condition compacts are wanted, as long as the compact is complete. Unusual, Art Deco and precious metals are preferred.

> Vivian Temes
> Bird In the Cage Antiques
> 110 King Street
> Alexandria, VA 22314
> (703) 549-5114   <bird_in_the_cage_antiques@compuserve.com>

◆ **Ladies' compacts.** "I am a buyer and seller, always looking for the unusual, enameled, novelty, in the shape of other items, or compacts that are part of purses of other items. I prefer items in good to mint condition, but have been known to buy lesser condition, but priced accordingly. Please include an SASE if you want photos returned. I do ask you to set the price wanted but will make offers when necessary."

> Sue Murphy
> 29668 Orinda Road
> San Juan Capistrano, CA 92675
> (949) 364-4333

★ **Metal mesh purses with colorful designs** painted into the mesh. Prefers mint condition items but will consider some with minor wear or a few disconnected links. Among items sought are:

- Very large bags, 6" x 10" or larger;
- Very small bags, 2" x 3" or so;
- Bags with designs portraying scenes, animals or people;
- Bags with cartoon characters;
- Bags with ornate frames set with polished stones, fake jewels, or enameled decorations;
- Bags with elaborate Art Deco designs on the mesh and or frame;
- Mesh vanity bags which combine a compact and a purse (these usually bring the highest prices);
- Beaded purses, but only older bags with very small glass beads (18 to 22 beads to the inch) which are strung into a scene, a figure, or into the design of an Oriental rug.

Must be in mint or nearly mint condition. A Xerox™ copy is a good way to describe your purse.   Illustrated wants list available for SASE.

Mike and Sherry Miller
303 Holiday Avenue
Tuscola, IL 61953
(217) 253-4991   <miller1@net66.com>

◆ **Purses from before 1930.** Primarily seeking:

- Enameled mesh purses in bright colors, scenic designs, etc. from the late 1920's, especially with jeweled frames or in odd shapes or made with unusual mesh;
- Beaded purses, with interesting patterns, scenes of people, pictures of places, Persian carpet or Egyptian motifs;
- Bakelite purses;
- Plastic compacts which are actually small purses;
- Trinity plate very small purses made of brass with complex filigree work and stones, often with tassels.

Good purses must be without wear in mint to near mint condition and will bring prices from $50 to $300 depending on style, rarity and condition. "I'm looking for the out of the ordinary." Your description should include the style, design, and color. A photo or Xerox™ is a good idea. Dealers should price their goods. Amateurs may request an offer from this veteran collector. If she is not interested in your item, she will be happy to tell you what an appropriate price should be.

Leslie Holms
PO Box 596
Los Gatos, CA 95031
(408) 354-1626   <melas@ips.net>

◆ **Compacts.** Wants unusual compacts:
  • Shaped like phone dials, pistols, hot air balloons, suitcases, hands, drums, guitars, lady bugs, flying saucers, etc.;
  • Enameled Art Deco designs;
  • Jeweled vanities;
  • Molded plastic *Bakelite* vanities;
  • Mesh and beaded purses with compact tops;
  • Canes or hat pins concealing compacts.
"I don't buy 1940's and 50's carryalls (usually 3"x5" or 4"x6"), nor am I interested in plain brass, sterling, or silver plate without color." No compacts with damaged enamel. Photo helpful.

> Lori Landgrebe
> 2331 East Main
> Decatur, IL 62521
> (217) 423-2254

◆ **Fancy lipsticks and compacts,** especially those in combination with purses, bracelets, etc. Wants gold, sterling or enameled pieces only. Will consider vanity cases, chatelaines and cigarette holders. Values range from $15 to many hundreds" but items must be near mint with no chips, dents, or broken hinges. Make a Xerox™ copy.

> Rita Berman
> 1807 Baton Rouge
> Henderson, NV 89052
> (702) 617-1551   fax (818) 349-3923   <rrberman@lvcm.com>

◆ **Thimbles, sewing tools, and scissors**. Wants old, interesting items, especially gold, sterling or enameled. Please, no common modern thimbles or scissors. Old and unusual ONLY.

> Helen Arendt
> 43601 Florida Avenue #84
> Hemet, CA 92544
> (909) 927-0543   <thimblelady@pe.net>

AVON BOTTLES

TONY'S TIP: *Avon bottles are everywhere, and I have not been able to locate a buyer for collections of Avon items.*

In my experience it's difficult to find buyers for common items. They generally sell one at a time, for $1 or $2 at flea markets. Only a few Avons are sought after and bring higher prices.

TONY'S TIPS ON SELLING DOLLS AND TEDDY BEARS

Doll collecting is the second largest hobby in the United States. Doll lovers spend one-half billion dollars each year.

Collectors want all types from the high priced 19th century mechanicals and French fashion dolls which cost many thousands of dollars to modern plastic dolls worth a fraction as much.
Because you are more likely to have the more modern dolls, a greater emphasis has been placed on them in this book.

Buyers of most dolls want the following information:

(1) *Length of the doll, important because some dolls made in multiple sizes have different values;*
(2) *How big around the head is, important on old dolls; use a seamstress's tape or string to measure;*
(3) *Material from which the head, hair, hands, feet and body are made (may be from different materials);*
(4) *Type of eyes (painted, button, glass), their color and whether or not they move;*
(5) *Whether the mouth is open and whether teeth (molded, painted, or attached) show;*
(6) *Marks incised into the scalp, neck, shoulders, or back of the doll;*
(7) *How the doll is dressed and whether the clothes seem to be original;*
(8) *Any chips, cracks, repainting, or other repairs.*

When offering a doll for sale, a photo can be helpful, but you can often get better results faster, easier, and cheaper with a photocopy machine. **Photocopies are particularly useful for showing how a doll is dressed.**

The original box for your doll may add as much as 50% to the doll's value. *When describing modern dolls such as Barbie™ whose accessories are frequently marketed in plastic bubble packs mention packages that are unopened and unfaded as they make a doll worth two or three times the value of loose dolls or accessories.*

ANTIQUE DOLLS

◆ **Dolls, antique and modern.** Buys dolls of bisque, china, wood, cloth, papier-maché, composition and hard plastic from the beginning of time to the 1960's. Especially interested in:
  • **Hard plastic dolls** of the 1950's;
  • Early **bisque Heubach babies and children;**
  • Bisque **bathing beauties** in various poses, a few inches long;
  • **Kewpies** by Rose O'Neill, especially in action;
  • **Stuffed bears, and other animals** before 1960**;**
  • **Doll accessories** like shoes, clothing, wigs, purses, combs, opera glasses, dresser sets, and the like;
  • Small props like **buggies, furniture, tea sets,** and the like.
"I prefer things priced, but will make offers."
  Madalaine Selfridge
  Hidden Magic Doll Museum
  33710 Almond Street
  Wildomar, CA 92595
      (909) 674-9221   <ms@majornet.com>

◆ **Character dolls.** Buys a variety of character dolls:
  • **Barbie dolls** from 1964 and before, especially the "Color-Magic" and "American Girl" models. Also buys factory-made Barbie clothes, but not home-made ones;
  • **Raggedy Ann and Andy** and related items, including **Beloved Belindy.** She pays top prices for early high quality dolls;
  • **Howdy Doody dolls and marionettes.** Also interested in dolls of all other characters on the show: Clara Belle, Mr. Bluster, Princess, Flubba Dub, and Dilly Dally;
  • **Little Lulu & Tubby** dolls and related items in all sizes;
  • **Red Riding Hood** and related items;
  • **Cinderella** and related items.
Follow the basic rules for describing what you have to sell, including dimensions and an accurate statement of condition. "I don't want reproductions, common items, or junk."
  Gwen Daniel
  18 Belleau Lake Court
  O'Fallon, MO 63366
      (636) 978-3190 anytime   <gwendaniel@aol.com>

★ **Collections of antique dolls** are sought for cataloged specialty auctions by this well known New England auctioneer. No junk, reproductions, or dolls made after 1940 will be considered.
  James D. Julia Auctioneers
  PO Box 830
  Fairfield, ME 04937
  (207) 453-7904 fax (207) 453-2502   <jjulia@juliaauctions.com>

◆ **Old dolls and their parts.** "I buy, both as a collector and as a dealer, a large variety of old dolls and doll parts.
  • Old **German dolls** (a particular favorite);
  • **Cloth comic characters** such as Lulu, Tubby, Nancy, or Sluggo;
  • **Raggedy Ann or Andy** dolls, but only old ones;
  • **Bisque snow babies;**
  • Wooden jointed **creche-type dolls** for display at Christmas;
  • Damaged dolls if priced reasonably;
  • **Accessories for old dolls,** such as shoes, clothing, wigs, purses;
  • **Doll carriages and quality furniture;**
  • **Buster Brown china dishes.**
I have no interest at all in Japanese bisque or currently made dolls. Send a Xerox™ or photo of what you have."
　　　　Patricia Snyder
　　　　My Dear Dolly
　　　　PO Box 303
　　　　Sparta, NJ 07871
　　　　　　　(973) 729-8087   <dolly@mydeardolly.com>

◆ **Dolls, doll buggies, doll furniture and doll dishes.** This 30 year veteran doll dealer wants collections or single:
  • **Antique dolls from France, Germany or the U.S.** made from
    bisque, wood, china, composition or other material;
  • **Shirley Temple** dolls;
  • 1950's and 60's dolls such as **Ginny, Terri Lee, Buddy Lee,** etc.;
  • **Barbie dolls** and accessories, especially made before 1970; all
    limited edition porcelain Barbies, Bob Mackie designer dolls,
    store specials, convention dolls, or other special issues;
  • **Kewpie** dolls;
  • **Doll buggies, furniture and dishes.**
"I pay especially well for these dolls in their original packages." Prices vary widely depending on the individual doll, its rarity and its condition. "I do not want any dolls that are still available in stores or any new reproduction porcelain or artist dolls. In most cases, I need you to tell me the size, any marks or identifications, and what you know of its history. Dealers, price your goods; amateurs may request an offer."
　　　　Donna and Al Purkey
　　　　All About Dolls
　　　　PO Box 2104
　　　　Anaheim, CA 92804
　　(714) 828-5909　　(714) 826-4699 days <aboutbrbe@aol.com>

◆ **Dolls of all types.** This active dealer will consider a wide range of good looking fine condition dolls made of papier-maché, wood, china, or bisque, including:
- Expensive **French fashion dolls,** character dolls, etc.;
- Early **cloth dolls;**
- **Teddy bears;**
- **Steiff character and animal dolls;**
- **Vogue Ginny dolls;**
- **Kathe Kruse, Chase, Madame Alexander,** or **Izannah Walker;**
- **Doll houses.**

Follow guidelines on page 110 for describing dolls correctly.

Valerie Zakszewski
1319 Shore Road
Magnolia, MA 01930
(800) 897-2933   (617) 576-0796   <valeriezak@adelphia.net>

◆ **Teddy bears** that are fully jointed with glass or shoebutton eyes. Wants pre-1920 Steiff bears in any condition and will pay $1,000+ for those larger than 20" long.   Not interested in any non-jointed bears or bears made after 1940. Also teddy bear books, postcards, photos, trays, etc. Polly also buys stuffed animal toys on cast iron wheels.

Polly Zarneski
5803 North Fleming
Spokane, WA 99205
(509) 327-7622

◆ **Teddy bears** that are fully jointed with glass or shoebutton eyes. "I'll pay the best prices for early German bears in very fine condition." Follow basic rules for describing.

Gwen Daniel
18 Belleau Lake Court
O'Fallon, MO 63366
(636) 978-3190 anytime   <gwendaniel @aol.com>

◆ **Mohair teddy bears** with long arms and big feet made between 1903 and 1915 are wanted in all sizes as long as they are fully jointed. Also wants perfume and compact bears in various colors and any unusual mohair teddy or teddy related items. Also looking for early Steiff cats and dogs with printed ear buttons. **Also wants Billy Possum stuffed dolls with shoebutton eyes and all Billy Possum items** including doll dishes and silverware, banks and postcards. Mimi wants you to know your dolls are going to a "loving home, not a dealer."

Mimi Hiscox
12291 St. Mark
Garden Grove, CA 92645
(562) 598-5450   (714) 897-9289   <mimihiscox@yahoo.com>

◆ **Raggedy Ann & Andy dolls and other items.** Dolls of interest are those made by Volland, Georgene, or Molly-es. Volland dolls are seldom marked, but can be identified by their narrow, black outinled nose. A fine condition one can bring $1,000. Georgenes have tags sewn to the body, apron or trousers and are worth around $100. Mollyes can be identified by their multiple colored striped legs, and can put $400 in your pocket. A black Beloved Belindy doll by Volland is worth $2,000 in fine condition. Books before 1960 in good condition are wanted, as are **quilts and dishes** featuring the twins. Anns and Andys she does not want include: hand made dolls, modern dolls by Applause, ceramic figures, music box dolls, marionettes, or dolls by Knickerbocker (except the very large ones). Photos or a Xerox© copy are most helpful.

Catherine Smith
PO Box 247
Perrysburg, NY 14129
     (716) 532-5154   <panman@panman.com>

◆ **Cabbage Patch Kids** are wanted but only a select few. Ann is a collector who wants 1983 Colecos (black signature) with freckles, boy dolls with fuzzy or shag hair, dolls from molds 4, 6, 19 or 30. She also wants UT tags, dolls sold in foreign countries, and mint clothing accessories. A color photo and SASE is a must. Ann is the author of an inexpensive ($7) book that describes the types of CPK's. If you have Kids for sale other than those listed above, you are encouraged to advertise your CPK's for sale in the monthly Newsletter which she edits. Many CPK's sell below issue price but some originals bring $200-$300 and rare models by Coleco bring $150 and up. If you want to sell your doll, determining its value requires expertise and a lot of information. If your doll is in its original box, open it from the bottom and untwist the wire holding the CPK in place. Your letter should contain the following information for an accurate response:

• Head mold number impressed on the back of the neck;
• Hair style and color;
• Eye color and whether there are freckles or not;
• Description of the clothing (look for a tag and CPK logo);
• Color of the Xavier Roberts signature found on the left butt;
• If the CPK's butt has a date, please give it as well;
• The name of the manufacturer and the factory ID letters in the circle on the body tag found under the diaper on the left side (letters should be J, P, IC, KT, OK, PMI or UT);
• And lastly, whether the box and birth papers are present.

Values of these once popular collectibles have remained stable

Ann Wilhite
The Cabbage Connection
610 West 17th
Fremont, NE 68025

◆ **Barbie dolls.** Wants to buy all Barbie dolls, fashions and accessories, 1959-1972. "Anything Barbie related," she says, especially prototypes, gift sets, licensed Mattel products, watches, ponytails, color magic, bendable leg Barbies, and the rest of Barbie's family, especially Francie, introduced in 1966. Will pay $1,000 for a mint in box airplane and $500 for a mib Barbie boat. She does buy Bob Mackie Barbies, porcelain, holiday, Xmas, and FAO Schwartz Barbies too. It's worth your time to look for early dolls, especially for the clothes and accessories in their original boxes, because some were made for a very short time or sold in very limited markets. Some inside tips:

The first Barbie sleep eyes were introduced in 1964.

If the knees bend, the doll was made after 1965.

Rooted eyelashes came into use in 1966.

Talking Barbie family arrived in 1968.

Black Barbies Julia and Christie arrived the same year.

Dolls that are easy to pose, and those with growing hair, are both products of the 1970's and too late to interest most Barbie collectors. To describe a Barbie, you must give the name of the doll, hair color, lip color and condition. "Please," she asks, "do not send or write about Barbies because they say 1966 on their back. Today's dolls still say 1966 on them." Marl offers an important clue about how to tell if your Barbie is old. "If it does not say "Japan" on the buttocks or foot, I don't want it." Marl buys dolls for her personal collection and for resale.

Marl Davidson, WS10
10301 Braden Run
Bradenton, FL 34202
(941) 751-6275   fax (941) 751-5463
<marlbe@aol.com>   <http://www.marlbe.com>

TONY'S TIPS:
The first Barbie wore a black and white swimsuit and had copper tubes set in holes in the bottom of her feet. Barbie stood on a round black plastic disk.
Her white irises and black eyeliner looked Oriental.
The second Barbie was like the first except the stand holes were gone.
Barbies three through six had blue eyes.

The first (ponytail) Barbie from the late 1950's and early 60's had MCM LVIII embossed on her behind. This remains until 1962. **For 30 years, beginning in 1966, Barbie was marked "1966" on her behind.**

Barbie was made worldwide, and marked accordingly. Only ones marked "Japan" are sought by most collectors.

◆ **Barbie dolls and accessories** from 1958 through 1966 are wanted, especially items still in their original box. "I'll also buy other members of the Mattel family of dolls from that era, and clothing for them all. **Hint: Barbie's clothing is numbered.** The earliest clothing is in the 900 series, but I also want the 1600 series outfits sold in the early 1960's. Call even if your outfit isn't all there, because you may have just the parts I need to complete a set. Of all the Barbie items, the one I'd like to find the most is the case of 30 or 31 Barbies that was carried by salesmen in 1958 in an effort to sell the doll to toy stores. It contains #1 Barbies wearing the old outfits that were going to be available. If you have one of these in perfect condition it could be worth as much as $100,000. Pink display box dolls that retailers used in the early 60's containing dressed Barbies are also sought, and can put from $3,000 to $5,000 in your pocket if in fine condition. In 1964 when Mattel introduced the bendable Barbies, they tried a variety of hair styles, so Barbie came with bubble cuts, pony tails, and page boys. **The American girl dolls with side-parts in their hair are among the rarest** of the Barbie dolls, and can be worth $2,000 to $4,000 or more if in their original boxes." She is not buying Barbies from the 1970's and 80's, or earlier dolls with serious flaws such as damaged fingers or toes or missing limbs. Describe your Barbie and accessories thoroughly, paying particular attention to condition. Describe the condition of the box as well. You may set the price wanted or request an offer if your doll is for sale.

Linda Brundage
2625 West Alameda Avenue #110
Burbank, CA 91505
(818) 843-8616   Fax: (818) 845-2119   <herbrun@aol.com>

◆ **Barbie dolls and accessories** (especially pre-1970), all limited edition **porcelain Barbies, Bob Mackie** designer dolls**, store specials, convention dolls,** and other **special issues**. "I pay especially well for these dolls in their original packages." Prices vary widely depending on the individual doll, its rarity and its condition. "I do not want any dolls that are still available in stores or any new reproduction porcelain or artist dolls. "Dealers, price your goods; amateurs may request an offer."

Donna and Al Purkey, All About Dolls
PO Box 2104
Anaheim, CA 92814
(714) 828-5909   (714) 826-4699 days   <aboutbrbe@aol.com>

TONY'S TIP : *Ask the reference librarian at your public library for help in locating books about dolls. If you have dolls made in the 20th century,* ***books by Pat Smith may be of help.*** *The library can obtain these and other doll books through interloan if you can't find what you need locally.*

★ **Nancy Ann Storybook Dolls** were created in the mid 1930's. These early dolls were bisque (unglazed china) made in Japan, and usually marked with a sticker reading "Nancy Ann Dressed Doll." After 1942, dolls were "frozen legged." Nancy Anns were the number one selling girls' toy in the 1940's. In 1947 they introduced plastic arms, then all plastic bodies. In 1949, eyes opened and shut. Many different series were created including Sports, Masquerade, and Famous pairs like Hansel and Gretel (all desirable). You may also find:

- Nursery Rhymes, Days of the Week, and Months of the Year (the most common of her dolls);
- Margie Ann is same doll but dressed as a little girl in a suit;
- Audrey Ann in an organdy dress and white boots is hard to find;
- Geraldine Ann with eight outfits and a "movie set" with a director's chair, lights, etc., is fragile and very desirable;
- Judy Ann/USA dolls, which are very scarce;
- Muffie and Debbie, 8" and 10" hard plastic dolls, were the tops of the line, and came with many matching outfits.

Nancy Ann made a great many dolls, so values range from $20 to $175 with a few over $500. Dolls must be individually evaluated, however, because there are so many different costumes. **In general, the frozen leg and plastic dolls are less valuable, but boy (male) dolls are rare and desirable in any form as is some furniture.** McCalls pattern #811 for making cardboard furniture at home is $50+ to you! All Nancy Ann dolls have a hat or ribbon in their hair. **A missing hat reduces the value of a doll by more than half**, and "you can't put just any old ribbon in the hair." **To sell a Nancy Ann, you must** tell whether it's plastic or bisque, has moving or frozen legs, has eyes that move or not (and their color), and the height. Make a photocopy of the doll which shows the dress. If you have the original box, copy that too, since some boxes are more valuable than others.

Elaine M. Pardee
3613 Merano Way
Antelope, CA 95843
(916) 725-7227   <epardee@rcsis.com>

◆ **Kewpie dolls and figures.** "I am the great-grand nephew of Rose O'Neill who created Kewpies, and have been an avid collector for fifteen years." Despite owning 400 items, there are still many he seeks. If you have any questions about Kewpies, don't hesitate to call.

Dave O'Neill
506 College
Springfield, MO 65806
(417) 864-0092

TONY'S TIP ABOUT DOLL INFO:
*Many readers want info about their heirloom. **If you're not planning to sell**, make that clear up-front when you contact someone in Trash or Treasure.*

★ **Annalee dolls.** Wants 1950's, 60's, 70's and 80's versions of these felt dolls with painted faces, most of which have internal wires for positioning arms and legs. All types considered, including human, animal, and holiday, especially those with feather or yarn hair. Look for embroidered (or woven) tags as tags, more than copyright dates, are indicators of when a doll was made, although early dolls didn't always have tags, and doll owners often cut them off. Dating dolls by their tags is a job for experts, and never foolproof, as many different tags appear on the oldest dolls. Some Annalee Dolls were custom made, some limited production, and others factory made in fairly large quantities, so Sue will often need to talk to you or inspect the doll before giving an offer. Dolls tend to be worth $20 to $150 with a very few worth more. "I'll analyze your doll and will always give you a fair price." **Pictures are helpful, but "if you can't send a photo, you must tell me what the doll is (human or animal) and what it's doing and how it's dressed.** I also need to know the height of the doll, as they come in many different sizes. Condition is important in determining price. If you have an Annalee Doll, I want you to call with the doll in front of you. Before you call, please make a careful inspection for moth and silverfish damage in the form of holes, pock-marks, etc., and for any signs of fading in the doll or clothing." Please include your phone number. If you're a picker, her detailed informative wants list is a must. Please include your telephone number and a Stamped envelope addressed to yourself with all inquiries.

Sue Coffee
10 Saunders Hollow Road
Old Lyme, CT 06371
(860) 434-5641   fax (860) 434-2653   <suecoffee@aol.com>

◆ **Dolls of the 1950's,** but only in excellent condition with original clothes. Call, fax, or write a description if you have the following:
- **Nancy Ann Storybook** dolls, particularly Muffie;
- **Vogue Ginny dolls;**
- **Betsy McCall dolls;**
- **Alexanderkins;**
- **Hard plastic dolls in interesting costumes,** such as cowboys, Hawaiians, ethnic dress, etc. "The costume's the thing."
- **Doll houses and furniture** from before 1960.

A complete description of the doll, costume, and box is helpful, but a photo is the best. Dimensions from head to toe are also helpful.

Leda Andrews
2110 Staples Avenue
Key West, FL 33040
(305) 296-4195   fax (305) 293-0904   <in1era@aol.com>

★ **Madame Alexander dolls of the 1950's.** Mid 1920's dolls were cloth, then composition. The 1950's Alexanders were made of hard plastic jointed at neck, shoulders and hips, and often knees, elbows, and even ankles! In the early 1960's, these hard plastic dolls gave way to squeezable vinyl dolls with rooted hair. "I only want good condition hard plastic dolls with glued wigs and original clothes but they can be any size from 8" to 21". The same doll might have 80 or more different costumes, and a variety of hair. "Some that don't look too exciting may actually be rare and valuable because they didn't sell and were only offered for a short time." The 1950's dolls she seeks were generally tagged and marked. To sell your doll, give her the information on the clothing tag, a description of the costume, and a statement of condition. Note whether you have the original box. Have the doll in hand if you call. "I will consider older composition or cloth Alexander dolls, but only if in mint perfect condition. They don't have to be in the original box, but must otherwise be like new."

Lia Sargent
74 The Oaks
Roslyn Estates, NY 11576
(516) 621-4883   fax (516) 621-7517   <liasargent@aol.com>

◆ **Madame Alexander 8" dolls** especially Red Riding Hood, Wendy, Elaine, Maggie Mix Up and Little Genius made 1953 and 1965. Also wants company catalogs, store ads for Mme Alexander dolls. A photograph would be most helpful. Make sure to note anything missing.

Ann Bergin
PO Box 105
Amherst, NH 03031
<acbergin@aol.com>   fax (978) 649-6807

◆ **Topper Dawn and other dolls from the 1960's and 70's.** "I am interested in anything Dawn doll related, especially the Aladdin Dawn Brunch Bag and catalogs and other printed Dawn material. I am also looking for the following dolls:
  • **Hasbro Love, Leggy, Jem and Disco Girls;**
  • **Kenner Blythe and Darcy;**
  • **Mattel Liddle Kiddles, Talk-Ups, Major Matt Mason and**
       Upsy Downsys;
  • **Galoob Baby Face;**
  • American Character **Emerald the Witch;**
  • Ideal **Flatsys** (but only boxed or carded).
"I am also interested in any catalogs that include toys and dolls, thingmakers, Oily Rubber Creatures and the like.

Joedi Johnson
PO Box 565
Billings, MT 59103
(406) 248-4875 voice/fax   <starbase@mcn.net>

★ **Skookum Indian dolls.** Skookums are blanket wrapped male and femal Indian dolls made for the tourist trade, 1914-1960. All sizes will be considered in they are in fine condition with no missing parts, but especially interested in dolls taller than 15" which are $300 and up. She DOES NOT BUY Japanese dolls made of celluloid or dolls in poor condition. Description should include size and condition with any flaws noted. Note what foot cover the doll has: leather, tape, or plastic.
Linda Larouche
606 Carlton Ave.
Brooklyn, NY 11238
(718) 230-3830 fax: (212) 244-1775 <skookumgal@aol.com>

★ **Skookum Indian dolls** wearing colorful Indian pattern blankets from the smallest sizes up to those five feet tall, if in perfect condition. Some dolls are marked "Skookum" and/or "Bully Good" under the feet. He does not want Skookums with plastic parts. Send a photo for offer.
Barry Friedman
PO Box 55492
Valencia, CA 91355
(661) 255-2365   <barryf@thevine.net>

◆ **Betsy McCall dolls** and clothing in original package or loose, one item or an entire collection. The "Designer Studio" and "A Day at the Ranch" gift sets are particularly sought, as are puzzles, cookie cutters, coloring books, figurines, etc. "I'm interested in anything and everything Betsy McCall." Marci produces a *Betsy-On-Line* newsletter.
Marci Van Ausdall
PO Box 719
McCloud, CA 96057
(530) 964-2468   fax (507) 226-5407   <dreams@snowcrest.net>

◆ **Metal doll house furniture by Tootsietoy and Kilgore** from the late 1920's and early 1930's. Both companies produced furniture in a variety of colors and sizes and are usually, but not always, marked as to maker. A large Kilgore baby carriage is particularly valuable. No plastic or other metal items are wanted. "If a magnet doesn't stick to your furniture, I'm not interested." Complete description important.
Jana Saputo
PO Box 3475
Shell Beach, CA 93448
(805) 773-8636   <taylans@aol.com>

TONY'S TIPS ON SELLING TOYS AND GAMES

Games and toys are often treasures, *especially if they are colorful, in their original box, and in excellent condition. There is a market for lesser items, but* **prices drop to nothing for anything shabby.** *It seems as if nearly every toy is collected by someone, and you'll find some great buyers in the following pages.*

If you carefully read sections in Trash or Treasure about Toys, Dolls, Games, and Pop Culture, you will see a wide range of small and seemingly insignificant items sought by collectors. Games based on movies and TV usually find ready buyers in the $20 to $100 range (see pp111-126). You will also find a buyer for nearly all toy vehicles made from tin, steel or cast iron. The market is not good for plastic vehicles, though some other plastic toys, especially comic characters will sell. Baby boomer toys of the 1960's and 70's are particularly popular right now.

Common games with names you recognize are seldom collectible, unless they are prototypes or hand made.

To sell something, you should provide the potential buyer with a complete description, including the following information:

(1) *What you have, including its size, color, and the material from which it is made;*
(2) *Names, dates, and numbers printed, embossed, stamped, or labeled on the item;*
(3) *Condition, including mention of any damage, missing parts or pieces, or missing paint;*
(4) *Whether it has the box and/or instructions, especially important when selling games.*

Wooden, tin, and iron toys were usually painted. **The amount of paint that still remains is vital information,** *as is any evidence that the toy might have been repainted. You should estimate what percentage of original paint remains.*

Don't forget your Self-Addressed Stamped Envelope.

MISCELLANEOUS TOYS

◆ **High quality kaleidoscopes** from the 1800's, made of wood and/or brass by makers such as Bush, Brester, Carpenter, or Leach. Prefer perfect original condition brass instruments in wooden cases with the Royal seal, but will consider less. He does not buy cardboard or other inexpensive kaleidoscopes. Nothing made in the 1900's. Include your phone number and time you're home so he can phone.

    Martin Roenigk
    Mechantiques
    75 Prospect Avenue
    Eureka Springs, AR 72632
(479) 253-0405   cel (443) 831-6211   fax (479) 253-0406
        <mroenigk@aol.com>

◆ **Fine old kaleidoscopes** made of wood and/or brass especially elaborate inlaid or complex instruments from the mid 19th century. No cardboard toys.

    Lucille Malitz
    Lucid Antiques
    PO Box KH
    Scarsdale, NY 10583
            (914) 636-7825   <lithophane@aol.com>

◆ **Polyramapanoptiques and megalethescopes.** The former are early 19th century cardboard or wooden boxes with flaps for slides, which permit viewing of hand painted or pin-pricked scenes. Megalethescopes, invented in 1860, are large wooden cabinets, often heavily carved, also devices for slides, usually seen as day and night views of the same scene in 3D. **Lucille also buys and sells slides for these early optical toys.**

    Lucille Malitz
    Lucid Antiques
    PO Box KH
    Scarsdale, NY 10583
            (914) 636-7825   <lithophane@aol.com>

TONY'S TIP: 19th century toys with moving parts usually top the $500 mark and regularly bring more than $2,500. At least one Trash or Treasure find resulted in an $18,000 sale. Be very careful how you dispose of any old toy in fine condition.

◆ **Antique toys** including cars, carousels, character and comic wind-ups. German and American tin toys, penny toys, nested blocks, still banks and pop-up books are all sought. Has special interest in toys by Gibbs, Arcade, Tootsietoy, Buddy L, Hubley (motorcycles), and 1950's Matchbox. He DOES NOT WANT dolls or trains. List manufacturer, size, and condition. Fine condition items only. Photo desirable.

> James Conley
> 2758 Coventry Lane NW
> Canton, OH 44708
> (330) 477-7725

★ **Collections of fine tin and iron toys** are sought for cataloged specialty auctions by this well known New England auctioneer. No junk, reproductions or items made after 1940.

> James D. Julia Auctioneers
> PO Box 830
> Fairfield, ME 04937

(207) 453-7904   fax (207) 453-2502   <jjulia@juliaauctions.com>

◆ **Cast iron bell toys,** working or not. He will consider incomplete specimens of these early toys which move and ring a bell when pulled on a string. Send clear photos taken from more than one angle, or phone with the item in hand.

> Gregory "Dr. Z" Zemenick
> 1350 Kirts Blvd. #160
> Troy, MI 48084

(248) 642-8129   (248) 244-9495   <drzzeezz@aol.com>

◆ **Victorian toys:** Jack-in-the-boxes, animals on rolling platforms, nine pins bowling games, and other traditional toys, especially those with nursery rhyme tie-ins. All items MUST BE AT LEAST 100 years old. This 25 year veteran requests a photo or photocopy of what you'd like to sell. Prefers to find toys in like-new condition, because they are frequently used as part of Christmas theme displays.

> Dolph "Father Christmas" Gotelli
> PO Box 188977
> Sacramento, CA 95818

(916) 456-9734   fax (916) 457-1559   <degotelli@ucdavis.edu>

◆ **Any sand-operated self contained toys,** including the "not very old" enclosed boxes with figures set in motion by flipping over the box. Also small toy scales made of tin.

> Donald Gorlick
> PO Box 24541
> Seattle, WA 98124
> (206) 824-0508   <seashore8@hotmail.com>

◆ **Tin wind-up toys made in Germany or Japan,** as well as a "few select American wind-ups" are sought by this collector/ dealer who says he prefers automotive and character toys. He does say that some battery operated and non operating toys will also be considered, especially cast iron cars and motorcycles as well as "carnival ride" toys. He does not buy plastic items or anything in poor condition. He'd like to know if your toy is complete, how much paint is missing, whether it works and if you have its box. If it's newer than 1960, it's not wanted.

> Richard Trautwein
> Toys n' Such
> 437 Dawson Street
> Sault Ste. Marie, MI 49783
> (906) 635-0356   <rtraut@portup.com>

◆ **Antique toys** of many different types:
  • **Mechanical banks,** pre-1920, made of tin or iron;
  • **Cast iron bell toys,** circa 1890;
  • **Figural clockwork toys,** in tin or iron, from the 1870's;
  • **Political campaign toys** and banks;
  • **European tin toys** and large boats;
  • Colorful paper on wood boats and trains from the 1890's;
  • Colorful **Victorian children's games** and block sets;
  • Hand painted tin wind-up toys.

He's not interested in anything after 1940, nor does he want banks marked "Book of Knowledge," repainted items or things that have been dug up. Broken mechanical banks or rare toys that are incomplete may be of minor interest. Give the size, condition of the metal, and the condition of the paint including fading. List all repairs and note if the item has been lacquered or refinished. This 20 year veteran insists you set the price you want for your items.

> Mark Suozzi
> PO Box 102
> Ashfield, MA 01330
> (413) 628-3241   fax (413) 628-3241   <marklyn@valinet.com>

TONY'S TIP: You should give the following information:
(1) What you have, including its size, color, and the material from which it is made;
(2) Names, dates, and numbers printed, embossed, stamped, or labeled on the item;
(3) Condition, including mention of any missing parts, pieces, or paint, or damage to what remains;
(4) Whether it has the box and/or instructions.

Don't forget your Self-Addressed Stamped Envelope.

◆ **Clockwork (wind-up) toys** from before 1910, made of tin or iron, working or not, complete or not. "I want wind-up cars, boats, horses and buggies, people, and what have you, with particular interest in large ocean boats and steamships." Send a good clear sharp photo of both sides of the toy and include your telephone number.

> Greg "Dr. Z" Zemenick
> 1350 Kirts Blvd. #160
> Troy, MI 48084
> (248) 642-8129 eves   (248) 244-9426 days   fax (248) 244-9495
> <drzzeezz@aol.com>

◆ **Schoenhut circus animals, milk and bread wagons, trolleys, and other other toys,** games and dolls made by Schoenhut. No pianos. He asks for pictures and an accurate description. No offers, so research is in order before making any inquiry.

> Harry McKeon, Jr.
> 18 Rose Lane
> Flourtown, PA 19031
> (215) 233-4094   fax (215) 233-3639   <toyspost@aol.com>

◆ **German or French tin clockwork toys** by makers such as Martan, Lehman and Marklin. He asks for pictures and an accurate description. He does not make offers, and these can be quite valuable.

> Harry McKeon, Jr.
> 18 Rose Lane
> Flourtown, PA 19031
> (215) 233-4094   fax (215) 233-3639   <toyspost@aol.com>

See Teddy bears and Dolls for other buyers of early toys.

◆ **Old one of a kind kites** from before 1940 especially those made by important inventors may have value. Names on desirable kites include Hargrave, Lecornu, Saconney, Conyne, Perkins, Bell, and many others including Barrage Kite, Target Kite, and the U.S. Weather Bureau. If your kite is old, interesting, or unusual, you can learn about it, and perhaps get help finding a buyer here at the Bookstore. Kite technology has changed a lot, the market for antique kites is small, so only the best items have a market. The Kite Lines Bookstore's catalog may be seen at <http://www.kitelife.com> Please, no collector wants your paper drug store kites from the 1940's and 50's.

> Valerie Govig
> Kite Lines Bookstore
> PO Box 1775
> Millsboro, DE 19966
> (302) 945-0449   fax (302) 945-0550   <kitelines@compuserve.com>

★ **Yo-yos from 1920 to 1980 with original maker's seal intact.** Will buy some Duncans, but most interested in "off brands" like Cheerio, Royal, Flores, Hi-Ker, Chico, Goody, Cayo, Tom Kuhn and other less common makers. Jeweled yo-yos are wanted, as are the tin ones that whistle as they go up and down. Yo-yo's that are carved by Philippino demonstrators are wanted, if you can assure authenticity. Yo-yos with foil seals in perfect condition are wanted, as are those in original boxes. **In addition** he wants yo-yo strings in glassine envelopes with the maker's name displayed, yo-yo trophies, patches (the bigger the better), awards, pins, boxes, posters, store displays, ribbons and sweaters. We DO NOT WANT yo-yos with missing or heavily damaged seals, red and black Duncans, plain yo-yos, plastic Duncan Imperials, or Duncan wooden crossed flags tournament yo-yos. Include the color, size and the *exact* wording on the seal, A photo or Xerox™ is helpful.

Jason Colwell & Julie Martensen
1432 Howard Street
Dearborn, MI 48124
　　　(313) 506-4342　　<j2@peoplepc.com>

◆ **Collectible toys of the 1970's and 80's.** "We will be happy to identify and evaluate any toy from that era." Provide names, dates, or numbers on your toy and a brief accurate description of condition including paint or color loss, damage, and condition of the package it came in." They do not want plush (stuffed) animals, sports toys, NASCAR, Beanie Babies or glassware of any kind. Jack has edited various space and action toy price guides; more information is available from him. Email is the preferred way of contacting.

Jack Klodsinski & Rich Levy, Critical Mass Toys
PO Box 470
Geneva, FL 32732
(407) 327-8223 days　<askdoctorjack@hotmail.com> <cmitoys.com>

◆ **Baby rattles** from before 1950 in gold, silver, wood, celluloid, plastic or rubber, especially Art Nouveau, Georgian, Victorian, Oriental, and early American. No repros or common. Send photo and description. You must price what you have for sale.

Marcia Hersey
106 West 69th Street
New York, NY 10023

◆ **Erector sets** by A.C. Gilbert. Will buy complete sets, partial sets, manuals, signs, and sales catalogs. Give model numbers and dates whenever it's possible.

Michael Wagner
28 East Willow Street
Carlisle, PA 17013
　　　(717) 258-0839 M-F 11am-9pm　fax (610) 296-2258
　　　<w5344@aol.com>

TOY BANKS

◆ **Cast iron mechanical banks,** 1870-1920, and Japanese tin battery operated banks, 1946-1960. Include a bottom tracing. Indicate whether it works or not and if you still have the original box. Battery banks must be in near mint condition. No plastic banks.

    Rick Mihlheim
    PO Box 128
    Allegan, MI 49010
        (616) 673-4509

TONY'S TIPS: *Tin and iron toys were painted.* **The amount of paint that remains is vital information to a collector.** *So is evidence that the toy might have been repainted. You should estimate the percent of paint remaining.*

Toy banks are desirable, particularly 19th century originals. These were sold in boxes, which can add hundreds of dollars to the value. Banks marked "Book of Knowledge" on the bottom are not of interest. Advertising cards which depict banks sell for $300 to $1,000+ each!

◆ **Mechanical banks in the form of rocket ships** used by financial and insurance companies as promotional giveaways. "I want banks with all the original parts in excellent condition. Photo is helpful."

    Anthony Glab
    407 East Wheel Road
    Belair, MD 21015
        (410) 235-1777 voice/fax

◆ **Still banks** made of cast iron or metal with special emphasis on unusual or rare examples in excellent to near-mint condition. Letters should include an accurate description including an estimate of how much of the original paint is still there. Carefully measure the length, width, and height. Photos are appreciated. Private collector answers all letters which include SASE.

    Ralph Berman
    3524 Largo Lane
    Annandale, VA 22003
        (703) 560-5439

◆ **Mechanical and still banks made of cast iron, tin, or wood.** Especially any mechanical bank with its original box, packing, and receipt. Also buys painted and stenciled cast iron or tin still banks shaped like buildings. Will consider incomplete, broken and non-working specimens, if old and genuine. No banks made after 1930, especially those which say "Book of Knowledge" on the bottom. Also buys trade cards, catalogs, empty packing boxes, advertising depicting mechanical banks and photos of children with banks. Send sharp photos of the bank from different angles, or phone with it in front of you. Greg is the former president of a club for bank collectors.

Gregory "Dr. Z" Zemenick
1350 Kirts #160
Troy, MI 48084
(248) 642-8129 eves   (248) 244-9426 days   fax (248) 244-9495
<drzzeezz@aol.com>

◆ **Still and mechanical banks in all materials,** including pot metal, lead, cast iron, zinc, glass and wood. Also buys packing boxes, trade cards depicting banks, photos of children with their mechanical banks, and other ephemera related to banks. Pays from $1,000 to $100,000 for mint condition, like new, 19th century banks. He does not want any mechanical bank made after 1935, nor does he buy reproductions or modern banks. He does not buy broken still banks but will consider buying some broken mechanical banks, "but for a lot less." To sell your bank, include a full and accurate description noting any defects. Describe the paint and what percentage of it remains. Measure it carefully and give the exact length and width of the base. Include sharp color photos. Sy has written a column on antique banks in *Toy World Magazine* for 20 years.

Sy Schreckinger
PO Box 104
East Rockaway, NY 11518
(516) 536-4154 any time

TOY SOLDIERS & TOY GUNS

◆ **Toy soldiers, farm figures and zoo animals** and related buildings and vehicles made of metal, composition or plastic. "I buy single pieces, sets, and entire collections. Prices vary widely, but complete sets of toy soldiers mint in their box will bring from $50 to $1,500. I am not interested in reproductions or damaged figures. Please send a photograph, an accurate description, or a sample figure."

Dave Francis
PO Box 16
Wadsworth, OH 44281
(330) 335-3717   fax (330) 335-3617   <fphadv@bright.net>

◆ **Toy lead soldiers** and related items by the following companies, especially when packed in original boxes: Britains, Mignot, Heyde, Lineol, and Elastolin. When writing, please give a brief description of the soldiers, the name of the maker whenever possible, whether or not you have the original box, the number of soldiers and include a photo.

> Craig McClain
> Old Toy Soldier's Home
> 977 South Santa Fe Avenue #11
> Vista, CA 92083
> (760) 758-5481 voice/fax

◆ **Toy soldiers of all types** including dime store soldiers, 1930-50, made in the USA of painted lead, boxed sets of fine British soldiers, or German composition soldiers of WWII. Xerox™ gets a free appraisal.

> Larry Bruch
> PO Box 121
> Mountain Top, PA 18707
> (800) 549-toys   <bkinglar@aol.com>

◆ **BB guns.**   Older BB guns with cast iron parts, and USA made spring-air BB guns in excellent condition. Many brands are wanted, although Daisy guns are preferred from the Plymouth, MI, factory. Does not want recently made guns, or those that are damaged, broken or in less than very good condition. You must list everything broken or missing. Is the stock, forestock, or grip broken, cracked or worn? Describe the finish on all metal and wooden parts. Include all names, numbers and addresses found on the gun. Indicate if it works or not.

> James Buskirk
> Toy Gun Collectors of America
> 3009 Oleander Avenue
> San Marcos, CA 92069
> (760) 599-1054   <toygun@earthlink.net>

TONY'S TIP: Minor differences in castings, handles, or decoration can put extra money in your pocket.

◆ **Daisy air rifles and Daisy company advertising** and other memorabilia from the Plymouth, MI, plant only. Give model number and description of condition, including all damage or missing parts for guns. Paper and advertising items are best to photocopy (Xerox@).

> Johnny Spellman
> 10806 North Lamar Blvd.
> Austin, TX 78753
> (512) 836-2889 days   (512) 258-6910 eves   (512) 750-2838 cel
> fax (512) 832-0242   <dvm69@swbell.net>

★ **Cap pistols.** "I'll buy Western style cap guns made before 1965 by Kilgore, Hubley, Stevens, Leslie-Henry, Chas. Schmidt, Nichols, Mattel, and others. Especially looking for Kilgore "disc cap" guns such as the American, Big Horn, Long Tom and Roy Rogers models. Also seeking any cap gun or holster sets associated with cowboy movie and TV actors like GeneAutry, Hoppy, Paladin, the Lone Ranger, etc. Condition is important. Guns must be complete, working, and have little wear. Top prices paid for guns or holster sets in their original box. Photo if possible. Xerox™ your gun if you don't know what it is.
Bill Hamburg
PO Box 536
Woodland Hills, CA 91365
(818) 346-1269   fax (818) 346-0215   <whamburg@aol.com>

◆ **Quackenbush air guns.** Send a complete description, including a sketch or photo. Will make offers, but appraisals are for a fee.
Charles Best
11523 Pinevalley Drive
Franktown, CO 80116
(303) 660-2318   <budbest@aol.com>

◆ **Cap pistols.** Especially interested in cast iron guns by Kilgore, Stevens, Hubley and Kenton. Premium paid for character guns such as the Kilgore Long Tom, Big Horn, Roy Rogers, Lone Ranger or American, the Kenton Lawmaker, the Stevens Cowboy King, or any of the many different models of Gene Autry guns made by Kenton. Also interested in the 1950's and 60's die cast guns. Buys any guns marked Gene Autry, Roy Rogers, Dale Evans, Trigger, Lone Ranger, Tonto, Paladin, Alan Ladd, Hopalong Cassidy, Hoppy, or Shane. Particularly seeks character guns made in Los Angeles by the Schmidt Company or by LATCO. Must give all identifying marks, numbers, etc., found on the guns and a complete accounting of damage or wear to the gun, finish, or handles (grips). Buys only guns in fine condition. Publishes the *Toy Gun Collectors Newsletter*, available with club membership for the bargain price of $15/year.
James Buskirk, Toy Gun Collectors of America
3009 Oleander Avenue
San Marcos, CA 92069
(760) 599-1054   <toygun@earthlink.net>

◆ **Cap pistols** made of cast iron, especially animated guns from the 1800's or guns featuring movie cowboys and other Pop Culture heroes before 1940. A magnet must stick to your gun or he's not interested.
George Fougere
67 East Street
North Grafton, MA 01536
(508) 839-2701

GAMES & PUZZLES

◆ **Antique and collectible board and card games** made in the U.S. from 1840-1950's. Any game before 1860 is wanted, especially those made by Ives, Crosby, Magnus, or Adams, for which they will pay $500 and up. Other items of particular interest are baseball games before WWI and games about cartoon characters, space exploration and pop culture (including movies) of the 1930's-1950's. They also buy wooden jigsaw puzzles, blocks, and paper toys. No chess, checkers, *Pit, Lotto, Rook, Flinch, Autobridge, Parcheesi, Touring*, variants of Bingo, TV "game show" games, or "kiddie" games like *Chutes and Ladders*. Give the name of the game, the maker, size, condition, copyright date, and the degree of completeness.
> Dave Oglesby and Sue Stock
> 57 Lakeshore Drive
> Marlborough, MA 01752
> (508) 481-1087   <djoz@mediaone.net>

◆ **Games.** Buys children's and adult games in colorful pictorial boxes copyrighted before 1970 including:
- Victorian games before 1900;
- Comic character games;
- Television games from the 1950's and 60's;
- Sports games with famous players named on the box;
- Space and science fiction games before 1970;
- Games based on children's book series;
- Lesser known games with colorful names or pictures.

Does not want generic games, or any common game. Condition of games is very important as he buys for resale. Give the name of the game, the maker, copyright (©) date, and list all missing pieces, if any.
> Paul Fink's Fun & Games
> PO Box 488
> Kent, CT 06757
> (860) 927-4001   <paul@gamesandpuzzles.com>

◆ **Almost any complete playable game,** especially out-of-print titles by Avalon Hill, 3M, SPI, pre-1964 Parker Bros., war games, sports games, political games, and TV related games. Include the name of the manufacturer and copyright date. Please thoroughly check the contents and note if anything, no matter how small, is missing. Describe how much wear shows on the box and pieces. Also buys gaming magazines such as *The General, Wargamer, The Dragon,* and *Games & Puzzles*. Please, no checkers, chess or common children's games like *Authors*.
> H.M. Levy
> PO Box 197-TH
> East Meadow, NY 11554
> (516) 485-0877   <gamers@pipeline.com>

◆ **American boxed games, all types and all years.** "I buy:
- Board games;
- Card games;
- Skill and action games;
- **Jigsaw puzzles;**
- **Mechanical puzzles;**
- Paper games published in magazines and newspapers;
- Games with themes reflecting American history and culture, sports, politics, social issues, fads or leisure;
- Mystery games;
- Space games;
- Games depicting specific events or persons;
- Games with fictional or cartoon characters;
- Games based on radio, television, movies or books;
- Games which have advertising or were sponsored by products;
- Games made in upstate New York;
- Games with colorful illustrations on the box or game board;
- Game boards, parts and pieces before 1900;
- Advertising or ephemera related to game companies.

"Specific games I want include *Philo Vance, Charlie Chan, Boom or Bust, Star Reporter, Red Barber's Baseball, Troque*, and *Elvis* but I buy most games by McLoughlin Brothers and E.G. Selchow, and pre-1920 games by Parker Brothers, Selchow & Righter, Milton Bradley, Singer, Bliss, Ives, Cadaco, National, Games of Fame, Jim Prentice Electric Game Company, and others, especially small regional companies. **I do NOT want games that don't indicate the manufacturer, or common games such as** *Authors, Backgammon, Beano, Bingo, Bridge, Charlie's Angels, Checkers, Chess, Chinese Checkers, Doctor Busby, Fish Pond, Flinch, Jack Straws, Keno, Kojak, Lost Heir, Lotto, Monopoly, Old Main, Parcheesi, Peter Coddles, Pick-Up-Sticks, Pit Rook, Snap, Tic-Tac-Toe, Tiddly Winks, Touring* or *Whist* unless there is something very striking or unusual about your edition. Please don't offer games that are not complete and in near mint condition unless they are before 1900 or priced so cheaply that I can buy them for parts." When describing a game, give the name, date, manufacturer, box size, box contents, and the material from which the pieces are made. Tell whether the game has all parts and instructions. Make a Xerox™ of the cover of the box and board. Bruce charges a fee for appraisals. Dealers should price their goods, but amateurs may request offers with the understanding that Bruce buys for resale. Bruce has written more than 100 articles on games, past president of the American Game Collectors Ass'n and author of the definitive price guide to games: *American Boxed Games and Their Makers, 1822-1992.*

Bruce Whitehill
The Big Game Hunter
11 South Angell Street #116
Providence, RI 02906
   <games@thebiggamehunter.com>

◆ **Checker ephemera,** primarily books about checkers or draughts, but also old checker sets made of wood, rubber, *Catalin* or *Bakelite*. Call about anything unusual related to checkers.

> Don Deweber
> 3520 Hillcrest #4
> Dubuque, IA 52002
> (563) 556-1944   <checkers21@hotmail.com>

◆ **Chess sets,** as well as books and art related to chess.
- "I'll buy figural or very ornate sets" made of ivory, bone, amber, wood, silver, metal, glass, or porcelain. Sets from before 1900 are preferred. Artist signed sets are of particular interest as are ivory sets from 19th century Europe or Russia. Standard looking sets are not wanted.
- Art sought includes paintings, prints, figurines, and anything else with a chess related theme.
- Books related to playing chess, chess pieces, or chess history. "Will consider any book related to chess" including those on other topics with chess sections.
- Ephemera such as photos, autographs, postcards, score cards of well known players, medals, souvenirs from chess Olympiads, and what have you.

Chess sets should be complete, but early and rare items will be considered even if damaged. A photo or Xerox™ is helpful. When offering a set for sale, note the material from which it is made and measure the height of a pawn and the king. Note whether pieces are boxed or loose. Dealers, price your goods. Amateurs may request an offer.

> Jeffrey Litwin
> PO Box 494
> Princeton Junction, NJ 08550
> (609) 275-0996   fax (609) 275-1427   <jsl58@comcast.net>

◆ **Chess sets,** especially figural sets based on themes that are topical, historical, geographical, cultural, political, fictional, etc. "I'm looking for workds of art or imagination, particularly sets that are out of the ordinary in theme, design or material." Your full description should include color of the pieces, what they are made of, and the condition. Give the exact hight of the king and a pawn. He wants to know how you came to own the set, including when and where you bought it. He DOES NOT WANT any plastic or ordinary looking sets, nor does he want books on chess strategy. Send an SASE and a photo of the pieces.

> Dennis Horwitz
> PO Box 301
> Topanga, CA 90290
> (310) 202-7393 after 6 pm Pacific

★ **Jig saw puzzles with advertising,** mostly from the 1930's. They want die-cut cardboard puzzles with the advertiser's product or name printed on the face of the puzzles. Puzzles must be complete, in good to excellent condition. The original envelope or container and all the enclosures add to the value.

> Liz & Dick Wilmes
> 38W567 Brindlewood
> Elgin, IL 60123
> (847) 697-9679   fax (847) 742-1054
> <dick@bblocksonline.com>

◆ **Games and puzzles, including jigsaw, based on maps** as long as they're complete and made before 1960. Description should include the name of the game, the publisher, copyright, condition and whether pieces are missing. Photo or Xerox© of the cover is helpful.

> Murray Hudson
> Antiquarian Books & Maps
> 109 South Church Street
> Halls, TN 38040
> (800) 748-9946   fax (731) 836-9017   <mapman@ecsis.net>

◆ **Mechanical and dexterity puzzles.** Wants all types of mechanical and dexterity puzzles. Not interested in jigsaw or paper and pencil puzzles. Please send a photocopy, sketch, or clear photo of your puzzle.

> Cary Basse
> 6927 Forbes Avenue
> Van Nuys, CA 91406
> (818) 781-4856

◆ **Mechanical puzzles of all types** including trick locks and match-safes "and all others." Also expresses some interest in advertising for trick locks and puzzles. A photocopy, photograph, or good sketch is appreciated. Dealers should price their goods, but he will help amateurs to determine the value of what they have.

> Jerry Slocum
> 251 South Palm Drive
> Beverly Hills, CA 90212
> (310) 273-2270   fax (310) 274-3644   <jslocum@earthlink.net>

TONY'S TIP: Pencil and paper puzzles like rebuses and crosswords are sought by a different type of collector. You will find this type of puzzle in the section on paper. Look in the index under "crossword puzzles" and you'll be steered to pages 556 and 570.

MARBLES

★ **Better quality marbles and marble related items** such as original boxes, tournament trophies and medals, and marble literature. "We run marble auctions, and if you send a detailed description or close-up color photo, we'll give you an idea of what your items will bring at auction and what we will pay you to purchase them outright." Stan is the chairman of the Marble Collectors Society of America. Son Robert is author of *Marbles Identification and Price Guide* available for $24.

     Stan and Robert Block
     PO Box 2321
     Shelton, CT 06484
     (203) 924-2802 voice/fax   <blockschip@aol.com>

◆ **Marbles and marble-related toys.** Wants include clay, china and porcelain marbles decorated with flowers, people, animals or geometric designs. Pays up to $2,000 for colored sulfide marbles with unusual objects or people in them and up to $1,000 for china marbles decorated with flowers, ships, birds, or people and animals. He also wants early boxed sets of marbles made by Christensen Agate Co., Peltier Marble Co., or Akro Agate. Toys related to marbles are also often of interest. He does not want Chinese Checker marbles and boards or any cat's-eye marbles. If you know your marble's history, tell him. A good description should include what is on or in the marble and its diameter.

     Edwin Snyder
     PO Box 156
     Lancaster, KY 40444
        (606) 792-4816 eves

◆ **Marbles and marble-related items.** "I'll buy marbles with pontil marks (from where they were hand-blown), toys or games using marbles, marble bags, tournament pins and medals, and boxes of marbles. Also pictures, magazine ads, and postcards which depict marble games." He does not buy "beat up" or chipped marbles, machine made marbles, homemade games, or Chinese Checkers. When selling marbles, it is important to give the diameter as part of your description.

     Cathy & Larry Svacina
     7812 NW Hampton Road
     Kansas City, MO 64152
        (816) 587-1203   <marbleldy@aol.com>

◆ **Marbles and marble related ephemera.** Will buy postcards, magazine covers, ads, trade cards, stories, calendars, or "anything depicting or written about kids playing marbles."

     William Nielsen
     PO Box 1413
     East Dennis, MA 02641
        (508) 385-9247

TOY & ELECTRIC TRAINS

★ **Toy trains and accessories,** U.S. or foreign, made between 1900 and 1970. Will buy any maker and gauge except HO gauge trains. Items do not have to be in perfect condition to be considered. Also buys train catalogs and literature. A wind-up American Flyer train with cars marked Coca-Cola is worth $350 in mint condition. This 40 year veteran will make offers only if you're serious about selling. Lazarus is past president of the Toy Train Operating Society. Make certain to include a stamped envelope for a reply.

> Hillel Don Lazarus
> 14547 Titus Street #207
> Panorama City, CA 91402
> (818) 762-3652 eves   <hillylaz@earthlink.net>

TONY'S TIP:
When describing electric trains,
give the brand name, any model numbers found on the engine, and a list of the cars. It's worth your time to indicate the color of each car, it's purpose, and RR line name, since minor variations can affect value. If the car has been repainted or otherwise modified by someone other than the factory, be certain to note that fact.

If you have the original box, describe its condition. Make a list of any accessories, noting the condition of the paint of each. Some buildings and other items will bring you $100 or more.

◆ **All makes of old toy trains** except HO gauge and hand made scale models. Buys Lionel, American Flyer, Ives, Marx and all foreign trains larger than HO. "I'll buy engines, cars, accessories, signals, and incomplete sets that are new, like new, used, and even incomplete but useful for parts. No layouts, rusty junk or other toys." This 45 year veteran hobby shop owner offers a large price guide to trains for $7, which is refunded on your first purchase.

> Allison Cox
> 18025 8th Avenue N.W.
> Seattle, WA 98177
> (206) 546-2230 voice/fax   <coxtrain@gte.net>

★ **Toy trains in all gauges and types** are wanted, including electric, wind-up, floor type, etc. Lionel, American Flyer, Ives, Dorfan, Marx, and others, in any gauge. O, HO, G, GAO and all others. "Age is not the main consideration, but I do want items from before World War II. I like to buy large collections, but will buy smaller units, and consider properly priced junkers, but no reproductions." Wants to know the train's gauge, maker, condition, the number of pieces and the markings on each, and how many of the original boxes you have.

  Jay Robinson "The Chicago Kid"
  522 Rivershire Place
  Lincolnshire, IL 60069
  (847) 913-1106   fax (847) 913-1274   <jcomcent@megsinet.net>

◆ **Marklin and other European toy trains** and metal toys powered by clockwork, electricity, or live steam. Other toys such as airplanes, boats, circus toys, and others made by Marklin will also be considered for purchase. "I want anything by Marklin before 1955 in decent condition." Most Marklin toys are marked with the company name but some have an entwined "GM" or "Germany." **Also wants** trains and toys by Bing, Schuco, Doll, Lehmann and Carette in very good or better condition. "I will buy common items in excellent condition, but don't want repros, fakes, or toys with pieces missing. I'm a collector not a dealer so prefer people not contact me unless they actually want to sell or trade what they have. I pay fair prices and am willing to travel to inspect collections." Marklin trains from before WWII are worth from $500 to $10,000 to Ron so check carefully.

  Ron Wiener
  1650 Arch Street, 22nd Floor
  Philadelphia, PA 19103
  (215) 977-2266   fax (215) 977-2334   <rwiener@wolfblock.com>

◆ **HO and N gauge trains** and accessories, preferably in running order, but they don't have to be old for him to be interested. Cliff also buys **railroad books and magazines.**

  Cliff Robnett
  7804 NW 27th
  Bethany, OK 73008
      (405) 787-6703   <clrob@swbell.net>

◆ **Trains and other vehicles.** Will make an offer on trains in any gauge, especially HO, Standard, and O. He is also in the market for any fine old toys, but especially steam engines, tin plate toys, and airplanes. A color photo must accompany your description if you wish to sell to this long time dealer.

  Heinz Mueller, Continental Hobby
  PO Box 193
  Sheboygan, WI 53082
  (920) 693-3371   fax (920) 693-8211   <continental@lsol.net>

◆ **Electric trains by Marx** with metal or plastic cars that have eight wheels. Especially wants complete sets in original boxes. "I'll pay $100 for Marx Pennsylvania RR car #53941. Not interested in plastic engines numbered #400 or #490 or in any plastic cars. " When writing, give him all numbers you find on boxes or cars.

> Robert Owen
> PO Box 204
> Fairborn, OH 45324
> <gardnerst8@aol.com>

TONY'S TIP: If toy trains interest you, join the Toy Train Operating Society, Their Bulletin is one of the truly fine club publications. For information write to them at 25 West Walnut Street, Room 408, Pasadena, CA 91103. They'll send complete information and a sample copy.

TOY MOTORS & ENGINES

◆ **Toy outboard motors,** either battery or wind-up, alone or mounted on toy boats. "I'll buy motors by K & O Fleetline made between 1952 and 1962 with names of popular manufacturers of real outboard motors." Pays $75-$400 for your toy depending on the model. Describe the decals and color. Author of *Toy Outboard Motors.*

> Jack Browning
> 214 16th Street NW
> Roanoke, VA 24017
> (540) 982-1253   (540) 890-5083   fax (540) 342-1283
> <jbrow9945@aol.com>

◆ **Books, magazines and catalogs of toy and full size electric motors and devices** from before 1930, especially *Electrical Review* and *Electrical World* publications. Pre-1920 **electrical devices** also considered. Give make, model, serial number, and dimensions. DO NOT TEST OR PLUG IN.

> Rick Padrone
> 1005 E. Idlewild Ave.
> Tampa, FL 33604
> (800) 991-0165   fax (800) 991-0166
> <ricpadron@webtv.net>

◆ **Model airplane engines,** both foreign and domestic, built between 1930 and 1970. Buys both spark and glo plug ignitions as well as diesel. "I am particularly interested in .15 cubic inch (2.5 cubic centimeter) displacement glo and diesel engines." Generally, engines with ball bearings are more valuable than those with plain bushings. Engines should be complete with proper carburetor and no disfiguring marks. Engines can be worth form $4 to $400 depending on rarity and condition. Does not buy model boat engines, steam engines or stationery engines, but a few small car engines may be acceptable. Give the name of the engine if known, and all markings stamped on the crankcase. Give serial numbers, if any. A picture is preferred. SASE is a must. Dealers price your goods; amateurs may request an offer or appraisal.

> Jim Dunkin
> 29805 Southeast Ryan Road
> Blue Springs, MO 64014
> (816) 229-9671 voice/fax   <dunkin@discoverynet. com>

◆ **Toy electric battery driven motors** for kids, 1910 to 1930, made by Ajax, Lil Hustler, Porter, Kent, Edison, Leavitt and others. These range in size from lemons to large apples and had a variety of applications. Send complete information and the price wanted.

> Steve Cunningham
> 3200 Ashland Drive
> Bedford, TX 76021
> (800) 991-0165   fax (800) 991-0166   <sacunningham@attbi.com>

◆ **Miniature outboard marine motors** used on model boats before 1970. Wants fuel type motors only. No electric motors or boats. Condition must be described carefully. Offers made only on items sent for his examination. Owner pays postage for return of your motor if my offer is not accepted.

> Sven Stau
> 181 Crestmount Court #3
> Tonawanda, NY 14150
> (716) 693-4011   <svenstau@cs.com>

◆ **Toy outboard boat motors** made of metal labeled Oliver, Mercury, Evinrude, Scott, Johnson, Fuji, Sea-Fury, Gale, Orkin and the like. A Gale Sovereign 60HP toy metal outboard will bring $200 as will an Oliver 35HP. Boxes are worth an additional 10% **No plastic motors.** Please send a photo (not a Polaroid ™) and describe the condition.

> Richard Gronowski
> 1100 Peninsula Drive
> Traverse City, MI 49686
> (231) 941-2111   <rgrono3381@aol.com>

PLASTIC MODEL KITS

★ **Plastic model kits** especially from the 1950's made by Monogram, Hawk, Aurora, Bachman, Comet, ITC, Frog, Allyn, Monogram, Revell, Strombecker, and others. Models can be autos, airliners, commercial ships, spacecraft, TV and movie subjects, science fiction and other figures. **Also manufacturers' catalogs, and store display models.** Kits must be complete and unbuilt, with minimal damage to the box. Sealed unopened kits are best. She offers to send a copy of the grading system used by kit collectors for an SASE.   Starline publishes *Vintage Plastic*, the journal for kit collectors.

>Edith Keller
>Starline Hobbies
>PO Box 38
>Stanton, CA 90680
>(714) 826-5218 days   <prsdog@aol.com>

◆ **Plastic model kits** of airplanes, tanks, ships, figures, cars, buildings, or what have you if complete, unbuilt, and in original box.   Your description should include the manufacturer and kit number. John publishes *Kit Collector's Clearinghouse*, a bimonthly newsletter for kit collectors and is the author of *Value Guide for Scale Model Plastic Kits*, available for $30, and other model books.

>John Burns
>3213 Hardy Drive
>Edmond, OK 73013
>(405) 341-4640   <cheersjwb@aol.com>

◆ **Plastic model kits.** "If it rolls, floats or flies, I like it! The early items are always of interest but I like all eras. Planes, trucks, cars and sci-fi models are my primary interests." His #1 want is the Revell atomic power plant from 1960. Give the name of the kit, the scale, the maker, model number (all found on the box). Note whether it is complete with all parts, decals and instructions. Has any of if been painted or assembled? He says the proliferation of re-issued models has caused prices of older originals to drop as much as 75%. Herb has been a manufacturer of plastic models for more than a decade, specializing in Sci-fi kits.

>Herb Deeks
>1516 East Santa Ana Street
>Anaheim, CA 92805
>(714) 774-7326   fax (714) 774-9631

126 TOY VEHICLES

★ **Larger pressed steel toy cars and trucks** are wanted by this 10 year veteran collector-dealer. "I'll buy **Smith Miller, Doepke, Tonka, Buddy-L, Keystone, Arcade** and other makes of toy vehicles including construction types, boats, airplanes, and farm tractors." To sell your vehicles, tell him [1] the maker if you can, [2] what it looks like, including what type of vehicle it is, [3] how many you have, and [4] the condition of each. Make an estimate of what percentage of the original paint is left. "I prefer not to buy rusty or damaged vehicles, but this policy is not written in stone."

Jay Robinson "The Chicago Kid"
522 Rivershire Place
Lincolnshire, IL 60069
(847) 913-1106   fax (847) 913-1274   <jcomcent@megsinet.net>

◆ **Metal vehicles and toys,** pre-1959, including cars, trucks, boats, airplanes, trains and construction equipment:
  • Large steel toys by **Buddy-L, Sturditoy, Turner, Kingsbury, Sonny, Keystone,** and **Structo;**
  • **Tootsietoys** with white rubber tires or all metal wheels;
  • Old tin toy boats, the larger the better;
  • **Pedal cars** and trucks made before 1940;
  • Steel Smith-Miller or M-I-C trucks made between 1945 -1957;
  • **Tin windup automotive, aviation, or comic toys**, U.S. or
       European, working or not. Will pay $8,000 for an 8" truck
       with "Aunt Eppie Hogg" in perfect condition;
  • **Dinky toys,** pre-1964, from England or France;
  • **Any metal motorcycle** 8" or longer, especially Hubley Indian
       delivery cycle, worth $2,500 in original condition;
  • Japanese scale models of U.S. cars;
  • **Cast iron toys** by Hubley, Arcade, Kilgore, and Williams.
Plastic, rubber, or wooden vehicles are not wanted. Describe the condition carefully, paying particular attention to the quality of the paint and whether or not all the parts and pieces are present. Describe the condition of the wheels and tires. Dimensions are helpful.

Larry Bruch
PO Box 121
Mountaintop, PA 18707
       (800) 549-toys   <bkinglar@aol.com>

◆ **Tonka, Doepke, and Smith-Miller toy trucks** and catalogs, ads and photos of them. He does not want Tonka's "Mighty" or "Mini" series trucks or anything repainted. Photos of both sides are necessary.

Nollie Neill, Jr.
PO Box 38
Enice, NC 28623
       fax (336) 657-8084   <saddlemtn@skybest.com>

★ **Cars, trucks and race cars made of metal** before 1960 wanted.
- Toy cars by **Hubley, Dinky, Arcade, Kilgore, Williams, Tootsietoy, Sun Rubber,** and **Auburn Rubber** are wanted;
- Race cars, with or without engines, are wanted made by Cox, Thimbledrome, Ohlson and Rice, Rodzy, and others;
- Trucks by **Smith-Miller, MIC, Tonka, Marx,** and others.

Please send a photo and good description. "Prompt response assured."

Bill Hamburg
PO Box 536
Woodland Hills, CA 91365
(818) 346-1269   fax (818) 346-0215   <whamburg@aol.com>

◆ Toy **tin automobiles made in France and Germany** before WWI that run by steam, batteries, or clockwork. "The item, its size, and the condition all determine value. Some early autos by Bing are worth thousands of dollars. A photo is almost a must."

David Bausch
252 North 7th Street
Allentown, PA 18102
(610) 432-3355   fax (610) 820-9368   <oldtoy@aol.com>

◆ **Hard rubber toys,** especially vehicles, motorcycles, trains, airplanes, ships, animals, soldiers, football and baseball players, especially by Rainbow Rubber Co. **Hard rubber toys only. No vinyl.** Hard rubber is painted. Vinyl is made in the color of the toy and is the same color throughout. Give the maker, size, colors, condition, and description of features. **Also buys all toy vehicles of all sizes, from Dinky to pedal cars made before 1950**. "Photos are best."

Steve Kelley
PO Box 695
Desert Hot Springs, CA 92240
          (760) 329-3206   <kskelley@earthlink.net>

◆ **Matchbox and other small toy cars.** "I want to buy old Matchbox cars produced before 1970. I am interested in buying 1-75 series, Major Packs, King Size and early Yesteryears. Send a list of what cars you have and an accurate description of their condition and I'll make an offer." Also buys Matchbox accessories such as buildings and store displays, as well as cars made by **Hotwheels, Corgi, Husky, Johnny Lightning and Aurora slot cars.** Any Matchbox cars with metal wheels that are new in their box are worth a minimum of $50, but he does not want cars with chips, scratches and missing parts. This 20+ year veteran prefers items in original box.

Richard Okula, Rit's Cars
PO Box 6393
Wolcott, CT 06716
          (203) 879-6883

◆ **Toy farm tractors and equipment** from 1980 or older, including the large cast metal riding tractor toys. "I want toys with real farm equipment company names like John Deere, Farmall, Oliver, Ford, Allis-Chalmers and the like, in plastic or metal, and pay over $200 for some tractors. Even broken ones are wanted for parts." Also wants Caterpillar dozers and heavy equipment toys. Does NOT want anything made after 1980. Give the color, size, brand, model, condition, and the status of the original box, if available. "A photo is helpful."
>
> Dave Nolt
>
> PO Box 553
>
> Gap, PA 17527
>
> (717) 768-3554   <nolt@dnolt.com>

★ **Hot Wheels, Corgi, Matchbox and other die cast metal cars from 1979 or before.** Items in original packages can sometimes bring thousands of dollars, and so can a few loose rarities. Red lines are of particular interest. Call with what you have. If you have a very large collection, he'll come to you.
>
> Michael Herz, Whiz Bang! Collectibles
>
> 9 Hitching Post Lane
>
> Casselberry, FL 32707
>
> (407) 260-8869   fax (407) 260-2289   <majicherz@aol.com>

★ **Hot Wheels.** With 700 basic body styles, 5,000 color combinations, and 10,000 minor variations it's important to get expert advice before disposing of these toys. most are only a few dollars, but some can bring $1,000 each! If you want to sell, give the name of the car, the color, and the condition, including an estimate of the percent of original paint remaining. If all you want is an estimate of value, Mike wrote *Price Guide to Hot Wheels,* available from him for $30. "I give honest evaluations and pay fair prices," says this 20 year veteran collector/dealer, "but condition is important in the value of cars, and sellers really don't know how to properly evaluate condition, so I will never send money without seeing the cars first."
>
> Mike Strauss
>
> 26 Madera Avenue
>
> San Carlos, CA 94070
>
> (650) 591-6482 after 6 PST   fax (650) 571-7935
>
> <hwnewsltr@aol.com>

★ **Tin toys, wind up toys, cast iron toys and die cast metal toys.** "I really like toys made before 1940, but will buy high quality post war items as well." Condition is critical to determining value when dealing with this well known collector/dealer.
>
> Jay Robinson "The Chicago Kid"
>
> 522 Rivershire Place
>
> Lincolnshire, IL 60069
>
> (847) 913-1106   fax (847) 913-1274   <jcomcent@megsinet.net>

★ **Atlas, Aurora and all other electric slot cars**, car bodies, artwork for boxes and ads, kits, stock closeouts and markdowns, literature, parts, samples, prototypes, sets, displays, etc. "No limit," he says, but prefers to buy entire collections. He particularly wants complete sets and original boxes or store displays and stock, but "will consider any electric race cars you have." Look for shiny chrome, unopened packages, the newer looking the better. He DOES NOT WANT rusted track. DO NOT clean, polish, rub, wash or buff anything. Sell everything as it sits. Photos are requested, but if you have a large collection for sale, you are encouraged to phone him. "I also collect colorful **hockey related games**, preferably complete in original box, but will consider incomplete sets if the boxes are good."
Joe Bodnarchuk
62 McKinley Avenue
Kenmore, NY 14217
(716) 873-0264 voice/fax   <mratlas@bodnarchuk.com>

◆ **Dinky toys** of all types except army vehicles. Also wants to buy all types of toy motorcycles.
Don Schneider
PO Box 1570
Merritt, BC
V1K 1B8 CANADA
(250) 378-6421

◆ **Gasoline powered toy cars and car parts.** Wants all types of race cars made by Dooling, Rexner, Morrison, Bremer, Duesenberg, JL Special, BB Corn, Popp, etc., as well as all Mite cars such as Thimbledrome, O&R, McCoy, etc. Also buys damaged cars, 60 size racing engines, parts, coils, condensers, spark plugs, ignition leads, etc. Also buys **toy diesel engines, steam engines,** and home made engines.
Richard Gronowski
1100 Peninsula Drive
Traverse City, MI 49686
(231) 941-2111   <rgrono3381@aol.com>

★ **Aurora Thunderjet and AFX electric race cars/slot cars in 1/87 HO scale.** Wants cars, track, accessories, parts, complete sets, and collections of miscellaneous pieces. Original boxes not necessary, but welcome. Photos requested, "or give me a call." Also buys **HO trains.**
Pat Jacobsen
PO Box 791
Weimar, CA 95736
(530) 637-5923   <pjacobsen@neworld.net>

PEDAL CARS

★ **Pedal cars and planes,** three fender **tricycles, and tricycles with sidecars** in any condition. I will pay over $1,000 for the better examples." Also wants any pedal car advertising, sales catalogs, and the like as well as photos of kids with their pedal cars. He does not want pedal cars with plastic wheel covers and/or plastic steering wheels, as they are considered too new by collectors. The one exception to that rule is the **Ford Mustang pedal car** which he does want. Give the name of the manufacturer and the length of the vehicle. "I prefer to make offers only if you include a good clear color photo of both sides."

> Frank Martin
> 7669 Winterberry Drive
> Youngstown, OH 44512
> (330) 758-4470   <martin7669@aol.com>

◆ **Pedal cars and planes.** "I'll buy any pre-WWII pedal car, pedal plane or pedal truck, and will consider some from the mid-1950's. I'm a most generous buyer, as I buy to keep not to resell. Condition is not a problem. I'll even buy half a vehicle if that's all you have. Please send photos." Will also purchase large (bigger than 12") **metal cars, trucks, and planes made by Keystone, Buddy-L, Dayton,** etc. No interest in Tonka.

> Sandy Weltman
> 39 Branford Road
> Rochester, NY 14618
> (585) 442-8810   <blanchewelt@aol.com>

◆ **Pedal cars and planes** and other child-propelled vehicles including boats, planes, trucks, tanks, etc., made before 1940 "I prefer complete original toys but will consider units requiring restoration, but I'm not interested in basket cases. I especially want pedal airplanes and will pay from $1,500 to $4,000 for excellent originals. Perfectly restored planes will also be considered. I do not want any vehicle that has any plastic parts. Please give the maker if you can and note all missing parts or other damage."

> Stan Phillips
> 438 8th Street
> Oakmont, PA 15139
> (412) 828-7351   <nimbus66@nauticom.net>

POP CULTURE: TRASH THAT CAN BE TREASURE

*Pop Culture is "the fun stuff in life."
When folks talk about Pop Culture,
they mean radio, television, music,
magic, celebrities, cartoons and
comic characters. Pop Culture is
Little Lulu, Donald Duck and Superman.
Pop Culture is Tom Mix, G.I. Joe, and
Star Wars. It's Elvis, P.T. Barnum, and
Batman. It's Frankenstein! And Gilligan.*

Advertising has become part of pop culture. *More 7
year olds recognize Mr. Clean than Santa Claus. Aunt
Jemima, Speedy Alka-Seltzer, The Campbell's Soup kids,
and Reddy Kilowatt are among advertising icons that
have become collector favorites.*

*Lots of this stuff is only worth $10 or $20, but someone
paid $2,000 for a cardboard cereal box and $2,000 for a
plastic model less than 30 years old. Prices for Pop Culture
reflect the law of supply and demand perfectly.
Desirability (demand), not rarity, drives the market place.*

**Pop Culture collectors want rare, brightly colored items
in original boxes and mint condition.** *Sometimes, but not
always, they will settle for less. Depends on how highly
sought after the item is. That's the advantage of dealing
with the people I'm suggesting. They know what you
have and what it is worth; they know what the market is,
and they're committed to paying you fair prices for good
items.*

*Whether you already own this stuff, or whether you
want to make money by finding it at other people's yard
sales,* **the best way for you to cash in is to read all the Pop
Culture entries as well as those in the closely related
Entertainment and Advertising sections** *to see what's hot.
By selling to buyers in Trash or Treasure you can cash in.*

*Good close-up photos or Xerox© copies are important
since many vehicles, dolls, robots, and other Pop Culture
toys and games are worth $100+ and a surprising number
bring $1,000 or more. Buyers want to see exactly what
you are offering, as the condition affects value greatly.*

POP CULTURE

★ **Americana and Pop Culture** of all sorts is wanted by Ted Hake, the longest established mail dealer and auctioneer of pop collectibles. The wide range of items Ted buys includes:
  - **Pin back buttons** for politics, advertising products, sports, gum, Scouts, comic characters, movies, radio shows and all else;
  - **Premiums from radio, TV or cereal;**
  - **Disney characters** from before 1970;
  - **Animation** art from Disney and other cartoons;
  - **Battery or wind up toys,** especially comic and movie characters;
  - **Television related toys,** games, lunchboxes, etc., 1950's to 60's;
  - **Singing cowboys** and other western film heroes' guns, etc.;
  - **Robots and space toys;**
  - **U.S. Space Program** items;
  - **Elvis Presley** pre-death items;
  - **Beatles and other famous rock and roll personalities;**
  - **Movie posters,** lobby cards, etc.;
  - **Toys of the 1960's** like GI Joe, Capt. Action, Batman, etc.

"I'll buy almost any item related to a famous character or personality." Ted wants to know the material your item is made from, its size, any dates you can provide, and general condition. Firm offers are made only after inspection of your item. Hake has written four books on pin back buttons which are the basic reference works in the field. No reproductions are wanted, nor are political items after 1968.

Ted Hake
Hake's Americana Dept. 333
PO Box 1444
York, PA 17405
(717) 848-1333 10-5 Eastern Mon thru Fri   fax (717) 852-0344
<hake@hakes.com>

TONY'S TIP ON HOW TO SELL POP CULTURE ITEMS:
To sell Pop Culture items, give the following info:

(1) What it is, its size, color, and the material from which it is made;
(2) Names, dates, and numbers found on the item;
(3) Accurate statement of condition, noting missing parts, pieces, or paint and all other damage;
(4) Description of all repairs or repainting;
(5) Whether the original box, packaging and paper work are included and in good condition.

It's not hard, and a Xerox™ machine can be a big help.

◆ **Comic character toys and collectibles** from the 1930's and 40's, made of any material from cardboard to cast iron, especially **Disneyana, radio premiums,** and all **children's play suits** from Western heroes to sailor suits. No Halloween costumes. There are also many pieces of **comic character related sheet music** Ralph is seeking.

Ralph Eodice
Nevermore
77 East Emerson Street
Clifton, NJ 07013
    (201) 742-8278   <silverclip@aol.com>

◆ **Disney TV shows dealing with space.** Wants to obtain anything you have related to the 1950's TV shows produced by Disney: *Man in Space, Man and the Moon, Tomorrow the Moon* and *Mars and Beyond.* Photocopies are helpful.

David Enter
23851 Windmill Lane
Laguna Niguel, CA 92877
    (949) 363-8113   <dventer@webtv.net>

◆ **Pop culture toys and books from all periods**, including those items "that everybody else isn't buying and selling."
- Action figures such as DC and Kenner Super-Powers;
- Mego action figures;
- Star Trek and other 1970's and 80's toys;
- RoboTech and other Japanese animation related toys;
- **Hot Wheels** and other small die cast cars;
- Space and Monster figures and toys;
- Plastic model kits, especially space and monsters;
- Toy guns, especially space guns, up to the mid 70's;
- Comic Character related toys of all types and periods.

Give a complete description, including condition.

Dave Sheldon
9000 Williams Road
North East, PA 16428
(814) 897-1894 days   (814) 725-1394 <drskull9@hotmail.com>

TONY'S TIP ABOUT CONDITION: Buyers agree that every stain, scratch, tear, fold, crease, dent, chip, crack, faded spot, speck of rust, spatter of paint, or evidence of water damage makes an item less desirable.

There is no such thing as "good for its age." It does not matter how old an item is. Damage is damage. A buyer needs to know what the damage is, where the damage is, and what is affected.

◆ **Pop culture toys** of many types.
  • **Comic books and Big Little Books;**
  • **Disney;**
  • **Lunchboxes;**
  • **Robots and Transformers;**
  • **Comic, Sci-Fi, horror and action plastic models;**
  • **Monster & horror collectibles;**
  • **Action figures of any hero/superhero;**
  • **Rock concert posters.**

"We will be happy identify what you have and estimate the value." Give all names, dates, or numbers on your toy and a brief accurate description of condition, including the condition of the package it came in. We don't want plush (stuffed) animals, sports toys, NASCAR, Beanie Babies or glasware of any kind. Mail or Email preferred.

Jack Klodzinski & Rich Levy
Critical Mass Toys
PO Box 470
Geneva, FL 32732
(407) 327-8223 days <askdoctorjack@hotmail.com> <cmitoys.com>

◆ **Pop culture** items, including:
  • **Radio premiums** from children's adventure programs such as
    The Lone Ranger, Jack Armstrong, Tom Mix, Sky King,
    The Shadow, Doc Savage, Buck Rogers, Dick Tracy, etc.;
  • **Cereal boxes** offering premiums from the 30's through the 60's;
  • Superhero **action figures,**
  • **Space adventure items;**
  • **Disney.** "I'll buy anything that isn't pictured in one of the
    price guides to Disney that I wrote."
  • **Mickey Mouse** from the 1930's only (the "rat" Mickey) in all
    materials and forms: wind-up, dolls, figurines, etc.;
  • **Any odd Pop Culture item** in its original box.

Prefers items to be priced, but will make an offer only after seeing the item in person. Write first, with complete details and photo.

Tom Tumbusch
3300 Encrete Lane
Dayton, OH 45439
        (513) 294-2250   fax (513) 294-1024

◆ **Comic character pin back buttons,** 1896-1966, from the earliest *Yellow Kid* to all comic strip and comic book characters since then except no Pep pins, please. This *Star Trek* actor (Chekov) pays up to $1,000 for rare buttons like the *Buck Rogers 25th Century* and *Washington Herald Mickey Mouse.* Ask and he'll send an illustrated wants list. Include your phone number.

Walter Koenig
PO Box 4395
North Hollywood, CA 91607   <gineokw@aol.com>

★ **Pop Culture toys related to radio, television or movie characters and superheroes** including :
  • **Western movie & TV toys,** watches and premiums from riders of the range like: Roy Rogers, Gene Autry, Hopalong Cassidy, The Lone Ranger, Red Ryder and Tom Mix;
  • **Western style cap guns** made of metal;
  • **Disney** and other comic character toys;
  • **Doll houses** of tin in fine condition and Renwall plastic doll houses and accessories;
  • **Toy vehicles by Smith Miller, Tonka, Doepke, Dinky, Renwall (plastic), Auburn (rubber), Arcade, Marx, and Wyandotte;**
  • **G.I. Joe dolls,** accessories, pre-1970, in the 12" size;
  • **Toys which advertise** nationally known products.
Condition is critical and only excellent condition items are wanted. Items in original box always preferred. Descriptions should include dimensions. Photo helpful. "Generous prices paid, but all offers not final until I've seen the item in person." Will answer all inquiries that have an SASE. Calls welcome.
    William Hamburg
    PO Box 536
    Woodland Hills, CA 91365
    (818) 346-1269   fax (818) 346-0215   <whamburg@aol.com>

◆ **Pop Culture** treasures, especially made of paper, including:
  • **Comic books,** 1890's-1980's, but only hero comics after 1963;
  • **Sunday comics** from the 1890's to 1959;
  • **Original comic strip art;**
  • **Walt Disney books** and anything else before 1960;
  • **Big Little Books,** 1933-1950;
  • **Movie magazines,** 1920-1945;
  • **Television collectibles,** 1948-1970;
  • **Radio and cereal premiums** and giveaways pre-1960;
  • **Song magazines,** 1929-1959, like *Hit Parader* and *400 Songs;*
  • **Popular music magazines** 1920-1959 like *Downbeat, Billboard;*
  • **Pulp magazines,** 1930-49, except love, Westerns, and crime.
Wants nothing in poor condition. Ken has been in business 25 years. He pays Americans in U.S. dollars and drafts for quick payment.
    Ken Mitchell
    710 Conacher Drive
    Willowdale, Ontario   M2M 3N6 CANADA
        (416) 222-5808

TONY'S TIP: Pop rings worth 2¢ and rings worth $1,500 can look quite similar to the inexperienced. Don't take chances. Deal with my buyers.

★ **Comic, cartoon, TV and other Pop Culture** items such as:
- **Advertising product figures** *Mr. Clean, Speedy Alka-Seltzer*, and others can be worth up to $500 or more;
- **Original animation** and comic strip art from before 1970, with a particular interest in Disney films;
- **Watches and clocks** but only if pre-1978 and in original box $1,000 for Betty Boop pocketwatch, 3 pigs wristwatch or the Donald Duck wristwatch from the 1930's;
- **Empty boxes for toys, watches, and models;**
- **Cereal, gum, candy and food wrappers and boxes,** some of which, like the *Kix* atom bomb box, are worth $500+;
- *PEZ* candy dispensers, premiums, and store displays (worth up to $1,500 for rarities);
- **Premiums from radio and TV shows, comic books or cereal,** 1920-70's; pays $10,000+ for Superman of America member rings or Superman secret compartment rings, and $2,000+ for Superman and Captain Marvel wooden statues;
- **Monster toys and games** of Frankenstein, *The Creature,* others;
- **1960's TV characters** such as *Munsters, Addams Family, Jetsons, Flintstones, Lost in Space, Batman* and the like;
- **Children's books** (coloring, sticker, paper doll, cut-out, pop-up) that feature TV, movie, cartoon, or pop personalities before 1975, if they are in near mint condition. $2,500+ for Mickey Mouse or Wizard of Oz Waddle Books;
- **Celluloid, battery, wind-up or friction toys**, especially Disney and Popeye; pays $10,000+ for German Mickey and Minnie on a motorcycle or celluloid Horace Horsecollar pulling Mickey in a cart;
- **Captain Action and G.I. Joe dolls** with painted hair, their accessories and vehicles, but only if in their original boxes ("I'll pay $3,500 for a boxed *Capt. Action Spiderman* outfit");
- **Trash cans made of metal** with colorful pictures of cartoon or advertising characters from the 1960's if in perfect condition;
- **Robots made before 1970** only, with a primary interest in metal robots from the 1960's or earlier (some boxed robots are worth $10,000); Marx's *Big Loo* and a few other older plastic robots may be of interest ("Watch out for reproductions");

Condition is crucial. Make certain to note all damage and if there are missing parts. Make certain to mention if item is in its original box or wrapper since they can be "worth more than the item they held." Photos are "very helpful." Does not buy reproductions. David stresses, do not sent items without first contacting him. David is the author of two books on Pez dispensers, both available through him.

David Welch
PO Box 714
Murphysboro, IL 62966
(618) 687-2282   fax (618) 684-2243   <pezdude1@aol.com>

◆ **Robots and space toys** made of tin before 1965, either wind-up or battery operated, are wanted. "I'll pay $2,000 for *Mr. Atomic* and $750 for the *Robby Space Patrol* vehicle. Condition is important with these toys, so I'll pay an extra 10% for any toy in its original box." Also buys tin wind-up comic character toys made in the USA or Europe, whether working or not, and **any Disney toys**, especially celluloid toys from the 1930's. **Santa Claus** toys are also of interest.

> Larry Bruch
> PO Box 121
> Mountaintop, PA 18707
> (800) 549-toys   \<bkinglar@aol.com\>

◆ **Robots, Transformers and space toys from all periods.** Provide any names, dates, or numbers on your figure and a brief description of condition. Email preferred. Jack has been the editor of various space and action toy price guides.

> Jack Klodzinski & Rich Levy
> Critical Mass Toys
> PO Box 470
> Geneva, FL 32732

(407) 327-8223 days   \<askdoctorjack@hotmail.com\> \<cmitoys.com\>

◆ **Disney from before 1946,** especially:
  • Mickey or Donald painted plaster lamps;
  • Waddle Books from the 1930's (these have been reproduced);
  • **Animation cels** from before 1960, including drawings and
      background paintings;
  • Mickey, Minnie, and Donald costume dolls in Western, Mexican,
      Russian or bandleader outfits;
  • Vernon Kilns ceramic figurines;
  • Tin or celluloid plain or wind up toys of Disney characters;
  • Wood or porcelain figurines;
  • **Original art** for WWII combat insignia and other wartime items;
  • Cartoon **movie theater posters.**

Items can be foreign or domestic, but nothing newer than the 1950's is of interest. "Do the best you can in describing the dimensions, color, maker's markings, condition (mention all damage or missing parts)." Dennis will make offers for items "only when I'm holding it in my hand," preferring you to set the price. Include your phone number when you write.

> Dennis Books
> Comic Characters
> PO Box 99142
> Seattle, WA 98199
> (206) 283-0532

◆ **Pop Culture toys,** including
- Older **comic books;**
- **Marilyn Monroe** memorabilia;
- **Elvis** memorabilia from before 1977;
- **Disney** paper collectibles;
- **Non-sports cards;**
- **Rock 'n' Roll** records and memorabilia from before 1970;
- **B-movie cowboy** collectibles.

This well known magazine collector/dealer has expanded into the above related ephemera. Please describe what you have fully. Items are purchased for resale.

> Stan Gold
> 7042 Dartbrook
> Dallas, TX 75240
> (972) 239-8621   fax (972) 239-9622   <record@astimegoesby.com>

TONY'S TIP:
Dealers make their living buying and selling.
They can't and don't stay in business long
if dishonest. The world of collecting is small.
Word gets around fast.

◆ **Wacky Packages stickers** and related items by Topps Chewing Gum from 1967 to 1977. The cards satirized food and other household products (Pupsi Cola, Ratz Crackers, Band-Aches, etc.). "I want stickers, checklists, original artwork, advertising, display boxes, wrappers, uncut sheets, wall posters, T-shirts, beach towels, etc., with Wacky Package designs. Original artwork brings $1,000 and up. Ratz Crackers and Cracked Animals stickers bring $500 unpunched. "I don't want any stickers with ©1979 or ©1980 or ©1991." Condition is very important so mention any creases or writing. There is a big difference in price from sticker to sticker so make a list of what you have and note whether the back of the sticker is white, tan or has a camel on it.

> David Gross
> 15 Delavan Street
> New Brunswick, NJ 08901
>   (732) 246-1589   <salandrei@aol.com>

★ **Wacky Packages stickers** and related items by Topps Chewing Gum from 1967 to 1977.

> David Welch
> PO Box 714
> Murphysboro, IL 62966
> (618) 687-2282   fax (618) 684-2243   <pezdude1@aol.com>

◆ **Comic character and science fiction toys** made in Germany, Japan, or the U.S. **Also merry-go-rounds and airplanes** (no jets). "I'll pay over $1,000 for a *Mr. Atomic* robot or *Mickey the Magician,* two battery toys." He does not want common items like the Charlie Weaver bartender toy, plastic toys, wind-up dogs, toy trains, dolls, items with missing parts, or toys made in the third world. Tell this toy consultant and restorer the condition of the item and box, and about any restoration or repainting.

Don Hultzman
5026 Sleepy Hollow Road
Medina, OH 44256
(330) 225-2668   <d.hultzman@gte.net>

TONY'S TIP: *To sell Pop Culture items, tell the buyer:*

(1) What it is, its size, color, and the material from which it is made;

(2) Names, dates, and numbers found anywhere on the item;

(3) Accurate statement of condition, noting missing parts, pieces, or paint. Mention scratches, dents, dings, tears, stains, etc.

(4) Description of all repairs or repainting;

(5) Whether the original box, packaging and paper work are included and in good condition.

It's not difficult; a Xerox™ machine can be a big help.

★ **Playsets and plastic figures from the 1950's** to early 1970's by Marx, Archer, Auburn, Giant Plastics, Lido, MPC, Multiple, Remco, Ideal and others.. These toys came with metal buildings and loads of plastic people and accessories. Particularly desirable are boxed sets of *Lost in Space, Batman, Justice League, Gunsmoke, Wells Fargo, The Civil War, Disneyland, The Untouchables, Alaska, Ben Hur, Johnny Ringo*, and the Revolutionary War. If clean and complete in the original box, these can be worth up to $2,000. If yours isn't in perfect shape, inquire anyway as a few rare individual parts can be worth $500. Condition is extremely important, as damaged pieces have no value. Small TV and cartoon figures from one inch to six inches tall that were sold individually rather than in boxed sets are are also wanted.

David Welch
PO Box 714
Murphysboro, IL 62966
(618) 687-2282   fax (618) 684-2243   <pezdude1@aol.com>

G.I. JOE & OTHER ACTION FIGURES

★ **G.I. Joe figures and accessories.** "I'll buy anything related to all eras of G.I.Joe from 1964 to the present day. The most valuable items are from the 1960's, however **fuzzy headed and small G.I. Joe items are of interest** as well. Many boxed G.I.Joe items can bring over $1,000." Mike buys for his collection as well as for resale, and requests you call with what you have. If it sounds good, you will be asked to send it to him at his expense for inspection and for an offer. Do not send things unannounced. "For large collections, I'll come to you." Mike is the promoter of the official Hasbro sponsored G.I.Joe Convention.
    Michael Herz
    Whiz Bang! Collectibles
    9 Hitching Post Lane
    Casselberry, FL 32707
  (407) 260-8869   fax (407) 260-2289   <majicherz@aol.com>

◆ **G.I. Joe toys** produced between 1964 and 1969 including dolls (dolls from this period have molded/painted hair not flocked hair), guns, uniforms, vehicles and accessories. Vietnam War Joes are particularly sought after, including the Airborne Military Police, Marine jungle fighter, and the Air security helmet and radio, all of which can be worth several hundred dollars. Among vehicles he particularly wants the crash crew fire truck and desert patrol jeep among others and will pay up to $500 for complete sets, more with boxes. A complete Canadian Mountie set would be worth from $150 to $300 even without its box. Items must be marked gi joe or hasbro. "I'll buy one or a collection and am happy to identify your items over the phone. When you call, have the items handy and be ready to answer questions about colors, letters stenciled on them, and the condition of the box. Original packaging is a plus. If you write, send photos when possible. I insist on return privileges if the item is not exactly as described. If I do not wish to buy what you have for sale, I will refer you to another collector whenever possible." "Some items can be repaired. Call if you have questions." He does not buy the small figures made in the 1980's.
    Matthew McKeeby
    156 Old Post Road
    Lebanon Springs, NY 12125
        (518) 794-0964   <advteam@capital.net>

TONY'S TIP ABOUT GI JOE & CAPTION ACTION DOLLS:
Painted hair dolls are usually more valuable than those with flocked hair. Boxes can be very valuable! Condition is very important. An item worth hundreds of dollars mint and packaged can be worth nothing when stained, ripped, damaged or missing pieces.

★ **G.I. Joe action figures.** "I'll buy figures, uniforms, vehicles and accessories." Prefers items from the 1964-69 era, but "will consider anything in good condition whether boxed, carded or loose." Especially seeks store displays and stock, dolls, novelties, puzzles, games, vehicles, and carded stock but will buy nearly anything. He notes that painted headed dolls are more valuable than fuzzy headed ones, and that a 1967 nurse doll, mint in her box, could bring $2,000. Purchases both for his personal collection and for resale.

> Joe Bodnarchuk
> 62 McKinley Avenue
> Kenmore, NY 14217
>   (716) 873-0264   <gijoe@bodnarchuk.com>

★ **Superhero, action and cartoon character figures** especially Captain Action, G.I.Joe and Mego Superheroes. "I buy, sell, and trade most any character collectibles including superheroes, cartoon characters, and action figures like *Star Wars* and G.I. Joe. I specialize in premiums, rings, and superhero items from the 1940's through the present such as Superman, Batman, etc." He does not buy books except comics. He requests you call with what you have. If it sounds good, you will be required to ship it at his expense for inspection and an offer. Do not send things unannounced. "For large collections, I'll come to you."

> Michael Herz
> Whiz Bang! Collectibles
> 9 Hitching Post Lane
> Casselberry, FL 32707
> (407) 260-8869   fax (407) 260-2289   <majicherz@aol.com>

TONY'S TIP: Experienced dealers make their livings buying and selling. They can't and don't stay in business long if dishonest. The world of collecting is very small. Word gets around fast.

★ **Captain Action and G.I. Joe dolls with painted hair**. Also wants their accessories and vehicles, but **only** if in their original boxes. "I'll pay $3,500 for a boxed *Capt. Action Spiderman* outfit." Condition is crucial. Make certain to note all damage and if there are missing parts. Make certain to mention if item is in its original box or wrapper since they can be "worth more than the item they held." Photos are "very helpful." Does not buy reproductions. David stresses, do not sent items without first contacting him.

> David Welch
> PO Box 714
> Murphysboro, IL 62966
> (618) 687-2282   fax (618) 684-2243   <pezdude1@aol.com>

SCIENCE FICTION & MONSTER TOYS

★ *Star Wars* **toys, Transformers, action figures** and related memorabilia. "I only buy toys and figures in excellent condition. Items do not have to be in their original packaging, but packaged items bring a much higher value. A loose action figure can be worth from $1 to $300, whereas carded figures can be worth over $1,000." He is interested in loose and carded action figures, dolls, vehicles, posters, or any other *Star Wars* items, except he DOES NOT WANT vehicles that are broken or missing parts. Mike requests you call with what you have. If it sounds good, you will be asked to send it to him at his expense for inspection and for an offer. Do not send things unannounced. "For large collections, I'll come to you." DOES NOT BUY paper items or anything after 1985 or associated with Episode One (the prequil).

Michael Herz
Whiz Bang! Collectibles
9 Hitching Post Lane
Casselberry, FL 32707
(407) 260-8869   fax (407) 260-2289   <majicherz@aol.com>

◆ **Space toys and ray guns** from the 1930's through the 1950's, particularly *Buck Rogers, Flash Gordon, Tom Corbett, Capt. Video, and Space Patrol*. Fine condition toys of all types are wanted, even rocket shaped pedal cars. He does not want *Star Wars, Star Trek,* the new TV *Buck Rogers* and other characters from after 1960. Leslie is author of the *Zap! Ray Gun Classics* available for $16 postpaid.

Leslie Singer
7 Shackleford Plaza #C
Little Rock, AR 72211
(501) 221-2885 voice/fax   (501) 228-9982 eves
<zenmotel@aol.com>

◆ *Famous Monsters of Filmland* **and other monster magazines** from the 1950's and 60's. Will also consider other inexpensive monster films memorabilia. Especially seeking video entitled *"Best of Famous Monsters of Filmland"* or *"Hooray for Horrorwood"* hosted by Forest Ackerman. This relatively new collector will buy in any condition, but at substantially reduced prices for lesser grade copies. Will consider seriously damaged copies of numbers 1 through 27. Describe condition and note anything missing or badly damaged.

Michael Malone
16820 Lunn Court
Weed, CA 96094
<rhk1@thegrid.net>

★ **Model kits of human, monster, comic or science fiction characters** from before 1975 are sought. Kits were produced by Aurora, Hawk, Revell, MPC, Multiple, and Lindbergh. Any kit containing figures (not cars and boats) may be of interest as long as it is unbuilt in its original box. Will also buy empty boxes, factory promos, store displays and advertising and manufacturer's catalogs. A few items like *Godzilla's Go-Cart* or *King Kong's Thronester* can bring $3,500 if still factory sealed. Has a special interest in gift sets with two or more kits in the same box made by any model company in the 1950's or 60's.

David Welch
PO Box 714
Murphysboro, IL 62966
(618) 687-2282   fax (618) 684-2243   <pezdude1@aol.com>

◆ **Monster items of all types** including:
- **Gum cards,** display boxes and wrappers such as *Mars Attack, Outer Limits, Terror Tales, Spook Stories,* etc.;
- **Plastic model kits** of Frankenstein's monster, wolfman, mummy, *King Kong, Rodan, The Munsters,* and so on, built or unbuilt. Will even purchase some broken models for parts, and pay up to $50 for some empty boxes;
- **Toys and games,** puzzles, novelties, and the like that feature any movie, TV, or comic book monsters or creatures. Will pay $75 for the board game, *Outer Limits*;
- **Halloween masks of monsters,** especially masks by Don Post;
- **Comic books** by Zenith, E.C. and other 10¢ monster titles;
- **Magazines and record albums,** especially *Famous Monsters, Castle of Frankenstein, World Famous Creatures, Monster Parade* and similar titles.

"I welcome any calls or letters, and am always happy to talk with anyone who has monster items." If you write, include where you got the item. Don't forget your phone number.

Joe Warchol
Small World
2316 Hassell Road
Hoffman Estates, IL 60195
(847) 843-2442 days   (847) 698-1467 eves

◆ **Robots, Transformers and monster toys and models.** Provide any names, dates, or numbers on your figure and a brief description of condition. Email preferred. Jack has been the editor of various space and action toy price guides.

Jack Klodzinski & Rich Levy
Critical Mass Toys
PO Box 470
Geneva, FL 32732
(407) 327-8223 days   <askdoctorjack@hotmail.com> <cmitoys.com>

POP CULTURE FOOD

◆ **Plastic advertising and comic characters by F and F Mold and Die Works.** This Dayton company was responsible for an enormous number of Pop characters including *Aunt Jemima, Uncle Mose, Keebler Elf, Dennis the Menace, Yogi Bear, Bugs Bunny* and the like. They made cups, bowls, cookie jars, salt and pepper shakers and other items. Pieces are marked, usually on the bottom or lower back, and the mark can sometimes be hard to see. "I do not want broken items or those with excessive paint chipping (though some chipping is to be expected). *Aunt Jemima* has been reproduced, but without the "F and F" logo. I am not interested in repros. I pay from $5 to $30 for items and have paid as much as $400 for rare cookie jars. Pictures are helpful or phone with the item right in front of you."

Tom Basore
715 West 20th Avenue
Hutchinson, KS 67502
(620) 665-3613 eves

★ *PEZ* **candy items.** "I'll buy any-thing related to pez: old candy or dispensers without feet, premiums, paperwork, store displays, ads, etc. Pays up to $2,000 for Make-A-Face dispenser if the package is unopened; $1,000 for the full body shiny gold robot; and $1,500 for the shooting star lighter with no head. Dave is author of *A Pictorial Guide to Plastic Candy Dispensers* ($22) and *Collecting PEZ* ($44) .

David Welch
PO Box 714
Murphysboro, IL 62966
(618) 687-2282   fax (618) 684-2243   <pezdude1@aol.com>

◆ **Cereal boxes,** 1930-1959, depicting comic characters or giveaways. A series of 1940's *Cheerios* boxes featuring Disney characters is particularly desirable as is the 1946 atom bomb ring box of *Kix*.

John Fawcett
PO Box 1156
Waldoboro, ME 04572
(207) 832-7398 before 8pm EST   <fawcetoy@qwi.net>

TONY'S TIP: Many other food and drink related items are collected. ***You'll find buyers listed in Trash or Treasure under Liquor, Beer, Advertising, and Soft Drink*** *as well as among the general Pop Culture dealers you can find at the beginning of the Pop Culture section.*

POP CULTURE COWBOYS

◆ **Tom Mix** collectibles including *Shredded Ralston* cereal boxes from the 1930's and 40's with Tom Mix markings, arcade and gum cards, postcards, unusual photos, feature films, short subjects, various radio premiums, and the 1930's Tom Mix Ingersoll pocket watch. This 40 year veteran is author of *The Tom Mix Book* available from him for $24.95. Note that he does not want lobby cards, movie posters, newly made items, common photos, Big Little Books, clothing, video tapes or any material that is not in good condition. He insists that sellers price what they have.

    Merle "Bud" Norris
    1324 North Hague Avenue
    Columbus, OH 43204
        (614) 274-4646   <budntom9@aol.com>

◆ **Hopalong Cassidy** collectibles. Offer any in good condition.
    Ron Pieczkowski
    1707 Orange Hill Drive
    Brandon, FL 33510

◆ **Lone Ranger** items. Wants wide range of 1933-55 items including cereal boxes, dolls, games, posters, premiums, gun sets, carnival plaster figures, books with dust jackets, autographs, and other items associated with the Lone Ranger's radio days.
    John Fawcett
    PO Box 1156
    Waldoboro, ME 04572
  (207) 832-7398 before 8pm EST   <fawcetoy@qwi.net>

◆ *Gunsmoke* items from both radio and TV. "I'll buy nearly anything associated with either show except magazines and recently made stuff. I want autographs, contracts, production documents, scripts, advertising, gifts, awards, belt buckles, toys, promotional items, props, and anything personalized belonging to a cast member. I don't buy anything severely damaged." He can send you a list of nearly 30 cast members whose autograph and photo he wants. He's a collector and dealer who charges to make appraisals and expects you to tell him what you want him to pay for your item.
    Hank Clark
    PO Box 812
    Waterford, CA 95386
        (209) 874-2640   fax (209) 874-5750

TONY'S TIP: TV, movie and radio cowboy collectibles may also be of interest to general pop culture dealers found in the beginning of the Pop Culture section.

SUPERHEROES

◆ **Superman items.** Buys all rare or unusual Superman items, particularly dating from 1938 to 1966, but "I purchase interesting items from all years." Seeks toys, figurines, puzzles, watches, games, buttons, advertising, etc. "Please write me about any good Superman item because I buy duplicates and quantity." No comic books, except free premiums. No homemade items. Give a complete description, including every defect, and include its color, manufacturer, copyright date and country of origin. Photo or photocopy is appreciated. Danny has collected Superman for 30 years and is co-author of *The Adventures of Superman Collecting.*

> Danny Fuchs
> 209-80 18th Avenue #4-K
> Bayside, NY 11360
> (718) 225-9030 fax (718) 225-3688 <superdf62@aol.com>

◆ **Captain Marvel, Captain Marvel Jr.,** and **Mary Marvel** items including toys, buttons, posters, comic books, mechanical items, and statues produced between 1940-1953. Also items related to similar Fawcett Comics characters.

> Michael Gronsky
> 10328 Royal Woods Court
> Gaithersburg, MD 20879
> (301) 704-8620 <mjgronsky@aol.com>

◆ **James Bond 007** and Ian Fleming memorabilia including first edition hard and soft cover books, magazines with articles about Bond, movie posters, record albums, toys, dolls, plastic model kits, beer cans, clothing, games, comic books, and much more. Especially wants books autographed by Fleming, the British 1st edition of *Casino Royale,* and one of the signed and numbered limited editions of *On Her Majesty's Secret Service.* Give standard bibliographic information on any books, paying attention to the condition of the dust jacket (or the covers on paperbacks). On other items, indicate whether you have the original packaging; if you do, describe its condition. He does not want *Saturday Evening Post, Life* or *Look* magazines. Neither does he want Signet paperbacks after 1961 or U.S. Book Club editions.

> Gary Pimenta
> 64 Lakeside Drive
> Tiverton, RI 02878

TONY'S TIP: Super Hero, literary and comic strip character collectibles may also be of interest to general pop culture dealers found in the beginning of the Pop Culture section on page 132.

★ *Green Hornet, The Shadow,* and other character items from the 1940's to the present. A mint *Green Hornet Captain Action* suit in a mint box could be worth as much as $4,500, and some posters and premiums can bring as much as $2,000. Mike asks that you call with what you have. If it sounds good, you will be asked to send it on approval at his expense for inspection and offer. Do not send things unannounced.

Michael Herz, Whiz Bang! Collectibles
9 Hitching Post Lane
Casselberry, FL 32707
(407) 260-8869   fax (407) 260-2289   <majicherz@aol.com>

◆ **Action hero figures of all types from 1960 to the 1990's.** "We have extensive knowledge in this field and will be happy to identify and price any action figure or accessory. We especially encourage children to email us with questions about their hobby, even if they don't wish to sell." Give names, dates, or numbers on your toy, the dimensions, and a brief accurate description of condition of the figure and the package it came in. Email is the preferred way of contacting us. Jack has been the editor of Action Figure Collector PriceGuide, available from him.

Jack Klodzinski & Rich Levy
Critical Mass Toys
PO Box 470
Geneva, FL 32732
(407) 327-8223 days   <askdoctorjack@hotmail.com> <cmitoys.com>

◆ *Tarzan* **and Edgar Rice Burroughs memorabilia** including books, magazines, and collectibles. This enormous library collection still seeks items, such as the 1915 edition of *Return of Tarzan* with a dust jacket for which they'll pay over $1,000. Also seeking early Tarzan movies, foreign editions, Armed Services Editions and many smaller items associated with Burroughs or any of his characters. George advises, "Don't waste your time if your items aren't in fine to mint condition, including dust jackets. Please describe what you have carefully, give a guarantee, and tell us in what form you'd like payment."

George McWhorter
Burroughs Memorial Collection
University of Louisville
Louisville, KY 40292
(502) 852-8729   <gtmcwh01@gwise.louisville.edu>

◆ *Tarzan* **toys, games, movie items and autographs.** Describe condition of the book, include standard bibliographic information (that includes publisher and date), and note whether dust jacket is there.

Jim Gerlack
1621 Boundbrook Lane
Irving, TX 75060
(972) 790-0922   <j.gerlach@attbi.com>

COMIC CHARACTER COLLECTIBLES

◆ **Comic character items** from the 1920's and 30's are wanted, especially Disney but also *Betty Boop, KoKo the Clown, Felix the Cat, Maggie and Jiggs, Mutt & Jeff, Krazy Kat and Ignatz, Little Nemo, Barney Google*, and more. Wants figurines, masks, toys, premiums, posters, dolls, pins, original art, lamps, radios, store displays, etc.

>John Fawcett
>PO Box 1156
>Waldoboro, ME 04572
>(207) 832-7398 before 8pm EST   <fawcetoy@qwi.net>

◆ *Yellow Kid* **memorabilia.** Wants tins, toys, buttons, postcards, advertisements, "and anything else with the Kid on it."

>William Nielsen
>PO Box 1413
>East Dennis, MA 02641
>(508) 385-9247

◆ *Felix the Cat* pictured on china, or anything else, as long as it's from the 1930's or before. She is not interested in any of the Felix items reproduced in the 1950's. Please include a clear photo as she will be able to tell old from new in most cases.

>Marilyn Baseman
>Birdcage Antiques
>PO Box 1166
>Sheffield, MA 01258
>(413) 229-2294   <abca@bcn.net>

◆ **Cartoon and comic character books** such as Big Little Books, Pop-Up Books, Fast Actions, Fawcett Dime Action Books, Cupples and Leon, and other early comic reprint books from 1910's, 20's and 30's. Also coloring books, Whitman hard cover children's books with dust jackets, Whitman Penny Books, Nickel Books, Buddy Books, and any similar books published by Salsfield, Mclaughlin, Lynn Publications, Engel Van Wiseman, etc. "Let me know what you have and what you want for it, or ship for my immediate offer."

>Alan Levine
>PO Box 1577
>Bloomfield, NJ 07003
>(973) 743-5288   <posterking@aol.com>

*TONY'S TIP: Cartoon and comic strip character collectibles may also be of interest to general pop culture dealers found on pages 132-139 as well as toy buyers. **Use the index!***

◆ *Dick Tracy, Sparkle Plenty* and *Bonny Braids* **collectibles.** "I'm buying toys, games, premiums, original art, store displays, posters, books, paper, figures...anything! SASE gets his for sale list. "I will give free appraisals if you send a description, good photo and an SASE.

Larry Doucet
2351 Sultana Drive
Yorktown Heights, NY 10598
(914) 245-1320   <elgeed47@aol.com>

◆ *Peanuts* **cartoon character toys** and memorabilia of all types and characters including advertising, music boxes, ceramics, jewelry, etc., as long as it's marked UNITED FEATURES SYNDICATE and in fine condition. Especially wants a musical ice bucket and the Ansi and Schmidt music boxes made of wood. Not interested in Avon, squeak toys, or other common items, though. A picture is appreciated. She reminds you not to assume the © date is when the item was produced. "It's not," she says.

Andrea Podley, Founder
Peanuts Collector Club
539 Sudden Valley
Bellingham, WA 98226
(360) 733-5209   fax (360) 733-5239   <acpodley@nas.com>

MAD MAGAZINE

◆ *MAD* **magazine collectibles,** dolls, busts, straight jackets, bookends, jewelry, and all collectible items related to Alfred E. Newman. Wants only first printings of softcover books and hardcover books only if complete with dust jacket and all inserts. Does not want anything in poor condition. Also wants original art by any of the mad artists. Promises to answer all letters accompanied by an SASE.

Dr. Gary Kritzberg
PO Box 47
Yorkville, IL 60560
(630) 553-7653 eves   <yorkmaddoc@aol.com>

◆ *MAD* **magazine collectibles:** dolls, jewelry, hand puppets, busts, straight jackets, bound volumes, and other EC comic items. Also wants any and all pictorial representations of Alfred E Neuman's face from pre-*Mad* days. Nothing made after 1974 or in poor condition.

Grant Geissman
Box 56773
Sherman Oaks, CA 91413
(818) 501-0884   fax (818) 501-0886   <ggeissman@aol.com>

◆ **Walt Kelly and** *Pogo* **items.** This dedicated collector/historian seeks items produced by and associated with Kelly and his work, not only on *Pogo,* but as an illustrator for Disney, *Peter Wheat,* advertising, and various children's books. Of interest are first edition books, comics, records, plastic and porcelain figures, pin-back buttons, magazines, newspaper strips, original artwork, and what have you. Prices can be high for items like the 1968 button set, porcelain figures, plastic figures, records, and other scarce items. Books other than first editions are not wanted unless they are signed by Kelly. Photocopies are helpful. Complete bibliographic information should be provided for all books. Give specific information about all flaws. Steve publishes a wide variety of Kelly originals and reprints, including a bimonthly newsletter (membership is $20/year) and the *Walt Kelly Collector's Guide* (with prices) available for $16.50 postpaid.

> Steve Thompson
> 6908 Wentworth Avenue South
> Richfield, MN 55423
> (612) 869-6320 < thomp034@tc.umnedu>

◆ **Pogo.** "I want first edition paperbacks, comic books, the Pogo mobile, Puce stamps and any signed drawings. I don't want 2nd editions of his books, or those where two titles were reissued together. Paperbacks must be in near perfect condition, like new. The best way to describe what you have is with a Xerox™ copy. Jim has been buying books for 50 years.

> Jim Presgraves
> Bookworm & Silverfish
> PO Box 639
> Wytheville, VA 24382
> (276) 686-5813 <bookworm@naxs.com>

TONY'S TIP: *give the buyer the following information:*

(1) What it is, its size, color, and the material from which it is made;
(2) Names, dates, numbers found anywhere on the item;
(3) Accurate statement of condition, noting missing parts, pieces, or paint. List s scratches, dents, dings, tears, stains, etc.
(4) Description of all repairs or repainting;
(5) Whether the original box, packaging and paper work are included.

◆ **Giveaway and other toy rings of all type.** "I am interested in all novelty toy rings and premium rings from the 1930's through the 1970's. They can be from radio, TV, gumball machines, cereal boxes and other sources. Subjects can be Western, comic character, celebrities, TV and radio personalities including but not limited to the Lone Ranger, Sky King, The Phantom, The Shadow, Green Hornet, Jack Armstrong, Roy Rogers, Gene Autry, Hopalong Cassidy, Howdy Doody, Sgt. Preston, Cisco Kid, Captain Midnight, and simar action heroes. Photograph or photocopy helpful. Include a statement of condition and SASE. Dealers price your goods.

Bruce Thalberg
23 Mountainview Drive
Weston, CT 06883
(203) 227-8175   <mightyfinejan@yahoo.com>

◆ **Radio show giveaways,** membership cards, pins, photos, games, rings, toys, etc. from *Lone Ranger, Tom Mix, Sky King, Capt. Midnight, Charlie McCarthy, Gene Autry*, etc.

John Fawcett
PO Box 1156
Waldoboro, ME 04572
(207) 832-7398 before 8pm EST   <fawcetoy@qwi.net>

◆ **Radio show giveaways** such as rings, badges, decoders, etc. Wants *Captain Midnight, Superman, Little Orphan Annie, Buck Rogers, Howdy Doody, The Shadow, Sgt. Preston, Doc Savage, Sky King*, and other characters. Also buys the manuals from old radio, TV and cereal advertising campaigns. "Please advise what you have and what you want for it, or ship for offer."

Alan Levine
292 Glenwood Avenue or PO Box 1577
Bloomfield, NJ 07003
(973) 743-5288   <posterking@aol.com>

TONY'S TIP: *Cartoon and comic strip character collectibles may also be of interest to general pop culture dealers found in the Pop Culture section starting on page 132. Many buyers of toys could also be interested. These same buyers frequently also want radio show premiums and advertising as well.*

TV SHOW COLLECTIBLES

★ **Items of all sort related to television shows** are wanted by Ted Hake, the longest established mail dealer and auctioneer of pop collectibles. The wide range of items Ted buys includes:
- **Pin back buttons** for TV shows and their advertisers;
- **Premiums from radio, TV or cereal;**
- **Cereal boxes** featuring TV shows or personalities;
- *TV Guide* **magazines** before 1970;
- **Lunchboxes** featuring TV shows;
- **Disney** items from the *Wonderful World of Disney* or from the *Mickey Mouse Club;*
- **Animation** art from Disney and other TV or movie cartoons;
- **Television related toys** and games from the 1950's to 70's;
- **Cowboys** and other western TV shows like *Roy Rogers, Gene Autry, Hopalong Cassidy, Have Gun will Travel, Gunsmoke, The Lone Ranger, Maverick, Wild Wild Wes*t, etc.;
- **Robots and space toys** from *Star Trek, Lost in Space, Munsters, Outer Limits, Addams Family, Space Patrol* and other TV space and science fiction shows;

"I'll buy almost any item related to a famous TV show, character or personality." Ted wants to know the material your item is made from, its size, any dates you can provide, and general condition. Firm offers are made only after inspection of your item. Hake has written four books on pin back buttons which are the basic reference works in the field. No reproductions or damaged items are wanted.

Ted Hake
Hake's Americana Dept. 333
PO Box 1444
York, PA 17405
(717) 848-1333 10-5 Eastern Mon thru Fri   Fax: (717) 852-0344
<hake@hakes.com>

◆ **Television private detective and spy memorabilia.** Wants to buy games, puzzles, toys, books, photos, gum cards, wrappers, dolls, model kits, autographs, comic books, and just about everything else you can think of from shows like *77 Sunset Strip, Dragnet, Surfside 6, Peter Gunn, I Spy, The Man from U.N.C.L.E., The Wild Wild West, Secret Agent, Hawaiian Eye, Adventures in Paradise, The Untouchables* and others. This relatively new collector/dealer says he's interested in everything in good condition. Include photocopy or good description as condition is very important. Describe the package if you still have it.

Gary Pimenta
64 Lakeside Drive
Tiverton, RI 02878

★ *I Love Lucy, The Lucy Show* and everything else associated with **Lucille Ball and Desi Arnaz** from any era, including Desilu, their movies, records, and other activities, including toys, dolls, board games, magazines, comic books, paper dolls, advertising, scripts, tickets, props, costumes, autographs, and the like. If if says Lucy or Desi on it, he probably wants it. No newspaper or magazine clippings, please. He is the author of *For the Love of Lucy,* available though bookstores for $35.

> Ric Wyman
> PO Box 436
> Falconer, NY 14733

TONY'S TIP:
To sell TV related items, give the following information:
(1) What it is, its size, color, and the material from which
it is made;
(2) Names, dates, and numbers found on the item;
(3) Accurate statement of condition, noting missing
parts, pieces, or paint and all other damage;
(4) Description of all repairs or repainting;
(5) Whether the original box, packaging and paper
work are included and in good condition.

◆ *Charlie's Angels* and **Farrah Fawcett** memorabilia including cups, puzzles, walkie-talkies, pillows, Halloween costumes, radios, store displays for dolls, etc. Also wants original photos, magazines, posters, displays, videos, etc. Does not want lunchboxes, dolls, doll outfits, games, models or bubble gum cards. He prefers items in absolute mint condition, never used or played with, with no bends, crushes, or tears. Wants list available.

> Jack Condon
> PO Box 57468
> Sherman Oaks, CA 91403
> (818) 789-0862   fax (818) 501-1004   <chrlangels@aol.com>

◆ *I Dream of Jeannie* items, especially board games, comic books, scripts, photos, or original film. Wants the Libby Majorette doll but none by Remco. Send a photo or Xerox™ and include your phone number. He is author of the 450 page *Diary of a Genie: A History* available from him for $42. He has a few copies of Wood's *Dreaming of Jeannie* for $12. Send SASE for more information.

> Richard Barnes
> 1520 West 800 North
> Salt Lake City, UT 84116
>   (801) 521-4400   fax (801) 292-1947

◆ **Older Lucille Ball** memorabilia from any Lucille Ball show or project. Wants dolls, comic books, magazines with Lucy stories, etc. Buys, sells and trades in Lucilee Ball items.

> Cari Purkey
> Lucy Collectibles
> 16463 Harbour Lane
> Huntington Beach, CA 92649
>> (714) 377-1918   <cpurkey@socal.it.com>
>> <www.lucycollectibles.com>

◆ **Pee Wee Herman** items such as props from his TV show, movie promotional items, souvenirs, ads, fan club newsletters, giveaways and other toys. Also any size clothing put out by JC Penny Stores with the Pee Wee Herman label and designs. Especially large displays! He does not want small dolls, including the ventriloquist one. Please send a Xerox™ or photo of what you have to offer.

> Everen T. Brown
> PO Box 296
> Salt Lake City, UT 84110
>> fax (801) 364-2646   <etbrown@everent.com>

◆ *Howdy Doody* memorabilia is wanted, including all items related to any character on the show. Especially seeks items in original boxes. He runs periodic *Howdy Doody* auctions, "so will buy anything in fine condition that can be resold."

> John Andreae
> PO Box 156
> Granger, IN 46530
> (219) 272-2337   fax (219) 271-1146   <jkandreae@aol.com>

◆ *Smurfs,* especially those produced in Europe before 1979.

> Suzanne Lipschitz
> Smurf Collectors' Club Dept TH
> 24 Cabot Road West
> Massapequa, NY 11758
>> <nysmurf@aol.com>   <http://www.esmurfs.com>

TONY'S TIP: Radio, TV and comic character collectibles may also be of interest to general pop culture dealers found in the Pop Culture section starting on page 132. Many buyers of toys could also be interested.

OTHER CHARACTERS

◆ **Junk food character premiums and boxes that advertise them from 1950-1980 kid's junk food such as cookies, candy, cereal, ice cream, drink mixes, and snacks.** "Characters I buy in include Choo Choo Charlie, Quisp, Quake, Cap'n Crunch, Milton the Toaster, Mr. Bubble, Frankenberry, Count Chocula, Marky Maypo, Twinkles, Trix Rabbit, Mr. Wiggle, King Vitamin, Freakies, Farfel and other cartoon ad trademarks. Products include *Jiffy Pop, Mr. Chips, Fizzies, Funny Face, Cocoa Marsh, Bosco, Scooter Pies, Bugs Bunny Cookies, Nestle's Chiller, Kool Aid, Otter Pops, Kool Pops, Royal Pudding, Keds, P.F. Flyers, Big Shot Syrup* and especially discontinued oddball products. Will buy watches, toys, puppets, figures, banks, fan club kits, T-shirts, and especially store displays such as posters, stand-ups, animated displays and large 3-D figures. **I don't want fast food, generic products with no premium or character.**" Give condition, your phone number and best hours to call.

Roland Coover, Jr.
1537 East Strasburg Road
West Chester, PA 19380
(610) 692-3112   <rlcoover@aol.com>

TONY'S TIP: Advertising character collectibles will probably also be of interest to Pop Culture dealers such as those found beginning on page 132 and to collectors and dealers in advertising and packaging as found on pages 402 through 424.

◆ **Smoky Bear** items of all sorts are wanted by this ten year veteran collector who asks for "very descriptive detailed data on your item, including the condition." He points out Smoky items have been produced in great variety and he'll consider anything. Dealers price your goods. Amateurs may request offers.

Ken Laaker
1109 South 22nd Street
Quincy, IL 62301
(217) 222-5691

◆ **Smoky Bear** ephemera.
Thomas McKinnon
Twin Magnolia Farm
8500 Odom Road
Laurinburg, NC 28352
(910) 268-1800

CHILDREN'S LITERARY CHARACTERS

◆ *Uncle Wiggily* **items** including books, toys, empty boxes, buttons, Sunday comics, puzzles, mugs, dishes, games, and "all other memorabilia." Especially wants *Uncle Wiggily's* paint books, drums, Put-Together puzzles, candy tins, Animal Crackers boxes, kid's tea sets, and wind-up toys. Does not want *Uncle Wiggily Game* or books published by American Crayon Company or by Platt-Munk. Pays you a fee if you find something he wants and report it to him.

> Martin McCaw
> 307 East Second
> Prescott, WA 99348
> (509) 849-2621

◆ *Uncle Wiggily* **items** including toys, paper dolls, comics, dishes, handkerchiefs, fabric, and any unusual items.

> Audrey Buffington
> PO Box 386
> South Thomaston, ME 04858
> (207) 594-2683

◆ **Little Red Riding Hood dolls and other ephemera** including small old books (especially German), figurines, greeting cards and advertisements. Anything that's colorful and attractive and in fine condition will be considered. DOES NOT WANT Hull or McCoy pottery or Ohio Art tin or anything made after 1940.

> Ann Bergin
> PO Box 105
> Amherst, NH 03031
> <acbergin@aol.com>   fax (978) 649-6807

◆ **Red Riding Hood toys,** books, and other items.

> Wes Johnson, Sr.
> 106 Bauer Avenue
> Louisville, KY 40207
> (502) 899-3030 extension 228 days only

◆ *Alice In Wonderland* books and memorabilia including films, figurines, tins, toys, games, puzzles, posters, greeting cards, dolls, etc. Especially wants a Beswick china figurine of the Cheshire Cat, but encourages all inquiries. Also wants other Lewis Carroll items, including books, letters, and personal articles associated with Carroll. No books published by Whitman or illustrated by John Tenniel but would love the Alice published by Appleton in 1866, worth at least $1,000!

> Joel Birenbaum
> 2765 Shellingham Drive
> Lisle, IL 60532
> (630) 637-8530

LUNCHBOXES

★ **Comic character children's lunch boxes,** both metal and vinyl, from 1975 or before. Must have pictures depicting space, cartoon, TV, sports, western, or other kid-related themes. Condition is very important. Boxes and bottles should look as if they were only slightly used, with no rust, bad rubbing, dents, serious scratches, or names written on the outside of the box. The most sought after boxes bring over $500, with *Matt Mason's Space Diver* a hot $1,000+.

> David Welch
> PO Box 714
> Murphysboro, IL 62966
> (618) 687-2282   fax (618) 684-2243   <pezdude1@aol.com>

TONY'S TIP: Inspect your lunch box carefully for a © date. Most boxes will have one somewhere. Boxes are more valuable if their Thermos© bottles are present and in good condition. The more colorful and action filled, the better, according to collectors. Damaged, rusty boxes are not wanted.

◆ **Lunchboxes.** "We will be happy to identify your lunchbox and tell you the value." Provide them with any names, dates, or numbers on your toy and a brief accurate description of condition including paint or color loss, damage, and condition of the package it came in. We don't want plush (stuffed) animals, sports toys, NASCAR, Beanie Babies or glasware of any kind. Mail or Email preferred.

> Jack Klodzinski & Rich Levy
> Critical Mass Toys
> PO Box 470
> Geneva, FL 32732
> (407) 327-8223 days   <askdoctorjack@hotmail.com>
>   <www.cmitoys.com>

◆ **Lunchboxes and Thermos© bottles**. Wants metal and vinyl lunchboxes in fine condition, especially with original bottles. Has a particular interest in promotional lunchboxes and plastic boxes in unusual shapes. Larry is the author of two books on lunchboxes and their prices.

> Larry Aikins
> 101 Trail Ridge Road
> Athens, TX 75751
> (903) 675-3765   fax (903) 677-3643   <lunchbox@aol.com>
>   <www.mrlunchbox.com/mrlunchbox.html>

CARTOON & CHARACTER GLASSES

★ **Cartoon and character glasses.** "We buy drinking glasses that have cartoon characters, superheroes, sports personalities, fast-food logos, soft drink company logos, horse racing, grand openings, world's far, advertising, and convention decorations. We particularly want cartoon character and horse racing glasses from 1930-79. We don't want common glasses that are out there by the millions like *Camp Snoopy, Smurfs, Care Bears, Popples* and *Holly Hobbie.* We buy collections, accumulations, and singles but don't want anything faded or chipped." Best if you can send a photo, but not essential if you describe height, picture, and condition of the picture. They've promised to help amateurs, but dealers are expected to price their goods. Note any missing paint or misprinting. Mark and Mike are authors of *Collectible Drinking Glasses.* They also publish the bi-monthly "Collector Glass News" devoted to glasses, yours for $15 a year.

Mark Chase and Mike Kelly
Collector Glass News
PO Box 308
Slippery Rock, PA 16057
(724) 946-2838   fax (724) 946-9012
<cgn@glassnews.com>

◆ **Cartoon and character glasses** issued by restaurants, fast food chains, TV shows, and others. Peter buys outright, and also accepts items on consignment from pickers, dealers and private parties for his twice a year auctions of glasses, mugs, steins and related items. Some cartoon characters bring as much as $100. He does not want foreign glasses, anything issued in the last 10 years, or anything not in mint condition. He suggests you send a picture whenever possible. His 60+ page auction catalogs are $11 each and come with prices realized for over 1,600 auctioned items. Back issues are available.

Peter Kroll
Glasses, Mugs & Steins Auction
PO Box 207
Sun Prairie, WI 53590
(608) 837-4818 eves   fax (608) 825-4205
<pkroll@chorus.net>

TONY'S TIP: Cartoon glasses may also be of interest to general pop culture dealers found in the beginning of the Pop Culture section of Trash or Treasure starting on page 132.

BOBBING HEAD DOLLS

★ **Bobbing head "nodder" dolls.** Wants sports, advertising, political, comic and character dolls made of papier mache or ceramic. Plastic dolls are not wanted. Dolls must be in nice condition with no head or shoulder cracks ("Look carefully," he cautions, "because they can be hard to see"). Decals must be complete, and there should be no other damage. Generic Oriental figures (that represent no particular identifiable celebrity) are not wanted, nor are animals except cartoon animals like Sylvester the Cat. Top dollar is paid for Black/Negro athletes, which start at $350. With the exception of Col. Sanders, nodder figures which advertise a product are $250 and up. Celebrity figures are $50 and up, with some as high as $200. Tim will be happy to sell you a handy small guide to sports nodders for only $6. Tim is the country's biggest nodder dealer, and pledges to pay "an honest 60% of retail for any doll."

 Tim Hunter
 4301 West Hidden Valley
 Reno, NV 89502
 (775) 856-4357   fax (775) 856-4354   <thunter885@aol.com>

TONY'S TIP: *Rising prices has led to increased attention for all these kitschy collectibles, now considered among Pop Culture icons. When you describe a nodder for sale, give the height of the figure and the colors of the clothing, hat (helmet) and base. Decals must be in fine condition. Today's fads will be tomorrow's collectibles, but at much lower prices.*

◆ **Bobbing head sports and non-sports dolls,** Japanese ceramic or composition models only, no plastic dolls or dolls made in Taiwan or Korea. Indicate team or character portrayed. Also give the size, color, and shape of the base. Will pay $150 for any Blackface bobbing baseball doll in perfect condition and $600 for a perfect Roberto Clemente. **Also wants sports and non-sports plastic statues by Hartland.** Will pay between $100 and $700 for excellent and complete statues, depending on the character.

 Chip Norris
 PO Box 235
 Leonardtown, MD 20650
 (301) 475-2951   fax (301) 475-3900   <j.harry@excite.com>

◆ **Bobbing head and nodder dolls.** Prefers people or famous characters. Special wants include the *Pillsbury Doughboy, Elsie the Borden's* cow, *Popeye,* Presidents Eisenhower and Kennedy, Minnie Mouse, and Elmer Fudd. Also wants double nodder salt and pepper shakers, nodder ashtrays and other unusual nodders.

> Roxanne Toser
> 4019 Green Street
> Harrisburg, PA 17110
> (717) 238-1936   <r_toser@nonsportsupdate.com>

GUM CARDS

◆ **Non-sports gum cards** from 1930-49. This *Star Trek* star (Chekov) wants cards featuring pirates, WWII, Indians, cowboys, and comic strip characters. Especially wants comic cards cut from 1930-50 candy boxes. Cards must be in fine condition.

> Walter Koenig
> PO Box 4395
> North Hollywood, CA 91607
> <gincokw@aol.com>

★ **Non-sports gum cards** from before 1980 only. Especially interested in 1960's TV cards and will buy singles, sets, unopened wax packs, display boxes and uncut sheets. Mike asks that you call with what you have. If it sounds good, you'll be asked to send it on approval at his expense for inspection and offer. DO NOT send things without asking first. For large collections, he'll come to you.

> Michael Herz
> 9 Hitching Post Lane
> Casselberry, FL 32707
> (407) 260-8869   fax (407) 260-2289   <majicherz@aol.com>

◆ **Non-sports gum cards** are priced in *Non-Sport Update* magazine, a slick bimonthly with a pull-out *Price Guide*, edited by Roxanne Toser and available for $21 a year. Ms. Toser, whom we have recommended for more than ten years, no longer personally buys cards or wrappers.

> Roxanne Toser, editor Non-Sport Update Magazine
> 4019 Green Street
> Harrisburg, PA 17110
> (717) 238-1936   <r_toser@nonsportsupdate.com>

TONY'S TIP: Trading cards have been packed in tobacco, candy, gum and other products for 120 years. Thousands of non-sports card sets depicting every imaginable topic from animals to zeppelins exist. Expect to get from 10¢ to $4 for most cards. 19th century cards occasionally bring more from Tobacco or pop culture collectors.

TONY'S TIPS ON SELLING COMICS AND COMIC ART

*Comic strips and books have been around since the turn of the century. Approximately 17,000 comic titles have been published, but **only 300± of these have serious collector interest.** Age has little to do with the value of comic books, and almost all comics, 1930's and 40's included, sell for $10 or less.*

__The popularity of the artist who drew the comic has more to do with value than any other characteristic.__ Other things that go into determining how much money you get are the popularity of the character, the popularity of the publisher, the historical significance of the series or specific issue, the condition and the current demand.

__Comic collectors are fussy folks.__ Every tiny crease, tear, wrinkle, misprint, and off-center or rusty staple affects the value. Collectors tend to follow the grading standards suggested in Overstreet's __The Comic Book Price Guide__, the reference used by most folks as it contains values for nearly every American comic book. It is available at bookstores, public libraries, and by mail order.

__Expect buyers to pay you from 30% to 70% of prices quoted in Overstreet.__ As a general rule, the more valuable the comic you are selling, the higher the percentage of the value listed in Overstreet's guide. Dealers don't want to buy lots of inexpensive comic books. They know top items move quickly. Low priced items don't sell. __Badly worn comics, even rare titles and issues, are nearly impossible for you or for dealers to sell.__

__Buyers will usually ask you to send comics for inspection prior to payment since the value of comics is linked to condition.__ Ask your post office for "return receipt requested" which costs about one dollar. Always include a list of what you are sending and keep a copy of the list for yourself. Cautious sellers photocopy the covers of what they send, since the creases on the cover are like a fingerprint and can identify your comic should it become necessary.

COMIC BOOKS

★ **All 10¢ comic books,** for which Gary has "unlimited funds" to pay 50% to 100% of price guide values. Send a list of titles and issue numbers along with a brief description of condition. This nationally recognized comic book expert and historian is not interested in any comics which originally sold for more than a dime. Gary is also interested in comic strip original art for daily or Sunday strips.

> Gary Colabuono
> Pop Culture Resources, Inc.
> PO Box 117
> Elk Grove Village, IL 60009
> (800) 344-6060   fax (847) 577-6292   <moondog100@attbi.com>

★ **Comic books originally costing 10¢,** especially war, superhero, Western, science-fiction, fantasy and horror. Especially comics published by the following companies: Timely, Atlas, Avon, Centaur, E.C., Marvel, DC, Fawcett, Fiction House and Quality. He does not need more *Classics Illustrated* comics. The comics most wanted are by Timely Titles including *Captain America, Marvel Mystery, Mystic, All Winners, Human Torch, Sub-Mariner, USA,* and *Young Allies.* **He does not want** any comics without covers, no matter how old or rare they are. When writing or calling, give the title, publisher, and issue number (usually found on the cover, inside front cover, or first page). Describe condition including cover gloss, creases, stains, tears, tape, and damage to the spine. Note loose or missing pages, bends, and folds, as well as browning of the pages. A b/w photocopy of the covers is helpful. Joe has been in the mail order comic business since 1978 and promises to answer all inquiries if you include a Self-Addressed Stamped Envelope.

> Joe Hill
> 223 Fairview Road   357 No Problem Drive
> Erin, NY 14838 (Apl-Nov)   Las Cruces, NM 88005 (Dec-Mar)
> (607) 796-2547 <jrhillerin@aol.com>   (505) 524-2093

◆ **Comic books from 1938 to 1969** that originally cost 10¢ or 12¢ on the cover. Seeking crime, horror, romance, science fiction, super hero, war and western titles. "I'll buy in fair+ or better condition, but no brittle, damaged or incomplete comics." Geoff offers to pay you cash or, if your prefer, to trade movie memorabilia for your comics. Geoff deals in movie memorabilia.

> Geoffrey Mahfuz
> 30 Phoebe Avenue
> Lowell, MA 01854
>   (978) 662-6170 7am - 9pm   <zufham@aol.com>

◆ **Comic books from all periods.** Give the name and publication date or issue number. Describe the condition. No books with missing pages or badly damaged covers. Value is highly dependent on condition. "We encourage children to email us with questions about collecting comics."
> Jack Klodzinski & Rich Levy
> Critical Mass Toys
> PO Box 470
> Geneva, FL 32732
> (407) 327-8223 days <askdoctorjack@hotmail.com>
> <cmitoys.com>

◆ **All comic books in fine condition 1900 to 1969** are wanted by this active Canadian dealer. He also buys Big Little Books and Better Little Books from 1932 to 1950. He has no interest in anything brittle or damaged. Pays in U.S. dollars and bank drafts.
> Ken Mitchell
> 710 Conacher Drive
> Willowdale, Ontario
> M2M 3N6 CANADA
> (416) 222-5808

◆ **Big Little Books** are wanted, but only if in fine condition with no missing pages, coloring, or trashed spines. Please give the title, catalog number, and a photocopy (Xerox™) when possible.
> Mike Rasmussen
> PO Box 726
> Marina, CA 93933
> (831) 759-0259 fax (831) 422-1529
> <rasspapercol@thegrid.net>

◆ **Comic strip books, 1897-1922.** "These are large books with cardboard covers measuring approximately 10.5" x 16" and have colorful graphics. Characters featured include *Buster Brown, Happy Hooligan, Katzenjammer Kids, Little Nemo, Pore Little Mose* and several others. By 1915, a new format of black and white books measuring 5.5" x 15" were introduced. Condition is very important, with prices ranging from $50 to $250 for most items. I am not interested in items other than the above or in reprints. Please give the name of the book, the dimensions, the publication date and the condition of the covers and pages, making sure that all pages are present."
> Robert Quesinberry
> 342 Merrimac Road
> Hillsville, VA 24343
> (540) 728-0919 days   <robert@goldenage.com>

◆ **Comic books of all types before 1980.** Unlike most dealers, Dave will consider just about anything in the way of comic books from the 1930's to 1980, including Westerns, Romance, Horror, Science Fiction, jungle, war, crime, funny animal and superhero. He'll buy (at appropriately lower prices) comics in less than fine condition and has actually been known to buy coverless comics (only from the 1930's to early 50's). You can offer him your small press comics from the 1980's and **underground sex and drug comics** from the 1960's and 70's.   He DOES NOT WANT reprint comics and comic books by a publisher called Valiant (still widely available at discount prices). Give the title, issue number or date, and a statement of condition. Note all damage, or send him a Xerox© of the cover. Large collections or single copies.

> Dave Sheldon
> 9000 Williams Road
> North East, PA 16428
>   (814) 897-1894 days   (814) 725-1394
>   <drskull9@hotmail.com>

◆ **Cartoon and comic character books** such as Big Little Books, Pop-Up Books, Fast Actions, Fawcett Dime Action Books, Cupples and Leon, and other early comic reprint books from 1910's, 20's and 30's. Also Whitman hard cover children's books with dust jackets, Whitman Penny Books, Nickel Books, Buddy Books, and any similar books published by Salsfield, Mclaughlin, Lynn Publications, Engel Van Wiseman, etc. "Let me know what you have and what you want for it, or ship for my immediate offer."

> Alan Levine
> PO Box 1577
> Bloomfield, NJ 07003
>   (973) 743-5288   <posterking@aol.com>

◆ **Flip books** from any period. FLIP BOOKS ARE small booklets with one picture a page, like one frame of animation. When you flip the pictures with your thumb, the images seem to move. Will pay $200 for *Santa Claus Play Pictures* and *Mother Goose Play Pictures*, which had pages to be cut out and assembled into flip books. He DOES NOT WANT Big Little Books with flip illustrations in the upper corner. He DOES NOT WANT recent reproductions by Merrimack or Shackman & Co. If you have a genuine old flipbook, make a Xerox© of the cover and give a brief description of the action. Give the dimensions, whether illustrations are color or b/w and whether the pictures are cartoons or photos. Describe condition.

> Jeff Jurich
> 175 South Jersey Street
> Denver, CO 80224

SUNDAY COMIC PAGES

◆ **Sunday comic sections,** 1895-1970. Prefers to purchase runs of several years, not singles. He especially wants the color comics from the Saturday issues of the Chicago or the NY *Journal American,* from 1934 to 1964 but buys all very good condition sections before 1970.

> Claude Held
> PO Box 515
> Buffalo, NY 14225
> (716) 634-4842

◆ **Sunday and daily adventure comic strips,** 1930-60 such as *Tarzan, Prince Valiant, Flash Gordon, Terry and the Pirates* and *Casey Ruggles.* No single daily panels, humor strips or torn items.

> Carl Horak
> 1319 108th Avenue
> SW Calgary, Alberta
> T2W 0C6 CANADA
> (403) 252-0878   <carl@canuk.com>

◆ **All Sunday comic sections** in fine condition from 1929 to 1959. Name all the strips pictured, the date, and the number of pages. He DOES NOT WANT anything brittle or damaged. Pays in U.S. dollars and bank drafts.

> Ken Mitchell
> 710 Conacher Drive
> Willowdale, Ontario
> M2M 3N6 CANADA
> (416) 222-5808

ORIGINAL COMIC ART

◆ **Original artwork for animation, comic strips and cartoons,** 1920-1960, especially animation cels from Disney and Warner Brothers, for which this 30 year veteran has paid as much as $50,000. Jerry also buys original art from comic strips and magazine cartoons. Information he wants includes title, artist, description, the year, and any documentation you might have. In your description of condition, note any yellowing, folds, tears, cracked or missing paint, paste overs, etc. He does not want reproductions from newspapers or magazines, nor does he buy posters or prints of any type. Museum Graphics publishes a free bimonthly newsletter and price list.

> Jerry Muller, Museum Graphics
> PO Box 11155
> Costa Mesa, CA 92627
> (714) 540-0808

◆ **Comic strip art** by any noted cartoonist. Dennis issues an illustrated annual catalog which you may write for.

> Dennis Books
> Comic Character Shop
> PO Box 99142
> Seattle, WA 98199
> (206) 283-0532 eves

◆ **Original artwork** by Walt Disney studios, Walt Kelly (*Pogo*), or George Herriman (*Krazy Kat*). Some others may be of interest.

> John Fawcett
> PO Box 1156
> Waldoboro, ME 04572
> (207) 832-7398 before 8pm EST <fawcetoy@qwi.net>

◆ **Original comic book or comic strip art, 1890 - 1960's.** This well-known Canadian Pop Culture dealer pays in U.S. dollars or drafts.

> Ken Mitchell
> 710 Conacher Drive
> Willowdale, Ontario
> M2M 3N6 CANADA
> (416) 222-5808

◆ **Original art used in creating comic books and strips.** Please make a photocopy of what you have.

> Charles Martignette
> PO Box 293
> Hallandale, FL 33008
> (954) 454-3474

TONY'S TIP: Most comic art sells for $50 to $2,000 but some Disney pieces have sold for more than $200,000. Value depends upon age, artist, subject and condition. Carl Barks at Disney is very popular as is Charles Schultz, Walt Kelly, George Herriman, Hal Foster, Al Capp, Frank Frazetta and a few other artists who bring premium prices.

You are wise to check out any cartoon originals, whether in color or black and white.

Collectors buy comic art that was used in a movie, magazine, advertisement or other published form but also buy unpublished works by top artists.

TONY'S TIPS ON SELLING ENTERTAINMENT ITEMS

Nearly everything associated with entertainment is Treasure to someone.

Movie related items are the most popular entertainment collectible, but "Entertainment" includes anything done on a stage, Disneyland, World's Fair souvenirs, and the like. Distinctions between entertainment, music, toys, advertising, sports and Pop Culture are arbitrary, so when selling an entertainment collectible also try looking in these sections of Trash or Treasure whenever it seems appropriate.

Stars like James Dean and Marilyn Monroe are hot and genuine autographed photos can be worth $1,000 or more, but most star photos and production stills from films bring a few dollars at most. Many movie star autographs and photos are signed by secretaries or machines. Real signatures on hand-written letters and on scripts are of much more interest to collectors.

Posters from popular stars and important or cult films can bring hundreds, even thousands, of dollars. Contact more movie poster buyers in the section on Posters.

Items sought by more than one type of collector are called "cross-over collectibles." A signed photograph of Marilyn Monroe would find buyers in movie, photo, and autograph categories. Cross-over items are often priced very differently by the different types of collectors.

Radio and television sets are popular with a different breed of collector than the "Entertainment" collector.

Radio collectors will often collect decorative "go-withs" to display with their sets. Go-withs are photos, catalogs, signs, and advertising related to a collector's main specialty. A photo of the interior of a radio store in 1923 would be a fine go-with for a radio collector. That same photo would also be of interest to a collector of photos of store interiors, or to a collector of something else pictured in the store. Many entertainment collectibles make attractive go-withs, so consider all possibilities when looking for a buyer.

MOVIE MEMORABILIA

◆ **Commercial motion picture and magic lantern projectors** and associated films, **slides** and other ephemera related to theatrical history such as tickets, programs, and posters from early performances. Especially wants to find cameras and projectors made by Sigmund Lubin Co. of Philadelphia, and will play $500 and up. Also buys old "persistence of vision devices" such as zoetropes, praxinoscopes, and outfits used by traveling itinerant showmen at the turn of the century. He emphasizes, "I have no interest at all in toy magic lanterns or toy slides, nor do I want any 8mm or 16mm film or projectors." When offering something for sale, indicate the maker's name, the model number, and other relevant data. Describe condition accurately.

George Hall
Professor Hall's Cinema Museum
PO Box 4081
Prescott, AZ 86302
(928) 777-9134   <profh@silentmovies.com>

TONY'S TIPS: Professional lantern slides are usually 3 1/4" square or 3 1/4" x 4" and were either hand-painted, mechanically printed, or made from photographs. Some were mounted in 4" x 7" wooden frames with moving parts which changed the picture in some way. Children's slides are usually one or two inches high and 5" to 12" long.

◆ **Magic lanterns and their glass slides.** He buys these early glass slide projectors from all countries in all sizes and shapes, colors and makes. Also wants all related materials such as glass slides, accessories, books, catalogs, handbills, and broadsides. "The older the better," with prices varying from $10 to more than $1,000." Does not want reproductions or small black magic lanterns with "EP" on them. Send a photo and indicate all markings found on the lantern. Dealers must price their goods; amateurs only may request an offer.

Jack Judson
Magic Lantern Castle Museum
1419 Austin Highway
San Antonio, TX 78209
(210) 805-0111   fax (210) 822-1226
<castle@magiclanterns.org>

◆ **Magic lantern glass slides.** These slides are usually 3 1/4" square or 3 1/4" x 4" with black paper taped edges. They were either hand-painted, mechanically printed, or made from photographs. Some were mounted in 4" x 7" wooden frames with moving parts which changed the picture in some way. "I give old-time magic lantern shows as a hobby and am always looking for interesting or entertaining slides to add to my repertoire. I don't want church hymn or scripture slides. I do buy a few of the small slides for children's toy magic lanterns, but only those that measure 1 3/4" x 6 5/8" and no others."

> Lindsay Lambert
> 41 Bellwood Avenue
> Ottawa, ON
> K1S 1S6 CANADA

◆ **Silent movie memorabilia** including coming attraction slides, posters, lobby cards, figurines, sheet music, pin back buttons, paper dolls, and spoons by Athens or Rogers Bros. (but not Oneida). Wants *Our Gang* handkerchiefs, Artamo needlework, star garment hangers, and the standee for Robin Hood shoes. Nothing from the talkies or from later stars. No autographs or photos from any period are wanted.

> Richard Davis
> 9500 Old Georgetown Road
> Bethesda, MD 20814
> (301) 530-5904   <rdavis9500@aol.com>
>
> January-March
> 1391 S. Ocean Blvd #504
> PompanoBeach, FL 33062
> (954) 783-5807

◆ **Silent movie programs.** Please Xerox™ the cover and describe the condition of the contents, including how many photos it has. Complete items, please.

> Gary Bart
> 620 Siena Way
> Los Angeles, CA 90077
> (310) 471-6980   fax (310) 471-1910

◆ **Manuals and catalogs for magic lantern and cinema projection,** from before1925.

> Lindsay Lambert
> 41 Bellwood Avenue
> Ottawa, ON
> K1S 1S6 CANADA

◆ **Japanese animation cels and toys.** Give a brief description, including what information you can. Describe the condition.

> Jack Klodzinski
> PO Box 470
> Geneva, FL 32732
> (407) 327-8223 days   <askdoctorjack@hotmail.com>   <cmitoys.com>

◆ **Movie posters of all sizes,** with particular interest in collections of pre-1940 posters. All posters printed in color will be considered. Give the film title, general description of the image and the exact outside dimensions (the size) of the poster. One sheet posters that he particularly wants include *Public Enemy* for which he'll pay $12,000 and *Flying Down to Rio* worth a cool $10,000. But the original one-sheet poster for *The Mummy, Dracula* or *Frankenstein* one could put ten times that much in your pocket!

     Dwight Cleveland
     PO Box 10922
     Chicago, IL 60610
  (773) 525-9152   fax (773) 525-2969   <posterboss@aol.com>

◆ **Movie ephemera** including posters, lobby cards, souvenir booklets and standees, both American and European. "I guarantee a fast decision and faster check."

     George Theofilis
     Miscellaneous Man
     PO Box 1776
     New Freedom, PA 17349
        (717) 235-4766 days   fax (717) 235-2853

◆ **Movie memorabilia,** including lobby cards (especially from B movies 1930-1960), theater souvenirs, tickets, programs, photos of theaters, and materials sent by studios to theater owners. Also wants magazines such as *Motion Picture Herald, Box Office, The Exhibitor,* and others aimed at theater owners and will buy them in any condition. This 20 year veteran collector does not buy items made after 1960.

     Chris Smith
     26 Ridge Avenue
     Aston, PA 19014
        (610) 485-0814   <glcody26@icdc.com>

◆ **Movie posters,** foreign or domestic, from 1900 to the present. Give the title of the movie, size, description of the image, year of release, and the condition of the poster. Jon wrote *Warren's Movie Poster Price Guide* at $22.50 and publishes *Collecting Hollywood* magazine.

     Jon Warren
     American Collectors Exchange
     2401 Broad Street
     Chattanooga, TN 37408
        (423) 265-5515   fax (423) 265-5506
        <jon@jonwarren.com>

◆ **Movie memorabilia,** especially paper, from an original old showbill to a warehouse full, this long time dealer is interested. **Movie magazines** from before 1940 are also wanted if uncut and not moldy. Mike is an expert in movie star and other celebrity autographs. DO NOT send things without asking first. Xerox™ copies are helpful.

> Mike Rasmussen
> PO Box 726
> Marina, CA 93933
> (831) 759-0259   fax (831) 422-1529   <rasspapercol@thegrid.net>

◆ **Cartoon posters from silent movies.** "I buy posters featuring cartoon characters like *Felix the Cat, Out of the Inkwell,* and other silent films, but will consider other silent movie posters as well."

> Richard Davis   January-March
> 9500 Old Georgetown Road   1391 S. Ocean Blvd #504
> Bethesda, MD 20814   PompanoBeach, FL 33062
> (301) 530-5904   <rdavis9500@aol.com>   (954) 783-5807

◆ **Paper movie ephemera,** 1925-1959, including movie magazines, pressbooks, heralds, posters, trade journals, studio rehearsal discs and "almost anything else having to do with movies."

> Buddy McDaniel
> 2802 West 18th Street
> Wichita, KS   67203
>   (316) 942-3561   fax (316) 945-2971

◆ **Original studio production movie scripts** with original binders or covers when possible. "I am not interested in photocopies, TV scripts, or unproduced scripts unless the latter are by very important writers." Indicate author's name, whether script has its cover, what draft (or the date), whether all pages are present, and whether there are notations.

> Grayson Cook
> 367 West Avenue 42
> Los Angeles, CA 90065
>   (213) 227-8899

◆ **Movie memorabilia** including autographs of stars, promotional stills, lobby cards, and posters. This dealer wants bulk rather than single items from private parties, unless the single item's unusually good. Everything is purchased for resale.

> Ralph Bowman's Paper Gallery
> 5349 Wheaton Street
> La Mesa, CA 91942
> (619) 462-6268 voice/fax   <ralph@thepapergallery.com>

★ **Movie props and memorabilia** "from an original old showbill to a single movie prop to a warehouse full." Because the category is so large and diverse, Mike asks that you call with what you have. If it sounds good, you'll be asked to send it on approval at his expense for his inspection and offer. DO NOT send things without asking first. For large collections, he'll come to you.

Michael Herz
Whiz Bang! Collectibles
9 Hitching Post Lane
Casselberry, FL 32707
(407) 260-8869   fax (407) 260-2289   <majicherz@aol.com>

◆ **Movie memorabilia** 1920-96, including posters of all sizes, inserts, and lobby cards. Also wants movie autographs and magazines. Stars of particular interest include Jean Harlow, Marlene Dietrich, Bette Davis, Errol Flynn, James Cagney, Humphrey Bogart, James Dean, and Marilyn Monroe. Condition is important. Include your phone number.

Gary Vaughn, Cinemonde
138 2nd Avenue North #104
Nashville, TN 37201
(615) 742-9256   fax (615) 742-1268   <cinemonde@earthlink.net>

◆ **Movie memorabilia.** Buys posters, lobby cards, pressbooks, heralds, fan photos and other memorabilia from 1898 to 1970. Also movie magazines before 1950. "Please let me know what you have and what you want for it, or just ship for my immediate offer."

Alan Levine
292 Glenwood Avenue   or   PO Box 1577
Bloomfield, NJ 07003
(973) 743-5288   <posterking@aol.com>

◆ **Autographs of film, TV, and Rock and Roll stars,** song and script writers, including both minor and major figures. "I do not want Country & Western performers or current sports figures. Photocopies are recommended. Tell me where you got the item and set the price wanted as I do not bid on items." SASE. Jim sells inexpensive books containing current addresses of movie, music, sport and sex celebrities.

Jim Weaver
405 Dunbar Drive
Pittsburgh, PA 15235   <weaverjim@aol.com>

◆ **Stereoviews of Hollywood,** old movie theaters, movie stars, and anything else that is movie industry related.

Chris Perry
7470 Church Street #A
Yucca Valley, CA 92284
(760) 365-0475   fax (619) 365-0495

ACTORS & ACTRESSES

◆ **James Dean memorabilia** including magazines, photos, records, sheet music, lobby cards, autographs, posters, scrapbooks, plates and novelties. Description should include size, year, and condition.
> David Loehr
> PO Box 55
> Fairmount, IN 46928
> (765) 948-3326   fax (765) 948-3389   <dl@jamesdeangallery.com>

◆ **Celebrity memorabilia.** "I buy, sell and collect celebrity memorabilia by mail. I'm looking for personal belongings of entertainment stars and historical figures, including movie costumes, props, and autographed photos. I'm not interested in most mass produced items, except very rare items like movie posters." Your description should include what the item is, its condition, and its history, including how you came to own it. Make certain to describe what authentication you have.
> Richard Wilson
> 3511 Turner Lane
> Chevy Chase, MD 20815
>   (301) 652-4644   fax (301) 907-0216
> <normasjeans@msn.com>   <www.normasjeans.net>

◆ **Sherlock Holmes and Dr. Watson actors.** "I want anything about the actors who have portrayed Holmes and Watson, including Basil Rathbone, Nigel Bruce, Jeremy Brett, David Burke, Edward Hardwicke, William Gillette, Ellie Norwood, Arthur Wontner, Peter Cushing, Christopher Plummer, et al. Please describe and include a photograph or Xerox™ of what you have whenever possible.
> Rev. Sherlock Holmes
> PO Box 3
> Worcester, MA 01613
> free (877) 306-4059   <antiques@sherlockholmes.com>

◆ **Shirley Temple items** are always wanted by this specialty collector.
> Rita Dubas
> 8811 Colonial Road
> Brooklyn, NY 11209
>   (718) 745-7532   fax (718) 921-6444
>   <rdubasdes@mindspring.com>

◆ **Humphrey Bogart items** including original posters and film or video copies of *Broadway's like that, A Devil with Women* and *Body and Soul.* No sheet music or reproductions
> Dennis Horwitz
> 10416 Irene Street #8
> Los Angeles, CA 90034
>   (310) 202-7393 after 6 pm Pacific

★ **Lucille Ball and Desi Arnaz memorabilia** from any era associated with the *I Love Lucy* show, Desilu productions, their movies, records, and other activities, including toys, dolls, board games, magazines, comic books, paper dolls, advertising, scripts, tickets, props, costumes, autographs, and the like. If if says Lucy or Desi on it, he probably wants it. No newspaper or magazine clippings, please. He is the author of *For the Love of Lucy*, available though bookstores for $35.

> Ric Wyman
> PO Box 436
> Falconer, NY 14733

◆ **Three Stooges memorabilia** of all types, especially related to their tour of England in 1939. Buys items associated with any Stooge except Joe Besser and Joe Derita, including toys, contracts, posters, tickets, autographs, checks, personal items, coloring books, records, puppets, etc., and will pay as high as $3,000 for some rare items. He does not want comic books, gum cards, or things made after 1968, but has strong interest in animation cels from cartoons in which they appeared.

> Neil Teixeira
> PO Box 20812
> Oakland, CA 94620
> (510) 658-9938   fax (510) 658-8757   <n.teixeira@worldnet.att.net>

◆ **Three Stooges and other comedy team memorabilia.** Frank buys and sells items associated with all the classic teams.

> Frank Reighter
> 10220 Calera Road
> Philadelphia, PA 19114
>   (215) 637-5744   <pbreighter@aol.com>

◆ **Ginger Rogers memorabilia:** posters, lobby cards, autographs, photos, sheet music, magazines with her on the cover, advertising, *Old Gold* cigarette ads, and "anything else pertaining to this great actress." All items must be in good condition.

> Thomas Morris
> PO Box 8307
> Medford, OR 97504
>   (541) 779-3164   <chalkman@cdsnet.net>

◆ **Jack Benny collectibles.** "I'll buy any items pertaining to Jack Benny, and have for 15 years." Please describe your item, indicate the condition and set a price. If she doesn't buy what you have, she might run an ad for it in their newsletter so other collectors can see it. She sells a complete log of Benny's films, records and books for only $15.

> Laura Lee Leff, International Jack Benny Fan Club
> PO Box 11288
> Piedmont, CA 94611
>   <jackbenny@aol.com>

◆ **Marilyn Monroe.** Wants "anything and everything" U.S. and foreign, including lobby cards, press books, sound track albums, collector plates, dolls, and the like. Will buy magazines with Marilyn on the cover if they are in uncut condition. He does not want scrapbooks, new posters, or new pictures. Photocopies are helpful.

Clark Kidder
3219 East County Road North
Milton, WI 53563
(608) 868-4185   fax (608) 868-6808   <ckidder@jvlnet.com>

◆ **Marilyn Monroe** paper items are wanted by this 10 year veteran collector. She especially wants foreign magazines with Marilyn on the cover, and various issues of popular magazines with important Marilyn features or covers. Her most wanted item is a digest size copy of the *So-Rite Fashion Catalog* for Fall of 1949. You'll be $500 richer if you can find a mint one for her. She does not want nudes, *Playboy, Life, Look, Modern Screen, Screen Stories,* books about Marilyn printed in the U.S., nor does she want dolls or plates. She will consider sheet music, some newspaper features, and 3D items.

Ann Bartoli
1230 Woodridge Court
Princeton, IL 61356
(815) 875-8925   <bartoli@theramp.net>

◆ **Bob Hope collectibles** of all types: scripts, props, photos, records, tapes, film, personal items, clothing, movie banners, promotional items, public service records, commercials, toys, games, USO and armed services items dealing with him, Christmas cards, etc. This 20 year collector says, "I'm eager to learn of any Bob Hope item!"

David Elford
11018 NE 14th Street
Vancouver, WA 98684
(360) 256-9529   <bobthope@qwest.net>

◆ **Jeff Chandler** data for biographical research. Seek articles, magazines, photos and personal information from friends and acquaintances. "Please price them so a senior citizen can afford them."

Chaplain Jeanne Ann Miller
19750 SW Peavine Mountain Road
McMinnville, OR 97128
(503) 472-1092 8-8:30 am or 9-9:30 pm PST

◆ **8"x10" studio glosses of sexy starlets** and actresses, 1920-1990.

Charles Martignette
PO Box 293
Hallandale, FL 33008

MOVIES

◆ *Gone With the Wind* **ephemera** associated with the book, movie, stage play, or its author Margaret Mitchell, including items from her newspaper career, as well as various editions of her novel and promotional material for the book over the years. Will buy catalogs, pressbooks, lobby cards, programs, record albums, candy boxes, scarves, jewelry, neckties, games, bookends, buttons, clothing, hats, and many other items. **He'd love to find an admittance card to Mitchell's 1949 funeral,** but does not want anything made after 1980 such as plates, figurines, music boxes, dolls, reproduction posters, etc. Please give the dimensions and an "honest description" of its condition. Edits *The Scarlett Letter,* available for $15/year.

> John Wiley, Jr.
> 1347 Greenmoss Drive
> Richmond, VA 23225
> (804) 771-3561 day   (804) 330-5484 eve
> <tsl_gwtw@hotmail.com>

◆ *Gone With the Wind* **items** associated with the film, the book, or its author. Wants book and Mitchell related items 1936-1965, foreign language editions of the book, movie scripts, movie posters, banners, props from the film, and all the promotional items such as dolls, games, scarfs, book ends, figurines, jewelry, nail polish, paint books, paper dolls, and more. Nothing printed after 1965. Herb no longer does free appraisals or makes offers.

> Herb Bridges
> PO Box 192
> Sharpsburg, GA 30277
> (770) 253-4934

◆ *Wizard of Oz* **items** from 1900 to the present whether associated with the books, the movie or various stage productions including posters, lobby cards, pressbooks, toys, games, magazine and newspaper features and original movie merchandise marked "Loew's Inc." The only exception: "No 50th anniversary movie merchandise except foreign or prototype." Your description should include all defects. Give the history you know. Dealers, price your goods; amateurs may request offers. *The Wizard of Oz Collector's Treasury* is available for $63.

> Jay Scarfone and William Stillman
> PO Box 167
> Hummelstown, PA 17036
> (717) 566-5538   fax (717) 566-7718
> <TheBBugle@aol.com>

◆ *20,000 Leagues Under the Sea.* Anything associated with Disney movie version of the novel: props, costumes, scripts, cast and crew autographs, banners, posters, standees, and other promotional items from the original 1954 release. I'm seeking many children's items like the Captain Nemo hat, the electric quiz game by Jacmar, the Whitman coloring book (uncolored), the Pressman periscope with cardboard backing, school bag, jigsaw puzzles, and other items. Disney items ONLY. Please give an accurate description and a price if you can."
David Enter
23851 Windmill Lane
Laguna Niguel, CA 92677
(949) 363-8113   <dventer@webtv.net>

◆ *Castle* **newsreels** from 1937 to 1975, sound or silent, 16mm or 8mm, as long as they are complete. No shortened 50' or 100' versions are wanted. Will also buy selected titles of *Castle* space and moon flight films. Private party requests you list the film number if possible.
Art Natale
Newsreels
278 North 11th
Prospect Park, NJ 07508

◆ **16 mm motion picture films of all kind**, silent or sound, black and white or color, preferably but not exclusively, before 1960. "I'll buy Hollywood features, documentaries, shorts, **cartoons,** serials, **training** films, industrial or school film, **newsreels,** even **home movies**. I'm not interested in porno films, but **burlesque** dancers are fine. My special interest is in three D films." Give title and length (or diameter of the reel). 16mm film is 16mm (about 1/2") wide. He buys any quantity in good condition, but DOES NOT WANTprojectors, empty film cans or reels. **Will also buy some interesting 8mm films.**
Chris Perry
7470 Church Street #A
Yucca Valley, CA 92284
(760) 365-0475   fax (760) 365-0495   <evildoctor3d@yahoo.com>

◆ **16 mm films made before 1970** including educational, documentary, **training,** promotional, **cartoons,** features, musical short subjects, **burlesque, sex films,** and **home movies.** Will consider 8mm and 35mm but no Super8. Also want **movie projectors** from the 1950's, 60's and 70's, but not interested in toys. "We have fun splicing odd things together and putting on shows at our Lawn Chair Drive-In."
Todd & Kristin Kimmell
PO Box 43737
Philadelphia, PA 19106
(215) 925-2568

WORLD'S FAIR EPHEMERA

◆ **Crystal Palace and the 1876 Centennial**. Only fine rare items, especially paper goods, from these two exhibitions are wanted. Describe carefully, noting all damage. Please price your item.
>Tammy Lau, Head of Special Collections
>Madden Library
>Fresno Stete University
>Fresno, CA 93740
>>(209) 294-2595

◆ **1876 Centennial collectibles** such as tokens, books, textiles, trade cards, tickets, posters, broadsides, pamphlets, medals, plates, and all other souvenirs of the exposition. Describe fully, noting all damage. Will make offers only on items he requests you send on approval.
>Russell Mascieri
>9 North Sunset Drive
>Voorhees, NJ 08043
>(856) 354-2154   fax (609) 953-7768   <rmascieri@aol.com>

◆ **1895 Atlanta Cotton States Exposition memorabilia,** especially medals, tokens, and postcards. No glassware, please. Agriculture medals from **Georgia state fairs and expos** are also wanted.
>R.W. Colbert
>4156 Livsey Road
>Tucker, GA 30084
>>(770) 938-2596   <rwc391@yahoo.com>

◆ **Tennessee Centennial Expo of 1897.** This major token collector asks that you describe your item well, including its condition.
>Joe Copeland
>PO Box 4221
>Oak Ridge, TN 37831
>>(865) 482-4215   <joenatca@icx.net>

◆ **Tennessee Centennial Expo of 1897.**
>Peggy Dillard
>PO Box 210904
>Nashville, TN 37221
>>(615) 646-1605 eves   <pdill43795@aol.com>

◆ **World's Fair ephemera from before 1940.** Wants tickets, badges, stationery, postcard sets, pin back buttons, tokens, medals, souvenirs. Please write or ship for offer." Does not buy single items after 1940 except in large collections.
>Rich Hartzog
>PO Box 4143 TOT
>Rockford, IL 61110

◆ **1893, 1901 and 1904 Expositions** (Columbian, Buffalo, St Louis). "I am interested in mugs, pitchers, china items, banks, watches, clocks, toys, games, trays, spoons with enamel bowls, celluloid buttons and mirrors, postcards, sheet music, passes to the Expo or a specific exhibit, stereo views, magic lantern slides, advertising and anything else unusual." Mugs will bring $75 up, banks $100 up, enamel spoons $75 up, and some postcards with metallic glitter up to $100. There are many items which he DOES NOT WANT including view books with b/w photos, items referring to Mckinley's assassination, postcards marked official souvenir mailing card, pot metal or brass trays, aluminum items, decks of cards or buttons picturing two women representing North and South America, ruby glass items (except in a set), and silver plated spoons. A photo or Xerox™ is preferred. Give size, color and condition. Please include an SASE for prompt response.

Fred Lavin
1 Fir Top Drive
Orchard Park, NY 14127
(716) 662-5261   fax (716) 667-3234   <panamxpo@adelphia.net>

◆ **1904 St. Louis World's Fair** and other U.S. expositions from 1876 to 1940. Especially wants Ingersoll souvenir watches, clocks, banks, lamps, steins, lithopanes, hold-to-light postcards, china and ceramic souvenirs picturing fair scenes, ribbons and badges from judges and officials, full sets of stereo cards, photographs, complete decks of playing cards, and more. "I have less interest in fairs after 1940."

Doug Woollard, Jr.
11614 Old St. Charles Road
Bridgeton, MO 63044
(314) 739-4662

◆ **World's Fair ephemera from 1904 or before** including china, wood, metal, textiles, paper, souvenirs, and glass. "Any and all items from a fair from 1851 to 1904 will be considered," although he has a particular interest in 1851, 1876, 1893, 1901, and 1904 fairs. A photo is requested, especially of any possibly expensive items. He requests you price your item; he will make offers on "things genuinely for sale."

Andy Rudoff
PO Box 111
Oceanport, NJ 07757
(908) 542-3712   <shoreguy@attbi.com>

◆ **1909 Alaska-Yukon-Pacific Exposition in Seattle.** Wants paper items and memorabilia.

Nick Nickell
710 North 102nd Street
Seattle, WA 98133
(206) 789-7901

◆ **1933-34 Chicago Century of Progress World's Fair.** "I want employee items such as uniforms badges and certificates, but also buy tickets for specific days (ie. "Oak Park Day"), souvenirs, toys, banks, models, replicas of buildings, statues, signs, posters, paintings, pins, and the like. I'd also like 16mm home movies and personal photos of the Fair, as well as quilts made for the Sears quilt contest. I am a collector and also run the "Century of Progress Collector's Show" which is held each year to commemorate the Fair."

> Rick Rann
> PO Box 877
> Oak Park, IL 60303
> (708) 442-7907 <rickrann@aol.com>

◆ **Trylon and perisphere at the 1939-40 NY World's Fair** pictured on paper items is sought by this major NY stamp dealer, in business for 50 years. Send a photocopy of what you have.

> Harvey Dolin
> Mezzanine floor
> 111 Fulton Street
> New York, NY 10038
> (212) 267-0216

◆ **1964 New York World's Fair.** Especially wants fabrics, jewelry, toys, and unusual items.

> Sue Stock
> 57 Lakeshore Drive
> Marlborough, MA 01752
> <djo2@mediaone.net>

◆ **All pre 1940 World's Fair memorabilia suitable for resale** or auction. All fairs before 1940 are wanted, especially very early ones. Rex is one of the larger mail order dealer/auctioneers in the country. He offers a large quarterly auction catalog, and constantly needs new quality items in outstanding condition. No items valued under $50 are wanted, but "the very rare always is!"

> Rex Stark
> Americana
> PO Box 1029
> Gardner, MA 01440
> (978) 630-3237 <rexstark@yahoo.com>

TONY'S TIP: World's Fair souvenirs and other items will also be purchased by dealers in Pop Culture found in Trash or Treasure starting on page 132.

◆ **Posters from all European countries.** Posters originated in 19th century Europe as an eye-catching way to advertise fairs and other public events, entertainment, theater and products like tobacco, liquor and bicycles, as well as vacation spots, ship lines and even books and magazines. Posters were instantly popular as a form of street art, easily understood by folks no matter what language they spoke. Because posters were intended to be ephemeral, transitory, short-lived, they were generally printed on cheap paper. The typical life span was only a few weeks until another poster hanger came along and pasted a new image on top or before an "art collector" removed it to decorate the walls of his or her apartment. The vast majority of posters have disappeared, unable to survive the rigors of the natural disintegration of age, two world wars, and careless handling. It is very rare that as many as fifty examples of a single poster survive.

These posters are now recognized as "graphic art" or "advertising art" or "commercial art" and other similar names...and have gone up in value. What was once free for the taking off the walls of Paris a century ago will now put money in your pocket. That could be anywhere from $25 or so for common posters of the 1950's to thousands of dollars for rare examples of posters designed by famous European artists of a hundred years ago. Vintage European Posters Company is actively in the market buying and selling European posters of all types made before 1950. Because they buy for resale, condition is important. Any restoration they must do makes the poster less valuable to them...and means less money to you.

If you have posters on any subject that are in good condition, take a photo of your poster or posters and send it, along with a self-addressed stamped envelope. Give the dimensions and any printing information found along the lower border of the poster. Note any and all stains, tears, creases, worm holes, silverfish or mouse chews or other damage. Alan travels throughout the U.S. and Europe buying posters, so individual arrangements will be made depending on the rarity and value of what you have.

> Alan Dickar
> Vintage European Posters
> PO Box 246
> Mt. Eden, CA 94557
>   (510) 887-1075
>   <posters@unforgettable.com>

TONY'S TIP: *Posters may also be purchased by folks who collect the item pictured: tobacco, bicycles, ships, magic and the like. Use the Index of Things You Can Sell to identify others who might be interested.*
General U.S. poster buyers are found on page 522.

MAGIC APPARATUS & EPHEMERA

◆ **Magic posters and memorabilia** including posters, books, lithographs, autographed photos and letters, and children's magic sets, particularly Mysto. Ken buys items from the famous and not so famous, including Kellar, Thurston, Blackstone, Nicola, Raymond, Germain, and especially Houdini. Prices offered will depend on the rarity and condition of what you have, so it is often necessary to inspect your item before a final offer can be made. Ken promises top dollar and prompt response to any item you offer that is of interest.

Ken Trombly
7112 Loch Lomond Drive
Bethesda, MD 20817
(800) 673-8158 (301) 320-2360 fax (202) 457-0343
<trombly@erols.com>

◆ **Harry Houdini memorabilia** including book, magazine and newspaper articles, photos, handbills, pamphlets, autographs, posters, personal apparatus and personal belongings. Anything relating to Houdini will probably be of interest. He especially wants to find copies of his silent movies (including home movies) except The Man From Beyond. If you are offering personal apparatus or effects you must explain why you know it is from Houdini. You may price or he will make offer. Provide bibliographic information for books. Arthur is a 15 year veteran collector and happy to provide free appraisals and make offers.

Arthur Moses
4205 Hildring Drive East
Ft. Worth, TX 76109
(817) 921-2840 fax (817) 732-3339
<aem102@aol.com>

◆ **Magic apparatus, books, posters, magic sets, memorabilia** and anything else magic related from all periods is wanted by this full time dealer, collector, author. "I have a particular interest in Taytelbaum magic as well as Houdini, Leroy, Kellar, Thurston, Thayer, Klingl, and Conradi. All priced depend on rarity and condition and you may be surprised just how fast and easy it is to sell to me. Items are added daily to my web site <www.ktmagic.com>." Send $5 for illustrated catalog of magic for sale.

Kenna Thompson
PO Box 260
Hebron, KY 41048
(859) 689-7080 fax (859) 689-0227
<kennat@ktmagic.com>

★ **Magic apparatus of all sorts** including all paraphernalia and props, escape devices, tokens, programs, books, and other ephemera. Has a particular interest in pre-1900 posters, original photos of Houdini, and a complete set of Houdini letters, one on each of his twelve letterheads (worth $5,000 if you have it). A complete set of Thayer Manufacturing's wooden turned devices (1910-20) is worth $12,000 to some lucky seller. No items after 1950, newspaper clippings, radio premiums, or pulp books issued by Wehman Bros. An illustrated catalog of magic books and devices is available for $5 from this veteran collector dealer.
> Mario Carrandi, Jr.
> 122 Monroe Avenue
> Belle Mead, NJ 08502
> > (908) 874-0630   fax (908) 874-4892
> > <carrandi@email.msn.com>

◆ **Magic posters, memorabilia, tricks, and books** printed before 1940. Describe condition and include a photo or Xerox™. If you are a dealer, price your goods. Amateurs may request an offer.
> Marvin Yagoda
> Marvin's Marvelous Mechanical Museum
> 31005 Orchard Lake Road
> Farmington Hills, MI 48334
> > (248) 626-5020   fax (248) 626-7945
> > <www.marvin3m.com>

◆ **Harry Houdini memorabilia** of all types, including apparatus, posters, letters and books.
> Joe and Pamela Tanner
> Wheeler-Tanner Escapes
> 6442 Canyon Creek Way
> Elk Grove, CA 95758
> > (916) 684-4006 voice/ fax
> > <jnpwlrtnr@aol.com>

◆ **Burlesque and vaudeville memorabilia,** 1870's to 1950's. Wants photos and film, posters, handbills, flyers, sequined costumes, comic shoes, routines on cylindrical or disk records, sheet music, scrap books for any stage act except "legitimate theater," such as strong men, animal acts, minstrels, and odd musical performances.
> Todd & Kristin Kimmell
> PO Box 43737
> Philadelphia, PA 19106
> > (215) 925-2568

◆ **Blackface minstrel ephemera** such as sheet music expressly for black face shows, playbills, posters, handbills, postcards, photos, scripts, sketches, songsters and the like. Also wants make up and other artifacts, and the **catalogs** of the companies that manufacture or distribute them. He DOES NOT WANT black stereotype items, only those with reference to minstrel shows or minstrelsy itself. Nor does he want black history books or items, cheap joke books. Jack also does not want items about Eddie Cantor, Al Jolson, or other blackface performers who did not work in a minstrel company.
> Jack Fleming
> 1825 Vine Street #2
> Berkeley, CA 94703
> (510) 526-4565

◆ **Minstrel memorabilia** of all sorts. "I'll buy playbills, autographs, letters written by minstrels, news clippings, postcards, posters, radio and TV programs, rare book and magazine articles, recordings, and miscellaneous artifacts." He can send you a lengthy wants list. Norm recreates minstrel shows and is a serious historian of this entertainment profession.
> Norman Conrad
> PO Box 184
> East Walpole, MA 02032
> (508) 668-6926 eves   <miniminstrel@yahoo.com>

◆ **Ventriloquist's memorabilia** including:
• Old puppets used professionally by ventriloquists;
• **Photos** of ventriloquists;
• **Books** about ventriloquism printed before 1970 (there are a goodly number of these that he seeks, so inquire);
• Event **posters** depicting ventriloquist's performances;
• Movie posters featuring ventriloquists.
Not interested in items made after 1970. He does not buy phonograph records of any sort, nor is he interested in toy puppets. He asks you to describe the item's condition and asks that you price what you have. He will make offers to amateur sellers only.
> Nick Pawlow
> PO Box 11343
> Philadelphia, PA 19137
> (215) 537-0558   (215) 309-0580

◆ **Ventriloquist's dummies, ephemera, photos and other items** related to early ventriloquism. Frequently closed, they can be difficult to reach; don't count on phone calls being returned too quickly.
> Ann Roberts, Vent Haven Museum
> 33 West Maple Avenue
> Ft. Mitchell, KY 41011
> (606) 341-0461 and leave message

◆ **Theater programs.** Please send a Xerox™ of the cover and indicate the date of the performance if you can (and if it's not shown on the cover). Clean complete items only, with a preference for older programs from the early NY stage.

> Harvey Dolin
> Mezzanine floor
> 111 Fulton Street
> New York, NY 10038
> > (212) 267-0216

◆ **Theater programs** and souvenirs especially items related to an anniversary such as 50th performance, 100th performance, closing performance, and the like. In general, he is mostly interested in theatrical productions from before 1920, but will consider others.

> Drew Eliot
> 400 West 43rd Street   #25-T
> New York, NY 10036
> > (212) 563-5444

◆ **Follies Bergere** programs and other items from before 1940. Make a photocopy of the cover, and "tell me how many photos it has" as part of your description. He only wants to buy "complete items, with nothing removed, please."

> Gary Bart
> 620 Siena Way
> Los Angeles, CA 90077
> > (310) 471-6980   fax (310) 471-1910

◆ **Theatrical lighting from the gaslight era.** "I'll buy anything relating to 19th century gas, oil or candle stage lighting. This includes actual lamps and parts, prints showing them in use, manuals, catalogs, or other written material containing lighting information up to about 1940. I am especially interested in limelight or calcium light spotlights. Some carbon-arc lamps and carbon rods are of interest, but most electrical stage lighting is too new to interest me.   I am gathering materials for educational purposes and would be grateful if people could set the price they want."

> Lindsay Lambert
> 41 Bellwood Avenue
> Ottawa, ON Canada K1S 1S6
> > (613) 730-7797

CIRCUS & OTHER AMUSEMENTS

◆ **Wild West show** items including posters, handbills, letterhead, photos, and cowboy and cowgirl outfits. Will buy anything in fine condition that can be tied to a show or one of its famous performers like Annie Oakley or Buffalo Bill including belt buckles, watch fobs, holsters, etc., except he does not want saddles, and specifies that he is not interested in rodeo items. You must send a photo or Xerox™ of what you wish to sell. Dealers price your goods. Amateurs may request offer.
> Emory Cantey, Jr.
> Our Turn Antiques
> 1405 Ems Road East
> Fort Worth, TX 76116
> (817) 737-0430 voice/ fax   <ourturn@swbell.net>

◆ **Emmett Kelly and Emmett Kelly, Jr.,** items related to their "Weary Willie the Clown" character including porcelain figurines, dolls, souvenirs, advertising, books, photos, posters, programs, and what have you. Does not want Emmett Kelly Senior items currently being made by Staton Arts, or Dave Grossman. A photograph "makes sure we are all talking about the same item." No other clowns.
> Nollie Neill, Jr.
> PO Box 38
> Ennice, NC 28623
> fax (336) 657-8084   <saddlemtn@skybest.com>

◆ **Circus ephemera.** "I'll buy anything directly related to circuses, especially Barnum & Bailey, but other tented shows as well. I want posters, programs, photos, route books, etc., but only before 1940."
> Al Mordas
> 66 Surrey Drive
> Bristol, CT 06010

◆ **Chalk carnival prizes.** Wants cartoon characters like *Popeye, Wimpy, Olive Oyl, Barney Google*, etc., as well as movie and radio stars, hula girls, nudes, fan dancers, sailors, cowboys, etc. Seeks figures marked Jenkins, Rainwater, Venice Dolls, or Gittins. No animals are wanted unless they are part of a larger collection containing desirable figures. His two volume illustrated price guide to *The Carnival Chalk Prize* are available for $15 each.
> Thomas Morris
> PO Box 8307
> Medford, OR 97504
> (541) 779-3164   <chalkman@cdsnet.net>

◆ **Amusement park memorabilia:** catalogs, brochures, photos, tickets, stationery, sheet music, letterheads, pennants, tokens, advertisements, books, postcards and anything else. Appreciates a nice clear photo or a photocopy (Xerox©) of what you have. Especially interested in items from before 1940, but will consider interesting or unusual later items.

Jim Abbate
7936 Park Ave.
Skokie, IL 60077
(847) 675-4511   <amuspark@aol.com>

◆ **Roller coaster and amusement park memorabilia** including official or amateur photos, prints, blueprints, postcards, souvenirs, home movies and anything else, no matter how small or odd, that is remotely related to roller coasters or amusement parks. Check your family photo album, because even snapshots may find a buyer in Tom.

Thomas Keefe
PO Box 464
Tinley Park, IL 60477
fax (708) 349-0722

◆ **Disneyland souvenirs** and memorabilia from the California park before 1980. Wants maps, guidebooks, tickets, food wrappers, brochures, ceramic items, special event programs, posters, passes, postcards, your personal color or b/w snapshots, and what have you. Nothing from Florida's Walt Disney World is wanted.

Linda Cervon
10074 Ashland Street
Ventura, CA 93004
(805) 659-4405   fax (805) 659-4776
<hopey4@earthlink.net>

◆ **Disneyland souvenirs.** Dean will buy all types including ceramic figurines, guidebooks, maps, buttons, pins, coins, postcards, employee materials, etc. All items should be marked disneyland. Also will buy *Disneykins,* tiny one to two inch high plastic figurines of Disney characters sold by Marx in the 1950's and 60's. Also will buy anything related to Tinker Belle. Special wants include Disneyland items from 1955-59, a *Tinker Belle Glow-in-the-Dark Wand,* and Walt Disney's autograph. Everything must be in mint to near mint condition. Items may be sent on approval or described in writing if you want an offer.

Dean Mancina
PO Box 2274
Seal Beach, CA 90740
(310) 431-5671 voice/fax   <dsnelnd@aol.com>

◆ **Mardi Gras souvenirs,** tokens, and other ephemera are wanted, especially pre-1900 ball invitations and colorful Carnival Bulletins originally printed in local newspapers. Hardy and his wife are always looking for photographs, postcards, early magazine articles, and other items from New Orleans before 1940 which they can reproduce in their annual *Mardi Gras Guide.* Please inquire about all illustrated items and this prominent New Orleans collector will help you with pricing.

>Arthur Hardy
>PO Box 19500
>New Orleans, LA 70179
>>(504) 838-6111   fax (504) 838-0100

◆ **Mardi Gras.** Specializes in Mardi Gras invitations and dance cards before 1950 from **New Orleans and other cities**, but also buys newspaper carnival bulletins, pennants, postcards, pins, buttons, metal badges, and colorful paper ephemera. "If you need any assistance, please write or call."

>Marilyn Bordelon
>Enoch's Gallery
>1750 St. Charles Avenue #303
>New Orleans, LA 70130
>>(504) 596-6550

◆ **Carnegie Hall memorabilia.** Seeking relics of its own past, the Carnegie Hall Corporation wants especially to find programs and stagebills from 1892-98, 1929-31 and 1944-45. Also photos of the building in construction, or any interior shots of performers or speakers on stage. Since private parties are not permitted to take photos inside Carnegie Hall, but do anyway, amateur snapshots may be the only visual record of a performance. The Corporation also wants recordings, films and posters of events as well as any historical records on paper. Interested in ephemera from any type of performance: drama, dance, music, comedy, vaudeville, you name it, Carnegie's seen it.

>Gino Francesconi
>Carnegie Hall Corporation
>881 Seventh Avenue
>New York, NY 10019
>>(212) 903-9629

TONY'S TIP: SELLING RADIOS AND TV SETS

Valuable radios and television sets are difficult for most people to recognize. Radios worth $500 are sometimes thrown away by people who keep other radios worth $50 because they looked more valuable.

"Get advice," is good advice.

The folks who buy old radios and televisions like to know the brand name, model name and number and cosmetic condition (what does the radio look like?). Describe whether it is scratched, faded, dented, chipped, cracked, or the paint or veneer is peeling.   Examine the chassis carefully for missing parts or damage. If the chassis has blank spots where a component or tube might have originally been, tell the potential buyer.

Radios and TV sets are among those few collectible items that do not have to be in perfect condition to find a buyer. Certainly, the better the condition, the better the price, but scarce radios and television sets will sell in almost any condition, because parts are always in demand by people who enjoy rebuilding them. That's not true of transistor radios, which must be in fine cosmetic condition (must look good) to be sellable. Whether they work or not is irrelevant.

Plastic table model radios can bring from $50 to $1,000 and transistor radios can top $100. The most valuable radios are those covered with blue or other color of glass. Large glass radios are $10,000 and up.

Do not test old electric equipment. Plugging it in may cause serious damage because insulation around wires deteriorates, resulting in short circuits or fire.

Buyers will arrange for packing and shipping of these bulky yet fragile items.

RADIOS

◆ **Radios of many types** 1905-40, including crystal sets, wireless receivers and transmitters, battery operated radios 1914-1928, and small electric table models 1928-35. Buys radios in wood, metal, or plastic cabinets. Especially interested in large collections of usable speakers, tubes and parts for radios from this period. No large console models of the 30's except those with chrome plated interiors. Also radio magazines, catalogs, service manuals, sales literature, and advertising, pre-1935, including novelties, radio dealer promotional items, and anything shaped like or depicting a radio such as banks, toys, pin back buttons, games, postcards, and dealer promotional items. Gary formerly published *Antique Radio Classified.*

> Gary Schneider
> 14310 Ordner Drive
> Strongsville, OH 44136
>   (216) 251-3714 days   (216) 582-3094 eves
>   <gbsptop@aol.com>

◆ **Radios of many types** including crystal sets, battery sets of the 1920's (usually in long rectangular boxes), wireless sets and parts, WWI military radios, unusual cathedral radios by *Grebe* or *Ozarka,* grandfather clock style, odd shapes, and all luxury models like *Zenith Stratosphere* (pays $6,000+). Other names and models to watch for are *Atwater Kent, McMurdo Silver, Marconi, De Forest, Leutz, Wireless Specialty, Norden Hauck, E.H. Scott, Grebe,* and *RCA Radiolas.* Also novelty radios like Snow White or the World's Fair. In addition, he likes radio dealer indoor and outdoor advertising signs, point of purchase displays, brochures, instruction books, service manuals, parts and radio magazines. Not interested in plastic radios of any kind. Don is former editor of *Radio Age* magazine. Don is a collector rather than a dealer but will consider buying large collections.

> Donald Patterson
> 636 Cambridge Road
> Augusta, GA 30909
>   (706) 738-7227   <thepatters@mindspring.com>

◆ **Old radios, tubes, test equipment, open frame motors, generators and other electrical apparatus,** switch board meters, knife switches, neon signs, fans, Tesla coils, quack medical devices, and electric trains and accessories, as well as early books on radio and electrical theory and practice. Give info from the item's ID plate. Include a sketch or photo. Phone or email only.

> Hank Andreoni
> California
>   (909) 849-7539   <hankjoy@webtv.net>

◆ **Radios** from the 1900 to 1955, including:
- Crystal and 1 or 2 tube radios, factory or home made;
- Radios with comic or pop-culture characters;
- Brightly colored *Bakelite* radios from the 1930's and 40's;
- Mirrored radios ($1,000 to $40,000 for a like new floor model);
- Black and chrome radios made by *RCA* or *Majestic;*
- 1950's pocket transistor radios;
- Tuners and other quality audio equipment by *Scott, MacIntosh,* and others. "If it's too heavy to pick up, I want it."

Harry says he'll buy the complete contents of a ham shack, radio collector or Radio/TV shop. "If you send a photo and an SASE, I'll give you a free evaluation. If I want it, I'll pay to have it picked up."
Harry Poster
PO Box 1883
South Hackensack, NJ 07606
(201) 794-9606   fax (201) 794-9553   <hposter@worldnet.att.net>

◆ **Wireless, crystal sets, and battery radios** from before 1930 such as *Atwater Kent, Crosley, Amrad, Deforest, Federal, Grebe, Kennedy, Firth, Paragon, Marconi, R.C.A.,* and *Zenith.* Also early vacuum tubes with brass or Bakelite base. Also *Jenkins* scanning disc television. Also all wireless and radio books and magazines printed before 1930. Also radio advertising, parts, relays, earphones, horn speakers, amplifiers, batteries, meters, etc. Will pay $500 for a *Marconi* CA294, $600 for a *Marconi* 106, $800+ for a *Pacific Wireless Specialty* audio receiver, and some others to $2,000. "I do not want anything made after 1940, floor model radios, or transistor radios."
David Shanks
115 Baldwin Street
Bloomfield, NJ 07003
(973) 748-8820

◆ **Mirrored glass radios.** "I'm especially fond of green mirrored glass radios and forever trying to acquire *Sparton* floor model mirrored glass radios (model 1186). I pay through the nose if I have to." That translates to as much as $35,000 for a perfect condition peach colored glass and up to $30,000 for a perfect blue glass radio. Glass covered radios do not have to work and the glass may be cracked as "I don't turn down mirrored glass radios offered to me." He claims to outbid anybody, and points out that he will either come pick up any radio or have it professionally moved so you don't have to worry about shipping. He also buys **colorful plastic radios** of the 1930's and 40's. He prefers you to price but will make offers if you seriously intend to sell.
Ed Sage
PO Box 13025
Albuquerque, NM 87192
(505) 298-0840

◆ **Radios with wood cabinets.** Give make and model number, condition, and price. Does not make offers.
>Alvin Heckard
>165 Orchard Grove Ave.
>Lewistown, PA 17044
>>(717) 248-7071   <aheckard@nittanylink.com>

◆ **Radios made in Eastern Europe or elsewhere around the world.** Seeks information, schematics, and radios worldwide, especially from former Soviet Bloc countries.
>Richard Brill
>PO Box 5367
>Old Bridge, NJ 08857
>>(732) 607-0299   <rgbent.com>

◆ **Radios from before 1950 bought, sold, appraised, and restored.** Offers professional restoration of electric components as well as cabinets for all tube type table and console radios.
>Bob Eslinger
>Antique Radio Restoration
>20 Gary School Road
>Pomfret Center, CT 06259   <radiodoc@neca.com>

◆ **Microphones,** 1940-1960, but only the short stand-up desk type mics used by broadcasters and radio stations. Especially wants to find microphones with the station or network letters still attached.
>Charles Martignette
>PO Box 293
>Hallandale, FL 33008
>>(954) 454-3474

HI-FI EQUIPMENT

◆ **Early tube high fidelity equipment** 1947-1960 especially monaural but also some early stereo from companies such as *Dynaco, Marantz, Fisher, McIntosh, Scott, Eico, Altec Lansing, JBL,* etc. Most makes and models are wanted, working or not, complete or for parts, as well as tubes, loudspeakers, schematics, manuals and hi-fi magazines. Of special interest are all early *McIntosh* amps. Nothing after 1970, "but I'll buy a wide range of things relating to early audio, from broadcast equipment to home systems."
>Jack Smith
>288 Winter Street
>North Andover, MA 01845
>>(978) 686-7250   <tia1910@yahoo.com>

◆ **Early tube-type stereo and hi-fi equipment** made by *McIntosh, Marantz, Dynaco, H.H. Scott, Western Electric, Heath, Leak, Harman Kardon, Acrosound, Altec-Lansing.* Also any manuals or literature for this equipment. Also want large audio transformers by *Acrosound* like their model TO-300. Old microphones from the 1930's to 50's by *RCA, Shure, Western Electric, Astatic, Turner,* and *Electrovoice.*

    Jeff Viola
    784 Eltone Road
    Jackson, NJ 08527
        (732) 928-0666

◆ **Early tube high fidelity equipment** including stereo and mono amplifiers, pre-amps, tuners (especially *McIntosh, Marantz, Western Electric* and *Quad*), large old speakers (especially *Altec, JBL, Tannoy, Western Electric,* and *Jensen*). Also radios before 1920, vacuum tubes, homemade amplifiers and kits by *UTC, Dynaco,* and *Heath,* movie theater sound equipment (including amps, speakers, and microphones), antique electrical, electronic, telephonic, and telegraphic items. Also wants old hi-fi magazines, books, and other literature. Does not want "department store console stereos" from Sears, Silvertone, Wards, etc., television tubes, or any TV's made after 1940. Give the maker's name, model number, cosmetic condition (what it looks like in terms of scratches, dents, etc.), and whether the original literature is included.

    Vernon Vogt
    330 SW 43rd Street #247
    Renton, WA 98055
        (202) 318-4321 voice/fax   <vcvmav@webtv.net>

◆ **Tube-type hi-fi equipment** including:
  • Amplifiers by *McIntosh, Marantz, Dynaco, Fisher, Scott,* etc.;
  • Audio tubes 2A3, KT-88, KT-66, 6550, 12AX7, etc.;
  • *Hickok* audio tube testers 539C, 580, 752, TV-7, TV-10, etc.;
  • 15" Hi-Fi speakers;
  • Recording studio limiters/equalizers by *Fairchild, Pultec,* others;
  • Record cutting machines by *Fairchild* and many others.
Describe what you have fully, including all information on the ID plate. Note if any tubes are missing or if anything seems damaged.

    Mr. Kim Gutzke
    7134 15th Avenue S
    Minneapolis, MN 55423
  (612) 866-6183   fax (612) 798-4169   <kgutzke@mn.rr.com>

TRANSISTOR RADIOS

◆ **Pocket-size radios,** 5" x 7" or smaller. "If they fit in a shirt or coat pocket, I'm interested, whether they are tube, transistor, or crystal radios. I want the old ones made in the USA or Japan between 1954 and 1964. I collect for appearance and for history. I like cute colorful radios with interesting shapes on the front such as boomerangs, arrows, etc. I do not care if your radio works and will buy useful ones in any condition, but prefer they be complete and without chips or cracks. Radios with their original boxes and papers especially appeal to me." The most valuable radios are the Regency TR-1, a 1954 radio from Indianapolis, and the earliest *Sony* transistors, such as the TR-55, TR-52, TR-2K, TR-33, TR-6, and TR-66. **A perfect condition *Sony* TR-55 would bring $750 and you'd make $250 for a *Regency*.** To sell your radio, give the brand name, model number, color, and country of origin. If your radio has no model number, Xerox™ the front. Important: **he does not want radios made in Hong Kong, Taiwan or Korea** or radios that claim to have 10 or more transistors.

Eric Wrobbel
20802 Exhibit Court
Woodland Hills, CA 91367
(818) 884-2282   <ewrrobbel@aol.com>

◆ **Pocket transistor radios.** Has a particular interest in the *Hoffman Trans-Solar,* offering to pay $250 each for fine specimens in various colors. "I don't want anything not in good cosmetic condition, but it doesn't matter whether they work or not. Give the make and model number (which you will probably have to open the case to get) or make a Xerox™ of the front of the radio and describe the color.

Mike Brooks
7335 Skyline
Oakland, CA 94611
(510) 339-1751   <miniwave@aol.com>

TONY'S TIP ABOUT RADIO CONDITION: *Collectors of transister radios care far more about how the radio looks than whether or not it plays, so no need to find batteries. In fact, if batteries are in your unused radio, take them out because they could cause damage. Collectors DO NOT WANT transistor radios made in Hong Kong, Taiwan or Korea. They DO WANT those made in the United States, England, Japan and European countries.*

TELEVISION SETS

◆ Early television sets. "I'll buy old or unusual TV's, such as:
  • All 1920-1940 scanning disc or electronic (paying to $10,000);
  • 1940's sets with 3", 7" or 10" tubes ($50-$1,000);
  • 1950's sets in unusual shapes and styles;
  • 1946-1956 sets with 9" -19" tubes and color adapters;
  • 1960-1980 unusually shaped transistor TV's;
  • 1980's LVD TV's like *Epson* Elf, *Sony* KV4000, etc.;
  • Dealer displays for TV's, catalogs, signs, neon, promotions, etc.;
  • All books and manuals about TV printed before 1940.
"Mechanical TV's are often mistaken for early electronic junk," he cautions, "so look for 12" metal disks containing tiny holes that spin in front of a neon glow lamp. These early TV's drew their sound from radio sets, and most had no cabinets. Also interested in mirror-in-lid sets by *Pilot, Andrea, Philco, RCA, GE, Garod,* and *Zenith.* I also buy *Fada* and *Meissner* 5" kit televisions. "I am willing to buy an entire TV shop, attic, or estate to get one TV I want." Harry offers free evaluations of TV sets if you send him a good photo and SASE.
> Harry Poster
> PO Box 1883
> South Hackensack, NJ 07606
>   (201) 794-9606   fax (201) 794-9553
>   <hposter@worldnet.att.net>

◆ **Television sets** from 1938 to 1950 especially those with a reflective mirror in the lid and only four or five channels such as the *RCA* TT-5, *RCA* TRK-9 or TRK-12, *GE* HM-225, *GE* HM-275 and the *GE* HM 171 (worth $2,000 each). Television sets from 1946 to 1950 with screen sizes of 7" and 10" are worth from $75 to $250 for nice sets. Also wants sales literature and dealer promotions.
> Donald Patterson
> 636 Cambridge Road
> Augusta, GA 30909
>   (706) 738-7227   <thepatters@mindspring.com>

TONY'S TIP: WHAT TV'S ARE GOOD AND WHERE TO LOOK:
Look for TV sets that have channel one, or that have no channels higher than seven. The earliest sets (1923-1939) are hard to identify as they don't look much like TV's. You are most likely to find early TV's in those cities where TV began: Los Angeles, New York, Chicago, Philadelphia, and Schenectady. We're a mobile society and they could turn up anywhere, however.

TONY'S TIPS ON SELLING MUSICAL ITEMS

Music collectibles fall into five categories, each type sought by different collectors.

*(1) **Musical instruments** can be valuable, especially quality guitars and violins. To sell any instrument, you need to state the maker and the model, and describe the type and quality of finish. Mention all cracks, dents, and the like. If you have a piano or organ to sell, no national market exists so it is best to offer it for sale in a local classified ad.*

*(2) **Mechanical music** refers to phonographs, record players, player pianos, music boxes, and other devices which play music by mechanical means. Describing what you have is usually a matter of taking a good photograph, listing all the information on the maker's ID plate, and describing the condition. Buyers of juke boxes, a form of mechanical music, are considered part of the "Coin-Op" world and are listed in Trash or Treasure on pages 215-219.*

*(3) **Sheet music** collectors are more concerned with the picture on the cover than with the musical content, so classical music and school scores are not of interest. Music must be in exceptionally fine condition, free of significant tears, writing, or other damage.*

*(4) **Phonograph records** are seldom exceptionally valuable, with most records still selling for $5 to $10 retail. Don't let the fact your records are worth only a dollar or two discourage you. Records come in piles, and can add up! Record buyers want to know the title, artist, record label, and catalog number (there's one on every record). Note the condition of the record, the record jacket, and the paper sleeve. Records in mint condition are preferred by collectors, but a few early 78's have never been found in perfect condition. If it lists for more than $15 in Les Docks' "American Premium Record Guide" collectors may want it even if it looks a little beat up.*

*(5) **Memorabilia of music**, musicians and singers is like other Pop Culture items. Rare, colorful, and in fine condition describes what collectors want.*

MUSICAL INSTRUMENTS

◆ **Fretted stringed musical instruments** such as banjos, guitars, mandolins, ukuleles, and the like. "A *Martin* D-45 guitar made prior to 1942 could sell for as much as $100,000," so instruments are worth selling properly. **Also related memorabilia such as manufacturer's catalogs, old photos of guitar shops and players, accessories, etc.** State the preservation of your instrument. Examine carefully for repairs. Look for any signs that it might not be original. Mention the type and condition of the instrument's case. Offers a monthly 24 page catalog of used instruments for $15 per year. "We display more than 2,000 instruments and offer free catalogs of new merchandise."

> Stan Werbin
> Elderly Instruments
> 1100 North Washington Dept. TT
> Lansing, MI 48906
>   (517) 372-7880 ext 102   fax (517) 372-5155
>   <swerbin@elderly.com>

◆ **Most string, wood, and brass musical instruments** are of interest for trade or resale. "I'll buy any museum quality instrument." For his own collection he wants instruments that are rare, very old, pretty, unique or hand crafted. He especially wants **trumpets or cornets that have extra keys,** fewer keys, or keys that are in unusual positions or shapes. Also **instruments of other cultures** including African, Asian, Pacific, etc., but no pianos or organs. A photo should go with a complete description, including all labels or markings.

> Sid Glickman
> PO Box 434
> Riverdale, NY 10471
> (718) 548-6008 voice/fax   <sidglick@earthlink.net>

TONY'S TIPS: TO SELL AN INSTRUMENT, YOU NEED TO

(1) State the maker and the model;
(2) Describe the type and quality of the finish;
(3) Give an indication of its condition. Include mention of all cracks, dents, scratches and the like.

If something seems unusual to you, make a sketch or include a photo. If you have a piano or organ to sell, unless it's a concert grade Steinway, there is no national market and it is usually best to offer it for sale in a local classified ad.

★ **American guitars, banjos, and mandolins** made by the following: *C.F. Martin, Gibson, Fender* (older models only), *Dobro, National, D'Angelico, B&D (Bacon & Day), Epiphone* (older), *Paramount, Vega, Fairbanks, SS Stewart, Washburn, Lyon & Healy, Stromberg, Gretsch, D'Aquisto* and *Rickenbacker.* "If you have fine condition instruments for sale by these makers you may call us collect for an offer. Have your instrument in your hand. Be prepared to answer specific questions about condition, originality, serial number, color, and the type of case it has. Without this information, we cannot provide meaningful evaluation. Serious sellers only may call collect. All others are welcome to call for advice or information." Among instruments Jay would most like to find are the *Martin* D-45 with abalone inlay, the electric *Gibson* Les Paul Standard made in 1958-60, and *Gibson* Mastertone banjos made during the late 1930's. Dates and models are very important. "Another model made at the same time might be worth only 1/20 as much. Original condition matters a lot." Offers an interesting catalog of high quality new and used instruments. Wants list available.

    Stan Jay
    Mandolin Bros.
    629 Forest Avenue
    Staten Island, NY 10310
  (718) 981-8585   (718) 981-3226   fax (718) 816-4416
  <mandolin@mandoweb.com> <http://www.mandoweb.com>

◆ **Stringed fretted musical instruments** including electric and acoustic guitars, banjos, mandolins and ukuleles. **No ukelins or mandolin-harps,** please. He buys the following brands of guitar: *D'Angelico, Gibson Les Paul, Martin, Stromberg National, Epiphone, Fender, Gretsch,* and *Rickenbacker.* Many guitars purchased for $100-$300 in the 1950's are worth five to ten times as much today, and a *Martin* D-45 would bring from $20,000 to $50,000. Buys gold plated four-string banjos and fancy five string banjos by *Fairbanks, Vega, Epiphone, Gibson, Weymann, Slingerland, Bacon & Day, Studio King, Recording King, Paramount,* and others. Mandolins by *Gibson, Martin* and *Washburn* are wanted, as are ukuleles by *Martin* and *Gibson.* Photos of the front and back of your instrument are requested. Pays all shipping costs. Appraisal services are available.

    Steve Senerchia
    The Music Man
    91 Tillinghast Ave.
    Warwick, RI 02886
        (401) 821-2865   <shortsonhighway@yahoo.com>

TONY'S TIP: Maker, models and finish are important in determining the value of any stringed instrument.

★ **High quality Italian violins and some of their imitators** are the prime interest of this 20 year veteran West coast dealer. Cremona school violins, 1650-1750, can be worth from $2,500 to $100,000 or more, but many copies exist. Jones will consider better French instruments and **your fake "Stradivarius" violins.** Most of the fake "Strads" sell for $100 or less, but a few more valuable "fake Strads" were made by fine craftsmen who affixed the Stradivarius label in an effort to sell the instrument. A few were high quality reproductions of the master's work, deliberately copied in homage to his craftsmanship. Many other guitars, banjos, basses, violas, and mandolins can be fairly valuable to Jones if you have one of better quality. It takes years of handling violins to be able to recognize originals or instruments of value. For this reason "it is difficult to buy through the mail, but not impossible." The reputation of the maker and the condition of the instrument are crucial in determining value. To sell a stringed instrument, you must describe all damage, the type and quality of finish, the bow, and give every word on the label. In many cases, he will request seeing the instrument before making a final offer. **No Oriental instruments are wanted.**

David N. Jones' Violin Shop
6911 Engineers Road
Julian, CA 92036
(760) 765-0887   <violins@inreach.com>

◆ **French and Italian violins, violas, and cellos.** "I'll pay high prices for quality instruments, both commercial and handmade from anywhere in the world, but especially France and Italy. I don't want children's or school violins nor any imitations of Stradivarius, Guarnerius, or other masters." Describe the label inside the instrument. Appraisal services are available.

Robert Portukalian's Violin Shop
1279 North Main Street
Providence, RI 02904
(401) 521-5145

TONY'S TIP: *Many readers own violins with labels proclaiming them to be made by Stradivarius in the 1700's. These are usually cottage industry pieces made in Germany at the turn of the century for Sears Roebuck, who sold them from $3 to $9 in their catalog. All genuine Stradivarius instruments are accounted for. A few "fake Strads" are quality instruments and can command a few hundreds dollars or more.*

◆ **Vintage saxophones by King, Selmer, Buescher, Martin and Conn as well as other useful woodwind and brass instruments** of all types as long as they are in good condition. In addition to saxes, he buys playable clarinets, bassoons, flutes, oboes, trumpets, French horns, trombones, tubas, Sousaphones, etc. **Will buy both student and professional instruments, and is particularly interested in useful 20th century instruments**, though will buy antique ones as well. "I don't want terribly beat up remains of horns, or student horns with lots of dents or poor quality finish. The price I offer reflects both the quality and condition of an instrument." Give the type of instruments, the maker, the serial number and any stamped or engraved information on the instruments. Describe the type and color of finish and its cosmetic condition (what it looks like). **Tom is a full time dealer in used contemporary playable instruments.**

> Tom Goodwin
> 621 Hancock Street
> Edwardsville, IL 62025
> (618) 692-9736 voice/fax

◆ **Brass musical instruments,** especially the unusual and obsolete. He wants "to know about all your old brass instruments since they all look the same to the untrained." Among other instruments, he especially wants a B-flat cornet with the bell pointing over the shoulder and a Schreiber horn with a straight up bell. He is attempting to assemble a representative collection of the hundreds of different brass instruments. Also interested in band related memorabilia such as photos of bands or individual musicians holding instruments, band programs, catalogs of instruments, mouthpieces, decorative or unusual wooden music stands, and old-style conducting batons. Also interested in your coffin shaped wooden instrument cases. If you regularly sell musical instruments, get his informative illustrated wants list.

> Jonathan Korzun
> 206 Michigan Avenue
> Dowagiac, MI 49047
> (616) 782-5594 eves   <jonkorzun@beanstalk.net>

◆ **Brass musical instruments** made in the 19th century U.S., especially keyed bugles and instruments which hang over the shoulder, worth $600 and up. **He does not want saxophones or modern brass instruments.** Give the maker's name, the number of valves, the shape of the instrument and whether it is made of brass or silver. Include a photo or drawing of the shape of the instrument. He also wants photos of bands and bandsmen as well as old instrument catalogs.

> Mark Jones
> PO Box 98
> Eden, NY 14057
> (716) 992-2074 voice/fax   <jonesmj@aol.com>

◆ **Rare and unusual musical instruments** including harps, bagpipes, hurdy-gurdies, wooden flutes, concertinas, ethnic instruments, and all manner of brass and woodwinds, stringed instruments, dulcimers, autoharps, and others. **No keyboards** except a folding "preacher's organ." Mickie repairs instruments and will purchase good ones in "any restorable condition." Can make arrangements for consignment selling of instruments he doesn't wish to buy. This 20 year veteran conducts annual seminars on musical instrument history and performance. He charges reasonable rates for insurance appraisals, and will make offers. An extensive illustrated catalog may be ordered for $3. Has no interest in accordions, pianos, pump or electric organs, or ukelins.

> Mickie Zekley
> Lark in the Morning
> PO Box 1176
> Mendocino, CA 95460
> (707) 964-5569 <mickie@larkinam.com>

◆ **Drums and drum catalogs** from the early 1900's to 1970. Buys sets or single tom toms, bass drums, or snare drums, and buys uncracked cymbals marked "K.Zildjian" but not those made by "A.Zildjian." To save everyone effort, a thorough and complete inspection of your instrument should be done before contacting them. Check and note modifications and/or damage of any kind including scratches, cracks, peeling, bulging, holes drilled, rim warp, rust, pitting, stains, or discoloration. Information needed to evaluate your drum(s): the brand name, shape and color of the ID emblem, the diameter of the head(s), the depth of each drum's shell (not including the rims), and the color and type of finish of the drum(s) on both the outside and inside. Does not buy drums or drum catalogs produced after 1970, exotic or ethnic drums, or parade basses. He requests "serious inquiries only, please. Kindly keep in mind that we do not offer appraisals or estimates by mail or phone. If you have no idea of the value of your item(s), I'll give you a retail price range that your item sells for in the vintage drum market and then request you quote me your wholesale asking price. I'm willing to educate sellers so they can make an informed decision and determine a fair price, keeping in mind that we must recondition items, resell them, and make a profit." One of the world's largest dealers in collectible drums, Vintage Drum Center publishes a quarterly catalog, available free to drum buyers. Encourages you to visit his website for more information about drums and prices.

> Ned Ingberman
> Vintage Drum Center
> 2243 Ivory Drive
> Libertyville, IA 52567
> (641) 693-8691 (questions and appraisals)   fax (641) 693-3101
> (800) 729-3111 ext 5 (buy or sell only)
> <vintagedrum@lisco.com> <www.vintagedrum.com>

◆ **Harmonicas and related items.** Seeking unusual ones other than the standard 10 hole 4" long instrument: harmonicas with attached horns, bells, or whistles, those joined together with other harmonicas, those mounted in brass funnel-shaped resonators, and instruments that are smaller than 2" long or larger than 12" long. He also wants:
- Toy instruments with harmonicas built inside;
- Canes with built-in harmonicas;
- Blow accordions (clarinet-like instruments with keys which when depressed make a harmonica note or chord);
- Advertising, display cases, posters, magazines;
- Catalogs with pages of harmonicas pictured;
- Records (old), sheet music, lapel pins, and what have you.

No instruments in poor playing condition or that have bad rust or dents. Provide the maker, model, number of holes, length, width, whether it is double sided, whether all notes play, physical condition and (very important) whether the box is included. Photocopy of both sides helpful. Dealers must price your goods. Amateurs who are actually selling may inquire as to value before shipment.

Alan Bates
426 Bayberry Lane
West Grove, PA 19390
(800) 597-7012   (610) 345-0601   <harmonicas@compuserve.com>

◆ **Selmer saxophones** made between 1924 - 1977 with serial numbers 22000 through 276000 (serial numbers are found on back-lower area beneath the thumb rest). A few other brands of sax are wanted, notably some models of Conn, Buescher and Yamaha. Large dents, welds and heavy scratches reduce the value. Mouthpieces can be valuable if made by Links, Meyers, Larsens, Dukoffs, Brilhart and a few others. He will appraise, buy, sell, or trade your sax or mouthpiece. Write or call giving details of what you have.

Ed Hakal
10126 Signal Butte Circle
Sun City, AZ 85373
(623) 972-3091   fax (623) 933-5484

◆ **Cigar box musical instruments.** Any musical instrument made from a cigar box is considered. When describing your item, please include any of the instrument's history you know. Mention whether strings, pegs, bow and carry bag are present, and describe any applied or painted decorations. Photo is essential. Also buys some **toys and other items made from boxes,** especially items which retain their basic "boxness" rather than items made from cut up pieces of boxes.

Tony Hyman
PO Box 3028
Pismo Beach, CA 93448
<thyman@fix.net>

◆ **Musical instruments,** but only the following types:
- **Older "name brand" electric and acoustic guitars, banjos, amd mandolins,** especially Les Paul, Martin & Gibson;
- **Ukuleles** by Martin or those made from Hawaiian Koa wood;
- **Violins and bows** made in Italy, France or Germany. Please, no "Stradivarius" violins;
- **Tube type guitar amplifiers** especially Fender, Gibson, Standell, Marshall, or Vox;
- **Portable analog keyboards** from the 1960's and 70's;
- **Guitar effects pedals** from the 1960's or 70's;
- **Older snare drums and drum sets** from the 1930's to 60's;
- **Portable pianos** by Fender Rhodes or Wurlitzer.

Please give the following: type of instrument, brand name, model, year (if you know) amd condition rated on a 1-10 scale. Indicate whether it appears to be all original of if it was repaired or modified. This long time guitarist, songwriter, and dealer in fine instruments DOES NOT WANT Asian instruments, fake Strads, pianos, organs, or ukelins.

John Nelson
Guitars & Vintage Gear
1519 North Gardner Street
Hollywood, CA 90046
(323) 876-9862 days   (661) 722-4435 eves   <gnelson@gnet.com>

MECHANICAL MUSIC

◆ **Musical instruments that "play themselves"** by motor, springs, pneumatics or other means: music boxes, roller organs, cylinder music boxes, musical bird cages, nickelodeons, and organettes. Will buy rough condition items for parts or repair. Also musical disks, cylinders, piano rolls, old photos, postcards or paper ephemera depicting anything in mechanical music. Doug does not make offers.

Doug Negus
Phonograph Phunatic
215 Mason Street
Sutherland, IA 51058
            (712) 446-2270   <negus@midlands.net>

◆ **Horn phonographs** in any condition. Will buy complete machines or parts from any machine. Especially seeking: *Berliner Gramophone, National Gramophone, Universal Talking Machine, Zonophone* or *Victor.* Photos are helpful. All inquiries answered promptly.

Charlie Stewart
900 Grandview Avenue
Reno, NV 89503
            (775) 747-1439 days   <x14@worldnet.att.net>

◆ **Any pre-1930 device that plays music mechanically** including disk and cylinder music boxes, clocks and watches that play tunes, disk players, automata dolls, player organs, monkey organs, nickelodeons, horn phonographs in any condition from perfect to incomplete. Especially a barrel operated monkey organ with pipes ($2,000-$4,000), large disc music boxes that play more than one disc at a time ($10-$12,000), and cylinder music boxes with more than 175 teeth, and early musical watches. No player pianos are wanted, but most other mechanical devices bring $300 up. Give measurements of any disk or cylinder. Please include your phone number with correspondence.

Martin Roenigk
Mechantiques
75 Prospect Ave.
Eureka Springs, AR 72632
(479) 253-0405   cel (443) 831-6211   fax (479) 253-0406
<mroenigk@aol.com>

★ **Phonographs, music boxes, and related ephemera.** Would like to hear from you regarding all disc and cylinder phonographs with outside horns, especially those with wooden horns. Also floor model wind-up phonographs in deluxe or fancy cabinets. Also antique disc or cylinder music boxes, especially those that sit on the floor. Will pay from $200 to $10,000, depending on type, style, and condition. "I am also interested in purchasing old record catalogs, posters, metal signs, *Victor* dogs, needle tins, and the like. Phonograph related paper items before 1910 are especially desirable, particularly items associated with Thomas Edison." Send descriptions and photocopies. Kurt paid one Trash or Treasure reader a whopping $11,000 for their phonograph!

Kurt Nauck
Nauck's Vintage Records
6323 Inway Drive
Spring, TX 77389
(281) 370-7899   fax (425) 930-6862   <nauck@78rpm.com>

◆ **Antique music boxes and phonographs.** Wants all types, 1850-1920, including cylinder, disc, paper roll, and cob organs. Brands like *Regina, Mira, Stella, Symphonian,* and *Kalliope* are sought. Especially interested in a *Regina* Changer, a 15 1/2 inch upright music box which changes automatically. He'd pay $12,000 for a nice one. He wants to know the brand, model, size, and condition. Pictures are most helpful. Is not interested in "late miniature music boxes."

Chet Ramsay
2460 Strasburg Road
Coatesville, PA 19320
(610) 384-0514

◆ **Phonographs and related memorabilia** from before 1930 including cylinder and disc records, catalogs, needle tins, postcards, stereoviews depicting phonographs, toy phonographs, signs and other advertising except magazine ads. Also buys cylinder records of speeches by Taft, Teddy Roosevelt, and other famous people, for which he pays $10-$50. Also all material related to Thomas Edison. List make, model, and condition. Include label, artist, and title of records. SASE for offer.
> Steven Ramm
> 420 Fitzwater Street
> Philadelphia, PA 19147
> (215) 922-7050 eves <stevenramm@aol.com>

◆ **Phonographs with outside horns,** complete or for parts. No *Victrolas*. Alvin doesn't want to be bothered unless you're serious about selling. Does not make offers.
> Alvin Heckard
> 165 Orchard Grove Ave.
> Lewistown, PA 17044
> (717) 248-7071 <aheckard@nittanylink.com>

◆ *RCA* or *Capehart* **radio-phonographs that automatically flip records** over to play the other side. Pays $500-$700 for these large complicated machines from the 1930's. "If your machine weighs less than 75 pounds, I'm probably not interested." Take a photo of the record changing mechanism or give him a call.
> Joseph Weber
> 604 Centre Street
> Ashland, PA 17921
> (570) 875-4401 from 3 to 5 p.m.

◆ **Catalogs of phonograph records and piano rolls** published by record and piano roll companies, 1890 to 1960. Prefers to buy collections or very early pieces. No records, magazine ads, or damaged items. Tim is past president of the Association for Recorded Sound Collections, a national club for recording historians.
> Tim Brooks
> PO Box 31041 Glenville Station
> Greenwich, CT 06831
> <tbroo@aol.com>

◆ **Phonograph needle clippers and sharpeners.**
> Don Gorlick
> PO Box 24541
> Seattle, WA 98124
> <seashore8@hotmail.com>

Equipment for cutting records may be found on p. 393

SHEET MUSIC

◆ **Sheet music in small or large collections or accumulations.**
Primary interest is in popular music of the 20th century (1890-1970).
Movie and show tunes are of primary interest, but "also any music that
falls into any of the main collectible categories, like presidential, political, patriotic, war, transportation, cartoon, baseball, Coca-Cola, advertising, historical, Black related, and anything else that has interesting
cover art." Particularly likes to find music published by the ET Paull
Music Company, and will pay between $10 and $300, depending upon
the title and condition. Does not want to buy classical music or sheet
music designed for teaching. "If the person wants to sell the music as
a lot, I need to know quantity, condition, and the rough percentage of
movie, show, and pop tunes. I also want to know the percentage of large
format (11" x 14") and small format (9" x 12") music."

> Wayland Bunnell
> Clean Sheets
> 199 Tarrytown Road
> Manchester, NH 03103
>   (603) 668-5466   <wtarrytown@aol.com>

◆ **Old popular sheet music** from 1820-1970, with pictorial covers,
especially music or songs from movies, shows, WWI or WWII. Wants
ragtime, blues, Negro, ethnic music, political, historical, and particularly likes covers with baseball, cartoons, fire, aviation, and automobile
songs. No classical, teaching or religious, please. Also buys *Downbeat,
Metronome, Billboard* and movie magazines.

> Beverly Hamer
> PO Box 75
> East Derry, NH 03041
>   (603) 432-3528   <hamersheetmusic@aol.com>

Wayland Bunnell says "Please don't describe sheet
music as "good for its age" as that means fair or poor
condition. "Excellent" and "mint" are terms reserved
for music that has almost never seen the light of day,
music store stock, or publisher's remainder."

TONY'S TIP: Sheet music collectors are very fussy about
condition. **Don't waste their time and yours by offering
items in poor condition. They won't buy them!** When
trying to sell a few pieces of sheet music, a photocopy
is the best strategy, but with large quantities, follow
Wayland Bunnell's suggestions, giving quantity, general
condition, number of songs in each of the two sheet
music sizes, and the percentage of the pile that are
movie, show, and pop tunes.

◆ **Sheet music about WWI and WWII** in fine to mint condition. Also wants sheet music with pictures of Frank Sinatra or Presidents of the U.S. Also buys music by Charles K. Harris and Irving Berlin. Please send a Xerox© copy of what you have.

> Herman Rush
> 10773 Ojai-Santa Paula Road
> Ojai, CA 93023

◆ **Bound volumes of sheet music** from before 1900. Pays $1 or more per title for illustrated ones, but rare publishers bring more. Prefers bound books with no titles removed. **Also songbooks with oddly shaped notes**. "I'll pay $25+ for singing school books with notes that are oblong, triangular, rectangular or oddly shaped, especially those in good condition published before 1860. Authors of popular versions of these books include Funk, Carden, Davisson, Swan, and others."

> Jim Presgraves
> Bookworm & Silverfish
> PO Box 639
> Wytheville, VA 24382
> (276) 686-5813   fax (276) 686-6636
> <bookworm@naxs.com>

◆ **Sheet music.** "I am a general sheet music collector who buys music in 500+ categories, so I look for whatever I don't have that interests me. What I don't need is the most popular songs of any era. I don't have much interest in "nice" music like love songs, moon songs, waltzes, etc. I'm more apt to buy music in major categories with strong illustrated covers such as movies, politics, cartoons, transportation, sports, or racism." To offer her your music, list the title, date, composer, name of the movie or show, condition, and what is on the cover.

> Sandy Marrone
> 113 Oakwood Drive
> Cinnaminson, NJ 08077
> (856) 829-6104   <smusandy@aol.com>

Sandy Marrone says: "Don't expect to get rich on piles of old sheet music. Few pieces of sheet music have significant value...and those must be in outstanding condition. On the other hand, some sheets are worth $100 or more, so it is important to check."

To sell hymnals, see Religion section, pages 308-312

CYLINDER AND 78 RPM PHONOGRAPH RECORDS

★ **Music cylinders.** The following cylinders (early phonograph recordings) are wanted by a well known music auctioneer:
- Cylinders colored brown, pink, purple, white or orange;
- Cylinders 6" long or 5" in diameter;
- Blue cylinders numbered 5000 to 5750;
- Cylinders with opera or historical content.

It is a plus if the cylinders are in their original boxes, but not necessary. Cylinders can bring from $5 to $200 each, depending on the size, color, and condition. List the title, artist, catalog number, color, length and diameter, and note whether you have the box. If your collection is very large, so listing is impractical, phone him to make other arrangements. "Cylinders break or scratch easily. Avoid touching the surface. Do not play them, even if you think you have the right equipment."

Kurt Nauck, Nauck's Vintage Records
6323 Inway Drive
Spring, TX 77389
(281) 370-7899   fax (425) 930-6862   <nauck@78rpm.com>

★ **Rare 78 rpm records.** Among his particular wants are:
- Jazz, blues, cajun and country records 1925-1935;
- Rock and roll records, 1948-1960;
- Records before 1903 (often 7" diameter with no paper labels);
- Speeches by historical figures on disk or cylinder;
- **Picture records** (transparent records w/ pictures under grooves);
- Advertising, promotional, and special purpose records, some of which are made of thin cardboard (don't play them!);
- Classical and opera before 1908, especially smaller than 10";
- Long play 78's marked "longer playing," "five minute record;"
- Rare labels, of which he can supply you a long list, including *Black Patti, KKK, Sunshine, Marconi, Vitaphone,* and more;
- Puzzle, or multi-track, records;
- Unusual sizes and shapes of records.

He urges you to read *The American Premium Record Guide* by Les Docks and to list any records you have that catalog for more than $15 in that publication. Include the label, number, artist, and any noticeable defects. "If you have a large collection so that making a list is impractical, call me and we can discuss the possibility of evaluating your collection in person." Send a long SASE and $2 for his wants list. **He does not want** big bands, Hawaiian, popular songs, religious music, album sets, country music after WWII, home recordings, or later opera and classical, nor does he want 45's or LP records of any type.

Kurt Nauck, Nauck's Vintage Records
6323 Inway Drive
Spring, TX 77389
(281) 370-7899   fax (425) 930-6862   <nauck@78rpm.com>

◆ **78 rpm recordings,** 1900-1940, including popular, dance orchestra, vocal, military band, classical, jazz, country & western, instrumental, spoken word, personality, humor, and recordings in foreign languages. Also seeks picture records. Highest prices are paid for records in good condition with no cracks or chips into the grooves. Values range from $1 to $1,000 with 80% of them under $5 each (but a pile of them adds up). When listing your records, include the label, artist and catalog (index) number. Song titles are not necessary. A Stamped Self-Addressed Envelope should be included if you wish records evaluated. David will buy a wider range of items than most record buyers. He is especially interested in entire collections and will travel anywhere in the East. Catalogs of record companies before 1930 are also sought.

> David Alan Reiss
> 141 Cabot Road
> Massapequa, NY 11785
> (516) 798-3381   fax (516) 798-2618   <dnreiss@optonline.net>

◆ **American 78 rpm pop records,** 1888-1949, especially in quantity. Pays 10¢ to $1 apiece, less if records are not in fine condition. Buys disks, cylinders, and sapphire ball recordings at higher prices. Likes to find pre-1960 versions of *Froggy Went a Courtin'*, especially the Victor black label version from 1926, worth $100 in fine condition. Some interest in sheet music for pop music and songs from 1890-1925.

> Ron Graham
> 8167 Park Ave.
> Forestville, CA 95436
>   (707) 887-2856   <old78rpm@juno.com>

TONY'S TIPS: When describing phonograph records the most important pieces of information are the record label and catalog number. Record experts recommended in Trash or Treasure will know what you have without your even listing the artist and title. Condition is not as important, but still should be mentioned. Some rare 78rpm records will be purchased in any condition.

If your record is of a very popular song, there are many copies available, so it doesn't have much value.

A leading record buyer once said, "If your records were bought by someone who is white and middle class, the odds are they have little value. Black, cajun, hillbilly and ethnic music is where the action is."

TONY'S TIP: Buyer Ron Graham says "Look on eBay. You'll see how low prices are for records, and how many that no one wants at any price. See what your records bringing, or if they are wanted at all."

◆ **78 rpm, 45 rpm, and 33 rpm jazz, blues, big band, hillbilly, rock and roll, rhythm and blues, rockabilly, and celebrity records.**
   • Jazz and dance bands from the 1920's and 30's;
   • Jug and washboard bands;
   • Radio transcription disks;
   • Anything recorded on *Autograph, Black Patti,* and 50 other
       labels (send long SASE for a list);
   • Records marked "Fox Trot," "Stomp," or "For Dancing."
He buys many rare, obscure and unpopular records but does not want easy listening, hit records, or pop singing stars like Al Jolson and Bing Crosby. If you have 78's to sell, send $5 for the Shellac Shack's Wants List, a 72 page book listing the prices they pay for thousands of records. Les is author of *American Premium Record Guide,* the basic reference book on phonograph records, available for $28 postpaid from him.
   Les Docks
   The Shellac Shack
   PO Box 691035
   San Antonio, TX 78269
       <docks@texas.net>

◆ *Vogue* **78 rpm picture records.** Will pay $500 for *Rum and Coca Cola.* Records must be clean and in excellent condition. Long SASE brings a list of other records John wants to buy.
   John Widmar
   Lake Side Towers
   5800 3rd Avenue #515
   Kenosha, WI 53140
       (262) 654-6802

◆ **Phonograph records, tapes, music videos, sheet music, books and magazines related to music,** 1900 to the present. Items must be in fine condition as they are purchased for resale. Buys in bulk, so indicate the type of record (78, 45, 33), the type of music (rock, country, classical, jazz, easy listening, spoken, soundtrack, etc.), and the number you have of each. SASE is a must. Produces *Record Finder,* a 56 page monthly for $12/year.
   W.H. Smith, Memory Lane Records
   PO Box 1047
   Glen Allen, VA 23060
       (804) 266-1154   fax (804) 264-9660
   <sales1@recordfinders.com>   <www.recordfinders.com>

★ **Children's 78rpm records,** 1900's-1960's, in all sizes on all labels. Children's records that do not have their original jackets or sleeves are usually not of interest unless they are picture records (with pictures right in the vinyl as these are usually not found in sleeves). Most items are $1-$10 but a handful can bring $100 each. The condition of the record and the sleeve should be described, along with the label name and catalog number. He's compiling a discography of 78rpm children's records, so welcomes all information you have. Peter was a CBS-TV "What's It Worth?" consultant.

Peter Muldavin
173 West 78th Street, #5F
New York, NY 10024
(212) 362-9606   <kiddie78s@aol.com>

◆ **Phonograph records in all categories:**
- 78 rpm including popular, vocal, instrumental, personality, jazz, especially big band, country & western, dance orchestra and blues, 1900-1959;
- **45rpm from 1947 to the present,** especially rock and roll "gems" from 1954-1964;
- **33rpm LP's** both 10" and 12" of many types including popular, instrumental, jazz, folk, etc., from 1947-1990;
- Novelty records..."I'm crazy about them!"
- **Radio Transcriptions** on shellac or vinyl.

When listing your records, please include the label, artist, and catalog number. If you want an offer, include a long SASE. Jamie buys large quantities of records for 10¢ to $1 and up but **he does not buy** any children's records at all.

Jamie Sager
House of Golden Oldies
3231 Edgeware Road South
Memphis, TN 38118
(901) 795-2739   fax (901) 794-9986

◆ **45rpm and 33rpm phonograph records** pressed between 1950 and 1975. Most interested in rock and roll, jazz, blues, soul and country. Top want is rhythm and blues from the early 50's. No interest in classical or "hit" records and pop performers. Condition must be "in nice shape." List the type and quantity, the condition of the records, and the condition of the sleeve or cover. This record convention promoter, author, and columnist has been in the business for 30 years.

Doug Hanners
PO Box 90806
Austin, TX 78709
(512) 288-7288 eves   fax (512) 288-7227
<ausrecs@inetport.com>

◆ **LP (long playing 33rpm) records** in the following categories may be of interest if they are in fine condition:
- Modern jazz, preferably from the 1950's (no Dixieland!);
- Soul, doo-wop, blues, and rhythm & blues from the 1950's and 60's; original albums only, not rereleases;
- *Bluenote* and *Prestige* jazz recordings in mono, not stereo;
- Obscure Broadway original cast albums, like *Clown Around;*
- Soundtracks to obscure or unpopular movies, or any spoken soundtracks such as *The Caine Mutiny* (especially desirable);
- Classical stereo recordings on *RCA Living Stereo, Mercury Living Presence Stereo, Decca FFSS* and *London* from the early days of stereo in the 1950's and 60's;
- Classical recordings of solo performers on piano, violin, cello, etc., especially of lesser known performers;
- Oddities, including test pressings, items never released, etc.;
- Some rare 1950's and 60's 45's;
- Depression era 78's, especially jazz, blues, and dance bands.

Many of these items are only a few dollars, but some are worth many hundreds, and a handful can bring $1,000 or more. There are some records which have no value and can be considered "yard sale" fare, including all easy listening, rock and roll recorded after 1960 (unless unusual in some way), and any LP's with no sleeves. If you want to offer records for sale, list the label, the catalog number, the title, artist, and condition to this 40 year veteran expert dealer.

Rod Baum
Rare Records
336 Main Street
Hackensak, NJ 07601
(201) 441-9034 (10am to 6pm)   fax (201) 441-9036
<rarerecords@compuserve.com>   <http://www.rarerecords.com>

*TONY'S TIP: If offering records, pay attention to the wants lists. These are the **only** 33's they want.*

★ **LP (long playing 33rpm) records** in the following categories are of interest if they are before 1975 and in very fine condition:
- Movie soundtracks;
- Children's TV cartoon characters;
- TV soundtracks or character albums;
- Weird, involving unusual characters or themes.

No 78's, Broadway sound tracks, cardboard records or generic children's records like nursery stories or Mother Goose are wanted.

David Welch
PO Box 714
Murphysboro, IL 62966
(618) 687-2282   Fax: (618) 684-2243   <pezdude1@aol.com>

◆ **Jazz LP's from the 1950's and 60's. Also buys jazz literature and magazines,** any years, and some other materials associated with jazz. No 45's or 78's. No music other than jazz. No records with poor condition covers. Please include your phone number.

Gary Alderman
PO Box 259164
Madison, WI 53725
(608) 274-3527   Fax: (608) 277-1999   <gjazz@tds.net>

◆ **LP (long playing 33rpm) records** in the following categories may be of interest if they are in fine condition:
- **Jazz and soul**, "but no big hit records because I probably already have them;"
- **Obscure Rock & Roll bands** from the 1960's and 70's;
- **Christian Rock bands**.
- **Black gospel**.
- **Radio station records of commercials, sound effects,** public service announcements, and non-copyrighted production music.

When writing, please list the performer, album title, and the label. Records should look well cared for. "I do not want opera, or any sets which contain more than three records."

Joe Flynn
274 West 12th Street, #1-R
New York, NY 10014
(212) 675-7440   <joef@post.com>

*TONY'S TIP: When describing 33rpm phonograph records the most important pieces of information are the **artist, title, record label and catalog number**. Since many albums went through editions, **mention the color of the label, too. It is also important to note whether it is a mono or stereo** recording, as some records are common in one form and rare in the other.*

Condition of 33's is very important. Buyers care about the condition of the cover as well as the record. Make certain to mention writing (like owner's names), banged corners, split seams, and missing inside sleeves. Poor condition 33's that look like licorice pizza will not find a buyer.

It is very difficult for you to know which albums have value, because of surprises like the Caine Mutiny soundtrack worth more than $1,000, or the Bob Dylan album with the "missing song" that is worth even more.

◆ **Odd 45's** from the 1950's and 60's. "I want **little known performers on little known labels.** I have no interest in Elvis and other popular artists or in labels like *Columbia, RCA, Capitol* and the like. I don't
buy 78's, classical music or other instrumentals. Be specific in your
descriptions, including label and catalog number."
>   Otti Schmitt
>   Finders-Keepers Collectibles
>   7724 Hayfield Road
>   Alexandria, VA 22315
>   (703) 971-4065   <mchughs1@erols.com>

◆ **Rhythm and Blues or Rock and Roll 45's** from the 1950's. Wants
original recordings of groups like the *Flamingos, Robins, Wrens,
Penguins*, etc. Will buy any 45's from race labels such as *Chance, Red
Robin, Blue Lake, Harlem, Grand, Rockin, After Hours, Aladdin,
Parrot, Flip, Allen, Rhythm, Club 51,* and *Swingtime.* No records that
are reissues, bootlegged, or damaged. When writing, give the label, catalog number and condition.
>   John Widmar
>   Lake Side Towers
>   5800 3rd Avenue #515
>   Kenosha, WI 53140
>   (262) 654-6802

◆ **Rock and roll, rhythm and blues, and country music records**
from the 1950's and 1960's, especially 45 and 33 rpm:
- 45's with picture sleeves;
- Odd ball items;
- Disc jockey radio promos;
- Rock, blues, or country sheet music and magazines.

Nothing having to do with classical, big band, opera, or polka music is
wanted at all, no matter how old or interesting.
>   Cliff Robnett
>   7804 NW 27th
>   Bethany, OK 73008
>   (405) 787-6703   <clrob@swbell.net>

◆ **45 rpm records in quantity** in unplayed or nearly unused condition.
Looking for store stock or radio station collections, but will also buy
small collections if they contain desirable records. Nothing worn or
scratched. "Phone if you think you have what I'm looking for."
>   Ken Clee
>   PO Box 11412
>   Philadelphia, PA 19111
>   (215) 722-1979   <waxntoys@aol.com>

TONY'S TIPS ON SELLING COIN-OPERATED MACHINES

"Coin-ops" is what collectors call slot machines, jukeboxes, arcade games, trade stimulators (games you play for product prizes), and other machines put into play by dropping a coin into a slot.

Most dealers will know exactly what you have if you give them the type of machine, the name of the manufacturer, the model, and serial number. Most electric machines will have an ID plate somewhere on the back.

A photo of older items is advisable, *especially of vending machines and trade stimulators since unfamiliar ones turn up regularly.*

When writing about a coin-op, indicate whether it works and whether parts are missing or broken. ***Coin-ops do not need to be in perfect condition to sell.*** *Most collectors and dealers restore them and are willing to buy older machines in any condition for parts.*

When describing pinball machines note how much paint is peeling off the back board illustration. *If the illustration is not in perfect condition you must include a photo as the condition of the backboard is very important.*

When taking photos of pinball machines, include the play field in one photo and back glass (vertical pictorial area) in another. Most of the value is in the back glass so make sure you send a clear photo.

Because the machines are large, heavy, and valuable, buyers will usually make shipping arrangements.

One of the larger single sales by a Trash or Treasure reader involved juke boxes. He had been paying rent to store dozens of machines for more than 30 years. Our buyer paid $185,000 for his machines, so he decided it had been worth it.

◆ **Coin-op machines of all types** including jukeboxes, nickelodeons, **arcade devices** such as diggers and claws, view machines, coin-op fans and radios, and **vending machines for gum, condoms, etc.** Has particular interest in slot machines and gambling devices that pay cash rewards. These have a minimum value of $500 with the more unusual machines bringing considerably more. Pre-1910 gambling machines made on the west coast are very desirable. Also **paper ephemera about coin-op machines** including catalogs, brochures, advertising, and anything historical. **No pinball,** video, or service machines like washers.

Fred Ryan
Slot Closet
PO Box 83135
Portland, OR 97203
(503) 286-3597   (503) 235-9559

◆ **Coin-op machines** including 78 rpm *Wurlitzer* jukeboxes from 1938 to 1948, **penny arcade machines** from before 1920, **vending machines** from before 1910, and all slot machines.

Martin Roenigk
Mechantiques
75 Prospect Ave.
Eureka Springs, AR 72632
(479) 253-0405   cel (443) 831-6211   fax (479) 253-0406
<mroenigk@aol.com>

◆ **Coin operated game machines with a sports theme.** Any machine made before 1970 that requires a coin to start it is of interest if it has a sports theme: baseball, football, hockey, and basketball especially. Machines can be worth from $50 to as much as $10,000. Price is dependent on rarity, desirability and condition, though he will buy sports related game machines in any condition. "A picture is worth a thousand words and a few pictures are worth many thousands of words!" Rob is a collector with more than 100 machines and anxious to add yours.

Rob Lahammer
4501 Shoreline Drive
Spring Park, MN 55384
(952) 471-6175   fax (952) 471-6084   <rob@lahammer.com>

◆ **Mechanical coin-op kiddie rides** in any condition. "I prefer to make offers only when you send a good clear photo of both sides."

Frank Martin
7669 Winterberry Drive
Youngstown, OH 44512
(330) 758-4470   <martin7669@aol.com>

◆ **Coin-op machines,** especially pre-1940 slots and jukeboxes. No solid state pinball machines. Ted publishes the monthly *Coin Machine Trader* ($20/year) devoted to ads and information about coin-ops.
> Ted Salveson
> PO Box 602
> Huron, SD 57350
>   (605) 352-3870   fax(605) 352-7590

◆ **Jukeboxes,** jukebox speakers, wall boxes, remote equipment, literature and brochures are all wanted by this dedicated collector who also buys magazines associated with the coin-op world including: *Automatic Age* (1925-46), *Automatic World* (1927-57), *Cash Box Coin Machine Journal, National Coin Machine News,* and many others. His interest extends to all brands of jukeboxes, especially those made before 1946, and will consider them in any condition. Not particularly interested in those made after 1962. Only wants items he doesn't already have, but pledges to help you find a buyer if he doesn't want your item. When you write, include the brand name, the model number, and a photo or video. Wayne is author of the *Jukebox Speaker and Wallbox Guide* available from the author for $30, and plans to open a jukebox museum. He can send you a list of specific items he seeks.
> Wayne Kline
> 23622 Calabasas Road #101
> Calabasas, CA 91302
>   (818) 569-7474 eves   fax (818) 840-2249
>   <wayne.kline@nbc.com>

◆ **Table model jukeboxes.** He will buy all pre-1960 jukeboxes if you live close enough for him to pick them up. Also jukebox literature, advertising and parts. If you live far enough away that your machine must be shipped, he only wants the small ones. He doesn't want to ship the larger machines.
> Alvin Heckard
> 165 Orchard Grove Ave.
> Lewistown, PA 17044
>   (717) 248-7071   <aheckard@nittanylink.com>

*TONY'S TIP: Most dealers will know what you have if you give the type of machine, the name of the maker, the model, and serial number. **A photo is advisable**. Indicate whether it works and whether parts are missing or broken. **Note how much paint is peeling off the back board illustration** or elsewhere.*

◆ *Wurlitzer* and *Rock Ola* **jukeboxes,** working or not, especially *Wurlitzer* model 42 (worth up to $1,800) and model numbers 500 or above (which begin at $450 for a #500 and can go to nearly $12,000 for a nice condition model #950). Also all slot machines, in any condition, complete or not, working or not. All but the most common working machines will bring $500, many over $1,000. He advertises widely that $50,000 is waiting for the finder of a working *Fey Liberty Bell* slot machine. Will pick up machines anywhere in the U.S.

> Frank Zygmunt
> Antique Slot Machine Co.
> PO Box 542
> Westmont, IL 60559
> (630) 985-2742   Fax: (630) 985-5151   <zygm1015@aol.com>

◆ *Wurlitzer* **jukeboxes** with model numbers lower than 500. These 1930's machines predate the "plastic-and-bright-lights era" favored by most collectors. Also *Capehart* **radio-phonographs** and jukeboxes from the 1930's that flip records over. Pays $500-$700 for *Wurlitzer* 416 or *Capehart* C20-30. He'll buy these in any condition, but condition does affect value. Will pick up anything east of the Mississippi and arrange for shipments in the West.

> Joseph Weber
> 604 Centre Street
> Ashland, PA 17921
> (570) 875-4401 between 3 and 5 p.m.

◆ *Wurlitzer* **jukeboxes** from the 1940's. Also paper ephemera, service manuals, and advertising related to jukeboxes of all types. Rick publishes the monthly *Jukebox Collector Newsletter* and is author of three books about jukeboxes, including "A Complete Identification Guide to the Wurlitzer Jukebox" available from him for $15.

> Rick Botts
> 2545 SE 60th Court
> Des Moines, IA 50317
> (515) 265-8324

◆ **All types of coin-operated machines,** including slot machines, pinball machines, pre-electronic arcade games made of oak and/or iron, and trade stimulators. The more unusual, the better. "Tell me what it is, its condition, and whether it works. Please send a photo." Dealers should price your goods, but amateurs may request offers.

> Marvin Yagoda
> Marvin's Marvelous Mechanical Museum
> 31005 Orchard Lake Road
> Farmington Hills, MI 48334
> (248) 626-5020   fax (248) 626-7945   <marvin@marvin3m.com>
> <http://www.marvin3m.com>

◆ **Countertop coin-operated machines** including **arcade machines,** trade stimulators, and **vending machines** from the 1920's through the 1950's. You must send a photo and the price wanted. Ken is publisher of *Antique Amusements, Slot Machine* and *Jukebox Gazette.*
Ken Durham
909 26th Street NW
Washington, DC 20037
<durham@gameroomantiques.com>   <www.gameroomantiques.com>

◆ **Penny arcade games** such as grip tests, target games, kicker and catcher, Pike's Peak, and the like. Prefers penny machines.
James Conley
2758 Coventry Lane NW
Canton, OH 44708
(330) 477-7725

◆ **Peanut and gumball machines**
Rick Padrone
1005 E. Idlewild Ave.
Tampa, FL 33604
(800) 991-0165   fax (800) 991-0166   <ricpadron@webtv.net>

◆ **Gumball and peanut vending machines** made of cast iron or porcelain before 1930, with glass globes that are faceted, shaped like light bulbs or otherwise unusual. **He does not want machines with square globes** from the 1940's to the present. List the make of machine, shape of the globe, material from which it is made, any decals, condition of the paint, and whether or not it is working. Dealers must price your goods, but amateur sellers may request offers.
Don Reedy
13 South Carroll Street
Frederick, MD 21701
(301) 663-4240 days   (301) 662-5503 eves   fax (301) 694-9190
<shineit4u@aol.com>

◆ **Various coin-operated machines** including *Wurlitzer, Seeburg and Rockola* **jukeboxes,** various **slot machines**, *Popperette* **popcorn machines, arcade games** with wood cabinets, **Ten pin bowling machine** by Evans or Williams and Chicago Coin Basketball. A description of your item should include your asking price. He will help amateurs decide the value of what they have.
Mr. Kim Gutzke
7134 15th Avenue S
Minneapolis, MN 55423
(612) 866-6183   fax (612) 798-4169   <kgutzke@mn.rr.com>

MUSIC, MUSICIANS & SINGERS

◆ **Country music autographs, photos, and other memorabilia.** "What have you?" Gary is general manager of a company specializing in movie and country music memorabilia in the heart of Nashville.

Gary Vaughn
Cinemonde
138 2nd Avenue North #104
Nashville, TN 37201
(615) 742-9256   fax (615) 742-1268   <cinemonde@earthlink.net>

◆ **Opera and classical music concert programs, autographs and photos.** Please give title, date, and other information. Xerox™ helpful.

Steve Jabloner
145 Kent Avenue #4
Kentfield, CA 94904
(415) 461-9541   < jabloner@marin.cc.ca.us>

◆ **Ephemera associated with the history of pianos** including advertising signs, posters, catalogs, photos of factory and store interiors, models of pianos and mechanisms, tools used by piano tuners and builders, and piano trade publications. He is not interested in magazine ads. Your description should include size and condition as well as noting the materials from which your item is made. Photo or photocopy helpful. "The history of pianos and of their manufacture fascinates me." **He does not want to buy your piano.** No exceptions!

Phillip Jamison III
17 Sharon Alley
West Chester, PA 19382
(610) 696-8449   <mortier@netreach.net>

◆ **Eubie Blake or Sissle and Blake memorabilia** and records, especially a 10" recording called *Jammin' at Rudi's.*

Steven Ramm
420 Fitzwater Street
Philadelphia, PA 19147
(215) 922-7050   <stevenramm@aol.com>

TONY'S TIP: When you ask someone for information or for an offer, include a long business size #10 envelope, address it to yourself, and put a stamp in the corner. This is a Self-Addressed Stamped Envelope (SASE). Use a long envelope because many buyers will send you information which won't fit into smaller envelopes.

◆ **Big Band memorabilia** from the 1930's and 40's especially of Glenn Miller or Bunny Berigan. Wants home recordings, tapes of concerts or radio performances, transcription disks, autographs, photographs, newspaper articles, magazine articles, movie short subjects, home movies, posters, and sheet music if it has to do with big bands. This 30 year collector will negotiate an item's value. **No records.**

John Mickolas
172 Liberty Street
Trenton, NJ 08611
(609) 599-9672   (609) 530-5568 days   <jmickolas.col.com>

◆ **Bobby Breen phonograph records** and song sheets dating from the late 1930's.

Ralph Eodice
77 East Emerson Street
Clifton, NJ 07013
        <silvercup@aol.com>

◆ **Frank Sinatra memorabilia** including records, sheet music with his picture, radio items, stuff from TV shows, scrap books, and what have you. Please send Xerox™ copies or good description.

Herman Rush
10773 Ojai-Santa Paula Road
Ojai, CA 93023

◆ **Alvin & the Chipmunks** and creator David Seville. "I want anything from the Chipmunks, Chipettes, Clyde Crashcup or David Seville including records (especially picture sleeves), books, comics, dolls, plush toys, clothes, posters, cups and mugs, figures, lunchboxes, puzzles, games, etc. Alvin items are dated from 1958 to the present, while Chipette items start in 1983. Pre-1961 items are especially rare. **I am not looking for** Soakies, Christmas albums, cassettes or CD's recorded in the 90's, or the 1983 10" tall chipmunks. When writing, make sure to include the date and copyright holder (Bagdasarian, Karman/Ross or Monarch). Please give condition and dimensions.

Kim Shriner
236 Lakeside Drive
Little Egg Harbor, NJ 08087
        (609) 296-2322

◆ **Rock concert T-shirts from any band** but must have a date from 1964 to 1975 printed on the shirt. They can be in any size, but must be clean and never worn. I will buy one or dozens." Send a brief description and your asking price. Will make offers to genuine amateurs.

Judy Polk Harding
4347 Farm House Lane
Fairfax, VA 22032
        (703) 503-7323   <thefivejs@aol.com>

ROCK & ROLL

◆ **Rock & Roll memorabilia.** You name it, if it's rock and roll related and made between 1950 and 1990, he'd like to know about it... photos, instruments, jackets, rare recordings, posters, props...what have you? Fine condition only. The more rare and unusual the better. Among items sought are:

- **Guitars and accessories** used by name artists for practice, recording, or live performance. Will accept autographed guitars if accompanied by photos of the performer with the instrument. Also straps, capos, and broken parts. Hendrix, Presley, and Vaughan most sought.
- **Pianos from the Beatles' studio work** or those autographed for charity by Elton John;
- **Synthesizers and other small keyboards** if star use can be proven;
- **Drums used on stage** or studio by major artists;
- **Clothing worn on stage** that is colorful; must have photos of artist wearing the clothes on stage;
- **Cars and motorcycles** if still registered in the star's name, or if paper trail is compete, especially with photos of star with car or cycle;
- **Handwritten song lists,** notations, lyrics, etc.;
- **Contracts, autographs,** and other paper;
- **Awards, gold records, Grammys,** etc.
- **Posters from any live performance,** especially 1960's and early 70's. No hand bills. Movie posters with a rock and roll or motorcycle theme are wanted;
- **Unused concert tickets;**
- **Original artwork for albums, posters,** etc.

Send Danny a complete description, including a photo when appropriate. If it was a personal item belonging to a famous performer, you must include any and all documentation for authenticity. Danny has "runners" in all parts of the country, so he can usually have important items evaluated or picked up within a matter of days. He buys for himself and as a representative of The Hard Rock Cafe chain and other commercial operations, so he can buy an unusual range of items, big and small. Include your phone number when you write.

Danny Perkins
17927 River Court
Pierrefonds, PQ
H9J 1A2 CANADA
(514) 624-8515   fax (514) 624-8942
<danny@backstage.ca>

◆ **Rock and roll memorabilia** is wanted, including the **Beatles, Kiss, The Monkees** and **other headliners. Autographs** of rock singers and musicians are especially desired. He does not purchase rock and roll records unless you have studio dubs or tapes or radio station promotional copies. No other exceptions.

> Robert Urmanic "Nostalgia Bob"
> 199 Brookvalley Drive
> Elyria, OH 44035
>   (440) 365-3550   <urmanic@mediaone.net>

◆ **Beatles, Elvis, Kiss** and the **Rolling Stones** are wanted by this active West Coast pop-culture dealer.
- **Beatles items** include toys, games, musical instruments paint sets, dolls, tickets, movie posters, talcum powder, hair spray, lunch pails. Has a particular interest in the movie *Yellow Submarine.*
- **Elvis** items must be marked "EP Enterprises 1956" and include sneakers, lipstick, dress, gloves, scarves, plastic guitar, sweatshirts, autographs, wallets, purses, etc.
- **Rolling Stones** and **Kiss** items similar to above.

Paul encourages you to ask about any authentic fine condition item, but cautions he does not buy recordings. He notes that there are many fake Beatles items and that a photo is essential. Elvis items marked other than 1956 are not wanted.

> Paul Scharfman, Chic-a-Boom
> 6817 Melrose Avenue
> Los Angeles, CA 90038
>   <chickaboom@earthlink.net>

◆ **Rock star clothing and personal effects.** Give a complete description, including a history of the item, who used it, when, and how you came to own it. Photos are helpful.

> Paul Scharfman, Chic-a-Boom
> 6817 Melrose Avenue
> Los Angeles, CA 90038
>   <chickaboom@earthlink.net>

◆ **Michael Jackson or the Jackson 5 memorabilia,** especially backstage passes and official issue lunchbox.

> Carolyn Jamison
> PO Box 111752
> Nashville, TN 37222
>   (615) 252-4083

★ **Elvis Presley collectibles.** After 30 years of avid collecting, Robin still buys Elvis items, especially:
- Autographed photos, records, and other items;
- 45rpm records in their original sleeve, 1950-1960;
- Personal items, including clothing;
- Tour books from 1955-1977;
- "EP Ent" (Elvis Presley Enterprises) items from the 1950's;
- Movie posters and lobby cards from Elvis films;
- Store displays and promotions for Elvis products.

Prices vary according to the item, condition, authentication and rarity. Not interested in shot glasses, ash trays, postcards, or anything made after Elvis's death. Give the condition, and describe how you got the item. Robin's collection is featured in *All the Kings Things* available from her for $18 postpaid.

> Robin Rosaaen
> All The King's Things
> 101 Glen Eyrie Avenue #202
> San Jose, CA 95125
> (408) 297-0861 eves   <kingthings@aol.com>

◆ **Elvis Presley memorabilia** dating from before his death, including all marked "EP Ent 1956," such as lipsticks, skirts, perfume, gloves, and anything else out of the ordinary. He also buys posters and promotional items from Elvis movies, records, and appearances. He'd especially like to find a plastic guitar with pictures on it, and issues of 1950's magazines such as *Dig* and *Teen Stories* with all Elvis features. Autographs are always wanted. No records except promotional copies.

> Robert "Nostalgia Bob" Urmanic
> 199 Brookvalley Drive
> Elyria, OH 44035
> (440) 365-3550   <urmanic@mediaone.net>

◆ **Duran Duran.** Wants to buy single items or collections associated with this group, including backstage passes, posters, promotional records, unreleased recordings, autographed items, instruments, you name it, and she might buy it.

> Tammy Clack
> Strange Behavior Discs and Collectibles
> 101 Queensbury Circle
> Goose Creek, SC 29445
> (843) 863-0857   <tammy5145@aol.com>

★ **Beatles memorabilia** from before their 1970 breakup. Everything is wanted, including games, toys, dolls, posters, movie related items, **candid photos**, concert posters and programs, tickets, and ads for merchandise or concerts. Would love any Beatles toy musical instruments picturing the group, and will pay from $200-$500 for Beatles bongos or banjos. Buys common items as long as they are old and original. Wants to know where you got your item, and requests your phone number. Co-author of *The Beatles Memorabilia Price Guide.*

Jeff Augsburger
507 Normal Avenue
Normal, IL 61761
(309) 452-9376   fax (309) 664-1771   <beatles.normal@verizon.net>

★ **Beatles memorabilia** including toys, dolls, games, tickets, cartoon kits, model kits, *Yellow Submarine*, Halloween costumes, wallpaper, talcum powder, shampoo, ice cream wrappers, blankets, jewelry, china, toy musical instruments, fan club items, etc., especially items sealed in their original factory cartons. Rick also looks for hard-to-find albums such as *Beatles vs the 4 Seasons* or *Yesterday and Today* with the butcher block cover. "I'll pay $800 for a Beatles record player in mint condition, $500 for an unopened pomade, and $250 for a *Kaboodle Kit* like new." Rick also buys **The Monkees ephemera** of all types. Co-author of *The Beatles Memorabilia Price Guide* available for $28.

Rick Rann
PO Box 877
Oak Park, IL 60303
(708) 442-7907   <rickrann@aol.com>

◆ **Kiss collectibles.** Buys only items with the Kiss logo or that picture the band in make up. I'll buy any toy, tour book, guitar pick, drum stick, display, song book, poster, t-shirt, reel to reel tape, sealed 8 track, picture disc, American or foreign concert items. I do not want bootleg videos, cassettes or unsealed 8 tracks, nor do I want concert photos or t-shirts without makeup." Xerox™ copies or photos are helpful. Tom is the author of Goldmine's *Kiss Collectibles Price Guide.*

Tom Shannon
PO Box 25056
Lexington, KY 40524
(606) 272-7371 before 10pm EST   <tshannon40@hotmail.com>

◆ **Kiss collectibles.** Buys only items with the Kiss logo or that picture the band in make up including toys, dolls, household items. Send a long SASE for a list of what he has for sale.

Bob Gottuso
PO Box 1403
Mars, PA 16066
(724) 776-0621 voice/fax   <bojo@zbzoom.net>

TONY'S TIPS ON SELLING SPORTS MEMORABILIA

This chapter is particularly important because of the large number of items you own or can find that have some value. I urge all readers to go through this chapter thoroughly. These are important people, good buyers... and mean profit for you.

Balls, gloves, bats, uniforms, programs, championship belts, trophies, photos... anything sports is collectible.
Professional championship rings, belts, and trophies brings top prices (within each category). Amateur sports, except The Olympics, generate little dollar interest.

It is possible to cash in very large. A Detroit listener followed my instructions and turned a baseball uniform into $176,000. Readers and listeners just like you have uncovered 29 Babe Ruth balls and thousands of other uniforms, bats, programs and other baseball items have turned up.

In terms of dollar volume, baseball leads all sports. Don't let baseball's high prices mislead you. Items you are likely to find in other sports categories may bring as little as 5% of the value of a comparable baseball item.

Thousand dollar prices are not unknown in other sports, but prices of $20 to $500 are more likely. Fishing tackle brings the most money to Trash or Treasure readers and listeners. Find one good tackle box, and you could be thousands richer. Buyer Rick Edmisten reports spending $100,000 a year with Trash or Treasure readers and listeners. Small plugs (wooden and metal baits) purchased in the 1920's and 30's for pennies sell for hundreds of dollars today. Some boxes they originally came in are worth $50! Don't let them gather dust. Rick or other fishing tackle buyer will give them a good home...and give you a fatter purse or wallet.

Keep alert for strings of old decoys *laying unused in barns, basements and boat houses. These regularly bring over $1,000 each and one sold for more than $300,000. Millions of dollars worth of decoys are still waiting to be found in New England alone, according to one expert.*

Baseball collectibles bring high prices because there are so many collectors. Competition is not as great in other sports (including minor league baseball) so prices remain generally reasonable.

For example, the top price for a baseball card is over $500,000 while top value basketball and football cards sell for only $300. Expert advice is essential in sports cards. Prices are down substantially from their over-inflated days, but really rare cards still can bring you $100 or more each. I personally don't like the long range prospects of cards, so would sell now and put the money to better use.

The importance of condition depends upon the item you have to sell. *Card collectors require near perfection while collectors of other baseball items prefer items to show wear because it shows proof of use during a game.*

When offering items for sale, provide the following:

(1) What it is, its size, color and the material from which it is made;

(2) All names, dates and numbers embossed, incised, labeled or decaled on the item;

(3) An accurate statement of condition, noting missing parts, pieces, or paint;

(4) Mention whether the original box, packaging and instructions are included and in good condition.

Since many sports collectibles are paper, remember that a photocopy (Xerox™) machine is your best friend!

Pop culture dealers like Ted Hake (found on page 132) and others will sometimes buy sports memorabilia.

SPORTS EQUIPMENT & EPHEMERA

★ **Baseball, football, and boxing memorabilia,** with particular emphasis on the Victorian era, including:
  • Baseball equipment from before 1920, especially early
      fingerless gloves;
  • Paper ephemera: **books** from before 1920, display posters,
      baseball scorecards pre-1900, baseball guides pre-1920,
      World Series programs, and early ads featuring baseball;
  • **Uniforms** from any sport before 1960;
  • **Football guides** and equipment, pre-1930;
  • **Trophies** for any 19th century sports;
  • **Gum and tobacco cards.**
"Premium prices paid for 19th century baseball items." This 30 year veteran collector offers from $1,000 to $10,000 for posters depicting 1890's baseball cards, equipment, or sports figures. He does not want or buy anything after 1970. A clear photo is helpful.
> John Buonaguidi
> Monterey Bay Sports Museum
> 883 Lighthouse Ave.
> Monterey, CA 93940
>   (831) 655-2363 days   (831) 375-7345 eves
>   <hawkrise@redshift.com>

◆ **Baseball, football, basketball, and Olympic memorabilia** is wanted including items such as:
  • **Uniforms, trophies,** and medals and pins from famous athletes;
  • **Baseball gum cards** pre-1920;
  • **Posters and advertising** pieces related to sports, pre-1940;
  • World Series (1903-30) scorecards, tickets, press pins, pennants
      and souvenirs;
  • All star game programs, tickets, posters and press pins;
  • Black baseball bats;
  • Autographed balls, contracts and documents from sports greats;
  • Song sheets related to sports pre-1930;
  • **Games and toys** related to sports pre-1930.
"Unique and unusual" sports equipment and other material especially related to Hall of Fame baseball players from the 1920's and 1930's is sought. All items must be old, rare, and original. The gallery is now open to the public to see and to purchase rare sports collectibles.
> Joel Platt
> Sports Immortals Museum and Memorabilia Mart
> 6830 North Federal Highway
> Boca Raton, FL 33487
>   (561) 997-2575   fax (561) 997-6949
>   <legends@sportsimmortals.com>

★ **Professional baseball and football equipment, especially game worn jerseys, bats, and equipment.** Does not want foreign items, other sports, paper ephemera, or cards. Each item must be evaluated individually as to value. For an offer, describe your item thoroughly, including age, condition, and history. David's *Vintage Baseball Glove Price Guide* is only $6. A *Pocket Guide to Collectible Bats* is $5.

>David Bushing
>Vintage Sports
>217 Homewood
>Libertyville, IL 60048
>>(847) 816-6847   (847) 816-6861 eves
>><dbushing1@aol.com>   fax (847) 816-0570

◆ **Baseball, football, and boxing memorabilia** especially autographs of dead Hall-of-Famers and other important players. Wants **yearbooks of New York sports teams** and programs from championship events in all three sports. Will buy tickets, pins, and advertising items which mention players or teams, but not interested in sports cards. "Sellers should be willing to send the item to me for inspection. In many cases a good photo or photocopy will do."

>Richard Simon Sports, Inc. TH
>215 East 80th Street
>New York, NY 10021
>(212) 988-1349   fax (212) 288-1445   <richsprt@aol.com>

◆ **Baseball memorabilia,** especially from before 1948. Wants gum and tobacco cards and silks picturing baseball players, postcards, photos, games, programs, yearbooks, guides, advertising, fans, sheet music and autographs from dead Hall-of-Fame players. This 25 year advanced collector-dealer-auctioneer does not buy anything after 1960. Be as accurate as possible with descriptions and include your phone number with your letter. Photocopies are helpful.

>William Mastro
>12410 Ridge Road
>Palos Park, IL 60464
>(708) 361-2117   fax (708) 361-3848   <mfinesport@aol.com>

◆ **Canadian sports memorabilia.** "I'll buy all items associated with **Canadian hockey** teams and players before 1960, **Canadian lacrosse** teams and players, and **Canadian basketball** teams and players. I'm particularly looking for game schedules and calendars, programs, autographed photos, gum cards, etc. If practical, a clear photocopy is best. Small items may be sent on approval as I will always refund postage."

>Michael Rice
>PO Box 286
>Saanichton, BC V8M 2C5 CANADA
>>(250) 652-9412 eves <mrice@pacificcoast.net>

◆ **Baseball, football, boxing and hockey collectibles from 1970 or later** such as posters, programs, autographs, equipment, uniforms, bats, pins, and cards are wanted by this 50 year collector-dealer. Include year, size and condition. Originals only. No reproductions.

> Patrick Quinn
> Sports Collectors, Ltd.
> 8135 Elizabeth Avenue
> Orland Park, IL 60462
>   (708) 873-1195   fax (708) 873-1322

◆ **Babe Ruth material.** Send Xerox© to this major ephemera dealer.

> Harvey Dolin & Company
> Mezzanene floor
> 111 Fulton Street
> New York, NY 10038
>   (212) 267-0216

◆ **Philadelphia Phillies memorabilia,** especially pre-1930 programs and pre-1950 baseball player postcards.

> Gary Gatanis
> 3283-B Cardiff Court
> Toledo, OH 43606
>   (419) 475-3192   <janis@buckeyeinet.com>

◆ **Baseball gloves,** bats, autographed balls, cut autographs, programs, ticket stubs, scorecards, and uniforms. Does not buy any baseball cards.

> Gary Alderman
> PO Box 259164
> Madison, WI 53725
>   (608) 274-3527   fax (608) 277-1999
>   <gjazz@tds.net>

◆ **Games with a sports theme that work with coins.** Any machine made before 1970 that requires a coin to start it is of interest if it has a sports theme: baseball, football, hockey, and basketball especially. Machines can be worth from $50 to as much as $10,000. Price is dependent on rarity, desirability and condition, though he will buy sports related game machines in any condition. "A picture is worth a thousand words and a few pictures are worth many thousands of words!" Rob is a collector with more than 100 machines and anxious to add yours.

> Rob Lahammer
> 4501 Shoreline Drive
> Spring Park, MN 55384
>   (952) 471-6175   fax (952) 471-6084
>   <rob@lahammer.com>

◆ **Older (pre-1950) sports equipment** is wanted, including:
   • **Basketballs made of leather with laces;**
   • **Football helmets made of leather;**
   • **Golf clubs with wooden shafts;**
   • **Tennis rackets made of wood,** especially unusual shapes, with names of old professional players;
   • **Baseball gloves and bats** endorsed by players;
   • **Unusual** items..."Tell me what you have."
Asks for a photo, along with a good description which should include the names of makers and endorsers. He asks that you include your phone number with all correspondence.
   Gary Alderman
   PO Box 259164
   Madison, WI 53725
            (608) 274-3527   fax (608) 277-1999
            <gjazz@tds.net>

◆ **Old sports equipment suitable for restaurant, theme, model home, and other decorative purposes,** including:
   • **Balls from various sports** including pre-1950 leather footballs, baseballs, soccer balls, and basketballs. Seeks moderately priced old leather balls from before 1940 for decorator use. Not interested in balls autographed by famous persons.
   • **Wooden skis and bamboo poles.** Brand name doesn't matter, and neither do bindings, as long as they are all wood and in reasonably good condition;
   • **Leather football helmets;**
   • **Lacrosse equipment** such as sticks, balls, and leather knee pads;
   • **Snow shoes,** which are preferred intact with original gut, but empty frames in fine condition will be considered;
   • **Croquet mallets** or complete boxed sets if old and if the paint is in good condition;
   • **Cricket bats and balls;**
   • **Riding equipment** including tall boots, leather **whips,** velveteen riding hats, English style ladies' side saddles;
   • **Wicker creels and inexpensive bamboo fishing poles,** nets, etc., that aren't collectible but are in good condition.
All items should be pre-1940 and be fairly well cared for. Please give a general description of what you have, or telephone with the item in hand. "I want low-end items suitable for decorating theme restaurants, not fine expensive antiques. If what you have is very valuable, take it somewhere else. If you find that it isn't valuable, but you want it pre-served, offer it to me."
   Joan Brady
   834 Central Avenue
   Pawtucket, RI   02861

◆ **Tickets and ticket stubs from sports events.** Wants World Series, All Star games, Stanley Cup, NCAA final four, Super Bowl, Indy 500, and other **significant events** from the world of sports, including golf, tennis, boxing, etc. Tickets for any major events, such as no hatters and historic games, are sought. No common tickets to ordinary games unless there was a milestone of some sort (1st game in the stadium, last game, Aaron's last homer, etc.). Value is closely related to condition. You must describe whether there is damage, creases, tears, tape, glue, etc. Give the game, seat location, and date. This 25 year veteran collector/dealer asks other dealers to price their goods. Amateurs may request an offer.

> Norman Segel
> Doubleheader
> 3447 5th Street
> Oceanside, NY 11572
> (516) 536-7600   fax (516) 742-7209   <dblheader@aol.com>

◆ **Rugby and soccer** memorabilia wanted for resale. Can be either U.S. or foreign. Wants prints, cigarette cards, stamps, postcards, and paper ephemera. Also buys large items like coin operated games and strength machines with soccer or rugby themes.

> Matt Godek
> PO Box 565
> Merrifield, VA 22116
> (703) 280-5540   fax (703) 280-4543   <mgodek@aol.com>

◆ **Soccer memorabilia** wanted for museum display. Especially interested in U.S. soccer, but will also consider World Cup relics. Wants uniforms, rule books, posters, photos, prints, home movies, etc. Particularly likes to find items from soccer played in places other than the Northeastern U.S. Also interested in games and coin machines with soccer themes that might be suitable for play in their museum. Describe what you have. Primarily looking for donations.

> National Soccer Hall of Fame
> 5-11 Ford Avenue
> Oneonta, NY 13820

◆ **Roller Derby memorabilia,** including programs, posters, uniforms, flyers, autographs and "anything collectible from any era." He requests that you set the price wanted whenever possible, but says, "I will entertain all offers."

> Royal Duncan
> 428 West Collingwood Circle
> Peoria, IL 61614
>   (309) 691-2772   fax (309) 691 2577

◆ **College football, basketball and hockey programs** from before 1970. "I want programs from historic games, or with famous players, or with colorful art work but don't want those that are damaged or have missing pages." Give the sport, date, and colleges involved. Prefers to make offers only after seeing the actual program, but you are advised that sending a good Xerox© copy would be helpful.

Lee Goldstein
8747 North Bay Drive
Chanhassen, MN 55317
(952) 974-9929   <cresellers@aol.com>

◆ **Basketball memorabilia.** Anything before 1905, when it was "mostly a girl's game," is particularly of interest, but he'll consider any card, label or package featuring basketball themes or motifs. "If it has a picture related to basketball and it's old, I may want it. If I don't, I know other collectors who do." He is particularly interested in the career of George Mikan, and will pay up to $1,000 for obscure card issues such as *Mikan's Bread for Health, Scott Potato Chips, Royal Dessert* and the like. He DOES NOT WANT basketball programs, books, magazines, or toys unless they date before 1910." A photocopy is suggested.

Rob Lahammer
4501 Shoreline Drive
Spring Park, MN 55384
(952) 471-6175   fax (952) 471-6084
<rob@lahammer.com>

◆ **Pro basketball ephemera** especially autographed team balls, All-Star balls, programs, and yearbooks. Anything before 1990 that is in fine condition will be considered. A Xerox© copy is suggested.

Gary Alderman
PO Box 259164
Madison, WI 53725
(608) 274-3527   fax (608) 277-1999
<gjazz@tds.net>

◆ **Pro hockey memorabilia,** especially autographed pucks, programs, and unusual items like the 1969 Rangers' paperweight/bottle opener.

Gary Alderman
PO Box 259164
Madison, WI 53725
(608) 274-3527   fax (608) 277-1999
<gjazz@tds.net>

◆ **Harlem Globetrotters** ephemera from before 1970 in good condition including uniforms, programs, advertising, pennants, and what have you. A few later items will be considered if they are unusual and in fine condition. If you have a uniform, tell how you came by it.

    Lee Goldstein
    8747 North Bay Drive
    Chanhassen, MN 55317
        (952) 974-9929   <cresellers@aol.com>

◆ **Running memorabilia.** "I'll buy medals, ribbons, trophies, cards, annuals, magazines, programs, and books related to running, track & field, road races and the Olympics." Not interested in items since 1960, but will consider reproductions of some posters and other printed material. Tell what you have and its condition. Ed is president of the Motor City Striders and writes for various running magazines.

    Ed Kozloff
    10144 Lincoln
    Huntington Woods, MI 48070
  (810) 544-9099   fax (810) 544-4601   <racebreak@aol.com>

◆ **Self defense magazines,** photos, books, courses, equipment, posters, trophies, etc., printed before 1975. Doesn't want anything currently published. Please send an SASE with inquiries.

    William Moore
    PO Box 20732
    Tuscaloosa, AL 35402

◆ **Recreational and competitive horseback riding.** Wants books and paper ephemera related to Morgan horses, Arabians, saddlebred horses, polo ponies, sidesaddles, and Lippizzaners. She would especially like to find books by or illustrated by Paul Brown and George Ford Morris. Books and paper only!

    Barbara Cole, October Farm
    2609 Branch Road
    Raleigh, NC 27610
        (919) 772-0482   fax (919) 779-6265
        <octoberfarm@bellsouth.net>

◆ **Horseshoe memorabilia.** Seeks early pitching shoes with no hooks on the points or shoes that are smaller than normal. Shoes are only $3 to $5 each but cased travel sets can bring $75 or more. Catalogs, photos and advertising related to the game may also be of interest. Does not want modern or foreign made shoes. Give brand and model name and style (hookless or with hooks) and condition of shoes and box.

    Bob Dunn
    6417 Georgia Ave North
    Brooklyn Park, MN 55428
        (763) 535-3884

★ *Flexible Flyer* **sledding.** Wants "anything" having to do with *Flexible Flyer* sleds, including membership cards, models, pins, advertising, company literature, and rare sleds. Thorough description, with a photocopy or photograph, is helpful. Author of *Flexible Flyer and Other Great Sleds* available at your bookstore.

> Joan Palicia
> 15 Canton Road
> Wayne, NJ 07470
> (973) 831-0527   <jpsledssnofn@nac.net>

◆ **Diving related items** especially hard hat diving gear, old two-hose scuba regulators, manufacturer's catalogs and brochures depicting underwater gear, and all magazines (especially foreign) about any aspect of sport diving. Will also buy comic books such as *Sea Hunt* and *Primus* which focus on diving. No hardcover books, please.

> Thomas Szymanski
> 5 Stoney Brook Lane
> Stratham, NH 03885
> (603) 772-6372   <tomski@nh.ultranet.com>

◆ **Surfboards and surfing related items** from before 1970, such as magazines, posters, stickers, patches, etc. Pays up to $1,000 for round nosed pre-1970 foam longboards. All wood boards can bring up to $5,000. No name garage-made paddleboards are less than $200, but Tom Blake, Catalina, and Mitchell paddleboards can bring ten times that. If you phone, please have your board right there so you can answer questions about it. Would love to find a board made by the legendary Duke Kahanamoku.

> Wayne Babcock
> 4846 Carpenteria Avenue
> Carpenteria, CA 93013
> (805) 684-8148   <oldsurfin@cs.com>

◆ **Dog fighting.** Wants to buy prints, paintings, and statuary, especially as related to bull terriers. Books on dog fighting also wanted. Provide standard bibliographic information.

> Ron & Isabel Lieberman
> 4887 Newport Road at the Old Mill
> Kinzers, PA 17535
> (717) 442-0220   fax (717) 442-7904   <rarebooks@pobox.com>

◆ **Loving cup trophies** from before 1950. May be awarded for sports, beauty, service, heroism, or anything else as long as they have handles on each side and are 8" high or taller. No other style of trophy is wanted, nor is anything dating after 1950.

> Joan Brady
> 834 Central Ave.
> Pawtucket, RI   02861

◆ **Sports photographs, amateur and pro,** from before 1920. Wants photos of men, women or children involved in basketball, baseball, hockey, football, track, bowling...you name it. Wants photos of all types including real photo postcards, and may even buy stained photos if interesting. The only buyer I know interested in kids and amateurs.
> Lee Goldstein
> 8747 North Bay Drive
> Chanhassen, MN 55317
> (952) 974-9929   <cresellers@aol.com>

★ **Pro and college football memorabilia** "I'm looking for vintage items from the glory days of football including helmets, balls, game programs and autographed items. I also buy buttons, pennants, nodders and ticket stubs to important games. I am particularly interested in **the Washington Redskins** for my personal collection but buy from other teams for resale." Because the category is so large and diverse, Mike asks that you call with what you have. If it sounds good, you'll be asked to send it on approval for his inspection and offer. DO NOT send things without asking first. For large collections, he'll come to you.
> Michael Herz
> Whiz Bang! Collectibles
> 9 Hitching Post Lane
> Casselberry, FL 32707
> (407) 260-8869   fax (407) 260-2289
> <majicherz@aol.com>

◆ **Green Bay Packers** and other pro football ephemera including autographed balls, programs and yearbooks from before 1990, and other items. No trading cards.
> Gary Alderman
> PO Box 259164
> Madison, WI 53725
> (608) 274-3527   fax (608) 277-1999
> <gjazz@tds.net>

◆ **Sports rings from the Super Bowl and other bowls and confrontations in football, baseball and other sports** including hockey, basketball. Major leagues, minor leagues, college, if it's championship jewelry, give him a try. Your description should include the event, and any engravings or dates on the ring or jewelry.
> Mike Safran
> 204 South Edisto Avenue
> Columbia, SC 29205
> (803) 771-6995   <collect1@scsn.net>

or

> M.B. Spragins
> 501 Adams Street
> Huntsville, AL 35801
> (800) 987-7464 ext 8424   <mbs501@aol.com>

THE OLYMPICS

◆ **Olympic memorabilia** of all types from 1896 to the present such as programs, pins, medals, flags, tickets, uniforms and actual mementos from gold medal athletes. "We pay the highest prices!"
> Joel Platt, Sports Immortals Museum Gift Shop
> 6830 North Federal Highway
> Boca Raton, FL 33487
> (561) 997-2575   fax (561) 997-6949
> <legends@sportsimmortals.com>

◆ **Olympic memorabilia** including all pins, badges, medals, torches, mascots, posters, and everything else Olympic. "Naturally, I'd rather collect items from before 1972, but when you come down to it, I like it all." Particularly interested in purchasing anything from 1904 St. Louis Games and winner's medals from any year. He warns that many items from the 1936 Berlin Olympics have been reproduced. When writing, tell what you know of the item's history.
> Jay Hammerman
> 15630 Softwood Road
> Elbert, Colorado 80106
(719) 495-8938 eves   fax (719) 495-8463   <mjwhammer@aol.com>

◆ **Olympic memorabilia** from the 1932 games held in Los Angeles, including tickets, programs, postcards, photographs, literature, patches, and souvenirs. The more colorful and unusual, the better. Please send a photocopy of what you have.
> Reed Fitzpatrick
> PO Box 369
> Vashon, WA 98070
(206) 567-0555 eves 5-7 Pacific   <reed369@attbi.com>

◆ **Olympic items** from any year they were played.
> Otti Schmitt
> Finders Keepers
> 7724 Hayfield Road
> Alexandria, VA 22315
> (703) 971-4065   <mchughs1@erols.com>

◆ **Olympic pins, medals and participant's medallions** from Olympics prior to 1984 and the following sports from anywhere anytime: soccer, equestrian, swimming, figure skating, gymnastics, track & field and cheerleading. Please make a Xerox™ copy of what you have.
> Margarita Volker, Designs by Margarita
> 19382 Woodlands Lane
> Huntington Beach, CA 92648
> (714) 536-9850   fax (714) 536-9908

★ **Olympic medals, posters, pins, badges,** patches, decals, diplomas, tickets, programs, torches, and souvenir items. Especially wants Olympic torches ($1,000 to $5,000), winner's medals ($1,000 up), participation medals ($100 up) and souvenirs of the 1980 Lake Placid games ($5-$500). Not interested in Olympic souvenir items made after 1980, reproductions, most after-market items, and anything severely damaged. Describe your item carefully, including note all damage. Photo is helpful. Jonathan has been a collector dealer for 20+ years, who also purchases football and baseball equipment. He is author of a recent book on Olympic memorabilia.

> Greg Gallacher
> 301-D Henry Street
> Lindenhurst, NY 11793
> (631) 669-2222 days   fax (631) 669-2581
> <clubhsport@aol.com>

◆ **Olympic medals, posters, pins, badges,** patches, tickets, programs, torches, and the like. Especially wants winner's medals ($1,000 up) and participation medals ($100 up). Not interested in Olympic souvenir items made after 1980. Describe your item carefully, including note all damage. Photo is helpful. Jonathan has been collecting 30 years and the author of three books on Olympic memorabilia.

> Jonathan Becker
> PO Box 4273
> Greenwich, CT 06831
> (203) 532-9112   (203) 532-9136   fax (203) 532-9136
> <jbecker@sportschamp.com> <www.sportschamp.com>

GOLF EQUIPMENT & EPHEMERA

◆ **Golf memorabilia** of all sorts, including:
- Matched sets of wooden shaft clubs and early golf balls;
- **Books, magazines and catalogs** related to pre-1940 golf;
- Paintings, prints and photos with a golf motif;
- Golf **trophies;**
- Paper ephemera, scorecards and programs, catalogs, etc.;
- Miscellany, such as statues and ashtrays.

"If it has a golf motif, I'm interested, and will pay premium prices for premium pieces." Does appraisals for a fee. Accepts select high quality items on consignment for sale or auction.

> Richard Regan
> 293 Winter Street #5
> Hanover, MA 02339
> (781) 826-3537   <foregolf@tiac.net>

◆ **Golf memorabilia** from before 1930, especially:
  • Wooden shaft golf clubs that are in some way unusual;
  • **Books, magazines, and catalogs** related to pre-1930 golf;
  • **China and pottery with a golf motif** by *Royal Doulton, Lenox,* and other fine makers;
  • Golf balls and golf ball molds from before 1930;
  • Miscellaneous items related to "the knickers era."
This 35 year veteran collector wants wooden shaft clubs and old bags. He does not buy trinkets, ashtrays, petty jewelry or reproductions. Frank prefers you set the price you want but makes offers on rare items.
>   Frank Zadra
>   N 5830 County Highway H
>   Spooner, WI 54801
>   (715) 635-2791

◆ **Golf memorabilia.** Wants unusual wooden shafted clubs with patent numbers. Also odd golf balls, such as the pre 1850 ball stuffed with feathers for which he will pay $5,000. "I also buy golf pottery, items of silver, golf medals, pre-1920 golf books, and original art featuring golfers. I do not want clubs with simulated wood grain shafts or anything made after 1920. I'm really interested only in the very old and rare." You should follow standard rules for describing condition.
>   Art DiProspero
>   Highlands Golf
>   25 Rolling Ridge Road
>   Watertown, CT 06795
>   (860) 274-4203   <seasidelinks@aol.com>

◆ **Golf award medals** from before WWII and other pre-1930 golf ephemera. "If it's early and in good condition, ship it insured for my top offer." Items are purchased outright or, if you prefer, taken on consignment for his international auctions. He does not want golf clubs.
>   Rich Hartzog
>   PO Box 4143 BVT
>   Rockford, IL 61110
> (815) 226-0771   fax (815) 397-7662   <hartzog@exonumia.com>

◆ **Golf ball markers** advertising products or tournaments, those used by famous players, male or female, or markers used in major championships. Markers are worth from $1 to $5, depending on their text, picture, and association. Does not want large quantities of a single type. Other golf items such as postcards and medals will be considered.
>   Norm Boughton
>   PO Box 1
>   Macedon, NY 14502
>   (315) 986-3851   <nbought1@rochester.rr.com>

BOXING MEMORABILIA

★ **Boxing ephemera of all types** dealing with James J. Corbett, Jim Jeffries or John L. Sullivan. A clear photo or photocopy is helpful.
>John Buonaguidi
>Monterey Bay Sports Museum
>883 Lighthouse Ave.
>Monterey, CA 93940
(831) 655-2363 day   (831) 375-7345 eve <hawkrise@redshift.com>

◆ **Boxing memorabilia** of all types. "I'm the world's largest dealer in boxing memorabilia. I sell to boxing collectors all over the United States and Canada. As a result, I need to continually replenish stock, which means I am always willing to buy, sell, or trade." Please send a photograph or photocopy of what you have.
>Jerome Shochet
>6144 Oakland Mills Road
>Sykesville, MD 21784
>   (410) 795-5879   <jshochet@radius.net>

◆ **Boxing photos** and autographs from before 1920. Please photocopy what you have.
>Johnny Spellman
>10806 North Lamar Blvd.
>Austin, TX 78753
(512) 836-2889 days   (512) 258-6910   <dvm69@swbell.net>

◆ **Boxing memorabilia** of all types. Private collector who operates a gym seeks posters, programs, tickets, films, photographs, books and magazines about boxing, boxing awards, medals, belts and trophies from any level, Golden Glove to World Championship. "If you have single items or a large collection, whether it's from the earliest days or the present champs, I'd like to hear about it."
>Fred Ryan's Arena Archives
>7217 North Jersey
>PO Box 83135
>Portland, OR 97203
>   (503) 286-3597

◆ **Championship boxing belts, robes, trunks, or gloves** worn by famous champions. Also wants items associated with famous championship fights. Posters, sheet music and games related to boxing. This giant museum buys only quality unusual items that are old and rare.
>Joel Platt, Sports Immortals Museum Mart
>6830 North Federal Highway
>Boca Raton, FL 33487
(561) 997-2575   (561) 997-6949   <legends@sportsimmortals.com>

TENNIS MEMORABILIA

◆ **Tennis memorabilia** such as trophies, figurines, art, postcards, cartoons, tableware, trade cards, lighters, first day covers, and all sorts of other little tennis-related knickknacks from before 1940. He does not want to buy rackets, photos, newspaper clippings, books, autographs, or programs, but "I'll buy any quantity of other reasonably priced items if they send a photo or photocopy and price what they have."

Sheldon Katz
18 Cliffside Drive
Port Jefferson, NY 11777
(631) 928-1800

◆ **Tennis rackets.** "My primary interest is in rackets produced in the 1940's through the 1960's, but earlier ones are considered. Most desirable are frames that were high quality in their day, and that are in excellent condition. Prices range from $1 to about $25 each depending on the age and scarcity." Identify the maker, model, decals, signature, length, any warpage, and the condition of the grip and strings. Also interested in catalogs and other literature picturing or describing rackets. "I can also advise on ball cans and other tennis related items."

Donald Jones
107 Rivers Edge Drive
Savannah, GA 31406
(912) 354-2133 voice/fax

◆ **Tennis ball cans** made of metal. Any can, foreign or domestic, made before 1970 with key type opener will be considered. "I'm not interested in any plastic ball cans or sleeves." Send photo if possible and indicate whether the can has been opened.

Rusty McInroy
1331 West Chapala Court
Tucson, AZ 85704
(520) 797-2030

◆ **Tennis items,** especially ball cans with metal lids, ball boxes, and 12 ball cans, for which he will pay as much as $300 if mint and unopened. "If it had tennis balls in it and it's old, I'm interested." Also buys pre-1940 rackets, lawn tennis sets, tennis trophies, "plus much more." Describe condition carefully.

Michael Murphy
3031 Fairfield Lane
Aurora, IL 60504
(630) 851-5446 eves   <husscutter@aol.com>

AUTO RACING EPHEMERA

◆ **Auto racing memorabilia.** If it's related to auto racing, and in good condition, George will probably want it. He'll buy one piece or a large collection: awards, arm bands, dash plaques, entry forms, flags, goggles, helmets, magazines, models (built or unbuilt), movies, photographs, paintings, passes, postcards, posters, rule books, toys, board games, trophies, uniforms, and "anything else auto racing related." If you know any history of the item, let him know when describing what you have and its condition. This ex-race driver has been collecting 25 years and will travel "a reasonable distance" to buy collections.
George Koyt
8 Lenora Avenue
Morrisville, PA 19067

◆ **Indianapolis 500 pit badges** from before 1952 are wanted, as are race tickets from before 1950, racing programs from before 1941, and all rings or trophies, any year. Jerry will pay $500 for a 1946 pit badge.
Jerry Butak
1496 Crestview Drive
Cottonwood, AZ 86326
(928) 634-6461   <race2collect@aol.com>

◆ **Auto racing ephemera,** including books, programs, posters, and what have you are purchased by this giant dealer in automobile parts, manuals, advertising, and ephemera.
Walter Miller
6710 Brooklawn Parkway
Syracuse, NY 13211
(315) 432-8282   fax (315) 432-8256   <info@autolit.com>

◆ **Auto racing** before 1916, especially items associated with the Vanderbilt Cup races or with the Long Island Motor Parkway.
George Spruce
33 Washington Street
Sayville, NY 11782
(631) 563-4211   <js2wv2@aol.com>

◆ **Drag racing and hot rodding** from the 1940's through the 60's is wanted including: posters, programs, trophies, jackets, racing apparel, speed equipment advertising, car club plaques, hot rod movie posters, hot rod and custom car magazines and hot rod papers. Hot rod club jackets are especially wanted. "The older the better!"
Michael Goyda, Car Crazy
PO Box 192
East Petersburg, PA 17520
(717) 569-7149   fax (717) 569-0909   <goydagang@aol.com>

HORSE RACING MEMORABILIA

◆ **Thoroughbred racing memorabilia** including:
  • Paintings, prints and photographs;
  • Paper ephemera including racing and breeding books, programs, posters, tobacco cards, postcards, games and "the unusual";
  • Kentucky Derby programs, glasses and anything unusual.
  • Phar Lap memorabilia, especially from his 1932 race at Caliente.
All material from all racing thoroughbreds worldwide will be considered, with foreign material and older items preferred. Not interested in anything having to do with harness horses or harness racing.

  Gary Medeiros
  1319 Sayre Street
  San Leandro, CA 94579
  (800) 227-6049   (510) 351-6193   <pharlap2@aol.com>

◆ **Horse racing collectibles** including programs, glasses, books, magazines, posters, photos, postcards, art prints, decanters, parimutuel tickets, lapel pins, buttons, admission items, etc. "I do not want Kentucky Derby glasses after 1974, paper items in poor condition or newspapers except the *Daily Racing Form*." Give the year, condition, and description. He conducts auctions of horse racing items every year.

  James Settembre
  5115 Woodstone Circle East
  Lake Worth, FL 33463
  (561) 964-5434   fax (561) 964-1143   <bigred573@aol.com>

◆ **Dan Patch memorabilia,** especially Dan Patch postcards and a *Dan Patch Coffee* can. Also wants pre-1950 Kentucky Derby programs and drinking glasses featuring horse racing. He will consider other horse racing programs from the turn of the century.

  Gary Gatanis
  3283-B Cardiff Court
  Toledo, OH 43606
      (419) 475-3192   <janis@buckeyeinet.com>

TONY'S TIP: If you haven't read the first 20 pages (thats pages iii through xx in the front of the book), stop what you're doing and read them NOW.
You'll find lots of important information which will make you more successful if you follow directions.

WRESTLING

◆ **Professional wrestling memorabilia** from the 1800's to the present day. "I want anything and everything from pro wrestling: ring worn gear (trunks, shoes, robes, jackets), trophies, championship belts, personal effects, autographs, photos, posters, and scrapbooks. I do have all the magazines and photos I need from the 1990's, though." An accurate description and photo will bring you an offer.

> John "Mr. Wrestling" Pantozzi
> 1000 Polk Avenue
> Franklin Square, NY 11010
> fax (516) 327-8984

◆ **Pro wrestling autographs** and other items are sought, especially signatures of Frank Gotch, Joe Stecher, Dan McLeod, Charley Cutler, Earl Caddock and Wayne Munn. When possible, please price what you have. He wrote Wrestling Title Histories, available from him for $40.

> Royal Duncan
> 428 West Collingwood Circle
> Peoria, IL 61614
> (309) 691-2772   fax (309) 691 2577

◆ **Ephemera related to Frank Gotch,** a turn of the century wrestling champion. He wants posters, postcards, books, photographs, etc.

> Don Olson
> PO Box 245
> Humboldt, IA 50548
> fax (815) 361 5360   <donolson@goldfieldaccess.net>

BODYBUILDING

◆ **Bodybuilding ephemera.** "I'll buy anything before 1975 related to strength, body building, physical culture, weight lifting, strongmen or women, etc. I buy books, magazines, training courses, photos, catalogs, posters, letters, trophies, medals, certificates and videos. I want (1) Weider magazines like *Your Physique,* etc., (2) anything Milo Barbell Company, and (3) anything by or about George Jowett or Eugene Sandow. No magazines after 1970, and nothing currently in print." Describe what you have, give date and condition.

> William Moore
> PO Box 20732
> Tuscaloosa, AL 35402

POOL & BILLIARDS

◆ **Pool tables** (fancier the better), cue sticks and racks, ball racks, antique advertising, catalogs and other items related to pool or billiard playing before 1940. Send a photo and dimensions.
>Ken Hash
>Classic Billiards
>4334 Chapel Road
>Perry Hall, MD 21128
>(410) 391-3333 days   <cbilliards@aol.com>

◆ **Pool and billiard tables** and related items. Wants:
* Pool tables with inlaid designs on the legs or bodies, or with ornate carved or cast iron legs; will also consider tables with round legs and tables in any condition;
* Cue racks with mirrors or in generally Victorian style;
* Cue racks that lock or revolve;
* Ivory balls, with or without numbers;
* Ball boxes that are old or unusual;
* Cues that are ornate and 30+ years old;
* Billiard lights, either gas or kerosene;
* Benches and chairs from billiard parlors;
* Prints, paintings, posters, and other art featuring billiards, especially by Currier & Ives;
* Books on pool, snooker, or billiards before 1940;
* Magazines and newsletters before 1940;
* Catalogs before 1900, especially for Brunswick & Balke or Brunswick Balke Collender;
* Newspapers containing prints or articles on billiards before 1900.

He does not want "bar type" pool tables, tables made after 1940, or plain square legged tables with no inlay. Send a photo of your item and give complete bibliographic information on books.
>Tim Lawrence
>2489 Bexford Place
>Columbus, OH 43209
>(614) 235-9472 eves   <billiard_books@hotmail.com>

◆ **Pool and billiard memorabilia.** Wants interesting and unusual items associated with pool such as light fixtures, cue sticks and racks. Also buys catalogs, advertising, prints and other related items.
>Dilworth Billiards
>300 East Tremont
>Charlotte, NC 28203
>(704) 333-3021 from 1 pm to 1 am

HUNTING & FISHING ITEMS

★ **Fishing tackle** from before 1945 including:
- **Lures** (especially wood with glass eyes or made of hollow metal). Easiest way to describe these is to make a Xerox™ and pencil in the colors of the lures. If made of wood or metal, most lures are $2 and up...and some are way up!
- **Reels:** quality-made fly, bait-casting, and ocean reels that have serial numbers or people's names engraved. Brass or very large reels, especially wanted. There are too many quality reels to list, so ask about all reels except *South Bend, Pflueger, True Temper Shakespeare,* or *Penn.* Dozens of makers have value, some in excess of $1,000. Reels with no names or serial numbers are junk.
- **Bamboo rods in three or four pieces,** stored in cases made of wood, aluminum or cardboard, often packed in a carry bag. Give the name of the maker or owner, usually found in ink or engraved on a metal fitting near where the reel attaches. Does not want "no name" rods or rods made in Japan, no matter how pretty. Other common rods not of interest include *Shakespeare, Montague* and *South Bend.*
- **Tackle boxes:** "If you have a tackle box that contains items from the 1930's or before, you may ship it for my free inspection, evaluation, and offer."
- **Catalogs of fishing tackle** before 1925.

Give names, model, patent dates and numbers, and serial numbers on all equipment. If you have a great many items, you may call collect. Don't overlook empty lure and reel boxes, as some of them can be worth $50 or more. caution: don't clean or polish fishing gear you'd like to sell. "You're likely to damage it. Leave the cleaning to me."

Rick Edmisten
PO Box 686
North Hollywood, CA 91603
(818) 763-9406   fax (818) 763-5974   <mfrogscale@aol.com>

◆ **Old fishing lures,** especially Heddon 7500 vamps. Also odd fish scalers. When writing, include a photocopy of your lures, and indicate their color. For a quick response, please include your phone number.

Thomas McKinnon
Twin Magnolia Farm
8500 Odom Road
Laurinburg, NC 28352
(910) 268-1800

◆ **Antique fishing tackle** including bait and fly reels, bamboo fly and bait casting rods, willow creels, wooden nets, fishing lures (especially those with glass eyes), and early tackle boxes made of leather. Wants to find brass *Snyder* bait casting reels from early 1800's. Also buys fishing equipment catalogs and books. Not interested in anything made in the last 25 years.

Robert Whitaker
2810 East Desert Cove Avenue
Phoenix, AZ 85028
(602) 992-7304   fax (602) 493-5598   <whitakr@msn.com>

◆ **Antique and classic fishing tackle** and ephemera from before 1950. Among items wanted are:
- **Wood or hard rubber lures** in good condition with or without glass eyes, maker marked or not, in good condition;
- **Metal lures** marked with the name of the maker or patent data;
- **Reels** of all types, especially high quality nickel silver or brass, or reels with unusual features, but all will be considered except modern spinning or spin casting reels;
- **Split bamboo rods** in excellent condition in original bag or tube. They do not want metal rods, fiberglass rods, or any rods in poor condition;
- **Flies and fly boxes,** and other fly fishing accessories;
- Fishing paraphernalia, creels, tackle boxes, equipment catalogs, minnow traps, and other tools, boxes and instructions;
- Early **fishing licenses;**
- **Paintings and prints** related to fishing, including calendars, advertising, and cigarette cards, but no damaged artwork.

"We do not want lead sinkers, nylon line, anything made of plastic, clothing of any type, metal rods, fiberglass items or modern spinning reels. We do not want anything made in China, Korea or Japan. We will deal with experts or with novice sellers, but make offers only after inspecting what you have, but do not ship anything without our permission first. Provide photos and as much detailed information as possible. You may call, not collect, between 8am and 10pm Eastern.

Ed and Carolyn Corwin
PO Box 1133
Hastings, FL 32145
(904) 692-2037 voice/fax   <reellures@aol.com>

◆ **Antique and modern fishing tackle** is wanted by an "avid fisher-man" who buys lures, rods, wooden tackle boxes, fly reels, large ocean reels, catalogs of hunting and fishing equipment, hardcover books on fishing, old calendars with fishing motif and early advertising items with fishing graphics. Fair offers made if you include an SASE.
> Lee Pattison
> 5025 Route 19-A
> Gainsville, NY 14550
> (585) 493-9656   <leegail@frontiernet.net>

◆ **Hunting, fishing, and trapping licenses** and tags from all states up to the present. Also interested in entry and use permits for state and national parks. "Photocopies are very helpful."
> Bill Smiley
> PO Box 361
> Portage, WI 53901
> (608) 742-3714 eves   <wsmiley@chorus.net>

◆ **Gun, trap, and ammunition company items** such as posters and calendars (worth to $4,000), catalogs (up to $1,000), empty cardboard shotshell boxes (up to $5,000), pinback buttons (to $500), glass target balls and traps (up to $5,000), gunpowder cans (up to $1,000) and any-thing decorative or informative from before 1940. Does not want paper items that have been trimmed. No NRA items. "I am fair and honest," he says, exhorting, "Try me!"
> Ron Willoughby
> 2281 Lime Kiln Road
> North Haverhill, NH 03774
> (603) 787-2060   <swillo@together.net>

◆ **Old animal traps** of all sizes. Must be in working or repairable con-dition. Especially wants a Newhouse #6 bear trap, which can be worth $1,000. Give the size of the trap and all the words on the item. Russ offers a catalog of hunting and trapping supplies for one dollar.
> William Russ
> 23 William Street
> Addison, NY 14801
> (607) 359-3896

◆ **Boomerangs**, especially signed models by Herb Smith, Al Gerhards, the Janetzki Bros, and others. Also aboriginals.
> Barry Friedman
> PO Box 55492
> Valencia, CA 91385
> (661) 255-2365   <barryf@thevine.net>

◆ **Old duck, crow, owl and goose calls and decoys.** "I'll buy wooden decoys and calls in any quantity." Send a note or call with the description and the price you'd like.

Jack Morris
821 Sandy Ridge
Doylestown, PA 18901
(215) 348-9561

◆ **Fox hunting.** "I collect saddles, jewelry, hunt buttons, clothes, prints and paintings, books, and practically any item depicting hounds, horses, riders, and/or foxes. I also collect any item used in fox hunting such as hunting whip stocks, whip lashes, hunting horns, liquor flasks, side saddles, and the like. Clothing items include old-style jodphers, tall boots, canary vests, and red hunt coats."

Trish O'Brien
PO Box 3014
Glendale, CA 91221

◆ **Wooden decoys** and calls for ducks, geese, crows, and fish. Buys ice fishing decoys, wooden plugs, and early reels made by Meek, Talbot, Milan, or KY Bluegrass (for which he will pay $100 up). Joe quotes prices of $200+ paid for turkey calls made by Gibson. Also buys **various advertising signs related to hunting or fishing**. He suggests you send photos, but may require you to send the item for inspection before he purchases it.

Joe Tonelli (spring-summer)
PO Box 130
Spring Valley, IL 61362
(815) 664-4580

(fall and winter)
PO Box 459
Lake Andes, SD 57356
(605) 337-2301

<tonelli47@hotmail.com>

◆ **Traps of all types** and sizes from fly to grizzly bear. Wants fine fly, mouse, rat, mole, and gopher traps, glass minnow traps and spring operated fish traps. Will buy anything unusual whether made of wood, plastic, wire, cast iron, glass, cardboard, and tin. Also buys patent models, books, catalogs, and advertising (pre-1940) about traps. Does not want rusty or broken traps unless they are odd 19th century items. Send a picture or drawing, a good description, and SASE.

Boyd Nedry
728 Buth Drive NE
Comstock Park, MI 49321
(616) 784-1513

◆ **Animal traps.** Has a special interest in oddly shaped and unusual traps. Will buy all sizes and pay up to $2,500 for unusually large ones. Will also buy pre-1940 trap and fur company catalogs, calendars, advertising items and scent and lure containers. All inquiries will be answered and everyone will be treated fairly and honestly."
> Ron Willoughby
> 2281 Lime Kiln Road
> North Haverhill, NH 03774
>> (603) 787-2060   <swillo@together.net>

◆ **Wooden decoys of any tpe or condition**, including damaged, missing heads, etc. You must include close up side views of both sides.
> Art Pietraszewski
> 60 Grant Street
> Depew, NY 14043
>> (716) 681-2339 eves   <pie48@hotmail.com>

◆ **Mouse traps** made of wood, metal or glass, as long as they are unusual. Also buy fly traps and very large bear traps.
> Steve Kelley
> PO Box 695
> Desert Hot Springs, CA 92240
>> (760) 329-3206   <kskelley@earthlink.net>

◆ **Traps, both animal and insect.** "I'll buy all sizes and types of traps prior to 1940, from large bear traps to small mouse traps, glass and porcelain insect traps, and all literature, advertising, and posters related to trapping. Traps made before 1900 are the most desirable." Please provide the manufacturer's name and any information you can read on the trap, including all numbers. Indicate the amount of rust and the length and type of chain if there is any. "If you can't identify the trap, please send photos and measurements, and I'll respond quickly."
> Frank De Bolle
> 1930 West Gunn Road
> Rochester, MI 48306
>> (248) 652-9148 eves   fax (248) 650-8358
>> <eldebolle@yahoo.com>

TONY'S TIP: Don't forget to include a stamped envelope when you write to someone and want them to answer. No stamped envelope means "don't reply unless interested in buying."

TONY'S TEN TIPS FOR HANDLING AN ESTATE

Handling an estate is difficult. There are people listed in the Yellow Pages who will do it for you. The problem is you will make far less money, perhaps losing tens of thousands of dollars. If you have time, Trash or Treasure can help you simplify the process.

There are only three ways to dispose of things: throw them away, give them away, or sell them. Each has its advantages. Each is appropriate for some types of items. My goal is to make certain you don't throw away or give away valuable items that could be sold.

(1) **Start by simply clearing trash** you can throw out. Trash is broken stuff, badly soiled stuff, moldy clothes and musty magazines, rusty cans, and **obvious** trash. **Don't throw out** piles of business paper, catalogs, brochures, calendars, road maps, etc., before 1940. **Don't discard things in fine condition** including old boxes or cans.

(2) **Don't waste time with poor condition anything.** There is no such thing as "good for its age." Mechanical items like radios, juke boxes, slot machines and similar machines can be sold for parts.

(3) **Sort things into major categories:** toys, furniture, jewelry, sports items, clothing, etc. Use the Table of Contents on pages IV and V as a guide to categories. Read the appropriate chapter in Trash or Treasure Guide to Buyers. Identify and contact possible buyers.

(4) **Focus on categories with high value potential.** Do not dispose of the following items without first finding out if yours have value: fishing tackle, fountain pens, costume jewelry, bicycles, pottery vases, children's marbles, toys and dolls in their boxes, plastic jewelry, designer clothes, plastic characters that advertise products, animation cels, cast iron cookware, lace, art glass, Oriental items, bobbing head sports dolls, catalogs for any product, perfume bottles, mystery fiction with dust jackets, tin cans in fine condition, swords, photos of things other than people, guns, 35mm cameras, briar pipes, posters for any event especially rock and roll, musical instruments, plastic table model radios, electric trains, watches, figurines (a few are valuable), pedal cars, carnival glass, beer mugs, Army and Navy uniforms and patches from any war, 33rpm albums, pre 1950 advertising signs for any products, plastic model kits, Boy Scout patches, Barbie and GI Joe before 1965 especially boxed, Christmas ornaments or lights, anything depicting comic characters ...and more. **Read your Trash or Treasure.**

(5) **Be especially careful of collections.** If large collections of coins, stamps, butterflies, books, records, or anything else is part of the estate, it is possible items of high value may be included. Expert advice is essential whenever substantial collections are involved.

TEN TIPS FOR HANDLING AN ESTATE con't

(6) **Don't waste time** with less valuable things. You won't get much for them which can leave you discouraged. The following items seldom have much collector value: Kodak folding cameras, furniture, fur coats, old sewing machines, Bibles, Jim Beam bottles, National Geographic, movie star autographs, Avon, books in less than fine condition, encyclopedias, plastic cameras, typewriters, 48 or 49 star flags, *Playboys* (other girlies do sell), pull tab beer or soda, comic books after 1960, collector plates, reprints of paintings, china and dishes not listed in Trash or Treasure.

(7) **Have a yard sale as soon as possible.** Lots of the items in an estate are useful to someone, but not collectible. Get rid of things easy to sell to make room in the house for you to work with the good stuff. A yard sale will give you immediate cash to help offset expenses. Sell clothing, books, magazines after 1950, kitchen appliances, autos, silverware, everyday china, modern tools, lawn or garden equipment (unless you're maintaining the house), tractors, washers and the like are good examples. These items are easy to sell through classified ads. Sell your refrigerator last as it's handy while you're still working in the house. Yard sales are fine as long as you're certain the item doesn't have value to a Trash or Treasure buyer. Allow only two days for your yard sale, never longer. You'll have more than one yard sale as you progress with the estate.

(8) **Don't talk about your business when strangers come to your house** to buy things. Don't say the house is sitting unattended; don't complain about handling an estate; don't give any clues that could open you to burglaries.

(9) **Get family members to help.** Negotiate in good faith with one another for family items you want personally. There's nothing like greed to cause hard feelings. Items in dispute can be auctioned within the family, locally or on <ebay.com> where family can bid against everyone else.

(10) **Don't get discouraged.** A good job won't be done in a single weekend. By starting with categories with high value potential, you make the most money and can quit anytime.

IMPORTANT: read the first 20 pages of Trash or Treasure **and** the Tips at the beginning of most chapters. There's lots of valuable information there. **Everything I suggest in these two pages assumes you have first done that.**

MAKE MONEY ON ALCOHOL, TOBACCO, SEX & GAMBLING

If that title doesn't get your attention I don't know what will. You should pay attention, because this is another chapter crammed with great buyers of an incredible array of items... lots of things you already own or can find relatively easily.

In tobacco and liquor collecting, top prices are paid for 19th century items with attractive pictorials, but there are lots of items less than 50 years old that you can profit from.

If making money is your goal, it's important for you to learn about tobacco and beer cans, both of which can put hundreds of dollars in your pocket in a single sale. Someone who wanted to make money would learn about lighters ($5 to $2,000), cigar boxes and labels ($5 to $500), and mugs, glasses, and steins given away by 20th century breweries and soda companies ($5 to $250).

You can profit by buying briar pipes for pennies at yard sales and second hand stores. To make money, look for Dunhill, Barling and Caminetto, worth $25 to $100 to collectors. The shape of a pipe can have a lot to do with the value. Since you probably don't know the difference between an apple, a pear and a bulldog...lay the pipe on a copy machine. A poor photocopy is better than a worse written description.

Thirty pages full of buyers are waiting to hear from you. Nice people, committed to helping you get a fair price and a quick, easy and private sale.

To sell, you should provide the following information:

(1) What is advertised and what is depicted;
(2) Size, color, and the material from which it is made;
(3) Names, dates, and numbers on the item;
(4) Statement of condition, noting missing chips, cracks, and missing parts, pieces, or paint.

When you offer paper goods, photocopy what you offer.

PLAYING CARDS

★ **Playing cards** made in the U.S., poker size (2.5" wide), complete in their original box, made before 1940. "I don't much care what's on the back, as long as it's a complete deck in fine condition." He does not want bridge cards (2.25" wide) or any made after World War II. Make a Xerox™ of the face of the Ace of spades, the joker and the back of any other card. **Also clay, ivory, mother-of-pearl and bone gambling chips** and "better chip racks and holders." No chips that are clay with no design, made of paper or plastic, or that interlock. Send a sample, rubbing or photocopy. Tell how many chips of each color.

> Robert Eisenstadt
> 140 Cadman Plaza West #26C
> Brooklyn, NY 11202
> (718) 625-3553   <chipe@ix.netcom.com>

◆ **Anything concerning playing cards and card games.** Unusual playing cards including transformation cards, non-standard decks, and decks with a different picture on the face of each card. Also single cards in quantity with colorful backs and unusual Jokers, Aces or court cards. Also **books, magazines, and other items on the games of contract bridge, auction bridge, and whist.** Will consider early or limited edition books on other card games as well as plates, figurines, and other **artwork depicting card playing.** Will pay $100 up for Royal Beyreuth china in the pattern called "Devil and the Cards." Photocopies almost essential. Include an SASE to get an answer.

> Bill Sachen
> 107 Victory Drive #227
> Lindenhurst, IL 60046
> (847) 265-3573   <futilewill@aol.com>

◆ **Playing cards and related ephemera.** "I want complete decks of pre-1920 American cards in excellent to mint condition," she says, but indicates a willingness to consider "modern decks of original design." What she doesn't want is double decks of bridge cards, incomplete decks, or single decks of narrow (bridge size) cards without advertising on the Joker or Ace of spades. When contacting her, a Xerox™ of the Joker, Ace, any face card, and the back of the card is the best idea. If you can't do that, you'll need to tell her whether the deck is bridge or poker width, whether it has gilt edges or not, whether the corners are round or square, and the condition. She also wants advertising for cards, and **will consider depictions of card playing** on postcards, trade cards, and the like. She is secretary of the 52 Plus Joker Collector's club.

> Rhonda Hawes
> 204 Gorham Avenue
> Hamden, CT 06514
> (203) 288-6584   <rhawes@snet.net>

★ **Playing cards,** pre-1945, from the U.S. and other countries, as well as **advertising with a card playing theme**. "Packs should be complete, including Joker(s) and other extra cards, and preferably in their original box. I am especially looking for non-standard cards, unusual designs, advertising, pin-ups, comics, political, souvenir, etc., on the faces of the cards. I'll occasionally have interest in a more recent pack, if very odd. I am not interested in standard cards or in foreign cards after 1900. I am also not interested in packs with damaged or missing cards, unless they are extremely unusual. No airline or gambling casino decks. Make a Xerox™ of the Ace of spades, Jokers, and any unusual cards as well as the back. It will help me to appreciate what you have."

> David Galt
> 302 West 78th Street
> New York, NY 10024
> (212) 769-2514   <davegalt@spacedominoes.com>

TONY'S TIP: Buyers usually want "poker size" decks that are two and a half inches wide not "bridge size" decks that are two and a quarter inches wide. Bridge decks date after 1930. **To sell cards the smartest way,** *Xerox™ the Ace of spades, Joker and the back of any card. Photocopies of poker chips are also smart.*

◆ **Casino chips, plaques, and poker chips** from around the world, old or new, as long as they are marked with the name of the casino or club, or the initials of the person for who they were custom marked. His favorites include chips from Cuba and closed Nevada and Atlantic City casinos. No plastic toy store chips, plain clay chips, or items currently in use in the U.S. Give the casino name, denomination, color, and how you came to own the piece. "Happy to give free appraisals."

> John Benedict
> PO Drawer 1423
> Loxahatchee, FL 33470
> (561) 798-2520 voice and fax   <benedict@webtv.net>

◆ **Clay, ivory, or mother-of-pearl gambling chips** and selected other memorabilia. No plain, paper, or interlocking chips. Send a sample, rubbing or photocopy. Tell how many chips of each color. Dale wrote *Antique Gambling Chips,* available with a price guide for $20.

> Dale Seymour
> Past Pleasures
> PO Box 50863
> Palo Alto, CA 94303
> (650) 948-0949   Fax: (650) 941-3695

◆ **Advertising playing cards** from all eras before 1970. Is the deck complete with jokers and original box? Make a Xerox© of the Ace of spades, any face card and the design on the back. Include the box in the photocopy. Cards advertising cigars, whiskey, beer, and politicians are best bets, but any product will be considered. Poker size decks are preferred but bridge size decks with good ads are also sought.

> Robert Newman
> 17220 Silver Lane
> Encino, CA 91316
> (818) 461-9229

◆ **Scratch off lottery tickets.** "I'll buy instant rub-off lottery tickets from the 1970's and 1980's."

> Bill Pasquino
> 1824 Lyndon Avenue
> Lancaster, PA 17602
> (717) 393-0843   <wpasquino@aol.com>

◆ **Lottery tickets.** "I buy instant scratch-off type lottery tickets from anywhere in North America, both used and unused, from before 1990. Special issue and short run tickets are most desirable, as are complete sets such as the Presidential Series, Landmarks, and Bicentennial sets issued by various states. Not every ticket is valuable, but older complete tickets can bring up to original cost or more. Unusual, short run, special issue tickets from the 1990's are purchased.

> Jim Sheridan
> RR#1 Box 72
> Meshoppen, PA 18630
> (570) 836-1626

◆ **Punchboards** that are graphically interesting and unpunched. Give the condition and a photo or Xerox™ copy.

> Clark Phelps
> 390 K Street
> Salt Lake City, UT 84103
> (801) 355-1394   <clarkp@aros.net>

◆ **Books on gambling.** "We can give information as to whether your book or gambling has value if you write, call, or preferably fax." Howard knows more about gambling literature than anyone else alive.

> Howard Schwartz
> Gambler's Book Club
> 630 South 11th Street
> Las Vegas, NV 89101
> (702) 382-7555 (2 to 5pm)   (800) 522-1777   fax (702) 382-7594
> <www.gamblersbook.com>

◆ **Gambling chips, equipment and related advertising** such as:
  • Gambling chips, embossed or made of ivory or pearl;
  • Small pieces of gambling equipment;
  • **Objects with gambling scenes** like lighters, match safes, etc.;
  • **Tins and other packages featuring gambling;**
  • Lobby cards and other movie items featuring gambling;
  • **Catalogs** and literature from makers of gambling supplies.
Please make photocopies or take photographs of what you have for sale.
All items except chips and catalogs should be preior to 1945. He DOES
NOT WANT toys, plastic or paper or plain chips, metal slot tokens,
recent chips, or heavy things like slot machines.
> Robert Eisenstadt
> 140 Cadman Plaza West #26C
> Brooklyn, NY 11202
> (718) 625-3553   <chipe@ix.netcom.com>

◆ **Slot machines,** especially pre-1940. Ted publishes *Coin Machine
Trader* ($20/yr) devoted to ads and information about coin-ops.
> Ted Salveson
> PO Box 602
> Huron, SD 57350
> (605) 352-3870   fax (605) 352-7590   <bjsfam@santel.net>

◆ **Slot machines,** *Wurlitzer* **jukeboxes** (1938-48), **penny arcade
machines** from before 1920, and **vending machines** from before 1910.
> Martin Roenigk
> Mechantiques
> 75 Prospect Ave.
> Eureka Springs, AR 72632
> (479) 253-0405   fax (479) 253-0406   <mroenigk@aol.com>

◆ **Gambling items including slot machines, poker chips, playing
cards,** and other early casino items and advertising. Says he seeks "any
fine condition advertising or ephemera on gambling, including books
and **catalogs on poker, playing cards, and gambling** that were produced before 1960." He requests you tell where you got the item, and
include a photo. Also buys **billiard items.** Sellers must set the price.
> Larry Lubliner
> Re-Finders
> 737 Barberry Road
> Highland Park, IL 60035
> (847) 831-1102   <joker1854@aol.com>

*TONY'S TIP: Slot machines are also purchased by
buyers of coin-operated machines. It might be worth
your while to look in that section as well.*

CORKSCREWS & WINE COLLECTIBLES

◆ **Bottle openers and corkscrews,** especially those that contain advertising for a product or that have patent numbers. "I'm looking for antique items of quality. I don't want openers or corkscrews in poor condition, reproductions, or common modern advertising." He is editor of the newsletter, *Just for Openers* and author of *Handbook of United States Beer Advertising Openers & Corkscrews.* Send a photocopy and, if you're a dealer, the price. Amateurs may request an offer.

> John Stanley
> Just For Openers
> PO Box 64
> Chapel Hill, NC 27514
> (919) 419-1546 <jfo@mindspring.com>

◆ **Corkscrews and wine related items.** Collects hand held and bar mounted corkscrews that are unusual in some way. Also wants wine related items such as wine tasters, pre-1930 bottles, silver or ceramic bottle labels, bottle cradles and buckets, etc. "I have little interest in paper labels." Make a photocopy of smaller items if possible. Describe the others. "I will answer all letters," says Joe.

> Joe Young
> PO Box 587
> Elgin, IL 60121
> (847) 695-0108 fax (847) 695-1679
> <istamp2@aol.com>

◆ **Corkscrews.** "I'm looking for older metal and/or mechanical types rather than the "basic-T" shape, although I will by those in silver or gold. Non "T-type" corkscrews bring $100 and up. Please give dimensions as part of your description." Xerox™ copies helpful.

> Mark Barlow's Winetiques
> 3107-A Medlock Bridge Road
> Norcross, GA 30071
> (770) 449-7610 days (770) 447-6649 eves fax (770) 449-1839
> <mrgbarlow@mindspring.com> <sbbassociates@mindspring.com>

◆ **Wine-related items** such as corkscrews, wine tasters and coasters, holders, cradles, and other fine condition pieces. Give dimensions as part of your description." Photos or Xerox™ copies helpful. No labels or bottles, please.

> Mark Barlow's Winetiques
> 3107-A Medlock Bridge Road
> Norcross, GA 30071
> (770) 449-7610 days (770) 447-6649 eves fax (770) 449-1839
> <mrgbarlow@mindspring.com> <sbbassociates@mindspring.com>

◆ **Corkscrews** that are rare, pretty or unusual, miniature corkscrews, signture corkscrews, old knives with screws, screws with ivory handles, mechanical screws, lady's legs or mermaids with corkscrews, cigar box openers or cigar cutters with screws, corkscrew art, and a good sized list of specific screws he seeks. Send an SASE or email him for a copy of the list. This veteran author and expert collector DOES NOT WANT ordinary "T-type" wood handled corkscrews, modern corkscrews, or broken corkscrews. You are encouraged to visit the corkscrew museum where more than 2,000 screws of the type collectors want can be seen. Don is the author of numerous fine books on corkscrews which may be obtained through him.

> Don Bull
> PO Box 596
> Wirtz, VA 24184
> (540) 721-1128   fax (540) 721-5468   <corkscrew@bullworks.net>
> <http://www.corkscewmuseum.com>

LIQUOR COLLECTIBLES

◆ **Ceramic *Jim Beam* type figural liquor bottles from all makers.** Your description should include the brand name, the figure, all marks on the bottom, the dimensions, and all colors. Bottles must have their original stopper. Mario buys and sells ceramic decanter bottles and offers a price guide to 6,000 different figural bottles for only $5.

> Mario Latello
> 146 Sheldon Ave.
> Depew, NY 14043
>   (716) 685-3031   <mlatello@hotmail.com>

◆ ***Dewar's* scotch figural liquor bottles** made by Royal Doulton. Called KingsWare by Doulton collectors, more than 100 different figural bottles were commissioned in the 1920's and 30's. These distinctive brown-glazed bottles feature various literary characters and English historical figures. He pays $300+ each, says this veteran Royal Doulton dealer, as long as the figure is not chipped or cracked. If you wish to sell yours, telephone with the item in front of you.

> Ed Pasco
> Pascoe & Co.
> 575 SW 22nd Ave.
> Miami, FL 33135
> (800) 872-0195   (305) 643-2550   fax (305) 643-2123
>   <ed@pascoeandcompany.com>

★ **Cocktail shakers and related memorabilia** made before 1960 are wanted by this 25 year veteran collector, especially unusually shaped shakers (golf bags, lady's leg, lighthouse) and designer shaker sets. Chrome sets by revere or manning bowman are also wanted. "I also want anything to do with cocktails including matches, ashtrays, recipe books, posters, etc., from before 1930." Please include a photo or sketch. Measurements are very helpful. Stephen is author of *Vintage Bar Ware Identification & Value Guide.*

> Stephen Visakay
> PO Box 1517
> West Caldwell, NJ 07007
> (914) 358-0024 <svisakay@aol.com>

◆ *Green River* **Whiskey advertising** and that for J.W. McCulloch Distiller, Cliff Falls Distillers or the Oldetyme Distillers, Inc. "I want paper, cardboard diecut signs, display bottles, watch fobs, giveaways, counter displays, and company receipts, letterheads, etc. Will pay $250 for *Green River* shot glasses. Clear pencil rubbings of advertising coins and fobs is a must, as many types exist. I also buy Whiskey or spirits trade magazines such as *Wine & Spirits Bulletin* from before 1920. "No *Green River* soft drink or repro tin signs, please."

> Elijah Singley
> 2301 Noble Avenue
> Springfield, IL 62704
> (217) 546-5143 eves (217) 786-2251
> <greenriver1899@yahoo.com>

★ **China whiskey jugs marked KT&K** on the bottom. Also miniature whiskey and apple vinegar jugs with mottoes, product names or names of liquor stores on them. American pieces only, please.

> Barry Friedman
> PO Box 55492
> Valencia, CA 91385
> (661) 255-2365 <barryf@thevine.net>

◆ *Jack Daniels, Green River Whiskey,* **and** *Lem Motlow* **memorabilia** including crockery jugs, embossed bottles, cork screws, shot glasses, lighters, and old paper advertising. Only older items are wanted.

> Don Cauwels
> 3947 Old South Road
> Murfreesboro, TN 37128
> (615) 896-3614 fax (615) 896-3614
> <colblackjack@msn.com>

◆ *Old Crow* **Whiskey advertising,** promotional items, store displays and signs. Anything interesting, drop him a line, describing completely. He prefers if you price what you have.

William Crow
100 Coupland Road
Odenville, AL 35120

◆ **Miniature whiskey bottles,** bourbons, blends, straights and ryes made in America from 1890 to 1960. Bottles should be two (2) ounces or less with most stating 1/10 pint. All bottles must have paper labels in good condition. Mike will buy one or a large collection, but warns that the price on large quantities may only average a dollar or two because many of the bottles, though old, are common and have minimal value. "Nothing made after 1960 is of interest," he says, pointing out that the date is often found embossed on the bottom of the bottle (often simplified to just two numbers). List the brand name and condition of the label. It's helpful to also give any dates, and the shape of the bottle ("most are flask shaped, he says). Indicate whether it is empty or full. **He has no interest in figural ceramic whiskey bottles** (*Jim Beam* type) or in wine bottles of any type from any period. A few of Mike's fellow collectors seek bottles of scotch, Canadian, vodka, and other booze although they are generally a lot less valuable. "I'll try to help you sell just about any good miniature liquor bottles, or larger American whiskeys from Prohibition or before if they are still sealed and full." More than 30,000 different mini liquor bottles range in value from 50¢ to $100, with half having no value at all. Mike says, "I don't know too much about large whiskey bottles as that's not my area of expertise." He adds, "If you recognize the brand name, it probably has no value."

Michael Olson
MELO
309 Knopp Valley Drive
Winona, MN 55987
          (507) 454-1499   <melosminis@charter.net>

TONY'S TIP: Liquor and beer advertising signs and premiums will often find a ready market among general Advertising collectors and with a few Pop Culture buyers.

If you have early ads for any liquor product...they'll sell!

TONY'S TIP: Don't forget your self-addressed stamped envelope.

BEER COLLECTIBLES

◆ **Anything with the name of a beer on it.** It's called breweriana, and includes glasses, coasters, trays, calendars, label collections, signs, mugs, and anything else used to promote beer. Lynn particularly wants tin signs and other display advertising from the turn of the century. Lynn operates an auction service exclusively devoted to items associated with the golden brew. **No** *Billy Beer* **or** *J.R. Beer.*

> Lynn Geyer
> 300 Trail Ridge
> Silver City, NM 88061
> (505) 538-2341

★ **Beer and soda cans from small regional companies** before 1965. Prefers cone top cans but also buys flat top cans, brewery advertising, signs, trays, statues and glasses from the same period. Especially likes to find items from the Manhattan Brewing Company owned by Al Capone and the Grace Bros. Brewing Company in California. Prices on cans from these two companies tend to start at $500. No rusty cans are wanted by this 10 year veteran collector/dealer, but "some light spotting and aging is natural. I do require cans be sent before a final purchase offer is made because condition so greatly affects the value and I need to examine cans closely."

> Tony Steffen
> 14 N 679 Route 25 #A
> East Dundee, IL 60118
> (800) 498-3215   (847) 428-3150 eves
> <steinland@aol.com>

◆ **Beer bottles and jugs** with painted labels. American breweries only. Most of these are 6, 7 or 8 oz. Has particular interest in finding bottles from NY towns of Horseheads, Buffalo, Rochester, Syracuse and Tonawanda. *Stoney's Beer* and *Bald Eagle* are two PA brands he'd especially like to find. Describe whether the paint is scratched or faded and whether there are neck chips. No soft drink bottles, please, even if bottled in breweries.

> Jim O'Brien
> PO Box 885
> Sugar Grove, IL 60554
> (630) 466-4679

TONY'S TIP: No one wants your Billy Beer or JR beer at any price. You can currently buy a full case of Billy Beer delivered to your door for $35.
The $600 Billy Beer can was a hoax by Billy Beer salesmen that the media fell for..

◆ **Beer cans from U.S. brands before 1950.** "I'll buy all fine condition conetop and flattop cans with no pulltabs. Price is dependent upon the condition and rarity. Mint cone-tops are worth $20 and up. I do not want pull-tab beer cans." Give the brand name, type (beer, lager, bock, etc.), can style and condition.
Steve Gordon
PO Box 632
Olney, MD 20830
    (301) 996-4666 eves   fax (561) 264-3292
    <sgordon@beercanman.com>

◆ **Hamm's brewery memorabilia** including advertising, packaging and bottles, souvenirs, foam scrapers, coasters, bottle caps, kegs, glasses, signs and so on, for all of Hamm's brands. These include *Buckhorn, Velvet Glove, Matterhorn, Burgie, Right Time, Old Bru,* and *Waldech.* When selling glasses or cans, it is important to include all writing that appears on the object. Pete wants everything he doesn't already have and says the areas around Houston, Los Angeles, San Francisco, Baltimore and St. Paul are particularly saturated with Hamm's breweriana, so watch carefully.
Peter Nowicki
1531 39th Avenue
San Francisco, CA 94122
    (415) 566-7506   <portfire86@aol.com>

◆ **Beer uniform sew-on patches** from anywhere in the world. Jim wants any sewn patch: arm, cap, shirt, all ages, all sizes, all breweries. He isn't interested in beer club patches. Please describe condition noting whether it is used or unused, clean or not, and indicate whether it is a "second" or has been cut from a larger patch. Photocopy helpful.
Jim O'Brien
PO Box 885
Sugar Grove, IL 60554
    (630) 466-4679

◆ *Dixie* **beer** and the Lexington Brewery Company ephemera including openers, trays, fobs, mirrors, letterheads, and other give-aways. Please describe what you have and include an SASE. Some company records and other paper might also be of interes.
Thom Thompson
1389 Alexandria Drive, #7
Lexington, KY 40504
    (859) 255-2727 voice/fax   (859) 873-8787 eves
    <thomt@iglou.com>

◆ **Pottery and glass ginger beer bottles,** metal signs, crates, and paper ephemera. Minor chips, scratches, surface crackling OK on most pottery bottles. Glass bottles must be mint (except for case wear on the shoulders). Start by sending a nice clear picture. If there's a serious chance the bottle has some value, you will be required to ship it for his inspection and offer. No offers are made on the basis of photos alone, but you won't be asked to ship anything that doesn't have potential for serious value. Upon inspection, Sven will make you a fair offer. If you refuse a fair and honest offer, "it's the seller's responsibility to pay return postage." Sven is the author of the book on ginger beer bottles, obtainable through him.

   Sven Stau
   181 Crestmount Court #3
   Tonawanda, NY 14150
      (716) 693-4011   <svenstau@cs.com

◆ **Beer related items from the Southeastern U.S.** Buys signs, glasses, labels, cans, bottles, etc., from old breweries in Alabama, Mississippi, Tennessee, Louisiana, Georgia, or Florida. Give a good thorough description, noting any problems with condition. Note all rust, chips, dents, bullet holes and the like.

   Kip Sharpe
   PO Box 8116
   Mobile, AL 36689
      (334) 343-6700 days   (334) 666-6222 eves
      fax (334) 344-1666   <kip3249@aol.com>

TONY'S TIP: Steins marked "Made in Germany" or "Made in Occupied Germany" are seldom wanted by stein collectors, who want their German steins to be made before 1940, and prefer them made before 1920.

Good steins have handles, lids, and decorations.

BEER STEINS & MUGS

◆ **Beer mugs and glasses** are sought by this well known auctioneer.
   Lynn Geyer
   300 Trail Ridge
   Silver City, NM 88061
      (505) 538-2341

◆ **Antique beer steins** are sought, "but I want only quality steins. I am not interested in low end, common steins which sell under $100." **Good steins have handles, lids, and decorations.** The type steins I buy include:

- Regimentals, depicting military themes, 1860-1945;
- Character steins (shaped like people, animals, or things);
- Glass steins, sometimes heavily etched, often colored;
- Steins hand carved of wood, ivory, or unusual materials;
- Steins advertising early breweries;
- Porcelain steins, especially Meissen or **Royal Vienna;**
- Steins and other items made by **Mettlach,** including vases, plaques, humidors, and bowls.
- A few modern steins will be considered: limited editions, U.S. Military, made for **Anheuser Busch** before 1980, made by Villeroy & Boch, or made by **Ceramarte.**

Steins marked made in occupied germany or made in west germany are almost never wanted. Gary conducts about a half dozen stein auctions a year, in various cities around the country. Bidding by mail is allowed at these live auctions. Gary also conducts mail-only auctions of less expensive (under $500) steins. You can sell your steins to Gary outright. He also accepts steins on consignment for auction. Commissions are based on each lot sold (single stein, plaque, pair of plaques, etc.). The commission will be 2% of the selling price plus $30 per lot for mail bid only auctions and $40 per lot for live auctions. There are no other charges. They pay insurances, cataloging storage, transportation, etc. They will pick up large collections anywhere in the country. You will be paid within 40 days of the completion of the auction. Contact Gary before shipping anything for auction. Their UPS address (NOT A MAIL ADDRESS) is Gary Kirsner, 1940 Augusta Terrace, Coral Springs, FL 33071. "If you have steins for sale," says Gary, "contact us. We can discuss the best possible way for you to sell your steins." Gary is the author of numerous books on steins. Three with the most general interest are:

The Mettlach Book (376 pp, 1500 items illus, 1994, $35);
The Beer Stein Book (416 pp, 2400 items illus, 1985, $40);
German Military Steins (112 pages, 340 items illus, $18).

For information regarding auctions, books, etc., call or fax.

Gary Kirsner Auctions
PO Box 8807
Coral Springs, FL 33075
(954) 344-9856   fax (954) 344-4421

TONY'S TIP: *Remember, dealers and collectors can't make offers on what they don't understand. Give clear complete descriptions.*

◆ **Antique beer steins** of all types, from $10 to $10,000 as long as it was made before WWII. This active collector/dealer will buy one or a large collection. A photo is helpful, as are all markings, measurements, and a description of what is portrayed. Don't forget to note the condition of both the stein and lid. He offers free appraisals with no obligation and, if you telephone him with your stein in your hand, "I can usually tell you its wholesale and retail value over the phone."

    Les Paul
    568 Country Isle
    Alameda, CA 94501
        (510) 523-7480   fax (510) 523-8755
        <oldsteins@aol.com>

◆ **Glasses and beer mugs** of all sorts, including:
- Beer glasses, mugs, and steins from closed U.S. breweries and older items from present breweries;
- Horse racing glasses from important races such as the Kentucky Derby, Belmont, and Preakness;
- Etched shot glasses with names of whiskeys;
- Whiskey pitchers;
- Soda glasses and root beer mugs, but only early ones;
- Cartoon and character glasses issued by restaurants, fast food chains, TV shows, and others.

Peter buys outright, and also accepts items on consignment from pickers, dealers and private parties for his twice a year auctions of glasses, mugs, steins and related items. *Budweiser* mugs from the 1970's bring $500+, early 1900's beer glasses $40+, and some cartoon characters as much as $100. He does not want foreign beer glasses, items issued by breweries in the last 10 years, or anything not in mint condition. He suggests you send a picture when possible. His 60+ page auction catalogs are $11 each and come with prices realized for over 1,600 items.

    Peter Kroll's Glasses, Mugs & Steins Auction
    PO Box 207
    Sun Prairie, WI 53590
        (608) 837-4818 eves   fax (608) 825-4205
        <pkroll@chorus.net>

◆ **Beer mugs and steins** made in the 1970's and 80's by the Ceramarte Brazil Company. "I'll buy lidded and unlidded varieties of *Budman*, Busch Gardens, Clydesdales, Olympics, etc."

    Tony Steffen
    14 N 679 Route 25 #A
    East Dundee, IL 60118
        (800) 498-3215   (847) 428-3150 eves
        <steinland@aol.com>

CIGARETTE PACKS & EPHEMERA

◆ **Cigarette dispensers and boxes** especially artsy types: Art Deco, Bakelite, chrome, enamel, glass, pop-ups, Egyptian themes. Near mint condition only. No Japanese wooden birds, plain items or floor models.
Richard Brinn, Maple Island Antiques
5460 Maple Island
Nunica, MI 49448
(616) 788-1154   <rickbrinn@earthlink.net>

◆ **Cigarette packs, tins, and cardboard boxes** from obsolete U.S. brands of cigarettes. No cards, premiums, silks, flat 50's tins, or cigar or tobacco items. Give the series number found on the tax stamp. Dick is president of the Cigarette Pack Collector's Association and editor of *Brandstand,* a monthly newsletter for cigarette pack collectors.
Richard Elliott
61 Searle Street
Georgetown, MA 01833
(978) 352-7377   <cigpack@aol.com>

◆ *Philip Morris* **cigarette packs,** cartons, advertising, signs, premiums, counter displays from the 1920's to the 1960's. He especially wants items with Johnny the Bellhop. The one *Philip Morris* item he does not want is magazine ads of any type.
Charles Evarkiou
3882 Liggett Drive
San Diego, CA 92106
(619) 222-8588   <evarkiou7@cs.com>

◆ *Philip Morris* **ephemera** prior to 1955, including cigarette packs, tins, advertising, signs, stand-ups, matches, buttons, and what have you. This beginning collector does not want reprints, and expects you to price what you wish to sell.
Stuart Morrell
8925 Laureate Lane
Richmond, VA 23236
<ibuycomics@aol.com>

◆ **Tire ashtrays.** Give the tire maker and the "size" printed on the tire. Note what is printed on the glass part of the ashtray.
Ed Natale, Jr.
PO Box 222
Wyckoff, NJ 07481
(201) 493-7172 voice/fax

TONY'S TIP: More buyers of rubber tire ashtrays may be found in the automotive and tire section on p. 344.

◆ **Metal ashtrays with three dimensional people, animals or things attached,** such as airplanes, frogs, etc., which advertise a product. Most are $5 to $15, but has paid $100+ for exceptional pieces. Send a clear photo or a good sketch. Sorry, no SASE, no answer. We DO NOT WANT glass or casino ashtrays, pottery ashtrays, bar ads, ashtrays shaped like states, ashtrays with drunks and lamposts, ashtrays with a guy patting a woman on the behind, etc.

> Tobacciana Resources
> 2141 Shoreline Drive #A
> Shell Beach, CA 93449

◆ **Ashtrays with bronze nude dancers.** Ashtrays are usually marble or seashells with bronze figures from 3" to 6" high. "I'll pay $75 to $125 for them!" Nothing damaged, please. Photo essential.

> Tony Hyman
> PO Box 3000
> Pismo Beach, CA 93448
> fax (805) 773-8436   <thyman@fix.net>

CIGARETTE LIGHTERS

★ **Cigarette lighters.** This veteran collector buys a wide range of quality lighters, but is especially interested in:
- *Zippos* of all type which pre-date the Korean war, fancy or not;
- Lighters made of gold, silver or platinum;
- Enameled lighters;
- Lighters with watches or clocks;
- Lighters in canes or walking sticks;
- Any highly decorated lighter with a complicated mechanism or that is in pristine condition;
- Butane lighters made by *Dunhill, Dupont, Cartier* or *Waterman,* but only by those makers, no others.
- Catalogs, fluid cans, lighter displays, and advertising.

What he doesn't want is silver plated *Ronson* table lighters, lighters made in Japan, Vietnam *Zippos,* and anything in poor condition or that has been tampered with. A complete description includes the name of the lighter, size, condition, color, material it's made of, and its history of ownership if known. Photocopies of the side and bottom are helpful. Terry is Vice President of the Pocket Lighter Preservation Guild and a contributor to *Flint and Flame*, its newsletter.

> Terry & Karen Cairo
> PO Box 1054
> Addison, IL 60101
> (630) 543-9120   fax (630) 834-4051
> <lightergod@aol.com>   <lightergoddess@aol.com>

◆ *Ronson* **cigarette lighters.** "I buy all *Ronson* strikers and touch tip lighters. In addition, I am trying to find all of the different patterns on Princess and Standard pocket models as well as on the Mastercase case lighters." Pieces are marked on the bottom, so please include all info you find there along with a Xerox© of the lighter. Don't forget your SASE if you want an appraisal or opinion of value. Good condition items only. Silver plated Crown and Queen Anne are very common and are not wanted by collectors.

> Barry Hoffman
> 7 Stonemeadow Drive
> Westwood, MA 02090
> (617) 267- 9000   <pakistan@tiac.net>
> fax (781 326-4444   cel (617) 584-5555

◆ **Cigarette lighters and fire making devices.** Buys a wide range:
- High quality *Dunhills, Ronsons,* and pre-1940 lighters, especially *Dunhills* with special features such as being built into a watch;
- Lighters with unusual mechanisms, burning lenses, etc.;
- Table lighters that are in the shape of people or things;
- Automatic lighters made before 1920 by *Thorens, Haway, RK;*
- Lighters consisting of cap, gear, and tinder cord;
- Flint and steel strikers and tinder pistols;
- Designer lighters made of 14K or 18K gold;
- Chemical lighters from 1790 to 1890.

Anything unusual. Has no interest in modern Japanese lighters, butane lighters, and most advertising lighters except those for political personages. Don't bother him with common or recent items. As a basic rule of thumb, he says, "If you've seen it before, I don't want it." Give a basic description including brand name, patent information, ornamentation, construction, and condition. This 20 year veteran collector says, "I'm happy to answer inquiries from beginners or advanced collectors."

> Tom O'Key
> PO Box 6516
> Anaheim, CA 92816
> (714) 630-8919   fax (714) 632-8275   <ibuylighters@aol.com>

◆ *Zippo* **lighters** with Navy and Marine Corps insignia, especially aircraft carriers, submarines, aircraft squadrons, and small craft like minesweepers and patrol boats. If the lighters have ZIPPO PAT 2032695 or ZIPPO PAT 2517191 they are more desirable. Square cornered *Zippos* are very rare. "If they are in fine to mint condition, I also buy fancy lighters by *Dunhill* and lighters made by *Ronson* which are marked ART METAL WORKS, AMW or LVA. Please send photocopies of your lighters along with your Sell-A-Gram and an SASE."

> Jeff Mogilner, Racine & Laramine, Ltd.
> 2737 San Diego Avenue
> San Diego, CA 92110
> (619) 291-7833   fax (619) 297-6653   <axracine@snet.com>

◆ **Advertising lighters, especially** *Zippos©.* Please send a Xerox© of the lighter showing the advertising design..
> Robert Newman
> 17220 Silver Lane
> Encino, CA 91316
> > (818) 461-9229

TOBACCO & OTHER INSERT CARDS

◆ **Cigarette and other insert cards.** Wants all 19th century U.S. cigarette insert cards. This 50 year veteran also wants cards from Brooke-Bond Tea Company and the Liebig Meat Extract Company. He will consider Liebig cards in English, plus menu and calendar cards. Give quantities, and send a photocopy showing samples of the front and back of the cards you have for sale.
> Ron Stevenson
> 4920 Armoury Street
> Niagara Falls, ON
> L2E 1T1 CANADA
> > (416) 358-5497

◆ **Tobacco cards issued by** *Murad* **cigarettes** in their "College Series" only. No other cards. Please photocopy, or send on approval.
> Jack Smith
> 288 Winter Street
> North Andover, MA 01845
> > (978) 686-7250   <smithjohn@mediaone.net>

◆ **Cigarette cards and silks for Canadian, British or U.S. cigarettes.** These world reknown card dealers and auctioneers want only fine condition complete sets of tobacco and other trade cards issued anywhere in the world. Emphasie, don't waste your time and their if your cards are not in fine condition and in complete sets, although they may purchase rare 19th century US cards in less than complete sets if they are in mint like new condition. Send them a Xerox© copy of what you have for sale. If you want catalogs and reference books on cards they are one of the best sources.
> Murray Cards International
> 51 Watford Way
> Hendon Central
> London, ENGLAND NW4 3JH
> > (murraycards@ukbusiness.com>

TONY'S TIP: An excellent book on US tobacco cards is "American Tobacco Cards" by Forbes and Mitchell.

◆ **Cigarette and tobacco insert cards, silks and leathers.** Wants 19th century U.S. items primarily, such as cards by Allen & Ginter, but buys many 20th century pieces. Also buys tobacco advertising trade cards and tobacco related match covers. "Please describe and price, or send on approval. I pay all postage expenses and respond within 48 hours of receipt of your cards. Condition is important as I do not collect trimmed cards, badly creased or otherwise battered items." Does not want flannel flags (often erroneously called "felts").
>William Nielsen
>PO Box 1413
>East Dennis, MA 02641
>   (508) 385-9247

◆ **Cigarette silks given away by cigarette companies** at the turn of the century. Has a particular interest in those illustrating Indians, actresses, colleges and rulers as well as those that are woven rather than printed. He does not want silks (which are actually satin) that are soiled, frayed, stitched or otherwise damaged. "When offering silks for sale, please describe the size and quantity and I will reply with an offer. Within 48 hours of receipt of the collection I will reply with a check for the agreed amount or return the items paying all postage. Xerox™ copies are helpful for estimating." He does not buy flannels (felts) or leather premiums except as part of a large collection of silks.
>Roland DeCesare
>11235 Valley Bend Drive
>Germantown, MD 20876

◆ **Items made of cigarette silks or ribbons** such as jackets, wall hangings, pillows or quilts are wanted. Buying for resale. Please take a photograph or make a photocopy of part of your item. List how many silks of each size, counting only those in fine condition. Also buys high grade American cigarette cards and advertising. Near perfect condition.
>Tobacciana Resources Co.
>2141 Shoreline Drive
>Shell Beach, CA 93449

◆ **Items made of cigarette flannels, silks or ribbons** such as quilts, pillows and wall hangings are wanted. "No junk with tears, stains or other damage," he emphasizes, since everything is purchased for resale. Please take a photograph or make a photocopy of part of your item. **Also buys fine condition collections of silks or flannels.** List how many of each size and indicate what is pictured. Count only those in fine condition.
>Michael Council
>130 Buttles Avenue
>Columbus, OH 43215
>   (616) 299-9099 voice/fax   <equilt@columbus.rr.com>

◆ **All high grade tobacco related collectibles:** "We'll **consider** buying tobacco jars, tobacco tins, cigar labels, catalogs, rare books about tobacco, cigar boxes, posters, advertising and other tobacco related paper, packaging and advertising. We buy only fine quality excellent condition items for resale or museum exhibition. We pay fair wholesale prices and your items get to the right home. An SASE is required for an answer; we regret unavoidably long delays in response for items we do not want to buy." Folks at Tobacciana DO NOT BUY pipes, pipe racks, ash trays, things covered with cigar bands, flat 50 cigarette tins, or anything after 1940. "We buy a **few** magazine ads, and will pay $50 for the 1920± magazine ad for *Cremo* about spit being used on cigars."
> Hank Anthony
> Tobacciana Resources Co.
> 2141 Shoreline Drive
> Shell Beach, CA 93449
> <hankanthony@tobacciana.com>

◆ **Tin tobacco tags and tag collections** are bought, sold, and traded by this very active collector, who offers a free "suggestion sheet for new collectors" that will teach you all about tin tobacco tags. A colorful 2' x 3' poster picturing more than 100 tags in color is available for $17.50. Xerox™ your tags.
> Lee "Tagger Lee" Jacobs
> PO Box 3098
> Colorado Springs, CO 80934
> (719) 473-7101

◆ **Tobacco tags.** Buys both tin and paper types, either individual tags or entire collections or accumulations. "No collection is too large or too small for me to look at." Tin tags should have no rust, paper tags no tears. Small nail holes in tin tags may be OK. Tags dealing with women, blacks and political tops are especially wanted. Give a brief description, the approximate number, and a list of a few of the names on what seem to be the most interesting tags. A photocopy (Xerox©) is helpful, but not essential. Values range from a few cents each to more than $50. He also buys advertising, cards, and posters for chewing tobacco companies.
> Louis Storino
> PO Box 189
> Los Altos, CA 94023
> fax (408) 746-2021   <storino@ix.netcom.com>

◆ *Seal of North Carolina* smoking and chewing tobacco advertising. Does not want tin cans, only lithographed ads. Fine condition a must. Photos appreciated.
> Lisa Van Hook
> PO Box 2666
> Spring Valley, CA 91979
> fax (619) 470-3430   <badbluzz@aol.com>

◆ **Tin tobacco cans** from before 1940. Wants very fine condition smoking tobacco, chewing tobacco and cigar cans and signs only. **Save time and effort by sending a photocopy of the top and front of your tin along with a description of the condition.** SASE is a must. If you regularly pick or deal, he will send you an informative flyer listing some boxes and tins to look for. He DOES NOT WANT *Between The Acts, Bond Street, Briggs, Buckingham, Bugle, Dial, Dills Best, Edgeworth, George Washington, Half & Half, Hickory, Holiday, Humo, John Middleton, Kentucky Club, Model, Philip Morris, Philadelphia Perfecto, Phillies, Prince Albert, Red Jacket, Revelations, Sir Walter Raleigh, Stag, Target, Tuxedo, Twin Oaks, Union Leader, Velvet,* and *Willoughby Taylor.* NO flat cigarette tins, please.
> Tony Hyman
> PO Box 3028 A
> Pismo Beach, CA 93448
> <thyman@tobacciana.com>

◆ **Smoking tobacco bags, pouches and rolling papers,** the earlier the better. Unopened bags are better than those that have been opened or emptied. Also wants information about factories and manufacturers of smoking tobacco. When describing , state the condition and give the date or series number of the tax stamp. Jim is editor of *Roll Your Own,* the newsletter of a club devoted to smoking tobacco collecting. A $20 membership includes their newsletter.
> Jim Cawthorn
> PO Box 1433
> Canyon Lake, TX 78133
> (830) 907-3438

◆ *Old Judge & Gypsy Queen* **Tobacco baseball cards** and other items. Wants any advertising pieces, trade cards, die cuts, and packages. Particularly wants *Dogs Head* and *Gypsy Queen* boxes. *Kalamazoo Bats, Four Base Hits* and S.F.Hess baseball cards and advertising is also of interest.
> Jay Miller
> 4 Tyler Drive
> Darien, CT 06820
(203) 355-5030   (203) 655-2656 eves   <jmiller@sempratrading.com>

TONY'S TIP ABOUT UNITED AND SCHULTE COUPONS:
For almost 30 years, the American Tobacco Company operated United Cigar Stores, the largest retail chain in America, found on street corners nationwide. Every product they sold was accompanied by coupons redeemable for merchandise. Hundreds of millions of coupons were given away. At one time there were 160 redemption centers. They have no value today.

CIGAR EPHEMERA

◆ **Cigar industry items related to making or selling cigars:**
  • **Cigar boxes from the US, Canada or Cuba** from before 1940. If
      the factory number on the starts with T or TP, it's common;
  • **Cigar labels** in sample books or booklets; if what you have is
      framed, he's probably not interested;
  • **Cigar advertising** trade cards, envelopes, and flyers, but no
      magazine ads after 1930;
  • **Photos of factories, cigar counters, floats, etc.;**
  • **Store figures, machines, trade stimulators,** and other items
      found in a cigar store or around a cigar counter.
  • **CMIU (Cigar Makers International Union) anything,** especial
      ly a Sam Gompers letter on letterhead;
  • **Books** w/ titles like **"Directory of the Tobacco Ttrade"** (these list
      cigar and tobacco factories);
Condition important. Please Xerox© the inside lid of boxes. Pays from
$5 to $100+ for cigar boxes. Pays $1,000+ for inlaid boxes owned by
Presidents of Cuba. Send a long SASE for an informative priced wants
list including a useful list of common boxes. Tony's *Handbook of Cigar
Boxes* is in very short supply (w/ Price Guide, $55). He warns, "I have
no interest in cigar bands or items covered with cigar bands."
  Tony Hyman
  PO Box 3028
  Pismo Beach, CA 93448
  (805) 773-6777   fax (805) 773-8436   <thyman@fix.net>
  <www.cigarnexus.com/nationalcigarmuseum>

◆ **Cigar bands** from pre WWII, preferably sets of royalty, Presidents,
playing cards, and other pictorials. No torn, damaged, or partial bands
are wanted. Give the quantity, description, and an SASE. Myron is the
former head of the International Label, Seal and Cigar Band Society.
  Myron Freedman
  8915 East Bellevue Street
  Tucson, AZ 85715
          (520) 296-1048   <miccind@aol.com>

*TONY'S TIP: When you ask someone for information
or an offer, include a long business size #10 envelope,
address it to yourself, and put a stamp in the corner.*
This is a Self-Addressed Stamped Envelope (SASE).
*Use a long envelope because many buyers will send
you information which won't fit into smaller envelopes.
If you do not include an SASE, you are telling buyers not
to bother answering your letter if they are not interested
in what you have to sell.*

◆ **Cigar tip trays, mirrors, watch fobs**, pocket pouches, matchsafes, matchbook holders, match box holders, ceramic table matchbook and match box holding ashtrays, ceramic table matchstrikers, ink blotters, and felt counter change mata. He DOES NOT WANT cigar boxes, labels, bands, tins, signs, posters, pinback buttons, insert cards, match covers or cigar box openers. Take a good photo or make a Xerox™ copy of what you have.

> Mike Schwimmer
> 1201 Yale Place, #610
> Minneapolis, MN 55403
> <reynolds@pro-ns.net>

◆ **Figural wooden smoking stands** of the 1940's and before. These usually depict butlers, bellhops, servants, and the like holding an **ashtray** made of tin. Would love to find patterns, catalogs, and other information regarding who, how and where they were made. Describe as well as you are able. Values range from $50 to $200.

> Claire Savitt
> 4141 Battersea Road
> Coconut Grove, IL 33133
> (305) 665-7348 eves   (305) 666-1466 days
> <thesavitts@aol.com>

◆ **Cigar humidors** by *Tiffany, Dunhill, Davidoff, Benson & Hedges* and *Meridan,* preferably in silver or exotic woods. Has less interest in glass or ceramic humidors, "although I will consider them." Will buy table top, free-standing, and travel styles, paying up to $5,000 for exceptional humidors. Prefers humidors with sporting motif, such as hunting dogs. Not interested in plain or damaged humidors. Give the maker's name, dimensions, and type of material. Photo if possible.

> Francis Lombardi II
> PO Box 181-TH
> Syracuse, NY 13208
> (315) 685-9806   <francis@stellingtank.com>

◆ **Cigar store Indians.** Wants full size wooden or metal figures, especially Punch, Captain Jinks, or Dandy. Take photos from more than one angle or phone with the item in front of you. Also wants items from tobacco factories in Detroit: signs, cans, advertisements, bills of sale, boxes, store figures, photos, cutters, lighters, match holders and trays. Especially wants Hiawatha by D. Scotten.

> Gregory "Dr. Z" Zemenick
> 1350 Kirts Blvd. #160
> Troy, MI 48084
> (248) 244-9426   fax (248) 244-9495
> <drzzeezz@aol.com>

ANTIQUE & BRIAR PIPES

★ **Antique smoking pipes and pipe parts. Also buys books and magazines on pipes, tobacco, and related items.** Primary interest is in meerschaum, but also buys other antique pipes, especially porcelains, and any historical or unusual items including pipes from any culture. Will purchase complete collections as well as individual pipes. Not interested in damaged pipes or reproductions. Give size (length and width), condition, and all other information you can provide.

> Frank Burla
> PO Box 446
> Lisle, IL 60532
>   (630) 271-1317   <fpburla@aol.com>

◆ **High quality pipes of all type** are wanted, including:
- Name brand "pre-smoked" used briar pipes, especially *Dunhill, Charatan, Barling, Castello, Radich, GBD, Kaywoodie* and "others too numerous to mention";
- Meerschaum pipes in good to excellent condition;
- Carved briar pipes;
- Clay pipes that are very large or that have been carved into faces, animals, and other figures;
- Pipe tobacco advertising and books;
- Lighters of many different sizes and shapes.

Larger pipes are particularly desirable. When describing a pipe, include the brand name, its dimensions, shape, finish and all stampings. If you are not familiar with standard pipe shapes, make a photocopy of the pipe and list everything written on the pipe's shank. He does not buy *Medico, Yellow Bole, Dr. Grabow* or other drugstore pipes.

> Gary Donachy
> 1 Forest Court
> Chester, IL 62233
>   (618) 826-3079

◆ **Antique pipes** including carved meerschaums, opium pipes, water pipes, porcelain figural pipes, early bas-relief and high-relief wood pipes and selected clays. Ben is a specialist in the literature of tobacco, and buys books, magazines and pamphlets on all aspects of tobacco culture and use, in any language, from any period. If you are seeking literature on tobacco, he has the world's largest selection on that topic. He has an extensive printed catalog, but please don't ask for it unless you are a buyer of tobacco literature. He is the author of two excellent books on pipes, the one on meerschaum particularly useful.

> Ben Rapaport
> Antiquarian Tobacciana
> 11505 Turnbridge Lane
> Reston, VA 20194
>   (703) 435-8133 until 10pm Eastern

◆ **High grade briar pipes.** Brand names of interest include *Dunhill, Charatan, Barling, Comoy, Castello, Caminetto, Sasieni, Preben Holm,* and *Peterson.* "I'll buy them smoked or new, as long as they are in good looking condition, with no uneven surfaces on the rim, no tooth holes in the stem, etc." Wants collections of pipes, but will buy singles. He especially wants *Dunhills* with "ODA" or "ODB" and patent dates marked on the stem and *Peterson* pipes with Irish Free State or Erie on the shank. Please, no "drug store pipes" like *Medico, Yellow Bole,* or *Dr. Grabow.* When offering pipes for sale, mention any writing on the pipe and its condition. There are dozens of standard pipe shapes, so if you don't know them, send a photocopy of your pipe.

    Marty Pulvers
    Sherlock's Haven
    275 Battery Street, Embarcadero Center West
    San Francisco, CA 94111
(415) 362-1405   fax (415) 362-7048   <priorbriar@aol.com>

◆ **High quality pipes** of all types are purchased by one of the nation's largest and oldest tobacconists. Both modern and antique pipes are bought for resale or for display, but don't bother them with junk. *Dunhill, Comoy, Petersen* and *Sasieni* are among briars purchased. "If they are part of a large collection, we'll buy any pipes, including inexpensive ones, as long as they are in fine condition." Highly carved meerschaum will also be considered. A Xerox© is a good idea. Check your item carefully for damage and mention any defects you find. Also buys antique cigar cutters, cigar cases, and *Dunhill* lighters, as well as other old lighters made of gold or silver.

    Charles Levi
    Iwan Ries & Co.
    19 South Wabash
    Chicago, IL 60603
(312) 372-1306   Fax: (312) 372-1416   <iwanries@att.net>

◆ **Pipes and tobacco items** including:
  • Antique meerschaum (ivory-like) pipes, carved or plain;
  • Briar pipes, old or modern, new or smoked;
  • Pipe tobacco, especially old English tins full;
  • Full old boxes of cigars from Cuba or Tampa only;
  • Books or catalogs about pipes or smoking;
  • Advertising for pipes and smoking tobacco.
Please send photos or Xerox™ copies of what you have and include all information stamped on the pipe. "I am a 40 year collector and will offer more than a dealer." Include an SASE for an offer.

    Lee Pattison
    5025 Route 19A
    Gainesville, NY 14550
        (585) 493-9656   <leegal@frontiernet.net>

◆ **Clay pipes** and clay pipe ephemera. Especially wants figurals, faces, or political clay pipes. Prefers American pipes marked with the name of a city, but buys others. This author-historian buys pipe molds, presses and anything else involved in the making of clay pipes. Also wants billheads, letterheads, checks, catalogs, and other advertising before 1950 for any clay pipe maker. Generally not interested in plain white clay pipes with no markings or decoration. Please make a photocopy of your items, indicating any markings, and tell what you know about their origin or background. Send a long SASE for a list of publications Paul has produced on clay pipes.

    S. Paul Jung, Jr.
    PO Box 817
    Bel Air, MD 21014
        (410) 638-1475   <spjrob@yahoo.com>

◆ **Hookah (water) pipes.** "I'll buy one hose or multiple hose hookahs made of brass, ivory, or other materials. I'm seeking antique pipes, not head shop items, common glass bongs, and other drug paraphernalia. Please send a picture and information about the pipe's background. Dealers should price your goods but I will make offers for amateurs."

    Mark Rivkind
    11265 NW 53rd Court
    Coral Springs, FL 33076

◆ **Pipes with a dog motif.** Meerschaum or briar pipes carved with a dog motif, new or old, smoked or not, even if missing stem. Photo or Xerox™ copy is suggested. Describe color, chips, cracks, holes, etc. Give dimensions, please.

    Mel Rosenthal
    RR #5 Box 5711
    Saylorsburg, PA 18353
        (570) 992-8282   <meljune10@yahoo.com>

◆ **Pipes named *the pipe, the smoke* and *Venturi*** which were made and sold 1965-76. *The smoke* and *the pipe* had bowls made of black pyrolytic graphite inset into pipes made of a variety of materials including real briar. *Venturi* pipes had no bowl liners. All three brands of pipe are clearly marked on the stem: (1) *the pipe* has the initial "p" of "pipe" in the shape of a pipe; (2) *The Smoke* reads THE SMOKE in a stylized script font; (3) *Venturi* has a star dotting the "i." All of these pipes were made of compression molded phynolic resin in a variety of colors. Billie would like to obtain catalogs from wholesalers who sold these pipes: Bissel Corp., Tar Gard and Venturi Corp. He appreciates all information about these pipes, even if the item itself is not for sale.

    Billie Taylor
    131 Snow Hill Avenue
    Kettering, OH 45429
        (937) 294-3817   <smoker@billietaylor.com>

ACCESSORIES, JARS & BOXES

◆ **Tobacco jars.** "If you have old tobacco jars, I may be able to assist you to identify what you have and decide its relative rarity. If you would like to sell a tobacco jar, I can advise you how to go about it, and may be able to steer you to members who may be interested." Joe founded the international club for tobacco jar collectors and edits their newsletter. He has also written *Figural Humidors - Mostly Victorian,* a very fine colorful limited edition you can order through him for $80.

> Joe Horowitz
> 3011 Falstaff Road #307
> Baltimore MD 21209
>   (410) 358-1323   fax (410) 318-6768
>   <jfigtobjar@aol.com>

◆ **Cigar humidors and tobacco jars.** "I collect both plain and figural china, wood, copper or glass. Many jars without a tobacco motif are mistaken for cracker or cookie containers. A cone-shaped receptacle in the lid to hold a sponge is a clue you have a tobacco jar. Please send photo, including any china markings on the bottom. SASE for offer.

> Lee Pattison
> 5025 Route 19A
> Gainesville, NY 14550
>   (585) 493-9656   <leegal@frontiernet.net>

◆ **Snuff boxes of all types,** including early American, Civil War period, and Oriental.

> Eli Hecht
> 19 Evelyn Lane
> Syosset, NY 11791

TONY'S TIP : If you shop yardsales, pipes can put money in your pocket year after year.

You can resell quality used briar pipes for $15 to $100 each, yet they are often found for under $5.

As a general rule, only a handful of brands are resellable, with Dunhill the #1 favorite. Other good brands include Comoy, Barling, Charatan, Castello, Caminetto, Sasieni, Savinelli, and Irish Free State.

Most wooden pipes you will find are what collectors call "drug store pipes," because that's where they were frequently sold, usually at low prices. Some familiar drug store brands are Dr. Grabow, Medico, Wally Frank, Kaywoodie and Yello Bole.

MATCHCOVERS, BOXES & SAFES

◆ **Matchcover collections, match boxes,** salesman's sample books, pamphlets, and other match industry ephemera. Send brief description and SASE to this head of the American Matchcover Collecting Club. Bill is author of the *Matchcover Collector's Price Guide*, available from him for $28 postpaid. This book is highly recommended if you have a great many covers or if you intend to collect or deal.

    Bill Retskin
    PO Box 18481
    Asheville, NC 28814
        (828) 254-4487   <bill@matchcovers.com>

◆ **Matchcovers and match boxes,** foreign or domestic. "I don't want damaged covers generally, but will consider those with minor damage if they're from the early 1930's or before." Wants to know approximately how many covers or boxes you have, whether they are U.S. or foreign, whether they are used or unused, whether the covers are in an album or loose, and whether the matches are present. John is secretary of the Rathkamp Matchcover Society.

    John Williams
    1359 Surrey Road TH
    Vandalia, OH 45377
        (937) 890-8684

◆ **Matchcovers and match boxes.** Wants interesting singles or entire estates. Hiller is a West Coast auctioneer who can handle large collections. The ideal condition for matchcovers is unused, open, with the staples carefully removed. No "grocery store" covers, "Thank You's," or covers not identified as to origin (like Holiday Inn covers that don't give a location). His favorite find would be a matchcover from the Lindbergh welcome home dinner, worth in excess of $100.

    Robert Hiller
    2501 West Sunflower #H5
    Santa Ana, CA 92704
        (714) 540-8220

TONY'S TIP: Matchcovers are not wanted if they are torn or dirty, or if their striker has been cut off. Collectors do not want matchcovers if they are glued, taped, or stapled into a book.

◆ **Match box dispensers** from days gone by are sought by this dealer in contemporary advertising match boxes. Please give a thorough description of the item and indicate whether it works or not. Photo is helpful. As a relatively new collector, he'd appreciate your setting the price, but will make offers if necessary.

> Ed Sabreen
> 907 Glenside Road
> Cleveland, OH 44121
> (216) 381-0100   fax (216) 382 0969

◆ **Match safes.** "I'll buy figural, fancy, trick and unusual match safes (pocket holders for loose matches) and related items such as catalogs, advertisements, and ephemera prior to 1915. I'll take one or a collection, but only quality items. Photograph or Xerox™ along with description and other information. Asking price helpful but not necessary. I will respond to all inquiries."

> George Sparacio
> PO Box 791
> Malaga, NJ 08328
> (609) 694-4167   fax (609) 694-4536   <mrvesta1@aol.com>

◆ **Match safes.** Buys small pocket match safes that are figural (shaped like some object) or if they advertise tobacco products. Xerox™ what you have, rather than take photos which show your safe as a small blur. Prefers you to price your safe(s), understanding that almost all are worth under $100 to him. Sterling match safes that are not in the shape of some object will only bring $15 to $20 depending on the pattern.

> Tony Hyman
> PO Box 3028
> Pismo Beach, CA 93448

◆ **Mechanical match dispensers that give you one match at a time.** Please take a good clear photo and describe what happens to make it dispense matches. Give the measurement of the length of match it takes to operate. Figural dispensers which look like animals, people, insects, etc. are most valuable with prices ranging from $100 up to a few thousand depending on its age, mechanism, condition, and appearance. They DO NOT WANT machines that sell boxes of matches unless they are more than 100 years old. Nothing from the 1900's.

> Tobacciana Resources Co.
> 2141 Shoreline Drive
> Shell Beach, CA 93449
> <curator@tobacciana.com>

EROTICA & GIRLIE MAGAZINES

◆ **Erotica of all types,** all languages, all eras, including hard and soft cover books, sex newspapers, hand typed hard X stories, mimeographed scripts and stories, sex comics, original erotic art, films, photos, statues, and sexually explicit objects of all types. He DOES NOT WANT most magazines. His catalog of items for sale can be yours for $3.

> C.J. Scheiner
> 275 Linden Blvd. # B2
> Brooklyn, NY 11226
> (718) 469-1089 voice/fax   <erosbooks@worldnet.att.net>

◆ **Erotic art in all forms and formats** including statues, paintings, prints, post cards, photography, and three dimensional objects of all kinds from the days of the Roman empire up to the present. Especially seeks Oriental and European bisque or porcelain figures with hidden erotic scenes, revolving lamps from the 50's with pin-up shades, arcade "peep" machines, and photos of all types. Also original art for pin-up calendars or illustrations 1920-1970, especially work by Alberto Vargas and George Petty, but other artists are wanted including Earl Moran, Gil Elvgren, Zoe Mozert, Armstrong, Alk Buell, Al Moore and others. Also Vargas Esquire calendars and prints, other calendar pin-ups, and some homemade erotica, including obscene letters written by private parties. Describe condition. A photograph or photocopy is suggested. Include your phone number when you write.

> Charles Martignette
> PO Box 293
> Hallandale, FL 33008

◆ **Erotica of all types,** including nude photos and photo books, original art and paintings, Oriental or European, and three dimensional materials of all sorts.

> Ivan Gilbert, Miran Art & Books
> 2824 Elm Avenue
> Columbus, OH 43209
>   (614) 236-0002

◆ **Girlie magazines** published by Parliament from the 1950's, 60's, and 70's. Buys *Playboy* from the 1950's only. Buys related girlie material, calendars, and paperbacks, but nothing from the 1980's. Fine condition only. Catalog of magazines for sale is $3.

> Warren Nussbaum
> 29-10 137th Street
> Flushing, NY 11354
>   (718) 886-0558

TONY'S TIP: Stains and cut outs are not acceptable.

◆ **Girlie magazines published by** *Parliament, Nuance, Marquis* **or** *Briarwood.* Will pay $1 or $2 each for these publishers **ONLY.** Will pay 25¢ to $1 each for similar girlie magazines from the 1960's to 90's by other publishers. Pays $5 each for *Puritan* or *Private* and $1 to $5 for other xxx. Complete clean copies only. "**No embarrassment. No need to write or call. Ship one or a hundred for immediate cash.** Ship via Post Office 'Media Mail' and I'll reimburse. **For safety, don't put more than 20 or so magazines in a carton.** Heavy packages tend to break in the mail. Every shipment evaluated individualy." He DOES NOT WANT bondage magazines, or those featuring fat or biracial. No *Playboy, Oui, Penthouse, Hustler, Chic, Club, Club International, Playgirl* or *Forum.* Thanks.

> Hank Anthony
> PO Box 88
> Avila Beach, CA 93424

◆ **Autographed** *Playboy* **playmate ephemera** including covers, gate-folds, and partial pages, but the photo must be from the magazine. Items may be dedicated ("To Bill," etc.), but those without dedications are preferred, and bring from $20 to $50. Autographs of other women (actresses, models, celebrities) who have appeared in Playboy will be considered but only if they have signed the cover or photo spread in which they appear. Photocopy what you have.

> David Kveragas
> 1943 Timberlane
> Clarks Summit, PA 18411
> <hiwind2000@aol.com>

◆ **Men's magazines** with two or three pictorials (*Adam, Stage, Rogue, Sir, Male,* etc.) from any period. Must be in fine condition, with no cut outs, moldy smell or other damage. No need to write. No embarrass-ment. Just ship. I pay 25¢ to $1 each and your postage in cash. No more than 20 or so magazines in a carton, so they're not too heavy.

> Hank Anthony
> PO Box 88
> Avila Beach, CA 93424

◆ **Alberto Vargas illustrations,** 1918-1960. "I'll buy magazine cov-ers, Ziegfeld Follies posters, and other Vargas art depicting nudes, but only his work before he began drawing for *Playboy.*" He does not want *Esquire* calendars unless they have their original jackets and is not interested in any of Vargas's *Playboy* art.

> David Kveragas
> 1943 Timberlane
> Clarks Summit, PA 18411
> (570) 587-3429

◆ **Condom tins,** especially those with "nice colorful graphics" are wanted. The *Akron Tourist Tubes* tin which pictures a blimp is worth "about $250" but your old *Sheik, Ramses* and *Merry Widows* have no value nor do any tins in poor condition. Best if you make a Xerox™ of your tin to show its condition.

> Dennis and George Collectables   **November to May**
> 3407 Lake Montebello Drive   323 Sandpiper Lane
> Baltimore, MD 21218   Delray Beach, FL 33483
> (410) 889-3964   \<dandgtins@aol.com\>   (561) 243-3072

◆ **Condom (prophylactic) and feminine hygiene vending equipment,** fine condition condom tins (the older and more colorful the better), and advertising relating to condoms or prophylactics, especially before 1960. Will buy single items or large lots.

> Mr. Condom
> 1635 Acorn Ano Road
> Somerset, KY 42501
> (606) 274-4848

◆ **Burlesque, strippers, and sexy dances.** Buys photos, posters, signs and any unusual items related to these skinful arts. Likes to find 3-D picture books and unusual pictorial items, especially art originals.

> Charles Martignette
> PO Box 293
> Hallandale, FL 33008
> (954) 454-3474

◆ **Betty Brosmer photos** and other items related to this 1950's pin-up queen, including magazine covers and stories, newspaper articles, film loops, and videos of her TV appearances. Xerox™ copies of paper items are helpful. Date them if you can.

> Harold Forsko
> 35 Abrazo Aisle
> Irvine, CA 92614
> (949) 261-6228 eves   \<harold_forsko@msn.com\>

◆ **Provocative or obscene photographs** including nudes, semi-nudes, candids, home made pictures, outdoor frolicking, etc., from teasing to hard core pornography. Also pin-up photos of dancers, starlets, and sexy ladies of all ages and periods.

> Charles Martignette
> PO Box 293
> Hallandale, FL 33008
> (954) 454-3474

MISC. HISTORIC EPHEMERA

◆ **"The Beat generation" ephemera.** Wants items associated with "The Beat Generation" of the 1950's including books, records, posters, handbills, leaflets, underground newspapers, pins, comics, buttons, and other items, with a particular interest in the poets and authors associated with that era: Ginsburg, Rexroth, Burroughs, and Kerouac. Please state the condition, date, and how the item was stored.

> Richard Synchef
> 208 Summit Drive
> Corte Madera, CA 94925
> (415) 927-8844

◆ **Civil rights movement.** Wants buttons and paper ephemera, flyers, handbills, and pamphlets related to the civil rights movement.

> Peggy Dillard
> PO Box 210904
> Nashville, TN 37221
> (615) 646-1605 eves   <pdill43795@aol.com>

◆ **Immigration memorabilia.** "I'll buy documents, photos, pin-back buttons, ribbons, passports, pre-1920 naturalization certificates, books, postcards, and other material related to immigrants, Immigrant Aid Societies, Immigrant Social and Political Clubs, Ellis Island, Castle Garden, and ethnic festivals before 1950." **Has particular interest in Chinese immigration memorabilia**, and will consider purchase of anything having to do with movement of Chinese in the U.S. prior to 1950, including items related to Chinese laundries and Chinese social and political clubs. Also Immigration and Naturalization Service forms and documents from before 1930. Photocopy please.

> K. Sheeran
> PO Box 520251
> Miami, FL 33152

◆ **Paper ephemera from radical movements** including the Tories of the American Revolution, the social and political radicals of the 1800's, the labor unionists, women's suffrage, etc., right down to and including the Black activists, Peace movement, and other "hippies" of the 1960's. Wants letters, documents, posters, broadsides, books, and pamphlets.

> Ivan Gilbert
> Miran Arts & Books
> 2824 Elm Avenue
> Columbus, OH 43209

★ **Hippie items.** Wants items associated with the Counterculture of the 1960's including books, records, posters, handbills, leaflets, underground newspapers and comics, buttons, bumper stickers, etc., representative of 1960's student activism, the anti-war movement, Haight-Ashbury, the 1968 Democratic Convention, Abbie Hoffman, Jerry Rubin, Timothy Leary, anti-LBJ, anti-Nixon, SDS, Yippies, Chicago Conspiracy Trial, the Black Panthers, drugs, Woodstock, Kent State, and the Grateful Dead. He does not want JFK items, jewelry, comic book reprints, Watergate, or common lp's. State condition, date, and how the item was stored.

> Richard Synchef
> 208 Summit Drive
> Corte Madera, CA 94925
> (415) 927-8844

◆ **Civil Rights movement** memorabilia emphasizing items relevant to Black Americans, including Jim Crow signs (but only if authentic). Rare or one-of-a-kind items with strong provenance connected to a Black historical event or issue are most desired. "I don't want to buy books, sheet music, stereoviews, postcards, or any reproductions." Send a description, including the condition. You may set the price wanted or request offers. "I buy, sell, and trade."

> Elizabeth Meaders
> 94 Mersereau Avenue
> Staten Island, NY 10303
> (718) 727-0703

◆ **Political protest buttons from the 1960's** or before including civil rights, anti-war, leftist and student movements, etc. "I'm interested in any and all items, but their condition must be excellent. I do not want cracked, scratched or foxed items at any price." Send a Xerox of what you have along with a self addressed stamped envelope. Most buttons are from $3-$10.

> Michael Engel
> 43 Bryan Avenue
> Easthampton, MA 01027
> (413) 527-8733   <mengel44@aol.com>

◆ **Slave tags.** These were small metal tags worn by slaves to indicate their status or occupation. Pays $200-$600 and up for tags reading servant, porter, mechanic, seamstress, fisherman, fruiterer, etc. Some rare types, dates, styles, or occupations can bring $1,500 or more. Call collect or ship insured for his offer. Do not clean the tags.

> Rich Hartzog
> Box 4143 BVT
> Rockford, IL 61110
> (815) 226-0771   fax (815) 397-7662
> <hartzog@exonumia.com>

◆ **Socialism and Communism in the U.S. before 1940.** "I'll buy anything pre-1940: books, magazines, leaflets, brochures, buttons, postcards, pennants, etc., that were produced by radical groups such as the Communist Party, Socialist Party, I.W.W. (Industrial Workers of the World), Socialist Labor Party, etc. Would especially like to find the magazines *Masses, New Masses,* and *International Socialist Review.*" Mike will purchase items written in Yiddish, Italian, and other foreign languages, but "I'm really not too interested in material not written in the U.S.A." What does Mike consider important? "Condition! Condition! Condition!"
Michael Stephens
2310 Valley Street
Berkeley, CA 94702
(510) 843-2780

◆ **Labor union and Socialist material.** "I buy just about everything relating to organized labor, unions, and working people" including dues buttons and books, pins, convention and parade ribbons and badges, photographs of workers or unions, programs, contracts, labor trade cards, union magazines, books, etc.s. "I'd like to find items about labor leaders, and the old and unusual from groups like the Knights of Labor, I.W.W., Railroad Brotherhood, AFL, and CIO. I'll consider anything but am most interested in learning about items before 1960."
Scott Molloy
550 Usquepaugh Road
West Kingston, RI 02892
(401) 874-2239 days   (401) 782-3614 eves   <molloy@uri.edu>

◆ **Cigar Maker's Union** and **Samuel Gompers.** "I'd like anything from or about the Cigar Maker's Union or its top officers, including pamphlets, regulations, photographs, and letterhead" especially **a letter by Samuel Gompers on CMIU stationery.** Include a photocopy.
Tony Hyman
PO Box 3028
Pismo Beach, CA 93448
(805) 773-6777   fax (805) 773-8436   <thyman@fix.net>

◆ **Mining and miner's Union items.** Wants United Mine Workers of America or the Western Federation of Miners Union including photos, books, letters, ribbons, badges, etc. Also photos of mining activity, especially in Southern California. Miner's carbide and oilwick lamps, candle boxes and explosive items are also of interest. He does not buy reproductions or anything in poor condition. Appraisals are for a fee, but he will make offers if your item is legitimately for sale.
Deric English
24261 Sage Avenue
Boron, CA 93516
(760) 762-6208   <djcenglish@ccis.com>

ROYALS & FRAT BROS

★ **British Royal commemoratives.** Buys nearly any fine condition pictorial item, including ceramics, textiles, tins, plates, mugs, medals, busts, jewelry, paperweights, dolls, postcards, programs and more from various ceremonies and events involving British royalty from Queen Victoria to Queen Elizabeth Reign, including Prince Charles, Princess Diana, and Prince William. Will consider single items or large lots. Please send an SASE with complete descriptions, including condition. Photo or photocopy is desirable. Please do not send anything without prior approval. Audrey is the author of *British Royal Commemoratives*.
> Audrey Zeder
> 1320 SW 10th Street #T
> North Bend, WA 98045
> > (425) 888-6697   <royalbritish@aol.com>

◆ **British and European Royalty.** "Anything that's colorful, interesting, and in fine condition. No junk, no plastic, and nothing damaged."
> Pat Klein
> PO Box 262
> East Berlin, CT 06023
> > (860) 828-6528 days   (860) 828-3973 eves
> > <pklein262@yahoo.com>

◆ **All fraternal order materials** that are small and flat, such as coins, tokens, medals, badges and ribbons. Especially interested in Masonic chapter pennies and hand engraved badges of precious metal. Will consider larger BPOE items or unusual fraternal items. If what you have is pre-1930, you may either make a Xerox© copy and send it with an SASE or you can ship your items to him for an offer. Hartzog will send you a check for the lot. He claims to pay higher prices than anyone else.
> Rich Hartzog
> PO Box 4143 BVT
> Rockford, IL 61110
> > <hartzog@exonumia.com>

◆ **Odd Fellows items** including badges, medals, banners, posters, jewelry, furniture, arks, collars, signs, windows, lighting fixtures, rugs, and anything else with the three link emblem on it.
> Greg Spiess
> 230 East Washington
> Joliet, IL 60433
> > (815) 722-5639 days   fax (815) 722-0171
> > <spiessantq@aol.com>

◆ **Mafia or organized crime** items including books about organized crime, magazines with major features on organized crime, photographs of criminals and crime scenes, autographs of members of organized crime, videotapes, recordings, government reports, and any other memorabilia or artifacts. **"I'd love to find a poster from the Italian American Civil Rights League meeting of June 28th, 1971."** Wants nothing fictional.

> Ron Ridenour
> PO Box 357
> Moorpark, CA 93020
>   (800) 457-7473 days   fax (213) 382-2501
>   <ron@pipe.org>

◆ **Newsboy statues around the U.S.** including souvenir replicas, advertising for the figurines, and photos of any statue of a newsboy. Replicas of the statues bring $50 or more. Give the material it's made from, the dimensions, and mention any damage.

> Gary Leveille
> 5 Brook Lane
> Great Barrington, MA 01239   <garyleve@aol.com>

◆ **3-D metal replicas of famous buildings** and monuments. Buys paperweights, banks, salt and pepper shakers, ashtrays...anything that is made of metal into a three dimensional representation of a famous place or structure. He does not want miniatures that you can buy today: Eiffel tower, US Capitol, Empire State building, Statue of Liberty, etc. Identify the building, give dimensions, and report any names or marks on the piece.

> Dave Forman
> 215 10th Avenue North
> St. Petersburg, FL 33701
>   (727) 553-9380   <forvid@aol.com>

◆ **Metal souvenir buildings** of all types, either presentation pieces, models, give-aways or souvenirs sold at the building. The older and more unusual the better. Condition is important. Please indicate what the building is (and where) and if it is part of an ashtray, lighter, award, etc. Size and material helpful and a photo is appreciated. Please include an SASE along with your querry. If you can't take a photo, a sketch will usually do.

> Barry Hoffman
> 7 Stonemeadow Drive
> Westwood, MA 02090
>   (617) 267- 9000   cel (617) 584-5555
>   fax (781 326-4444   <pakistan@tiac.net>

POLITICS

◆ **Presidential political items of all sorts.** Will buy buttons, banners, ribbons, and paper material, especially from candidates of the 1920's, Coolidge, Davis, Harding, LaFollette, Cox, Hoover, Smith, and Debs, with a strong interest in Calvin Coolidge. Please don't send him any Kleenex button reproductions, other reproductions, or anything in poor condition. This well known collector/ dealer has been active for 30 years. He requests a Xerox™ and thorough description. The price you'd like is appreciated but "I will make a fair offer if you have no idea of an item's value."

    Larry L. Krug
    Americana Resources
    18222 Flower Hill Way   #299
    Gaithersburg, MD 20879
        (301) 926-8663   fax (301) 926-7648
        <larry.krug@amres.com>

◆ **Abraham Lincoln presidential campaign memorabilia** including items related to his various opponents: Douglas, Bell, Breckinridge, McClellan, and Jefferson Davis. Will buy flags, banners, posters, tokens, ribbons, and photo badges. This 30 year veteran collector/dealer does not want autographs, engravings, newspapers, magazines, memorial items created after his death, or commemoratives of any sort. "I'll only buy items issued during an election or for Lincoln's two inaugurations." He wants a photocopy or photo, or a sketch with dimensions and information about material, inscriptions, and all defects. "I must see an item before I buy." Don edits *The Rail Splitter Quarterly*, available for $24/year.

    Donald Ackerman
    PO Box 3487
    Wallington, NJ 07057
        (973) 779-8785 eves   fax (973) 744-1517
        <provenance@viconet.net>

◆ **Political buttons, tokens, and ribbons** and other items from any election before 1925. Consignments to his auction are invited. Send a Xerox™ or ship your item for his offer.

    Rich Hartzog
    World Exonumia
    PO Box 4143 BVT
    Rockford, IL 61110
        (815) 226-0771   <hartzog@exonumia.com>

★ **Presidential memorabilia** including glass, china, campaign buttons and ribbons, **White House gift items**, inauguration medals, invitations, **Xmas cards**, etc. This long time veteran expert will pay $4,000 for a mint condition Theodore Roosevelt inaugural medal. Author of *Collectors Guide to Presidential Inaugural Medals and Memorabilia.*

H. Joseph Levine
6550-I Little River Turnpike
Alexandria, VA 22312
(703) 354-5454 fax (703) 914-0547
<jlevine968@aol.com>

◆ **Political campaign items of all kinds.** Top priority given to better 19th century items, especially those associated with Abraham Lincoln and his contemporaries in the Civil War period. "I'll buy buttons, badges, ribbons, banners, tintypes, portrait flags, and three dimensional objects," says this 25 year veteran dealer /collector, but he is not interested in any buttons later than 1960 (Kennedy/Nixon), or in 20th century buttons that do not have pictures or something unusual. Except for political quilts, he does not buy commemorative items not actually issued as part of a campaign. A photocopy or photo "is of great help." Third party candidates from all eras are a special interest as well.

Cary Demont
PO Box 16013
Minneapolis, MN 55416
(763) 522-0957 <caryd8@aol.com>

◆ **Presidential, gubernatorial, and Congressional campaign memorabilia.** "I'll consider any and all items used in a political campaign for president, governor, U.S. Senate or the House of Representatives, including buttons, ribbons, banners, pennants, posters, and 3-D items like canes and hats." You are encouraged to inquire as " an item may look common but be very scarce." Send a Xerox™ copy. If this is not possible, this veteran of 21 years collecting and dealing asks you to give the size, color and condition of your item.

David Quintin
PO Box 800861
Dallas, TX 75380
(972) 625-7189 (972) 625-6971
<dqtexas@aol.com>

TONY'S TIP: Political buttons after Johnson - Goldwater **are in little demand** *as most of them are widely available on the net.*

292 POLITICS

★ **Presidential campaign memorabilia** including political buttons are
wanted. Of special interest are:
- All pre-1896 campaign items including lapel badges, ribbons,
  bandannas, posters, cans, and "just about anything else"
  related to Presidential candidates;
- Campaign buttons and similar small items related to Presidential
  campaigns from 1896 through the campaign of 1972;
- Buttons for 3rd part candidates, social issues, labor, anti-war,
  civil rights and other causes from 1896 to 1972;

Ted would like to see Xerox™ copies and have you note any defects
such as stains, scratches or cracks as all damage has an effect on value.
For larger items, a photo is recommended, giving dimensions and again
noting any damage. Ted does not buy buttons newer than 1952 that
have only a candidate's name. You should check the inside of your button's edge and watch for the words "Kleenex," "A-O 1972," or
"Reproduction" as a great many reproduction buttons exist. Tentative
offers can be made from photocopies or photographs, but final evaluation depends upon personal inspection prior to payment. "Payments are
made immediately upon receipt if condition matches the description."
Ted is one of the country's largest buyers of campaign and pop culture
items (see his listing in that category) and is **author of numerous
books on political buttons, campaign collectibles and pop culture**
which are considered standard references among collectors and dealers.
You are encouraged to send an SASE for a catalog of available titles.

Ted Hake
Hake's Americana Dept 343
PO Box 1444
York, PA 17405
(717) 848-1333 10-5 Mon-Fri fax (717) 852-0344
<hake@hakes.com>

◆ **Presidential campaign items:** buttons, badges, ribbons, tokens,
canes, flags, china, posters, bandannas, banners, torches, lanterns, and
novelty items. Does not want books. Has been buying and selling these
items for 30+ years, and offers catalogs for $3 each.

Historical Collections
PO Box 42
Waynesboro, PA 17268
(717) 762-3068

◆ **Presidential campaign buttons, ribbons, and posters.** This active
collector does not want common buttons like "I Like Ike" or "Nixon's
the One." Offers free appraisals, but an SASE is a must.

Peggy Dillard
PO Box 210904
Nashville, TN 37221
(615) 646-1605 eves <pdill43795@aol.com>

◆ **Political buttons from state and local candidates** before 1930, the more odd and obscure, the better." Also buys other early campaign items, paper, ribbons, etc., used by mayors, congressmen, state legislators, county and municipal officials. Most desirable are buttons from famous persons and Presidents running for minor offices early in their career. "I'm interested in any and all items, but their condition must be excellent. Most buttons are $3-$10 with some much higher, but I do not want cracked, scratched or foxed items at any price." Send a Xerox of your button along with a stamped envelope.

Michael Engel
43 Bryan Avenue
Easthampton, MA 01027
(413) 527-8733   <mengel44@aol.com>

◆ **Election memorabilia of all types,** 1780-1960, for resale, especially higher quality items.. Wants china, ribbons, mirrors, clocks, glass, paintings, textiles, etc., that are political or patriotic in content. "I'll pay from $500-$5,000 for small historical medallions with pewter rims and lithographed portraits of military and political figures." Rex does not do free appraisals. Please don't contact him unless you want to sell. He does not want paper items after 1896.

Rex Stark Americana
PO Box 1029
Gardner, MA 01440
(978) 630-3237   fax (978) 630-2388
<rexstark@yahoo.com>

◆ **Women's suffrage items:** "I'll buy anything related to the suffrage movement. I'm particularly interested in pinback buttons, badges, posters, ribbons, banners and 3-D items that say votes for women and related slogans. I Especially seek items that picture or mention Victoria Woodhull, Belva Lockwood, Susan B. Anthony, or Carrie Nation. If you send a photocopy, I'll pay top dollar."

Cary Demont
PO Box 16013
Minneapolis, MN 55416
(763) 522-0957   <caryd8@aol.com>

◆ **Women's suffrage and political campaign items,** especially 19th century buttons, ribbons, posters, and pennants.

Ken Florey
84 Laurel Crest Road
Madison, CT 06443
(203) 245-1461   <florey@mail.snet.net>

◆ **William Jennings Bryan and Thomas Dewey memorabilia** of all types are wanted. Please send a Xerox™ or send your item for an offer.
   Rich Hartzog
   World Exonumia
   Box 4143 BVT
   Rockford, IL 61110
         (815) 226-0771   <hartzog@exonumia.com>

◆ **Richard M. Nixon collectibles.** "I'll buy campaign collectibles, anti-Nixon items, and Watergate related ephemera including, but not limited to, buttons, jewelry, textiles, glassware, medals, coins, games, novelties, pens and pencils, pocket knives, keychains, stamps, stickers, caricatures, matchbooks, postcards, puzzles, headgear…almost anything picturing or referring to Nixon." He does not want magazines, posters, bumper stickers, and newspapers. He is interested in Nixon's entire history as a public figure. Please send a "crisp photocopy or photo of the item along with a description of all flaws such as foxing, chips, scratches, fading, etc." Include the price you'd like (although he will make offers to amateurs) and SASE if you want photos returned.
   Eldon Almquist
   975 Maunawili Circle
   Kailua, HI 96734
         (808) 262-9837 eves   <nixcol@aol.com>

◆ **Gubernatorial (governor) or U.S. Senate race political buttons** from any state. Pays $25-$50 each for those he can use. Photocopy. Describe condition if there are any problems not evident.
   Dave Quintin
   PO Box 800861
   Dallas, TX 75380
   (972) 720-4714 days   (972) 625-7189   <qgtexas@aol.com>

*TONY'S TIP: Some collectors pay for information where a particularly rare item might be found. **So if you see something in an antique shop that you think is nice, you may get a fee for reporting it.** Give as much information as you can, but most important, don't forget the phone number of the antique shop in which the item can be found.*

◆ **Tennessee and other Southern political items.** Interested primarily in races for Senate, Congress and Governor in any Southern state. Pictorial buttons a favorite. Xerox© what you have.

> Peggy Dillard
> PO Box 210904
> Nashville, TN 37221
> > (615) 646-1605 eves   <pdill43795@aol.com>

◆ **North and South Carolina political buttons** and ephemera with a special interest in locating items from Taft's 1909 visit to Charlotte. Asks that you photocopy and describe all defects.

> Lew Powell
> 700 East Park Avenue
> Charlotte, NC 28203
(704) 358-5229   (704) 334-0902   <lpowell@charlotteobserver.com>

◆ **Canadian election memorabilia,** pin back buttons and badges from Canadian political campaigns before 1965, especially material on John MacDonald and Wilfred Laurier. Small items may be sent on approval. If Mike does not buy them, he will reimburse your postage.

> Michael Rice
> PO Box 286
> Saanichton, BC
> V8M 2C5 CANADA
> > (250) 652-9412 eves   <mrice@pacificcoast.net>

TONY'S TIP: It's important to remember things don't always go up in value.

Jim Beam bottles, Avon, Levis, and Cabbage Patch dolls are only a few of the items selling for less now than they were a few years ago.

The art market is still a long way from fully recovered from its large dip in prices. Tin cans are selling for less today than they did 10 years ago as are hula dolls and a good many electric trains.

When you save an item for a rainy day, the rain might turn out to be your tears.
Sell now.

POLITICAL SYMBOLS

◆ **American flags.** "I'll buy cloth flags from 6" to huge. Prices depend upon the pattern in the stars, size, condition, construction technique, etc. "The following will give an idea of the minimum prices that this particular social studies teacher pays for flags:
  - 13's are almost always reproductions and not wanted;
  - 15 to 35 stars bring $85 to $1,000 or more;
  - 36, 37, 38, 40, and 41's bring $65 to $500;
  - 43's and 47's are worth $95 to $500;
  - 44's are only $45 to $100;
  - 39, 42, 45, 46, and 48's are wanted only if they have an unusual configuration of stars or have pictures or advertising; these are definitely not wanted if the stars are in straight rows. Sellers may add 50% more for unusual configurations such as circular, stars in stars, overprinted flags containing some message, or if they are all hand sewn. If the flag advertises a political candidate, prices should be multiplied by at least five times. Description should include the size, condition, and star pattern. No repros or pictures of flags."

Mark Sutton
2035 St. Andrews Circle
Carmel, IN 46032
(317) 844-5648

TONY'S TIP: 48 star flags are common. They are also legal to fly, so do. It's not collectible.

◆ **Statue of Liberty.** Wants French bronzes of the statue, books from before 1890, advertising items depicting or satirizing the statue, tin signs or containers, bottles, thimbles, lamps, medals and tokens, and other 19th century items related to Liberty or sculptor Auguste Bartholdi. Wants U.S. Committee 6" or 12" pot metal models sold to raise money for the pedestal and will pay $300 to $1,000. Wants early ones only. Photo or photocopy requested. Not interested in postcards or centennial items.

Mike Brooks
7335 Skyline
Oakland, CA 94611
(510) 339-1751   <miniwave@aol.com>

◆ **Statue of Liberty items.** What have you? Send a photo or photocopy of what you have to this well known stamp dealer.

Harvey Dolin & Company
111 Fulton Street, Mezzanine floor
New York, NY 10038
(212) 267-0216

INDIAN ARTIFACTS

◆ **Indian artifacts** including arrowheads, stone axes, celts, pipes, flints, ceremonial pieces, bannerstones, birdstones, baskets, beaded items, pottery, rugs, blankets, masks, wooden bowls, and any other Indian related items. He will pay high prices ($500-$1,000) for ancient birdstones he can use for his own collection. Please list what you have and make a drawing or photocopy, giving all measurements. Include your home and work phone. This 40 year veteran holds 4-6 auctions a year of Indian artifacts and is always ready to buy or sell good items.

Jan Sorgenfrei, Old Barn Auctions
10040 State Road 224 West
Findlay, OH 45840
(419) 422-8531 days   Fax: (419) 422-5321
<obauction@webtv.com>

★ **Antique American Indian and Eskimo items.** Buys quality items made before 1920 by Indians and Eskimos: baskets, bead work, quill work, pottery, clothing, weapons, old Navajo rugs, and blankets. He'll even buy beaded souvenirs made by Indians (like match holders, picture frames, etc.). If you've got a 16 foot long birch bark canoe, he might buy that too. **He does not buy any Indian jewelry, arrowheads and other stone, books, or modern items purchased ten years ago at a trading post on the Interstate.** A photo is a must, and please list dimensions and any flaws the piece has in your first letter. Dealers, price your goods, as he makes offers to amateur sellers only. Answers inquiries promptly. This veteran collector is an advisor on Indian collectibles to several antiques publications, can handle any size collection, and is willing to refer you to other buyers. "If you have quality items to sell, chances are I can put a deal together for you."

Barry Friedman
PO Box 55492
Valencia, CA 91385
(661) 255-2365   <barryf@thevine.net>

◆ **Hopi and Zuni Pueblo Kachina dolls.** "I especially want those made between 1900 and 1940. Other Indian items, dance wands, costume parts, pottery, baskets, and jewelry from Southwest Indians are also of interest." Kachina dolls can range in value from $100 to $5,000 or more, but there are many fake Kachinas. "An expert can tell the difference." He'll need a photo and all background information.

John C. Hill
Antique Indian Art Gallery
6962 East First Avenue #104
Scottsdale, AZ 85251
(480) 946-2910   fax (480) 946-7410   <antqindart@aol.com>

TONY'S TIP: The value of an Indian artifact depends on its age, condition, workmanship, size, eye appeal and authenticity. Because values can be quite high, it's a good idea to check out all Indian items which have been in your family since before World War II.

◆ **Museum quality American Indian relics.** "I'll buy fine baskets, pre-1900 Plains bead work, quill work, weapons, Southwestern pots, pre-1940 jewelry, Kachinas, early Navajo weavings, blankets and rugs, Northwest Coast masks and carvings, Eskimo objects, old photos of Indians, and more. Some of these items can be worth $10,000 or more." Dan does not want arrowheads, stone material, anything modern, small pots, or reproductions of early work.

> Daniel Brown
> PO Box 149
> Davenport, CA 95017
> (800) 492-6786   (408) 426-0134
> <green-garnet@sbcglobal.net>

◆ **Indian baskets, pottery and other art** are wanted by this nationally known folk art expert.

> Louis Picek
> PO Box 340
> West Branch, IA 52358
> (319) 643-2065   <msantiques@bigplanet.com>

◆ **American Indian and Eskimo art and artifacts,** including rugs, crafts, baskets, pottery, weapons, and clothing, especially old beaded buckskin moccasins. The museum does not buy modern Indian items. Prefers a color photo be sent with your inquiry. Prefers you price what you have to sell, but "our appraiser will suggest a value for your item, but only after examination of it in person."

> Lynn Munger
> Potawatomi Museum
> PO Box 631
> Fremont, IN 46737
> (219) 495-2340

◆ **Indian totems and carvings** from before 1950, including good quality items made for the tourist trade. Please provide a physical description, noting all obvious signs of damage. If you know the history of the ownership of the item, please give that information as well. Photos are helpful.

Edwin Snyder
PO Box 156
Lancaster, KY 40444
(606) 792-4816 eves

◆ **Seminole Indian items of all type** made before 1930.

Douglas Hendriksen
PO Box 21153
Kennedy Space Center, FL 32815
(321) 867-2551 days (321) 452-0633 eves
<fl_collector@mpinet.net>

◆ **Stone age artifacts,** including stone and bone tools, arrowheads, blades, pottery and other art and utilitarian objects. This 18 year veteran collector/dealer does not want modern American Indian items. Please include a photo with your description.

Scott Young
PO Box 8452
Port St. Lucie, FL 34985
(561) 398-7506 <iceageman5@aol.com>

COWBOY ARTIFACTS

◆ **Silver mounted parade saddles** and spurs by all makers, especially G. S. Garcia, Edward H. Bohlin or Visalia Stock Saddle Company. Always seeking quality cowboy items, such as fancy antique chaps and boots. Please send complete details along with a photo. This veteran collector is Indian/Western advisor to several antique publications.

Barry Friedman
PO Box 55492
Valencia, CA 91385
(661) 255-2365 <barryf@thevine.net>

◆ **Antique cowboy regalia** such as chaps, holsters, belts, badges, hats, boots, saddles and lassos. Also buys *Colt* and *Winchester* guns and rifles pre-1900. No reproductions or fakes. You must include photo and your asking price, and will be expected to ship for inspection.

Pierre Bovis, The Az-Tex Cowboy Trading Co.
PO Box 5529
Santa Fe, NM 87502
(520) 318-9512 fax (520) 318-0023 <bovisp@hotmail.com>

◆ **Cowboy equipment and regalia** including:
  - **Spurs** of all types except English and new military. Especially wants unusual spurs that are silver and maker marked;
  - **Cuffs** made of leather, chaps, hats, scarves, and fancy boots;
  - Western **saddles,** pre-1920, all types if maker marked, including black military McClellan saddles;
  - **Saddle bags** with maker's marks;
  - Reatas, quirts and bridles that are marked, tooled, or carved;
  - **Horse bits** more than 50 years old with silver mounts or inlay; some plain and/or foreign bought; inquire about any old bit;
  - Prison made spurs, horse bits, quirts, belts, and lead ropes;
  - **Catalogs for saddle makers** pre-1936;
  - **Photographs** of old cowboy scenes;
  - **Advertising related to the frontier,** especially watch fobs;
  - **Movie posters of cowboy movies;**
  - **Casey Tibbs,** famous rodeo rider promotional items, scarves, endorsed items, movie posters, rodeo posters, personal items;
  - **Books** by Will James.

Especially wants marked spurs authenticated as having been made for some well known personality. Does not want anything made in the last 25 years or made in the Far East. In your description, make certain to describe all marks. Give dimensions and mention all damage or repairs. He prefers you to set the price, but will make offers to amateur sellers. No guns! Will buy single items or collections for resale.

Lee Jacobs
PO Box 3098
Colorado Springs, CO 80934
(719) 473-7101

◆ **Cowboy gear** from before 1940 including Western guns, chaps, spurs, bits, brand books, law badges, saddles, reatas, quirts, cowboy hats, boots, vests, neckerchiefs, leather cuffs, early knives, beaded or embroidered gauntlets, and fine braided bridles or other items. Also wants old related catalogs, photos, documents, books, maps, and other items related to the life of the cowboy. He is most interested in spurs, holsters and cartridge belts which have maker's marks. Exceptional items can bring many thousands of dollars. Send a good photo and a description of your item, including a statement of condition. This 30 year veteran collector and museum curator, does not want horse collars, harnesses, and other farm related items. Bill's Cowboy and Gunfighter Collectibles, complete with price guide, is $22.

Bill Mackin
Museum of Northwest Colorado
1137 Washington Street
Craig, CO 81625
(970) 824-6717

◆ **Cowboy clothing, gear, artifacts and ephemera.** Wants everything associated with both working cowboys and badmen and peace officers: clothing, trail maps and brand books, wanted posters, "historically important letters," photos of cowboys, badmen, and peace officers. Has strong interest in anything you have relevant to the lives of Samuel Colt, Sam Houston and Benito Juarez.

> Johnny Spellman
> 10806 North Lamar Blvd.
> Austin, TX 78753
> (512) 836-2889 day   (512) 258-6910 eve   <dvm69@swbell.net>

◆ **Antique Western items** including boots, Stetson hats, gold-braided Mexican sombreros, chaps, leather cuffs, saddlebags, holsters, photos, letters of lawmen or gunfighters, rodeo pennants, tack catalogs, horsehair items made in prison, trunks covered with hide, and the like. This veteran price guide advisor will buy or broker any size collection. "If you've got good stuff, I can move it for you."

> Barry Friedman
> PO Box 55492
> Valencia, CA 91385
> (661) 255-2365   <barryf@thevine.net>

◆ **Steer horns from the 1930's or earlier.** "Older horns are wrapped in various types of old cloth, buggy seat material, or natural hair. The wrapped center piece will usually be no more than 12" or 13" wide. Old horns will usually be various shades of yellow, brown, or dark green, frequently with black tips. Newer horns, which I absolutely do not want, are wrapped in tooled leather, vinyl or rope and are usually ivory or a mottled color. Newer ones also have wide, often 18" space between horns. The best old horns have heavy amounts of twist and curl, are mounted on a wood backboard, and are five to seven feet wide from tip to tip. The wrapping on most old horns is frequently in poor condition, so I am much more concerned with the condition of the horns themselves, with no cracks or serious bug damage. A photo is a must. Include the measurements from tip to tip and the measurements across the middle piece where the cow's skull would have been. If you can't send a color photo, make certain to describe the twist and the color of the horns, as well as the type of material." **He also wants to buy photographs of longhorn cattle.**

> Alan Rogers
> 1012 NE Shady Lane Drive
> Kansas City, MO 64118
> (816) 436-9008   <kcstockyards@aol.com>

WEIRD & MORBID THINGS

◆ **Anything odd, unusual or morbid,** especially:
- **Two headed calves and other freak animals,** natural or man-made, alive or mounted and preserved;
- **Mummies, skeletons** and human skulls;
- **Shrunken heads** and other headhunter and cannibal items;
- **Funeral equipment,** coffins, embalming kits, and tombstones;
- **Torture and execution devices** and photos of executions;
- **Mounted reptiles,** trophy heads and uncommon animals;
- **Man-made mermaids** (up to $300);
- **Medicine show photos** and literature;
- **Tattoo equipment,** tattoo photos, and tattooed skin;
- **Voodoo and black magic** ephemera;
- **Flea Circus props** and photos;
- **Human oddity photos** and artifacts.

For 50+ years, this wheelchair bound vet has been buying odd, unusual, and bizarre items for public exhibit in his traveling and stationary museums. He does not buy furniture, clothing, plates, or jewelry. If you have something you think he might want, send a photo, a description, a statement of condition, and your lowest price.

    Harvey Lee Boswell
    Palace of Wonders
    PO Box 446
    Elm City, NC 27822
       (919) 291-7181

◆ **Human skulls,** preferably with more than 30 teeth. Send a photo or description, any background of it you know, and your phone number.

    Mark Miller
    PO Box 52261
    Philadelphia, PA 19115
       (215) 464-3561 voice/fax
       <70176.1153@compuserve.com>

◆ **Giant people.** "I'll buy postcards, pictures and other information about American giants (not the sports team, but real giants) including giant rings, souvenirs sold by giants, books by or about giants, etc."

    Don Gorlick
    PO Box 24541
    Seattle, WA 98124
       (206) 824-0508   <seashore8@hotmail.com>

◆ **Animal trophies, skulls, skins, fur rugs, teeth, claws, horns, antlers,** etc. If it's an animal trophy of any sort, they may be interested. Condition of the fur is important. Please give your phone number with your description.

> David Boone
> Boone Trading Company
> PO Box 669 (mail)   562 Coyote Road (shop)
> Brinnon, WA 98320
> (360) 796-4330   (800) 423-1945   fax (360) 796-4511
> <sales@boonetrading.com>

◆ **Skulls, skeletons, tusks, teeth, fossils, shrunken heads and mounted insects.** This relatively new dealer does not make offers.

> Ronald Cauble
> The Bone Room
> 1569 Solano Ave.
> Berkeley, CA 94707
> (510) 526-5252   <evolve@boneroom.com>
> <www.boneroom.com>

◆ **Shrunken heads** from the Jivaro tribe. Please send a photograph or description, including whatever history of the item which you know, including how you came to own it, where you bought it, etc. Include your phone number.

> Mark Miller
> PO Box 52261
> Philadelphia, PA 19115
> (215) 464-3561 voice/fax
> <70176.1153@compuserve.com>

◆ **Funeral ephemera.** "I'll buy things having to do with funerals such as funeral parlor advertising, mirrors, ribbons, trays, badges, and other items issued by funeral parlors. I am not interested in caskets, funeral or embalming equipment, or cemeteries."

> Rich Hartzog
> PO Box 4143 BVT
> Rockford, IL 61110
> (815) 226-0771   fax (815) 397-7662
> <hartzog@exonumia.com>

◆ **Death and postmortem photos,** casket photos, black bordered photos, hair lockets with photos, as well as dissection and other unusual medical photos.

> Steve DeGenaro
> PO Box 5335
> Poland, OH 44514
> <sdegenaro@aol.com>

BLACK & NEGRO MEMORABILIA

◆ **African-American historical memorabilia.** This serious historian/collector/dealer wants artifacts and paper associated with the history of African-Americans in the United States.
- **Black militaria.** "I will buy any and all items specific to African-American participation in wars from the Revolution through Vietnam, especially named medals, uniforms, equipment, documents, photos, and prints.
- Books dealing with Black military history;
- Items associated with **historically important Blacks,** including sports and entertainment figures, "the earlier the better;"
- **Slavery items;**
- **Jim Crow signs,** but only if authentic;
- **Civil Rights movement** memorabilia.

Rare or one-of-a-kind items with strong provenance connected to a Black historical event are most desired. "I don't want books, sheet music, stereo cards or postcards, or any reproductions." Send a good description, including the condition. You may set the price wanted or request offers. "I buy, sell, and trade."

    Elizabeth Meaders
    94 Mersereau Avenue
    Staten Island, NY 10303
      (718) 727-0703

◆ **Items depicting Blacks in an exaggerated, comic or derogatory manner** "I'll buy anything made before 1920 with Black Americans (not African natives) such as minstrel posters, spoons, toys, advertising, figurines, sheet music, postcards, trade cards, and the like." Emphasizes that he does not want reproductions. This authority on Black American items wants a careful description of condition.

    Sam Ginsberg
    PO Box 24944
    Ft. Lauderdale, FL 33307
      (954) 566-3344   <losam@aol.com>

◆ **Black memorabilia that is comic or exaggerated** including cookie jars, plates, lamps, clocks, salt and pepper shakers, table cloths, towels, plaster or ceramic items, and other household items depicting Blacks. "I also buy advertising pieces of all kinds that depict a Black person, including whiskey ads, *Aunt Jemima* items, *Cream of Wheat* packs, *Uncle Ben's Rice* memorabilia, etc."

    Diane Cauwels
    3947 Old South Road
    Murfreesboro, TN 37128
(615) 896-3614   (615) 896-3614   <colblackjack@msn.com>

◆ **Items depicting Blacks in an exaggerated, comic or stereotypical way** including cookie jars, older dolls, toys, kitchen items, prints, Black folk art, children's books, *Uncle Remus*, advertising items, *Aunt Jemima*, *Cream of Wheat*, *Amos 'n Andy*, and "all items relating to Blacks in America. Buys one piece or a collection." Wants include Golliwogs, *Little Black Sambo*, Nicodemus, Pickaninnies, etc. "I also buy literature, poetry, humor, and other books by or about Blacks. I want vintage entertainment related minstrel material, Amos 'n' Andy, Josephine Baker, Hattie McDaniel, etc. I do not buy African art or artifacts, slave items, or KKK material. No magazine ads or reproductions. All offers welcome and will be answered if you include SASE."

Judy Posner, winter
PO Box 2194
Englewood, FL 34295
(941) 475-1725
<judyandjef@aol.com>

June-September
RR #1 Box 273
Effort, PA 18330
(570) 629-6583

◆ **All items depicting Blacks in a manner that is exaggerated, comic, or realistic** including dolls, folk art, sewing items, walking sticks, miniature bronzes, jewelry, paintings, valentines, playing cards, games, children's books, cookie jars, string holders, spoons, Golliwogs, linens, jigsaw puzzles, candy containers, Christmas ornaments, and items associated with the *Our Gang* comedy's Farina. No postcards, sheet music, trade cards, photos, outhouse figures, ads, large signs, damaged items, or reproductions. This active dealer/collector does not make offers.

Jan Thalberg
23 Mountain View Drive
Weston, CT 06883
(203) 227-8175   <mightyfinejan@yahoo.com>

◆ **Popular portrayals of Black dancers** on sheet music, figurines, postcards, etc. Wants dancers doing the cake walk, jitterbug, etc.

William Sommer
9 West 10th Street
New York, NY 10011
(212) 260-0999   <wgs2@columbia.edu>

◆ **K.K.K. items** of all type, including robes, swords, pamphlets, jewelry, knives, badges, medals, china, banners, books, letters, newspapers, magazines, figurines, rituals, etc. This buyer is a serious historian of this movement, not a Klan member. "Please, no hate mail."

Historical Collections
PO Box 42
Waynesboro, PA 17268
(717) 762-3068

SCOUTING MEMORABILIA

◆ **Scouting items from Boy Scouts, Girl Scouts and Lone Scouts,** especially before 1940.
- Uniforms, badges, and pins. Patches with WWW from Order of the Arrow lodges, and badges from Senior Scout and Explorer groups particularly needed;
- Rank and Honor medals: lifesaving medals, medals for war service, Eagle, Ranger, Silver, Ace and Quartermaster medals, and World Jamboree medals; he notes that some medals are worth $1,000;
- Girl Scout uniforms (either blue or khaki) with badges, Golden Eaglet pins, senior GS pins in blue or green, and leader pins;
- Cub Scout items marked CUBS USA, not with CUB SCOUTS BSA;
- Girl and Boy Scout dolls, soft or composition, in all sizes, if complete. Kenner *Steve Scout* dolls from 1975, if mint in box. All *Steve Scout* accessories, such as a summer uniform;
- Scout toys and games, including figures, boards, etc.;
- Scout table model *Bakelite* radios from the late 1930's;
- Official books and other literature including manuals and magazines before 1930, merit badge pamphlets and Cub Scout literature from before 1940, and "all Air Scout stuff".
- Historical items related to founders of Scouting, including Baden-Powell, Juliette Low, Seton, Beard, West, Boyce, and Robinson. Also wants books by or about these people.
When you are offering things to them for sale, they remind "a photocopy is worth 1,000 words."
> Fran and Cal Holden
> PO Box 264-H
> Doylestown, OH 44230
> (800) 663-2793   <goodoldayscal@aol.com>

◆ **Girl Scout memorabilia.** "Try me for anything that says or means Girl Scout." She especially wants very old items, Mariner and Wing Scout items, Senior GS items, all pre-1945 items, World's Fair items, war time items, and items from Camp Edith Macy, Our Chalet, and Our Ark. Make certain to note condition and whether any-thing is missing. Asking price is appreciated. Since she will buy so many items, it is important to note **she does not want** the following: handbooks after 1918, 1940's green uniform, 1960's green cotton or Dacron Brownie and Intermediate uniforms, 1960's forest green two piece senior uniform, 1970's or 80's uniforms, any mess kits, canteens, back packs, sleeping bags, and other big camping gear after 1925.
> Phyllis Palm
> PO Box 5272
> Mt. Carmel, CT 06518
> (203) 288-9190   <poohdingaling@worldnet.att.net>

◆ **Boy Scout memorabilia** and patches, especially Order of the Arrow patches with WWW on them (for which he will pay from $2.50 to $1,000+). Items from National Order of the Arrow conferences from 1948 and earlier are especially sought, although staff items from all NOAC's are needed. Early Order of the Arrow National Committee items are needed such as the red felt sash which is worth $2,000. Pre-1960 National Jamboree staff items are wanted, as are pre-1955 World Jamboree items. As a general rule, the older the patch, the better. However, this does not apply to patches which have only local interest such as camporees, Scout-O-Ramas, Scout circus, and other local items. Ron says, "before you sell, compare what I pay to other offers."
>   Ron Aldridge
>   250 Canyon Oaks Drive
>   Argyle, TX 76226
(940) 455-2519 eves   fax (940) 455-5094   <noacman@aol.com>

◆ **Boy Scout items** of all sorts wanted. Of special interest are Order of the Arrow patches (worth $3 to $150+), Eagle and other medals, pins, and items from World Jamborees 1920-1951 (worth $50 to $300). Interested in games, postcards, and books and uniforms before 1950. No camping items, tents, mess kits, canteens, etc.
>   Doug Bearce
>   PO Box 4742
>   Salem, OR 97302
>   (503) 399-9872   <bearce@prodigy.net>

◆ **Boy Scout items,** Eagle awards, and Order of the Arrow patches (marked OA., Lodge, or W.W.W.). "I'll pay from $1 to $100 for most, though some very scarce items may bring $1,000 or more. I need a photocopy, although you may send what you have for sale to me and if we can't agree on a fair price, I will return it and pay shipping costs both ways." He does not want handbooks printed after 1915, first aid kits, neckerchief slides, belt buckles, knapsacks, tents, or camping gear.
>   Greg Souchik
>   PO Box 133
>   Custer City, PA 16725
>   (814) 362-2642   fax (814) 362-7356
>   <director@armormuseum.com>

◆ **Girl Scout memorabilia.** Wants to buy pre-1960 catalogs, postcards, magazines, uniforms, equipment, and other items. Handbooks before 1921 only. Send Xerox™ or photo. Do not send items without prior arrangement.
>   Jerry King
>   8429 Katy Freeway
>   Houston, TX 77024
(713) 465-2500   fax (713) 465-0824   <jerryksl@ok.com>

RELIGIOUS ITEMS

◆ **Relics of the Saints.** This buyer seeks "first class relics" of Catholic Saints. A "first class relic" is a tiny fragment of bone displayed in a reliquary, a small metal or wooden container with a glass cover. It should include the Saint's name. "Second class relics" are fragments of something worn or used by a Saint, and not of particular interest. Please send a photocopy or brief description including the Saint's name. You may mail your relic on approval, and your mailing costs will be reimbursed whether he purchases your item or not. Hal notes that relics are not to be sold, but that he will "make a donation to any church or charity you name in exchange. I assure you, I will care for your relic and treat it with proper respect," Hal vows.

Hal Miller
PO Box 4005
Philadelphia, PA 19118
(215) 247-5051   <halmiller99@yahoo.com>

◆ **Protestant religious items** including old **Bibles, hymnals, bronze statues, old pictures and prints, oil paintings,** engravings, watercolors, books, autographs, and more. Gene asks you give a standard description, send Xerox™ copies or photos and estimate the age of what you have. Give standard bibliographic entries for any books.

Gene Albert, Jr.
12324 Big Pool Road
Clear Spring, MD 21722

◆ **Advent calendars up to 1950 are wanted.** These consist of pictures with numbered die cut "windows" to be opened each day before Christmas, a religious count-down. Behind each window is a verse or picture. A Xerox™ is the best way to describe what you have.

Ann Bergin
PO Box 105
Amherst, NH 03031
<acbergin@aol.com>   fax (978) 649-6807

◆ **Buddha images** in bronze, wood or stone. Well carved old figures with traces of gilding or the original paint is usually a good bet to be of value. Good pictures are helpful. Describe the material, height, any markings, repairs, or defects. Everything you know about the figure, including where it was purchased is helpful. **Images of the fat, happy, smiling Chinese Hotai Buddhas are not wanted.**

Eric Matthies
PO Box 470965
San Francisco, CA 94147
(415) 921-6604   fax (415) 563-4957   <mattdebois@aol.com>

◆ **Religious music, poetry and dance.** Wants hymnals, cantorial or choir music, religious poetry, sacred music, oblongs, indexes, books, magazines, leaflets, and original manuscripts (typed or handwritten, whether published or not) of religious music, poetry and dance notation or directions. May be in any language, English preferred. May be mixed collections of religious and secular music. Since these are "for use, not display, the appearance is unimportant" but items must be complete. Values range from 25¢ to $400. He does not want prose, blank verse, or secular music and has little interest in hymnology, data/discussions about music, dance, poetry, social causes, or religious topics. Doesn't buy duplicates, and offers to trade. Give the exact title, edition or revision number, latest copyright date, editor or compiler, and indicate the total number of religious music or verse selections or number of pages. This non-profit group encourages donations.

David Whitney, The Pealing Chord
8 Ellen Drive K.Twp.
Wyoming, PA 18644
(570) 696-2218

◆ **Methodist items** including histories, biographies, photos of preachers or churches, diaries, letters or manuscript material about Methodism, prints, posters, sheet music, copies of the *Discipline* and Hymnal printed before 1850 as well as all Methodist publications such as *Christian Advocate* from any year any edition, especially Southern. Also wants personal items of preachers, bishops or prominent laity such as canes, hats, gloves, etc. Does not want Sunday School material, holy cards or general material like a postcard of the Holy Land."

Rev. Kenneth Brown
243 South Pine Street
Hazelton, PA 18201
(570) 455-5548 <jinskip@ptdprolog.net>

◆ **Pentecostal religious items** including histories, biographies of preachers or leaders, photos of churches or services, sermons and sermon notes, and anniversary items from holiness and Pentecostal churches such as mugs, plates, etc. Will buy oils, napkins, snake handling boxes, and identified hymnals, Bibles and disciplines of denominations. Also wants any and all books, periodicals, and tracts on the subject of sanctification, holiness, perfection, second blessing, speaking in tongues, faith healing and healers, or snake handling and will buy single issues or bound volumes of Pentecostal magazines. Does not want Sunday School items, pictures of the Virgin Mary, etc., but is looking for historical books, documents, photos and artifacts only.

Rev. Kenneth Brown
243 South Pine Street
Hazelton, PA 18201
(570) 450-6382 <jinskip@ptdprolog.net>

★ **Missionary correspondence from Protestant or Catholic missionaries** in Asia, Africa, South Pacific and South America. The envelope must be intact as it is the stamps and cancellations (covers) that are of primary importance. These can be quite valuable so it is important to follow through. Advisable to first phone or send a photocopy of the envelope by mail or fax. Repays post on items sent on approval.

> Bruce Lewin
> Bridgewater Onvelopes Collectibles
> 680 Route 206 North
> Bridgewater, NJ 08807
> (908) 725-0022   fax (908) 707-4647

◆ **Judaica, especially silver religious items and old books.** "I collecti, buy and sell Judaica from before 1910. I want religious or ceremonial Jewish items, or American historical items with a Jewish connection, such as calendar plate advertising for a store owned by a Jewish person. Also letters and other paper. Use standard bibliographic information for books. Send a photo of religious items, and include all markings found on the piece.

> Jay Brand
> 253 North Stanwood
> Columbus, OH 43209
> (614) 238-3997   <jaybrand6@aol.com

◆ **Israel, Palestine, and the Holocaust.** What have you? It could be worth your time to make an inquiry.

> Harvey Dolin
> 111 Fulton Street, Mezzanine floor
> New York, NY 10038
> (212) 267-0216

◆ **Sacred books,** including **Bibles** before 1800, Books of Common Prayer, the Koran, and other unusual, beautiful or early sacred book.

> Ron & Isabel Lieberman, The Family Album
> 4887 Newport Road at the Old Mill
> Kinzers, PA 17535
> (717) 442-0220   fax (717) 442-7904
> <rarebooks@pobox.com>

◆ **Mormonism.** Buys all types of books, photos, letters, and other paper ephemera related to Mormons.

> Warren Anderson
> America West Archives
> PO Box 100
> Cedar City, UT 84720
> (435) 586-9497   fax (435) 867-8078
> <awa@netutah.com>

◆ **Shakers and other utopian groups.** "I buy and sell early and current (to 1970) books, hymnals, manuscripts, photos, and other ephemera by or about the Shakers and related utopian and communal groups. Particularly interested in 18th and 19th century items related to the American Shakers. An 1808 1st edition of *Testimony of Christ's Second Appearing* can bring $1,000, and other works can bring even more. Pamphlets for and against the Shakers printed in Ohio, Kentucky or surrounding states during the 1800-1840 period are of particular interest." Full bibliographic information on books is required, including full description of the condition. A photo or Xerox™ is suggested for other items. He produces catalogs of items for sale. Cost: $4.

> David Newell
> 39 Steady Lane
> Ashfield, MA 01330
> (413) 628-3240   fax (413) 628-3833   <shakerlit@aol.com>

◆ **Shaker artifacts and ephemera.** Specializes in Shaker furniture, tools, textiles and other crafts, books, pamphlets, photographs, and ephemera. Also buys and sells small Shaker artifacts such as bottles, sewing boxes, baskets, seed boxes, and the like, with emphasis on items from Kentucky communities. Send a clear photo or photocopy.

> Gary Gardner
> 200 College Street
> Hodgenville, KY 42748
> (270) 358-3222   <csapreservation@webtv.net>

◆ **Shaker furniture, books, diaries, and letters.** Will buy in any condition. Please write and describe what you have.

> James Williams
> 342 South Garnet Lake Road
> Warrensburg, NY 12885
> (518) 623-2831

◆ **Religious literature** and other items:
  • **Watch Tower Society books and Bibles** before 1940;
  • Old Judge Rutherford sermons on 78rpm records;
  • Yankee Stadium 1950's convention pennants;
  • Magazine bags with "Watchtower 5¢" on them;
  • *Millenial Dawn or Studies in the Scriptures*, from 1870-1920;
  • **Jewish uniform worn in WWII Nazi concentration camp.**

Give title, date and condition as well as whether or not it is complete. Please set your price. "I do not want anything newer than 1940 unless you are giving it to me free. I am a collector, appraiser and dealer."

> George Chartrand
> PO Box 334 Station Main
> Winnepeg, MB CANADA R3C 2H6
> (204) 774-1186

◆ **Watchtower Society literature,** books and other memorabilia from before 1930 are wanted. He'd like to hear from you if you have anything pertaining to the Watchtower Society, Tower Publishing, the International Bible Students Assn (IBSA), Pastor C.T. Russell, or George Storrs. Books of particular interest include N.H. Barbour's *Three Worlds* (1877, $200 "or a great deal more in fine condition"), J.H. Paton's *Day Dawn* (1880, $200+), C.T. Russell's *The Object & Manner of Our Lord's Return* (1877, $500+), J.F. Rutherford's *Man's Salvation from a Lawyer's Viewpoint* (1906, $500+), and various books by George Storrs. The special Watchtower Edition of *Human Linear Bible* (1902) is a $500+ prize. Numerous magazines, Journals, and Reports from before 1930 are sought, including *Watchtower, Golden Age, Herald of the Morning, Bible Examiner*, and *Overland Monthly*. This 35 year veteran collector/researcher wants to hear about anything you have from before 1930, books between 1930 and 1940, and nothing after 1950. Dealers should price their goods. Amateurs may request an offer.

> Jeffrey Neumann
> PO Box 171
> Wadsworth, OH　44282
> 　　　(330) 334-1784　　<jneumann@neo.rr.com>

◆ **Watchtower Society publications** and ephemera including *Golden Age, Consolation,* and *Awake* magazines, Millennial Dawn books, Watchtower books before 1927, items related to Pastor Russell, and any pre-1940 Jehovah's Witness literature.

> Mike Castro
> PO Box 72817
> Providence, RI　02907　　<ekim77@aol.com>

◆ **Mystical arts, crystal balls, tarot cards,** and ephemera related to **astrology, spiritualism, pyramids, palmistry, Yoga, numerology, psychic research, Atlantis, Tibet, UFO's** and the like.

> Dennis Whelan
> PO Box 609
> Melrose, FL　32666
> 　　　(352) 475-9520　　<samadhi@fdt.net>

◆ **Angels.** "I'll buy church type angels made of plaster or chalk, the bigger the better." Send a photo with dimensions.

> Gwen Daniel
> 18 Belleau Lake Court
> O'Fallon, MO　63366
> 　　　(636) 978-3190　anytime　　<gwendaniel@aol.com>

Angel figurines are also sought by a buyer on page 502.

HOLIDAYS

◆ **Holiday collectibles,** notably items associated with Christmas, Halloween and to a lesser extent non-religious Easter:
- **Halloween Jack O'lanterns** (at $10 an inch if mint);
- **Halloween, Christmas, or Easter candy containers** made in Germany of papier mache or composition (no glass);
- Santa related figures, especially bisque;
- **Halloween postcards** ($4 to $8);
- **Bubble lights** if working, at $2 to $4 each;
- Woolly animals, especially sheep and goats.

Things must be in fine condition for resale. She does not want Japanese made Santas from 1935 to the present, nor does she buy any Christmas item of plastic. She is not interested in, Halloween masks, or costumes. No Santas in magazine ads. Give a detailed description or good sharp photo. "Will buy one item or fifty."

> Jenny Tarrant
> Holly Daze Antiques
> 4 Garden View
> St. Peters, MO 63376
>   (314) 397-1763 any time   <jennyjol@aol.com>
>   <www.holly-days.com>

◆ **Holiday collectibles,** notably items associated with Christmas, Halloween and to a lesser extent Easter, including decorations from before 1920, and related items like:
- **Figural ornaments,** made of paper, tinsel, pressed cardboard, cotton batting, glass or other material;
- **Board games** with lithographed boxes depicting Santa;
- **Santa toys** and other ephemera: anything based on St. Nick, including advertising, banners, greeting cards, paintings, die-cuts, chromoliths, and prints;
- **Die cut children's books** 1880-1900 about Santa;
- Litho on tin candle holders for Christmas trees;
- **Halloween candy containers** in glass or papier-mache´;
- Papier-mache´ or composition Easter rabbit candy containers of rabbits wearing clothes..

He does not want anything made of plastic or vinyl, nor anything made after 1920. There are many reproductions of Santa items, some of which are quite valuable and require an expert to authenticate. This 25 year veteran requests a photo or photocopy of what you'd like to sell.

> Dolph "Father Christmas" Gotelli
> PO Box 188977
> Sacramento, CA 95818
> (916) 456-9734   Fax: (916) 457-1559   <degotelli@ucdavis.edu>

◆ **Greeting cards from any holiday,** 1840-1910. Nothing later. Everything must be in suitable condition for resale. No postcards.
> Madalaine Selfridge
> 33710 Almond Street
> Wildomar, CA 92595
> (909) 674-9221   <ms@majornet.com>

★ **German glass Christmas ornaments,** shaped like animals, people, and cartoon characters, made before 1920. Also wants painted cotton ornaments, paper Dresdens, and old candy containers shaped like Santa. Also Easter and Halloween decorations.
> Jim Bohenstengel
> PO Box 623
> Oak Park, IL 60303
> (708) 524-8870   fax (708) 386-1567

◆ **Early handmade folk art Christmas decorations.**
> Louis Picek, Main Street Antiques
> PO Box 340
> West Branch, IA 52358
> (319) 643-2065   <msantiques@bigplanet.com>

★ **Christmas tree ornaments.** Buys a variety of antique ornaments:
- Kugel ornaments;
- **Glass birds** with spun glass wings, tails, or crests;
- Czech beaded ornaments with satin glass rings;
- Birds perched in glass rings;
- Unusual **strings of glass beads**;
- Spun glass and **paper decorations**;
- Chandelier or fantasy ornaments (where two or three small bells, pine cones, or other items hang from a larger ornament);
- Delicate and unusual figural ornaments;
- **Catalogs and manufacturer's sales literature** in any language.

He wants a good description and if you still have the box, the information on it. "I generally avoid plastic items, and items newer than the mid 1950's." He requests return privilege if things aren't as described.
> David Speck
> 35 Arterial West
> Auburn, NY 13021
> (315) 252-8566 eves   <dspeck@relex.com>

◆ **Electric Christmas decorations** including figural light bulbs, pre-1940 items only, please. Send photo.
> Cindy Chipps
> 4027 Brooks Hill Road
> Brooks, KY 40109
> (502) 955-9238   fax (502) 957-5027   <holauction@aol.com>

★ **Matchless Wonder Stars Christmas lights.** "I'll buy all stars, working, dead or broken. Even empty boxes have value." This historian wants all factory wholesale literature and price sheets, as well as store display stands. **He also buys other Matchless products plus any old light sets that twinkle or bubble** by Paramount, Sylvania, Alps, Royal, Peerless, Mazda, Majestic and others. Especially wants nice boxed light sets by Propp and Clemco. He wants a good description and if you still have the box, the information on it. "I generally avoid plastic items, and Christmas lights later than the mid 1950's." Although he buys dead bulbs (except Sylvania fluorescents), he requests return privilege if things aren't as described.
David Speck
35 Arterial West
Auburn, NY 13021
(315) 252-8566 eves <dspeck@relex.com>

◆ **Hallmark Christmas ornaments,** one or a collection, are sought by this 14 year veteran collector/dealer. Especially interested in "first in a series" ornaments in mint condition in their original boxes such as: Frosty Friends, Rocking Horses, Mary's Angels, Nostalgic Houses & Shopes. She DOES NOT WANT round ornaments or any ornaments that are not part of a series but are "family or friend" oriented (such as Sister, Brother, Friend, Dad, Teacher, etc.). Please give the year the item was made, its condition, and the condition of the box. Boxes aren't necessary, but the best prices go for ornaments in their original boxes. She as thousands of Hallmark Keepsake ornaments for sale from 1973 to the present, miniature ornaments, Kiddie Car Classics, Barbie dolls, Beanie babies and other Hallmark collectibles. Her 60 page catalog costs $5 and is an excellent guide to determing the value of Halmark ornaments.
Kathy Parrott
Christmas in Vermont
51 Jalbert Road
Barre, VT 05641
(802) 479-2024 9 am to 8 pm <katparrott@aol.com>

◆ **Christmas collector's plates and ornaments,** but only (1) Royal Copenhagen plates; (2) Wedgwood Jasperware plates; (3) Bing & Grondahl plates; (4) Waterford crystal "12 Days of Christmas" ornaments. Indicate the year and whether you have the original box.
Old China Patterns Limited
1560 Brimley Road
Scarborough, Ontario M1P 3G9 CANADA
(800) 663-4533 (416) 299-8880 fax (416) 299-4721
<ocp@chinapatterns.com>

◆ **Russian Easter eggs** made of porcelain, solid glass, silvered hollow glass, and other materials. They are characterized by the letters "XB" or **XHRISTOS VOSKRECE** (Christ is risen) inscribed in paint, enamel, or other material. Value depends upon rarity, authenticity and condition.

> David Speck
> 35 Arterial West
> Auburn, NY 13021
>   (315) 252-8566 eves   <dspeck@relex.com>

★ **Halloween.** "I'll buy older paper items, Dennison *Boogie Books*, Halloween pins, jewelry, decorations, etc., but only if they were made before 1945. Nothing new is wanted." Stu is the author of *Halloween in America*, available through him for $35 postpaid.

> Stuart Schneider
> 820 Kindermack Road
> River Edge, NJ 07661
> (201) 599-4250   Fax: (201) 599-4251   <stuart@wordcraft.net>

4TH OF JULY MEMORABILIA

★ **Anything with a fireworks company name on it** including:
- Fireworks boxes that held salutes, torpedoes, sparklers, etc. (worth up to $200 each);
- Fireworks, rockets, Roman candles and wooden based items;
- Firecracker packs and labels;
- Salesmen's display boards and samples;
- Fireworks catalogs from before 1969 (often $150 up);
- Paper ephemera: stock certificates, posters, banners, photos, letters, billheads, magazine articles, and other paper about American fireworks companies.

"I would like to hear from any former employee of a U.S. fireworks company. Please include your phone number when you write."

> Barry Zecker
> PO Box 217
> Martinsville, NJ 08836
>   (908) 253-3400 from 9 to 9

◆ **Firecracker packs and labels,** especially of Chinese, Macao, and Hong Kong manufacture. Want none marked DOT or UNO336. Buys other fireworks related items such as firecracker cannons, cap canes, torpedo and salute boxes, catalogs and salesman's display boards. "I do appraisals and can store and import legally from all countries. Please send Xerox™. I pay postage both ways on all approvals."

> Hal Kantrud
> Route 7
> Jamestown, ND 58401
>   (701) 252-5639 eves   <halk995@daktel.com>

◆ **Firecracker labels.** "I'll buy pre-1940 labels with aviation, space, atom bomb, animal, and Americana themes." Also fireworks catalogs. Send a photocopy of what you have. No modern labels.

Stuart Schneider
820 Kindermack Road
River Edge, NJ 07661
(201) 599-4250   Fax: (201) 599-4251   <stuart@wordcraft.net>

◆ **Fourth of July fireworks,** firecrackers, and firecracker labels. Wants "anything prior to the early 1970's, especially packs of *Golliwog, Picnic, Tank, Oh Boy, Typewriter, Blue Dragon, Golden Bear, Green Jade, Santa Claus, Dwarf, China Clipper*, and many others." He wants most of these badly enough to pay $50 or more per pack! NOTE: if your package or label contains the letters dot and/or "Contents do not exceed 60 mg," he's probably not interested. He eagerly buys catalogs of fireworks too. Photocopy when possible.

William Scales
130 Fordham Circle
Pueblo, CO 81005
(719) 561-0603

VALENTINE'S DAY

◆ **Valentines.** Wants early die-cut and elaborate valentines made before 1910, but buys others "if reasonable." Please, no postcards.

Madalaine Selfridge
33710 Almond Street
Wildomar, CA 92595
(909) 674-9221   <ms@majornet.com>

◆ **Valentines** dating from 1889 to about 1920, but only the three dimensional fold-out stand-up type.

James Conley
2758 Coventry Lane NW
Canton, OH 44708
(330) 477-7725

◆ **Fine Valentines,** including handmade valentines from before 1940, interesting mechanical valentines, lacy 8" x 10" cards, large fan shaped token of love cards from the 1800's and anything unusual. Pays $25-$50 for folding ships, planes, and better fans. Photocopy what you wish to sell. NO children's 1¢ valentines from any era.

Evalene Pulati, Valentine Collector's Association
PO Box 1404
Santa Ana, CA 92702
(714) 547-1355

◆ **Holiday items of all types: paper cards, callendars and other collectibles of Christmas, Halloween, Valentines, St. Patrick's Day, Easter, May Day, Thanksgiving** and any other holiday as long as the item is 1880-1920, colorful, and in fine condition. \She is particularly interested in "mechanical" and pop-up and other very fancy cards or work by popular illustrators of the day. Also heavy **chromolithographed calendars with a Holiday theme.** A photocopy (Xerox©) is the best way to describe what you have to this 30 year veteran.

Ann Bergin
PO Box 105
Amherst, NH 03031
<acbergin@aol.com>   fax (978) 649-6807

MISCELLANEOUS

◆ **Large bells that weigh more than 50 pounds,** especially cast bronze church, mission, train, boat, and school bells. Brosmer buys, sells and installs large bells. The country's biggest dealer in used bells buys and sells a wide range of bells, but is not interested in glass bells or "the little ting-a-ling type." If you can pick your bell up in one hand, he doesn't want it. Write or call if buying or selling larger bells. You will be expected to state the price you want for your bell as he does not give free appraisals or make offers.

R.C. Brosamer's Bells
207 Irwin Street
Brooklyn, MI 49230
(517) 592-9030   fax (517) 592-4511
<sales@brosamersbells.com>   <www.usedbells.com>

TONY'S TIP: If you can pick your bell up with one hand Brosamer doesn't want it. If you struggle to pick it up with two hands, he might. If you can't at all, he'll buy it.

◆ **Items associated with celebrities, movies, historic events and the like.** This unusual company specialized in the odd, rare, unusual, and the curious, especially **movie and stage costumes, props** from movies and TV, promotional one-of-a-kind items, **belongings of famous people**, and historical relics and artifacts. They buy, sell and accept consignments. "Celebrities and consignors offering items are assured absolute discretion and confidentiality. We demand the best authentication from our suppliers and furnish our clients with letters, photos, videos and other provenance (history)."

Richard L. Wilson
Norma's Jeans
3511 Turner Lane
Chevy Chase, MD 20815
(301) 652-4644   fax (301) 652-9888   <normasjeans@msn.com>

◆ **Carved shells,** especially cowrie shells with the Lord's Prayer, personalized messages and/or dates, cities, foreign places with pictures (often sold as souvenirs), or events such as World's Fairs. "I buy any condition, any age, but do not want current souvenir shells made in the Philippines with zodiac signs and poor carvings of dolphins or fish done as souvenirs for coastal towns. I will buy modern items, but the quality of the carving must be exceptional." Values from $5 to $50 or more.

Vicki Tori Koonsman
3713 Hartwood Drive
Granbury, TX 76049

◆ **3-D movies, slides, magazines** and other items including:
- Any 3-D cameras, viewers, and projectors;
- *Viewmaster* views from before 1982;
- *Tru-Vue* filmstrips and viewers, but not *Tru-Vue* cards;
- 3-D color slides from the 40's;
- 3-D magazines and comic books from the 1950's;
- **Stereoviews of movie related subjects.**

He would pay $300 for the stereoview card set from the 20's sold in Germany called "The Making of the Hunchback of Notre Dame" but has no interest in (1) stereoviews that are printed rather than actual photos, (2) stereoviews of scenery, (3) cartoon subjects, or (4) Viewmaster reels that are damaged or dirty. He needs to know the brand and model of equipment and the title, subject, and catalog number of reels and stereoviews. If you have original packet envelopes, boxes, instructions or other paper, make certain to note the fact. When offering views, you should understand that most of them are worth only $1-$5.

Chris "Dr. 3-D" Perry
7470 Church Street #A
Yucca Valley, CA 92284
(760) 365-0475   fax (760) 365-0495   <evildoctor3d@yahoo.com>

◆ **Windup singling birdcages** from before 1920. Condition is critical.
Rick Padrone
1005 E. Idlewild Ave.
Tampa, FL 33604
(800) 991-0165   fax (800) 991-0166   <ricpadron@webtv.net>

◆ **Metal souvenir buildings** of all types, either presentation pieces, models, give-aways or souvenirs sold at the building. The older and more unusual the better. Condition is important. Please indicate what the building is (and where) and if it is part of an ashtray, lighter, award, etc. Size and material helpful and a photo is appreciated.

Barry Hoffman
7 Stonemeadow Drive
Westwood, MA 02090
(617) 267- 9000   cel (617) 584-5555
fax (781 326-4444   <pakistan@tiac.net>

◆ **Missouri Health buttons.** Buttons were issued annually from 1926 to 1974 and are found in various configurations with various ribbons attached. Most desirable are the issues of 1943-45 which were made of paper and/or plastic instead of metal. No damaged, stained, or faded buttons are wanted. Please Xerox©.

> Karen Ferguson
> 1010 Tarsney Lane
> Buckner, MO 64016
> (816) 650-5671   <dmlf@prodigy.net>

◆ **Peace symbols** from the late 1960's and early 70's. "I'm looking for jewelry, rings, watchbands, dogtags, belts, and anything unusual depicting the black and white symbol called a "chickenfoot" by detractors. Condition is very important, and items must not show damage or wear. Send a description, Xerox™, and asking price.

> Judy Polk Harding
> 4347 Farm House Lane
> Fairfax, VA 22032
> (703) 503-7323   <thefivejs@aol.com>

◆ **Yellow smile faces** from 1968 to 1975. "I want cups, pins, luggage, handbags, ice buckets, drinking glasses, cookie jars, flower pots, you name it. Smiley faces appeared on just about everything imaginable." Condition is very important, and items must not show damage or wear. Send a description, Xerox™, and asking price.

> Judy Polk Harding
> 4347 Farm House Lane
> Fairfax, VA 22032
> (703) 503-7323   <thefivejs@aol.com>

◆ **Badges, buttons, emblems or ribbons of all types.** This includes, but is not limited to, political buttons, union & labor items, old and new movie and cartoon items, fast food pins, fire and police badges, military medals, Olympic pins, and items given by gasoline companies and airlines, including wings. "I'll buy them all, common or rare, big quantities or small. Since the average reader doesn't have my 20 years experience, I will look at all items or Xerox copies of them and give an honest opinion."

> Fred Swindall, Button Exchange
> 2219 SE Salmon
> Portland, OR 97214
> (503) 224-0678 days   (503) 234-2454 eves

TONY'S TIP: Similar buyers can be found in the index under: buttons, badges, pop culture, tobacco, Olympics, sports, fire, unions, military, and specific companies. Ted Hake (p. 132) wrote 4 books on buttons.

◆ **Puzzle bottles.** "I'll buy bottles that contain unusual items such as chairs, carved human figures, etc. I do not buy ships in bottles. Things in undamaged condition only, please." Photo suggested.

> Barry Friedman
> PO Box 55492
> Valencia, CA 91385
> (661) 255-2365   <barryf@thevine.net>

◆ **Souvenir travel decals** of the U.S., Canada and Mexico including but not limited to States, parks, cities, highways, attractions, landmarks, motels, hotels, and the like. They must be the water dip transfer type. Most decals bring $1 to $6 each in small quantities, and sometimes more for rare and desirable locations like Route 66 attractions such as Petrified Forest, Meramec Caverns, Gallup, etc. Earlier types by EMCO, ENCO, Goldfarb Novelty (always labeled on the back) and Mastercraft (catalog #'s begin with MD) bring more. Early decals from the 1940's in their original envelopes can bring as much as $12-$15 each. The more obscure and off beat the place the better. Large quantities of the same decal, often drops the price considerably. He DOES NOT WANT vinyl self stick decals, bumper stickers, postcards, or water decals from colleges, scools, etc. Call or email if in doubt.

> Dick Schneider
> Lost Highway Art Co.
> PO Box 164
> Bedford Hills, NY 10507
> (914) 234-9029   <losthwyart@aol.com>

◆ **Occupied Germany.** Seeks a wide range of figures, china, toys, children's games, Christmas ornaments, kitchen items, tools and other items marked as having come from US Occupied Zone, British Zone, French Zone and USSR Occupied Zone. Items should be described clearly and be in good condition. A photo is helpful.

> Larry L. Krug
> Americana Resources
> 18222 Flower Hill Way   #299
> Gaithersburg, MD 20879
> (301) 926-8663   Fax: (301) 926-7648   <larry.krug@amres.com>
> <www.amres.com>

◆ **Texas A & M memorabili**a from before 1969. Nothing newer.

> Johnny Spellman
> 10806 North Lamar Blvd.
> Austin, TX 78753
> (512) 836-2889 days   (512) 258-6910 eves   (512) 750-2838 cel
> fax (512) 832-0242   <dvm69@swbell.net>

◆ **Electric and pre-electric vibrators** and hand held massagers. "I especially like those with metal casings rather than plastic, those with hand-cranks, and vibrators with wooden bodies, handles or parts. Not interested in battery operated devices. You won't make a fortune selling to me, but your item could reside in the world's only vibrator museum and will be happier than in your attic." No *Oster* vibrators which are worn on the back of the hand. Describe, give any numbers molded into the case, and indicate whether the box is present. Describe any attachments or instructional inserts. Will buy items which do not work but are not physically broken.

Jesse Proebstel, Curator
Good Vibrations Antique Vibrator Museum
938 Howard Street #101
San Francisco, CA 94103
<jessiep@goodv.com>

◆ **Sealing wax seals.** "We collect virtually any type of material or motif. While we are happy to look at (and sometimes buy) nice traditional pieces such as sterling art nouveau or agate seals, we are really seeking larger more unusual desk type seals. Upon occasion, we buy desk sets which include seals. Generally, we buy only items in perfect condition. We don't want fob seals, modern seals, or Oriental chops." To sell your seal you'll need good close up photos with notes about size, materials, and anything important that doesn't show in the photo. Include any pertinent history. If your seal is for sale they're happy to make offers. There may be a fee for formal appraisals.

Eileen & Irwin Prince
3500 West DePauw Blvd. #2015
Indianapolis, IN 46268
(317) 334-9200 days   (317) 255-1913 eves   fax (317) 228-3355
<noitall@inetdirect.net>

◆ **"Old Ironsides" memorabilia.** "I want relics of all types from the United States Frigate Constitution ("Old Ironsides"). These bronze or wood items items include: ash trays, dishes, anchors, cannons, etc., all marked this material was taken from us frigate constitution."

Tim O'Callaghan
PO Box 512
Northville, MI 48167
(248) 449-2652   <timothyo@ameritech.net>

◆ **Snowmobile, ski vehicle and *Ski-Doo*** toy models, literature, brochures, license plates and photos of them taken before 1970.

Don Schneider
PO Box 1570
Merritt, BC V1K 1B8 CANADA
(250) 378-6421

◆ **Hear no evil, see no evil, speak no evil figurines** are sought by this collector. Although not particularly valuable, she would like to hear from you if you have one for sale, and will make a fair offer. Describe the size, material, any markings on the bottom, and information about where you got it, if possible. Lois also buys some single figurines of monkeys. Most aren't particularly valuable, "but they make me laugh."

> Lois Dwyer
> 310 Lexington Ave.
> Syracuse, NY 13210
> (315) 476-1014

◆ **Mermaids and mermen.** "I will consider any item, made of porcelain, china, metal, stone, cloth, lace or paper which has a mermaid, merman, or merbaby motif. The item must be old and unusual, but may be advertising, folk art, scrimshaw, jewelry, bottles, fishing lures, and what have you. I do not want Japanese bisque, anything new, or anything cracked or broken. Indicate the size, markings, and condition as part of your description. Wants you to set the price.

> Stephanie Schnatz
> 17 Tallow Court
> Baltimore, MD 21244
> (410) 944-0819 <chelsealady@hotmail.com>

◆ **Billikens.** Naked pot-bellied figures sitting with the bottoms of their feet facing you. Promoted as the god of things as they ought to be, or the god of happiness, luck, etc. Found in a variety of sizes and materials. Wants original 1908-1910 Billikens as featured on flatware, ice cream molds, charms, jewelry, dolls, games, banks, thimbles, toothpick holders, postcards, and all other items in the shape of Billikens. No jade or tusk Billikens, which are more modern items from Alaska.

> Judy Knauer
> 1224 Spring Valley Lane
> West Chester, PA 19380
> (610) 431-3477 <winkjk@netaxs.com>

◆ **Golliwogs.** These cartoonish racist Black characters have appeared in many forms since they first arrived in England at the turn of the century. They can be found both store bought and home made, of nearly any material. She particularly wants them as small lead figures. These have been reproduced but "a photo will tell me a lot."

> Marilyn Baseman
> Birdcage Antiques
> PO Box 1166
> Sheffield, MA 01258
> (413) 229-2294 <abca@bcn.net>

◆ **Angels.** "I'll buy church type angels made of plaster or chalk, the bigger the better." Send a photo with dimensions.
> Gwen Daniel
> 18 Belleau Lake Court
> O'Fallon, MO 63366
>   (636) 978-3190 anytime   <gwendaniel@aol.com>

◆ **Key chains.** "I buy most types, whether they have advertising or not, including those that are souvenirs from places or events, of just decorative items. I pay from 25¢ to $5 for most key chains, though old commemoratives, old special event key chains and old advertising key chains (especially McDonald's and Tobacco companies) may be worth as high as $25. I do not collect the hand made crocheted type or ones made from yarn which form a design on plastic forms." Please make a Xerox© or describe as best you can. Buys one or a bagful.
> Joe Wagner
> 326 South Grant Street
> Westmont, IL 60559
>   (630) 971-0115

◆ **Mechanical exercise machinery** from before 1940. This exercise historian is not interested in stationary bikes, however. Give maker, model, brand name, patent info, whatever you can, including the condition. Dealers price your goods. Amateurs may request offers.
> David Landau
> Ultimate Exercise Books
> 18151 N.E. 31st Court #1505
> Aventura, FL 33160
> (305) 932-9879   fax (305) 937-7809   <exarchives@aol.com>

◆ **Trading stamps.** "I DO NOT WANT common ones like S&H, Gold Bond, Top Value, Plaid, and some others, but love to find loose stamps or a book full or partly full of small town issues by local stores 1896-1950. They're not worth much, a couple bucks or so a book, but you'll be contributing to history. I do reimburse postage."
> Vincent Marier
> 157 Berrywood Drive
> Severna Park, MD 21146
>   <marier@cs.umbc.edu>

TONY'S TIP ABOUT HANDLING ESTATES: I frequently get asked about handling estates, a difficult and often thankless job. In response, a few suggestions have been included on pages 251-252.

◆ **Youth hostel ephemera** such as handbooks, pins, magazines, etc.
Walley Francis
PO Box 6941
Syracuse, NY 13217
(315) 478-5671

◆ **Bride and groom cake tops.** "I collect German bisque bride and groom sets from the 1890's through the 1940's. Some of my favorites are still mounted on the icing cake top platforms. Paint and condition are very important to me. Clear close up photos are important to show subtle differences and detail since they all sound pretty similar over the phone." You set the price. If it's fair, she says she'll pay it.
Linda Vines
2911 4th Street #112
Santa Monica, CA 90405
(310) 314-0402 <lleigh2000@hotmail.com>

◆ **Wedding booklets and fancy invitations.** These romantic illustrated keepsakes were popular 1890-1925. Particularly fancy engraved invetations to weddings of Royalty or famous people are always wanted. She would like to find one illustrated by Ellen Clapsaddle.
Ann Bergin
PO Box 105
Amherst, NH 03031
<acbergin@aol.com> fax (978) 649-6807

◆ **Mannequins from the Victorian era** to the 1950's. "I'll buy heads or full body figures, in any size. I do not want plastic items, reproductions, or anything modern. Please send me a photo."
Gwen Daniel
18 Belleau Lake Court
O'Fallon, MO 63366
(636) 978-3190 anytime <gwendaniel@aol.com>

◆ **Hands.** "I'll buy wooden hands with fingers that move, generally used as glove stretchers, and Palmistry hands showing lines, zones, and mounds. I'm looking for wood or ceramic, not paper items."
Don Gorlick
PO Box 24541
Seattle, WA 98124
<seashore8@hotmail.com>

◆ **Scout knives** that are marked Boy Scouts, Cub Scouts, Explore, Girl Scouts or Brownies. Will consider them in any condition.
Michael Marshall
Box 16114
Shawnee, KS 66216
(913) 962-0085 fax (913) 962-4418 <mtmarshallks@hotmail.com>

EPHEMERA OF FAMOUS PEOPLE

★ **Celebrity yearbooks.** Celebrities of both yesteryear and today are sought in high school yearbooks. Politics, show biz, music, arts...If you went to school with anyone famous or infamous and have a yearbook with their picture, here's where you go to sell it. Typical prices start at $100 but can be higher for rare annuals with stars they need. "Our primary interest is in the celebrity's senior year and senior year photo, but will consider earlier if those aren't available." Their current "Most Wanted List" includes oldies like 1900 Groton, 1901 Independence Missouri HS, 1945 West Lake School for Girls, and 1947 Miss Porter's School, all of which will bring you $1,000 or more. Newer books include 1978 Collegiate HS in NYC and 1987 Buckley (Sherman Oaks, CA) which are worth $300. They do not want college yearbooks, nor do they want books that are mildewed or seriously damaged. If you do not know whether anyone famous is in your book, write to the Poppels, giving the name of the school, the city and state, and the year published. Please include a long SASE, for which they will also send you a list of books from your area they'd like to find. Great for serious yardsalers and pickers. **They would also like to hear from you were a HS friend or teacher of someone who became famous.**

Seth Poppel
Yearbook Archives
38 Range Drive
Merrick, NY 11566
(516) 867-6280   fax (516) 546-4128   <sethpoppel@aol.com>

◆ **Celebrity memorabilia.** "I buy, sell and collect personal belongings of entertainment stars and historical figures, including movie costumes, props, and autographed photos. I'm not interested in most mass produced items, except very rare items like movie posters." Your description should include what the item is, its condition, and its history, including how you came to own it. Make certain to describe what authentication you have.

Richard L. Wilson
Norma's Jeans
3511 Turner Lane
Chevy Chase, MD 20815
(301) 652-4644   fax (301) 652-9888   <normasjeans@msn.com>

◆ **Carrie Nation memorabilia** including vinegar bottles in her caricature, souvenir hatchet pins, photos, tickets to lectures, *The Hatchet*, newspaper articles about her, and anything else. You find it and you've got a buyer here if it's in any decent condition at all.

Cary Demont
PO Box 16013
Minneapolis, MN 55416
(763) 522-0957   <caryd8@aol.com>

◆ **Samuel Gompers ephemera** from before 1886 is sought, particularly items related to his career as a cigar maker or an NYC union officer, but please inquire about **any** Gompers item.
>Tony Hyman
>PO Box 3028
>Pismo Beach, CA 93448
>>(805) 773-6777   fax (805) 773-8436
>><thyman@fix.net>

◆ **John"Johnny Appleseed" Chapman** memorabilia including books and personal items. He's looking for artifacts from the real Johnny Appleseed, not the Disney cartoon character.
>Frederic Janson
>932 Glendale Court
>Burlington, ON L7R 1X0   CANADA

◆ **Commodore Matthew Perry material** including autographs, letters, and manuscripts, especially any artifacts or documents related to his expedition to Japan. Also all Lafcadio Hearn books, ephemera.
>Jerrold Stanoff
>Rare Oriental Book Co.
>PO Box 1599
>Aptos, CA 95001
>>(831) 689-0203   fax (831) 689-0204
>><jgs@rareorientbooks.com>

◆ **Frank Lloyd Wright material** including drawings, furniture, letters, photographs, books, smaller publications, and other ephemera.
>J.B. Muns' Fine Arts Books
>1162 Shattuck Avenue
>Berkeley, CA 94707
>>(510) 525-2420   fax (510) 525-1126
>><jbmuns@aol.com>

◆ **Horace Greeley memorabilia** of all types, especially campaign buttons from 1872 (worth $30 to $3,000) and copies of the *NY Tribune* newspaper from 1840 to 1872. If you know of other journalists who've run for public office and have materials from their campaigns, please contact him. Send a picture or photocopy. Dealers must price your goods. Amateur sellers may request an offer. "I am very selective."
>Walter Brasch
>Department of Journalism
>Bloomsburg University
>Bloomsburg, PA 17815
>>(570) 389-4565 days   fax (717) 389-2094
>><brasch@ptd.net>

◆ **Lillie Langtry memorabilia** including photos, cigarette and trade cards, letters, programs, posters, tickets, costume or set sketches, and cosmetics issued under her name. Wants a wine label produced on Langtry Farms, 1889-1906, worth up to $500. Langtry was also known as Langtree, the Jersey Lily, Lady Lillie de Bathe, Mrs. Jersey, and Emilie Charlotte Le Breton. In addition to his interest in Mrs. Langtry, he also wants material on Edward Langtry and Freddie Gebhard(t).

> Orville Magoon
> PO Box 279
> Middletown, CA 95461
>> (707) 987-2385 x207 days   fax (707) 987-9351
>> <omagoon@guenoc.com>

◆ **John Steinbeck memorabilia,** signed limited editions, first editions, first printings by subsequent publishers, appearances in anthologies, spoken word records and tapes, film and theater memorabilia, and things owned by him. Does not want book club editions, items in poor condition, or fakes. If a book originally had a dust jacket, slipcase, box or wrap-around, then it should still be present. Be specific about what you have, giving complete bibliographic information.

> James Dourgarian, Bookman
> 1595-A Third Avenue
> Walnut Creek, CA 94596
>> (510) 935-5033   <jimbooks@earthlink.net>

◆ **Mark Twain memorabilia,** autographs, photos, stories about, books about, and especially first editions of his books, "but no books that are falling apart." Include the color of the cover when providing standard bibliographic information.

> Duane and Eunice Bietz
> 6461 SE Thorburn
> Portland, OR 97215
>> fax (503) 233-1602   <heartbietz@aol.com>

◆ **Jack London memorabilia,** books and personal effects.

> Winifred Kingman
> Jack London Bookstore
> PO Box 337
> Glen Ellen, CA 95442
>> (707) 996-2888   (707) 996-4107

◆ **Items belonging to celebrities, singers, movie stars, politicians, etc.** "We demand the best authentication from our suppliers and furnish our clients with letters, photos, videos and other provenance (history)."

> Richard L. Wilson, Norma's Jeans
> 3511 Turner Lane
> Chevy Chase, MD 20815
> (301) 652-4644   fax (301) 652-9888   <normasjeans@msn.com>

◆ **Edgar Rice Burroughs and characters.** Wants rare items related to stories and characters created by Edgar Rice Burroughs, including:
  • Hardback books, reprints with dust jackets or 1st editions with or w/out dust jackets (1st editions in dj's of *Tarzan of the Apes, Return of Tarzan,* or *Princess of Mars* are worth $2,000+;
  • Pulp magazines, 1912 to 1919, featuring ERB stories;
  • Original Tarzan art by Ray Kuenkel, J. Allen St. John, Hogarth, Frank Schoonover, and Hal Foster;
  • Autographed items by ERB or by early movie Tarzans;
  • Toys, games and premiums before 1950;
  • Movie posters and lobby cards before 1945.

Does not want reprint hardbacks without dust jackets, paperbacks, recent comic books, or anything in poor condition. Make certain to include the publisher when describing a book. Give your phone number. Dealers must price your goods, but amateurs may request an offer.

  Jim Gerlack
  1621 Boundbrook Lane
  Irving, TX 75060
       (972) 790-0922   <j.gerlach@attbi.com>

◆ **Sherlock Holmes** items and specific related Victoriana. "Please call me if you have anything written about or showing Sherlock Holmes, Dr. John Watson or author Sir Arthur Conan Doyle. This includes all books, memorabilia, photos, movies, magazines, comics, ads, busts, ceramics, records, tapes, pipes, play books, scripts, etc., no matter where or when made. Also wants scientific apparatus and instruments, books, weapons and anything else made between 1850-1900 that was mentioned in Holmes stories. "I don't want currently published books containing just the regular 56 short stories and the 4 novels. However, if the book contains the stories plus commentary, analysis, notes, etc., then I would indeed be interested. If in doubt, please call." He adds, "Yes, it's my real name"

  Rev. Sherlock Holmes
  PO Box 3
  Worcester, MA 01613
  free (877) 306-4059   <antiques@sherlockholmes.com>
       <www.sherlockholmes.com>

◆ **Sherlock Holmes.** Wants "anything related to Sherlock Holmes or Sir Arthur Conan Doyle" including figurines, drawings, autographs, posters, photos, etc. Also wants items from actors who have played Holmes including Basil Rathbone, Peter Cushing and Jeremy Brett.

  Robert Hess
  559 Potter Blvd.
  Brightwaters, NY 11718
       (631) 665-8365   <hellmudlark@aol.com>

ANIMAL COLLECTIBLES

◆ **Royal Doulton flambe animal figurines.** Hundreds of different animals, both wild and domestic, are to be found in these attractive red pottery figures which range from 2" to 14" in size. They are still made today, so it's the older figures that are most sought after and bring the best prices. Have the figure(s) in front of you when you call this 20 year veteran collector. Or send a good description.

Ed Pascoe
Pascoe & Co.
575 SW 22nd Ave.
Miami, FL 33135
(800) 872-0195   (305) 643-2550   fax (305) 643-2123
<ed@pascoeandcompany.com>

◆ **Royal Doulton animal figurines.** "I'll buy any, large or small, as long as they are marked royal doulton and are in perfect condition. "Look for a number with the letters HN or K. Tell me the number and I'll make an immediate cash offer."

Carol Payne
Carol's Gallery
14455 Big Basin Way
Saratoga, CA 95070
(408) 867-7055 11-5 Wed-Sat

◆ **Camels.** Seeks prints, paintings, sculptures, and whatever you have, with a few exceptions. Please send photo or Xerox™ copy, along with the price wanted and your phone number. All letters will be answered promptly. He DOES NOT WANT small wood, or leather camels or in anything to do with *Camel* cigarettes.

Charlie Stewart
900 Grandview Avenue
Reno, NV 89503
(775) 747-1439 days

◆ **Zebras in many different forms,** including porcelain, carvings, paintings, folk art, etc. To be of interest, an item must be of a zebra, not just zebra striped. Please, no hides or parts of dead zebras.

Dave Galt
302 West 78th Street
New York, NY 10024
(212) 769-2514   <davegalt@spacedominoes.com>

◆ **Snakes, turtles, frogs, lizards, alligators and other reptile and amphibians.** Wants paintings and prints, wood carvings, ceramics, bronzes, stained glass, postcards, jewelry, folk art, pens, snake canes, stamps, posters, tribal art and gargoyles with reptile designs. Also wants zoological artifacts like turtle shells or snake skulls. Please send a good description or photo and phone number. If you call, let the phone ring a very long time before the fax picks up.

> Mark Miller
> PO Box 52261
> Philadelphia, PA 19115
> (215) 464-3561 voice/fax
> <70176.1153@compuserve.com>

◆ **Old butterfly collections** in Riker mounts, glass-topped drawers, or in paper triangles. He's trying to preserve lost species found only in antique collections, as well as supplying butterflies to museums and collectors worldwide. His personal favorites are swallowtails, the Solomon Islands version of which can be worth $900. Send photos of the collection or, if you can, a species list. He does not want endangered or protected species, butterflies with paper bodies or coffee trays or other items made from butterfly wings. A long business size envelope with 64¢ postage will get you *How to Butterfly Garden*.

> Marc Schenck
> The Butterfly Zoo
> 1151 Aquidneck Avenue
> Middletowne, RI 02842
> (401) 849-9519 7pm - midnight ET   fax (401) 847-2970
> <butterflyzoo@webtv.net>

◆ **Wild boar items.** "I'll buy paintings, bronzes, ceramics, advertising, and anything else that's nice and features a wild European boar or its American counterparts, the peccary or javelina." Describe what you have, including the dimensions. Point out any defects in the condition. Please don't forget your SASE. Henry travels worldwide, so reponses are sometimes delayed.

> Henry Winningham
> 3205 South Morgan Street
> Chicago, IL 60608
> (773) 927-3796

TONY'S TIP ABOUT CLEANING: I get asked about cleaning things before selling: "What to use and when to use it?" **My advice is simple: DON'T.** If it's something you want to keep forever, go ahead and polish it with whatever it takes. But if you're planning on selling it...no collector wants you to clean what you have. Don't wash. Don't polish. Don't anything.

HORSE COLLECTIBLES

◆ **Books, prints, and paper ephemera about horses.** "I buy books, prints, and paper only, but I buy on all horse related topics: polo, horseback riding, carriage driving, sidesaddle, draft horses, horseshoeing, veterinary, etc." Buys horse farm catalogs, brochures, posters, prints of riding and recognized horse breeds, books (1st editions in dust jackets only), magazines, postcards (if horse is named), stud books, and breed registers. "I don't buy common books still in print, book club editions, *Diseases of the Horse*, books on racing or horse race betting, or books with highlighting or underlining in the text. Please, I am not in the market for figurines, bronzes, or anything other than books, prints and paper about horses. Your items must be in fine condition for resale."

    Barbara Cole
    October Farm
    2609 Branch Road
    Raleigh, NC 27610
        (919) 772-0482   <octoberfarm@bellsouth.net>

◆ **Breyer plastic model horses** and other animals in good to excellent condition, without breaks or heavy scratches. "I'm interested in singles and in whole collections. I'm especially looking for Breyer horses of a different color, such as blue or gold, and am a little more lenient in condition for rarities. I pay up to $400 for rare colors, though most Breyer horses are worth from $10 to $60. Horses should be at least five inches tall and not made in Hong Kong." Describe your horse thoroughly, including the position in which it's standing or laying and the position of the feet, the color, and any mold information your might find on the bottom." She requests you include your phone number.

    Leslie Baldwin
    706 Pan Am Avenue
    Naples, FL 34110
        (941) 566-8412   <lbald34899@aol.com>

◆ **Hagen-Renaker porcelain horses and other animals,** as long as they're at least two inches tall. "I look for ones in good to excellent condition, but will consider animals with breaks. I'm interested in singles and in whole collections. Most Hagen-Renaker horses are worth from $10 to $60 but a few rare ones can reach $300, so please describe your horse thoroughly, including what it is, the position in which it's standing or laying and the position of the feet, the color, and any mold information your might find on the bottom." She requests you include your phone number.

    Leslie Baldwin
    706 Pan Am Avenue
    Naples, FL 34110
        (941) 566-8412   <lbald34899@aol.com>

CAT COLLECTIBLES

◆ **Cat items of all sorts,** especially high quality porcelain, paintings, carvings, prints, Orientalia, needlework, pottery, jade, ivory, jewelry, cookie jars, calendars, Art Deco, advertising, steins, medals, doorstops, bronzes, crystal, postcards, playing cards, toys, etc. Buys some cartoon cats (Felix, Sylvester, Kliban cats) but does not want any Garfield figures or reproductions in any form. Also she does not buy chalk figures, or anything broken or damaged.
Marilyn Dipboye
33161 Wendy Drive
Sterling Heights, MI 48310
(810) 264-0285

◆ **B.Kliban cat items of all types,** including figurines, candy dishes, banks, salt and pepper sets, mugs, cookie jars, cat feeders, kitchen and bath towels, framed pictures, stuffed animals, curtains, comforters, mugs, candle holders, magnets, place mats, etc. Ceramic items should be marked TASTESETTER/SIGMA. "I don't need sheets, soiled towels or broken items although I will consider ceramic items with small chips. Note that I want black and white cats, not black, white and gray cats as those are his newer ones. These are relatively inexpensive items, so please set the price you would like. Values can be from $5 to $100 depending on the item."
Sue Lucente
115 Marbeth Avenue
Carlisle, PA 17013
(717) 249-9343   <sooloo@webtv.net>

◆ *Felix the Cat* pictured on china, or anything else, as long as it's from the 1930's or before. She is not interested in any of the *Felix* items reproduced in the 1950's. Please include a clear photo as she will be able to tell old from new in most cases.
Marilyn Baseman
Birdcage Antiques
PO Box 1166
Sheffield, MA 01258
(413) 299-2294   <abca@bcn.net>

◆ **Garfield items** such as figurines, dolls, stuatuettes, etc. "I prefer second hand and cheap. If you are not fussy about the price, just mail them to me and I will pay a fair price and reimburse your postage. No need to include SASE as I will reply if interested."
George Chartrand
PO Box 334 Station Main
Winnepeg, MB CANADA R3C 2H6
(204) 292-8297 or (204) 775-3367 <place4plates@hotmail.com>

DOG COLLECTIBLES

◆ **Dog related collectibles** "especially figurines, jewelry and post-cards, but everything doggy considered." Russian Wolfhounds and Greyhounds are favorite breeds, especially in porcelain. Size, material, and markings are key elements in description, along with the breed if you know dogs well enough to tell.

> Denise Hamilton
> 899 Latta Brook Road
> Elmira, NY 14901
> (607) 732-2550

◆ **Dog art and ephemera.** Wants many different quality items:
- **Dog figurines** by well known porcelain companies from England, Germany, Denmark, Austria and America as well as a few others, especially artist signed pieces;
- **Ceramics** representing purebred dogs in lifelike colors; these are usually of lesser quality than the above, but are often signed or labeled;
- **Bronzes of dogs,** especially signed;
- **Wedgwood dog plates** by Marguerite Kirmse;
- **Woodcarvings** by ANRI of Italy;
- **Oil paintings** or etchings of purebred dogs;
- **Cigarette cards** of purebred dogs;
- **Kennel club, dog show, or dog club medallions** pre-1920 which have a lifelike representation of a dog on them;
- Other interesting three dimensional items depicting dogs.

"I am not interested in chalkware, Staffordshire, toys, doorstops, cast metal souvenir items, plastic, celluloid, poor quality items, or books, nor do I buy paper items other than etchings and cigarette cards. Figures must be lifelike portrayals of purebred dogs." Photo is preferred, along with the size and manufacturer. The condition is very important. All scratches, chips, flakes, breaks and imperfections must be noted.

> Sharlene Beckwith
> Exclusively Dogs!
> PO Box 457
> Lancaster, PA 17604
> (717) 892-1434   fax (717) 892-1435

◆ **Morton Studio figurines of dogs,** wild animals or people. These heavy ceramics are almost always marked on the bottom. Size, color, and shape are needed, along with condition.

> Denise Hamilton
> 899 Latta Brook Road
> Elmira, NY 14901
> (607) 732-2550

◆ **Bull terriers and dog fighting.** Especially wants prints, paintings, and statuary. Books on dog fighting also wanted.
>Ron & Isabel Lieberman
>4887 Newport Road at the Old Mill
>Kinzers, PA 17535
>(717) 442-0220   fax (717) 442-7904   <rarebooks@pobox.com>

◆ **Animated dog items.** "I buy dog items that move or are functional such as clocks, watches, toys and pop-up books. If it's got a dog on it and it moves or does something useful, drop me a line."
>Mel Rosenthal
>RR #5   Box 5711
>Saylorsburg, PA 18353
>(570) 992-8282   <meljune10@yahoo.com>

◆ **Pet license tags,** rabies tags, and all other metal tags related to animals. Especially interested in Illinois tags. Especially wants tags pre-1900 for which he pays $15 and up.
>Rich Hartzog
>PO Box 4143 BVT
>Rockford, IL 61110   <hartzog@exonumia.com>

◆ **Dog license tags** including: (1) tags from any state if they are shaped like the date of issue ($7-$25); (2) tags from anywhere in the world pre-1910 ($4-$100); (3) all NY tags issued before 1918 $5-$150); and (4) NY Conservation Dept. tags, 1917-35 (15-$50). Most tags before 1900 start at $25 and those before 1880 start at $40.
>James Case
>10189 Crane Road
>Lindley, NY 14858
>(607) 524-6606   <hftlicense@aol.com>

◆ **Dog license tags:** "I pay $1 each for tags 1930-1950, $5 each for tags from 1900 to 1930, and $20 each for tags before 1900. I'll buy licence tags in any quantity or condition, but no vaccination tags."
>George Chartrand
>PO Box 334 Station Main
>Winnepeg, MB CANADA R3C 2H6
>(204) 774-1186

◆ **Dog collars** from before 1930. Fancier or more unusual, the better. Fine condition only. Especially desirable when accompanied by a dog licence. Interesting fine condition **dog items of other types** are purchased for resale. No Japanese figurines, or other items after 1930.
>Rick Padrone
>1005 E. Idlewild Ave.
>Tampa, FL 33604
>(800) 991-0165   fax (800) 991-0166   <ricpadron@webtv.net>

WET CRITTER COLLECTIBLES

◆ **Tropical fish tanks, equipment and ephemera.** Wants old books, magazines, catalogs directly related to tropical fish, as well as "pet shop" or turtle magazines and other paper relevant to the hobby. Photocopy what you have. Priced items preferred but will make offers.
> Gary Bagnall
> 3100 McMillan Road
> San Luis Obispo, CA 93401
> (805) 542-9988 fax (805) 542-9295 <zoomed@zoomed.com>

◆ **Goldfish ephemera,** such as old **acquarium figures,** food containers, literature, magazines, advertising for related items. What have you?
> Thomas McKinnon, Twin Magnolia Farm
> 8500 Odom Road
> Laurinburg, NC 28352
> (910) 268-1800

◆ **Oyster memorabilia.** Got anything related to oysters? Cans, figurines, what have you?
> Sheldon Katz
> 18 Cliffside Drive
> Port Jefferson, NY 11777
> (631) 928-1800

◆ **Oyster related items** such as oyster cans, signs, posters, trade cards, labels, pinbacks, and what have you. Does not want oyster plates or reproduction signs. Describe the condition. Dealers, price your goods. Amateurs may ask for offers.
> John Baron
> 3636 Carpenter's Creek Drive
> Cincinnati, OH 45241
> (513) 563-7183 fax (513)946-6999

◆ **Whales and dolphins.** Interested in images of whales and dolphins that occur in books, photos, postcards, stereoviews, art of all types (paintings, prints, sculpture), advertising, posters, stamps, coins, money, toys and games. Also wants film footage (including home movies) of whales and recordings of whale sounds. Will also buy whale bones, baleen, and other whale artifacts. "We already have most items made after 1975." Send "a detailed description, including a photo" asks this collector-dealer-nonprofit organization.
> Steve King
> Whales & Friends
> PO Box 2660
> Alameda, CA 94501
> (510) 769-8500 fax (510) 865-0851 <whalefund@hotmail.com>

TONY'S TIPS: WHAT TO DO WHEN BUYERS DON'T BUY

Buyers in **Trash or Treasure Guide to the Best Buyers** aren't going to want everything you own. These are top experts, dealers and collectors and your item may be too common for their collection or shop. They may tell you that your item isn't collectible. Or they may tell you that it has "some value" but isn't important or desirable enough to interest them.

If that's the case, you still have other alternatives for selling.

You might think to offer your item to buyers who advertise in The Antique Trader, Antique Week, Newtown Bee, Collector, Maine Antique Digest, or other antiques publication. But, the reality is that those advertisers are many of the same people we recommend in here, or they're looking for the same types of items, the same rarity and condition.

That leaves yard sales, local auction houses, and the internet as alternatives for selling.

YARD SALES

If the Trash or Treasure Best Buyer experts told you that your item wasn't collectible, your alternatives are to offer it at a yard sale or donate it to charity.

Yard sales are fairly easy, but are best used for selling kid's clothes, post 1950 furniture, or things that you have already verified with experts that are yard sale quality, and not worth more. If you're moving or under press to handle an estate and haven't had time to check the value of your items, it may be cheaper to put stuff in storage and sell it slowly for top dollar than get rid of it quickly at a yard sale.

AUCTIONS

Amateurs believe that auctions always bring the highest prices. They think that because that's what they hear on the news. Whenever an auction house gets a record price they publicize the dickens out of it, sending press releases to the wire services, TV stations and to the antiques magazines and newspapers. Auction houses are quick to tell you of their successes. They don't tell you of their failures.

continued on page 362

TIPS ON SELLING ITEMS RELATED TO TRANSPORTATION, BUSINESS OR THE PROFESSIONS.

If it has anything to do with transportation, business, manufacturing, advertising, sales or commerce...someone buys it.

Some of these items are obscure, so there isn't a great deal of competition for them, and prices stay low. But small sums add up to substantial amounts of money. On the other hand, **some items listed on the next 100 pages sell for $10,000.** *You don't want to confuse the two.*

You are not qualified to judge what something is worth. *If you aren't absolutely certain what you have and what its current market value is, you should turn to experts in Trash or Treasure to help you. I've brought you the best in transportation, advertising and business buyers. Someone here will be just right for you.*

To sell your transportation, business, advertising or profession related item, your description should include:

(1) *What it is you wish to sell;*
(2) *What product or business it's associated with;*
(3) *What it depicts;*
(4) *What material(s) it is made from;*
(5) *Its size, shape, and color (especially colors of glass);*
(6) *All markings embossed (raised) or incised (stamped or etched in);*
(7) *Information contained on an ID plate;*
(8) *Accurate information regarding condition.*

The history and artifacts of some American industries is being preserved by fewer than a half dozen people, who can be difficult for you to find without this book.

Trash or Treasure sometimes puts you in touch with the only person in the country willing to buy what you have!

AUTOMOBILES & EPHEMERA

◆ **Old and antique cars and car parts.** "I buy and sell all types of antique cars and parts, foreign and domestic, as well as related materials such as parts, service manuals, advertisements and promotional toys." He specializes in **antique, classic, custom (hot rods), exotic and kit cars,** especially 1964 1/2 through 1968 Mustangs and Shelbys. Your description should include the type of item, and if a car, a description, including year, make, model, mileage, colors, and a brief history. Note its condition. "A color photo is helpful." Will make offers, but only if you intend to sell. Don't bother this busy 15 year veteran if you're only price fishing. Operates a national computer database on which you can advertise autos and cycles for sale or wanted, complete with color photos! Call for info.

Gregory Janaczek
Janaczek Engineering
Route 1   Box 1594
Gouldsboro, PA 18424
(717) 842-2277

◆ **Sports and race cars, 1950-1989.** We want cars used for slalom, drag racing, auto cross, and particularly road racing events. Most interested in obtaining German, Italian and British factory team cars, but well prepared amateur driven cars are also of interest. Will buy in any condition, but must be complete.

Paul Dunlop
PO Box 6269
Statesville, NC 28687
(800) 227-1996   (704) 871-2626 in NC

◆ **Race car "speed equipment" to hop up automobiles** from the 1930's, 40's, 50's, and 60's. Whether factory equipment or aftermarket, if it's designed to make a car go faster, and you want to sell it, give Dale a call. He'd especially like to find early Ford flathead engine cylinder heads, intake manifolds, and camshafts. 1955 to 1958 Chrysler aftermarket intake manifolds or valve covers will bring top prices. He personally does not want complete cars, complete engines, or "any items that can't be shipped U.P.S." But, if you have these things for sale, you might inquire as he adds, "I do have quality buyers for this type item." Describe what you have, including manufacturer and date, when possible. Dale publishes *RPM,* a monthly catalog which includes 30 pages of classified ads for folks buying and selling speed parts. You can subscribe for $20 a year.

Dale Wilch
2217 North 99th
Kansas City, KS 66109
(913) 788-3219   fax (913) 788-9682   <dale@rpmcat.com>

◆ **Paper ephemera, advertising, and promotional items associated with automobiles,** trucks, buses, campers, taxis, auto racing, police cars, ambulances, and hearses. Jay operates a large mail order business selling transportation memorabilia of all sorts and always needs clean old catalogs, promotional items, emblems, models given away by car dealers, auto company service pins, owner's manuals, and other small items associated with any form of vehicle. Will buy U.S. and foreign items, and multiples of some things. Will accept boxes sent on approval and "will make immediate offers to buy." Include your phone number. Does not want shop manuals, parts lists, and magazine ads.

> Jay Ketelle
> 3721 Farwell
> Amarillo, TX 79109
> (806) 355-3456   fax (806) 355-5743   <jayk.lit@amaonline.com>

◆ **Automobile sales catalogs, brochures, owner's manuals and repair guides** printed by the auto company. Wants material for all cars and trucks, American or foreign, especially pre-1970. No magazines, clipped ads, *Motor's Manuals, Chilton's Manuals*, or books not printed by the auto company. Also buys auto dealer promotional items including signs, salesman's awards, and the like. "Please send me a list of each item by year and make. If a list is not practical, give me a count by decade, such as 'so many brochures from 1950 to 1959,' etc."

> Walter Miller
> 6710 Brooklawn Parkway
> Syracuse, NY 13211
> (315) 432-8282   fax (315) 432-8256   <info@autolit.com>

◆ **After market hot rod add-on** items like fender skirts, sun visors, pipes, multi-carb manifolds, headers, hub cap sets, valve covers, etc., for building hot rods or customizing Detroit cars of the past. New old store stock especially wanted.

> Don Schneider
> PO Box 1570
> Meritt, BC
> CANADA V1K 1B8
> (250) 378-6421

◆ **Hot Rod and custom car magazines** from 1940-1964.

> Don Schneider
> PO Box 1570
> Merritt, BC
> CANADA V1K 1B8

◆ **Books, magazines, and factory literature about cars,** trucks, motorcycles, and bicycles. Also buys newsletters and magazines produced by automobile clubs devoted to one particular make of vehicle or another. Also buys documents related to vehicle history 1895-1990.
>
> Ralph Dunwoodie
> 5935 Calico Drive
> Sun Valley, NV 89433
>   (775) 673-3811

◆ **Books, catalogs, and owner's manuals.** Books may be on automobiles, auto history, racing, biography, auto travel, etc. Not interested in technical and repair manuals. Give standard bibliographic information, and note condition of cover, pages, spine, binding, and dust jacket. Also buys some photos of cars.
>
> David King's Automotive Books
> 5 Brouwer Lane
> Rockville Center, NY 11570
>   (516) 766-1561   fax (516) 766-7502

◆ **Automobile dealership ephemera** including signs for any make of automobile, sales literature, and what have you from the period 1930 to 1970. Nothing newer. No reproductions. SASE a must.
>
> Gus Garton, Garton's Auto
> 5th and Vine
> Millville, NJ 08332
>   (609) 825-3618

◆ **1932 Chevrolet parts,** accessories and paper ephemera including ads, showroom literature, catalogs, repair manuals, and what have you. As long as it's from a 1932 Chevy car or truck, he wants it.
>
> Reed Fitzpatrick
> PO Box 369
> Vashon, WA 98070
>   (206) 567-0555   <reed369@attbi.com>

◆ **Delorean items.** Wants "anything and everything related to John Z. Delorean and the Delorean car," including parts, newspaper clippings, magazine articles, posters, photos, commercials, certificates, and company greeting cards (worth $125 each!). Also items about the Delorean used in *Back to the Future* movies except bubble gum cards which are common. "The original Delorean sales brochure and John D's *On a Clear Day* are widely available; don't waste your time."
>
> Everen T. Brown
> PO Box 296
> Salt Lake City, UT 84110
>   fax (801) 364-2646   <etbrown@everent.com>

◆ **Ford Motor Company.** Buys and sells "almost anything" having to do with Ford Motor Company or Henry and Edsel Ford. Particularly interested in Ford aviation and Ford display and exhibition items from various World's Fairs up to 1964.

    Tim O'Callaghan
    PO Box 512
    Northville, MI 48167
        (248) 449-2652   <timothyo@ameritech.net>

◆ **Ford Motor Company.** Wants items related to Ford automobiles: postcards, books, photos, Christmas cards, sheet music, records, pens, pins, china, silverware, menus, sales literature, joke books, and what have you. Also wants items related to Henry Ford. Has a special interest in sales literature from 1928 to 1936.

    Cliff Moebius
    484 Winthrop Street
    Westbury, NY 11590
  (516) 333-3797   fax (516) 333-1712   <cmoebius@optonline.net>

◆ **Ford parts, 1932 to 1967,** that are new and unused, including fenders, grill assemblies, radiators, etc. Does not want reproduction parts.

    Gus Garton, Garton's Auto
    5th and Vine
    Millville, NJ 08332
        (609) 825-3618

◆ **Willy's automobile items** from 1933-42, including parts, showroom literature, shop manuals, dealer promos and signs. Also interested in 1950's and 60's Willy's drag racing items, photos of drivers, meets, etc. He DOES NOT WANT jeep items or any reprints.

    David Facey, Auto-Ads
    7015 Klein Road
    Lakeland, FL 33813
        (863) 644-8369

◆ **Volkswagen related memorabilia, literature, toys,** etc. "My preference is for older bug related items, with spilt window bug and oval window bug toys and memorabilia being the most desirable. However, any old VW items are of interest." Many foreign made toys are worth from $100 to $400 each, with some others, including some plastic ones, bringing even more! Does not want recent toys, *Avon,* or toys made in China. To sell toys, give the size, color, maker, and condition, noting whether you have the original box. Best to Xerox™ other items.

    Mike Wilson
    23490 SW 82nd Street
    Tualatin, OR 97062
        (503) 638-7074 eves   <rennopup@teleport.com>

◆ **Buick promotional items.**
Alvin Heckard
165 Orchard Grove Ave.
Lewistown, PA 17044
(717) 248-7071   <aheckard@nittanylink.com>

◆ **Mercedes and Rolls-Royce radiator mascots** and other parts, accessories, manuals, and literature made before 1960.
Joseph Weber
604 Centre Street
Ashland, PA 17921
(570) 875-4401 from 3 to 5 p.m.

◆ **Rolls-Royce advertising, pamphlets, cards, toys,** and other information. Has particular interest in all models from the years 1957 through 1962, Princess through Silver Cloud.
Richard Melcher
PO Box 1812
Wenatchee, WA 98807
(509) 662-0386

◆ **Parts and ephemera for Gardner autos.** Buys parts, hubcaps, mascots, owner's manuals, and the like. Will pay $75 for a single brochure on the front drive 1930 Gardner.
Robert Owen
PO Box 204
Fairborn, OH 45324

◆ **Radiator and hood ornaments from autos before WWII,** whether factory original or accessories. Does not want broken items or reproductions. Also buys catalogs, brochures, and advertising related to hood ornaments. Give a photo or detailed description.
Sy and Ronnie Margolis
17853 Santiago Boulevard #107-210
Villa Park, CA 92861
(714) 974-5938   fax (714) 921-0731   <smargol@adelphia.net>

◆ **Odd looking spark plugs.** "I'll buy as many as you have, the odder looking the better." He especially wants those with priming cups. No *AC* or *Champion* plugs.
Joseph Weber
604 Centre Street
Ashland, PA 17921
(717) 875-4401 from 3 to 5 p.m.

TONY'S TIP: *The basic book for getting an idea of the market for older and more unusual automobiles is* **Hemming's Motor News**, *available on most newsstands.*

◆ **Tire and tube repair kits** cans made of paper or tin. The older and more colorful the better. Photocopy what you have, please.

Ed Natale, Jr.
PO Box 222
Wyckoff, NJ 07481
(201) 493-7172 voice/fax

◆ **Car jacks.** "I'm a Baptist minister who owns more than 2,000 car jacks. I collect them, but also supply jacks to collectors and restoration shops. I am interested in buying:
  • Old bumper jacks with round or little I-beam upright shaft;
  • Small jacks with names of early car manufacturers on them;
  • Small screw jacks with protrusions like little shark's teeth;
  • Any unusual screw jack.
Please send a photo or drawing with the dimensions along with any patent dates or other numbers. I've been doing this for 14 years, and don't mind providing approximate values of jacks or making offers." No modern jacks, Volkswagen jacks or jacks with big screws.

Larry Olson
4125 56th Street
Des Moines, IA 50310
(515) 278-8487   <bigols@yahoo.com>

◆ **Tire company promotional items** especially **tire ashtrays,** tire clocks, pen holders, radios, globes, Tires magazines, tire catalogs, and other literature and promotional items. Also want foreign tires and those issued for promotions. Long priced wants list available. There are thousands of varieties of tires, so make certain to include all information printed on the tire and on the glass insert as well as the diameter (distance across) the tire. "I'll reply to any letters which include an SASE."

Jeff McVey
1810 West State Street #427
Boise, ID 83702
(208) 342-8447   <jeffrey_mcvey@waob.oas.sou>

◆ **Rubber tire ash trays** all sizes, colors, makes and ages, new or old.

Don Schneider
PO Box 1570
Merritt, BC V1K 1B8 CANADA

◆ **Rubber tire ashtrays.** Give the tire maker and the "size" printed on the tire. Note what is printed on the glass part of the ashtray.

Ed Natale, Jr.
PO Box 222
Wyckoff, NJ 07481
(201) 493-7172 voice/fax

◆ **Unused parts for Dodge, Plymouth and Chrysler products.** A private collector seeks new old parts and trim for three old Canadian version Chrisler product cars. Especially wants anything from a 1946-48 Dodge Club Coupe, a 1955 Plymouth 241 V8 or a 1965 Chrysler 413 V8. Wants **other Mopar (Chrysler) items including new old engines and transmissions, shop manuals, photos, sales literature**, etc.

> Don Schneider
> PO Box 1570
> Meritt, BC
> Canada V1K 1B8
>   (250) 378-6421

◆ **Mobile homes, trailer coaches, trailers and related ephemera.** "We're interested in full size trailers, motor homes and post war trailer coaches (early mobile homes) in goodcondition made between 1925 and 1959. Please send photos of the inside and outside of your vehicle along with an SASE for our offer." Also **all ephemera related to motor camping** including photos, articles, license plates, salesmen's samples, models, toys, amateur or professional film, sheet music, advertising, brochures, postcards, and promotional material of all sort, including that for **Volkswagen campers.** They publish *Lost Highways* about the heyday of trailering and motor camping. Sample issue $6. Compete information for a long SASE.

> Todd & Kristin Kimmell
> PO Box 43737
> Philadelphia, PA 19106
>   (215) 925-2568

◆ **Mullins Red Cap Trailer literature,** parts, and advertising.
> Cliff Moebius
> 484 Winthrop Street
> Westbury, NY 11590
> (516) 333-3797   fax (516) 333-1712 <cmoebius@optonline.net>

◆ **Engine rebuilding equipment and tools** for working on antique auto, marine, truck, tractor, and stationary engines. Wants equipment made by KR Wilson, Kent Moore, Hempy-Cooper, Waterbury Simplicity, Van-Norman, Peterson and others. Especially wants original equipment for Babbitt bearings including production equipment, smaller equipment for motorcycles and larger equipment for stationary engines. Not interested in home made equipment or items that have been "super modified."

> Shawn R. Aldrich
> Aldrich Engine Rebuilding
> 352 River Road (Rte. 32)
> Willington, CT 06279
>   (860) 429-3111   <www.babbitt-bearings.com>

LICENSE PLATES

◆ **License plates before 1920,** especially undated plates made of leather, brass, or porcelain. Will buy old collections or accumulations. Describe condition carefully, including damage, chips, and crazing. He offers to answer questions about license plates and says, "If I don't want your plates, perhaps I can find someone who does." Gary is secretary of the Automobile License Plate Collector's Association and a valuable source of information.

Gary Brent Kincade
226 Ridgeway Drive
Bridgeport, WV 26330
(304) 842-3773 eves

◆ **All license plates.** Will buy any good condition license plate; wants singles or collections and accumulations of plates:
• Undated or those made of porcelain, leather, or wood;
• **Any U.S. plate, any year, any condition;**
• All Alaska, Hawaii or foreign plates;
• **All motorcycle plates;**
• All plates issued on or for Indian reservations;
• **Personalized plates "with cute names or phrases";**
• Any pictorial plates;
• Mini plates from DAV, Goodrich, Wheaties, or Post cereals;
• Car club emblems such as AAA, especially foreign or pre-1925;
• Chauffeur's badges in good original condition, pre-1940;
List the type of item, place of origin, date, number, condition, quantity, and price (if possible). "If you don't like what I offer for your license plate, I'll let you run a free ad in my License Plate Corner magazine so you can try to sell it for more."

George Chartrand
PO Box 334
Winnipeg, MB R3C 2H6 CANADA
(204) 774-1186

◆ **Porcelain license plates from U.S. and Canadian cars,** trucks, and motorcycles before 1923. Also wants early photos and photo postcards of vehicles clearly showing readable plates. Pays especially well for plates from Southern and unpopulated Western states. Does not buy painted metal plates. Photocopies suggested.

Rodney Brunsell
55 Spring Street
Hanson, MA 02341
(781) 447-5384 <rodder781@aol.com>

TONY'S TIP: The best way to describe your license plate is by making a Xerox© copy of it.

★ **License plates of all types from anywhere** especially early porcelain plates. "I am happy to get your questions about license plates, rare or common. If I am not interested I will gladly try to help in other ways." Give the name of the issuing agency, type of plate, material from which it was made, the date, and its condition. Note any repainting or repair. Fluent in Spanish and French.

> Andy Bernstein
> 43-60 Douglaston Parkway #524
> Douglaston, NY 11363
> (718) 279-1890   (407) 793-8422   <andybnyork@aol.com>

◆ **License plates from anywhere in the world,** but primarily Washington and Alaska. "I'll buy singles or accumulations. Unusual plates such as mobile home, taxi, trailer, state representative, etc., are particularly welcome." Also buys plates that carry an advertising message and fasten just above or below a license plate. **Brass plaques, auto club insignias,** and the like are of interest. "When you contact me, I want to know the state, year and type of plate. Photocopy if you can."

> Reed Fitzpatrick
> PO Box 369
> Vashon, WA 98070
> (206) 463-0555   <reed369@attbi.com>

◆ **Expired obsolete license plates of all types and varieties** from anywhere. "I'll buy almost anything and everything ever used for registration or identification on a motor vehicle, front or back, domestic or foreign, from the earliest days of motoring up to and including current issues." Porcelain plates from before 1920, especially from less populous states, city and local issues and home-made plates bring the biggest premiums. Values depend on type of plate, numbers, rarity, condition, and degree of collector interest. He encourages you to write about any plate you think might be unusual, as long as you include a Xerox™ or clear color photo and a SASE. If a porcelain plate has a maker's name on the back, include that information. This long time collector/dealer asks that you also include your evening phone number.

> Dave Lincoln
> PO Box 331
> Yorklyn, DE 19736
> (610) 444-4144

◆ **License plates from Missouri, Kansas, and Colorado.** Also wants other states from the years 1936, 1976, and 1989. Also miniature key chain license plates produced by B.F. Goodrich or the DAV. Provide a list of the items you have and the price you'd like.

> George Van Trump, Jr.
> PO Box 260170
> Lakewood, CO 80226
> (303) 985-3508   fax (303) 985-7872   <jogeorge@qwest.net>

◆ **Bicycle license tags,** often called "sidepath licenses," from any state as long as they are dated before 1930. Value ranges from $20-$100 depending on the age, condition and place of issue.

> James Case
> 10189 Crane Road
> Lindley, NY 14858
> (607) 524-6606 <hftlicense@aol.com>

◆ **British Columbia license plates before 1922** in any condition. Later BC plates will be considered if unusual, as will pre-1960 Yukon plates, Canadian motorcycle plates, and BC chauffeur's badges.

> Don Schneider
> PO Box 1570
> Merritt, BC
> V1K 1B8 CANADA
> (604) 378-6421

◆ **B.F.Goodrich and DAV keychain license plate tags.** Pays 50¢ to $1 each, depending on age and state. The older the better.

> Dennis Schulte
> 8th Avenue NW
> Waukon, IA 52172
> (563) 568-3628

TONY'S TIPS: When a buyer asks for a photocopy they mean something made on a Xerox© machine not a photograph. This is the very best way of all to tell someone about your license plate. Be careful not to scratch the glass on the photocopier.

TAXIS, BUSES & TROLLEYS

◆ **Taxi cabs.** "If it pictures an American taxi cab, I'll probably buy it," says Henry, wo seeks a wide variety of taxi related items, including license plates, cabbies' hats, badges, cab ID medalions and what have you. Give a good description and include a photo or photocopy whenever possible. Responds to all letters with SASE.

> Henry Winningham
> 3205 South Morgan Street
> Chicago, IL 60608
> (773) 927-3796

◆ **Bus industry memorabilia from 1935 to the present** is wanted, including models, toys, banks, post cards of busses and terminals, time tables, bus manufacturer sales brochures, bus drivers' manuals, uniforms, driver's badges, promotional items, coach logos, bus industry trade magazines, and china, crystal, and flatware with bus company logos. This charter coach company owner **will even consider actual full size Greyhound style buses**. Please send a good description of the item and its condition for a fair offer. Regularly issues a catalog of bus related items for sale.

> Charles Wotring, Royal Coach
> 911 Conley Drive
> Mechanicsburg, PA 17055
> > (717) 691-1147   fax (717) 691-6623
> > <royal.coach@worldnet.att.net>

◆ **Greyhound and Trailways bus memorabilia.** Wants a wide range of items, such as cap badges, driver awards, etc., but mostly interested in toy Greyhound and Trailways busses, and Greyvan Moving truck toys. Prefers a picture or photocopy. No magazine ads, timetables, postcards or posters, but he does want internal company data like garage locations, driver assignments, and organizational directories.

> Eugene Farha
> PO Box 633
> Cedar Grove, WV 25039
(304) 340-3229 days   (304) 340-2296 eves   fax (304) 340-3356
> > <farha@mail.wvnet.edu>

◆ **Memorabilia from buses, taxis, hearses, ambulances, and any other public conveyance** before 1960 including emblems, badges, licenses, license plates, advertising, promotional giveaway trinkets, operator's manuals, sales literature, etc. May be foreign or U.S. as long as they are old and genuine. Will accept items sent on approval.

> Jay Ketelle
> 3721 Farwell
> Amarillo, TX 79109
> > (806) 355-3456   fax (806) 355-5743
> > <jayk.lit@amaonline.com>

◆ **Bus, trolley, and streetcar memorabilia pre-1940** including photos, artifacts, driver's badges, caps, bus emblems, route maps, and advertising. Has particular interest in Florida companies but says "I will consider any item if the seller describes it well and attaches a price."

> Sam LaRoue
> 5980 SW 35th Street
> Miami, FL 33155
> > (305) 237-7478   fax (305) 237-7534
> > <slaroue@mdcc.edu>

MOTORCYCLES & EPHEMERA

◆ **Motorcycles and motorcycle parts.** "I'm in the market for all American made parts for American motorcycles." Give marks and numbers when appropriate in your description. "I pay all shipping costs. I'm in the parts business and will travel to pick up large lots."

> Robert Fay
> Rusted & Busted Bob's
> Box 24
> Whitmore, CA 96096
>   (530) 472-3132   <yafer@shasta.com>

◆ **Harley-Davidson motorcycles, parts, and all other ephemera.** All types, all sizes, all things Harley. Ads, posters, leathers, cast iron toys, you name it. "If you got something great, I'll pay the price."

> Danny Perkins
> 17927 River Court
> Pierrefonds, PQ H9J 1A2 CANADA
>   (514) 624-8515   fax (514) 624-8942
>   <danny@backstage.ca>

◆ **Old European and Japanese motorcycles** with a particular interest in Moto Guzzi cycles. He would like the name of the manufacturer, the year, model and an accurate description of condition. "Very good photos" are requested. This 30 year veteran does not buy any Japanese motorcycles made after 1968. No exceptions.

> Michael Harper
> Harper's Moto Guzzi
> 32401 Stringtown Road
> Greenwood, MO 64034
>   (816) 697-3511   fax (816) 566-3413
>   <harpermoto@att.net>

◆ **Motorcycle memorabilia** including advertising, giveaway trinkets, watch fobs, and other items, both foreign and domestic, pre-1960. "I will accept boxes sent to me on approval and will make immediate offers to buy." Pledges to repay your postage if his offer not accepted.

> Jay Ketelle
> 3721 Farwell
> Amarillo, TX 79109
> (806) 355-3456   fax (806) 355-5743   <jayk.lit@amaonline.com>

◆ **Motorcycle racing autographs.** Please photocopy what you have.

> Royal Duncan
> 428 West Collingwood Circle
> Peoria, IL 61614
>   (309) 691-2772   fax (309) 691 2577

◆ **Motorcycle club or gang memorabilia** including photos, patches, pins, news clippings, business cards..."anything." Also buys cans of motorcycle oil, full or empty, "in all sizes and vintages." He notes that he'll pay from $50 to $200 for Indian and Harley Davidson cans and $20 each for oil can banks. Ed is the President of the American Iron Motorcycle Club and issues both wants and for sale lists.

Ed Natale, Jr.
PO Box 222
Wyckoff, NJ 07481
(201) 493-7172 voice/fax

◆ **Motorcycles and motorcycle ephemera** from before 1920. Wants advertising, factory sales catalogs, manuals, magazines, pins, fobs, trophies, medals, and related items.

Herb Glass
531 Burlingham Road
Pine Bush, NY 12566
(845) 361-3657   <hglass@pioneeris.net>

◆ **Can-Am motorcycle parts and ephemera** including Rotax motors, brochures, decals, gloves, leathers, goggles, and anything else marked Can-Am. This motorcycle is made by Bombardier of Canada.

Don Schneider
PO Box 1570
Merritt, BC V1K 1B8   CANADA
(250) 378-6421

◆ **Pre-1970 motorcycles** and motorcycle literature, manuals, magazines, postcards, toy and related items.

Don Olson
PO Box 245
Humboldt, IA 50548
<donolson@goldfieldaccess.com>

◆ **Motorcycles and motorcycle parts.** Wants Harley-Davidson, BSA, Indian and Vincent brands, not Japanese cycles. Your description should include the type of item, and if a cycle, a description, including year, make, model, mileage, and a brief history. Note its condition. "A color photo is helpful but doesn't replace seeing the actual item." Will make offers, but only if you intend to sell. Don't bother this busy 13 year veteran if you're only "price fishing." Runs a computer database on which you can advertise cycles for sale or wanted. Call for info.

Gregory Janaczek
Janaczek Engineering
Route 1   Box 1594
Gouldsboro, PA 18424
(717) 842-2277

BICYCLES & EPHEMERA

★ **Bicycles and everything related to them** including:
- Deluxe men's & boy's bicycles 1880-1960;
- Highwheeler bicycles by any manufacturer;
- All men's and women's hard tire safety bicycles;
- All Harley Davidson or Indian bicycles;
- All Schwinn bicycles with tanks and balloon tired bikes from 1933 on especially those with speedometers built into the handlebar crossbrace and Aerocycle, Autocycle and Motobike;
- All aluminum bikes by Monarch SilverKing, Wards-Hawthorne;
- All deluxe bikes with mechanical suspension systems and all bikes with rear suspension;
- **Schwinn Stingray, Orange Krates, Apple Krates, Lemon Peelers, Pea Pickers, etc. with 5 speed or coaster brakes;**
- Fiberglass streamlined bikes by Bowden, Sherrell, etc.
- **Motorized bicycles**, including Whizzers and Monarch Twins;
- All bicycle parts, accessories, clocks, etc., including trophies;
- Catalogs, advertising, signs, and the like.

Prices can be serious. He offers $5,000 for the early model Sears Elgin Bluebird and up to $5,000 for some hi-wheelers. He does not want reproductions or homemade, mismatched "phonied up" bikes and definitely no 1959 or newer girl's middleweight bikes with 24 or 26 x 1.75 tires. He requests you give the make, model (if known), tire size (printed on side of tire), sex and color of the bike, and a photo whenever possible. "Please don't call on the free (877) line if you do not have a bike to sell. If you want to chat or reminisce, use the other line."

Michael "Bike Mike" Kaplan
Funtiques
PO Box 440
Belmont, MA 02478
free (877) 652-BIKE   (617) 489-4779   fax (617) 489-1956
<bicyclemike@nostalgiamerchants.com>

TONY'S TIP: Collectible bikes usually have tires sized: 26" x 1.125", 24" x 2.125" or 28" x 1.5" and are especially good if colored red or blue.

◆ **Bicycles made before 1900** and associated memorabilia, medals, pins, LAW souvenirs, awards, ribbons, photos, whatever. Please send photo or Xerox™ copy, along with the price wanted and your phone number. All letters answered promptly.

Charlie Stewart
900 Grandview Avenue
Reno, NV 89503
        (775) 747-1439 days   <x14@worldnet.att.net>

◆ **League of American Wheelmen memorabilia** is sought by this expert 20 year veteran collector who buys pins, medals, ribbons, magazines, etc., from 1880-1955. You might try him for general early bicycle memorabilia as well. Not interested in anything after 1955.
>
> Walley Francis
> PO Box 6941
> Syracuse, NY 13217
> (315) 478-5671   <wfrancis@mailbox.syr.edu>

◆ **Balloon tire bicycles made between 1934-1960** in new or mint condition only, especially Schwinn, Shelby, Monarch, Columbia, or Elgin (Sears Roebuck). Please include a photo.
>
> Gus Garton
> Garton's Auto
> 5th and Vine
> Millville, NJ 08332

◆ **Whizzers and balloon tire bicycles** are wanted. Whizzers are motor driven bicycles, some of which were factory built, others made from kits with a belt drive attached to the rear wheel. If you're selling a Whizzer, include the serial number as part of your description, which ideally should include a sharp photo of the vehicle. The bicycles he wants have tires sized 20", 24", or 26" x 2.125". Especially looking for a 1933 Schwinn Aerocycle or a 1938-39 Shelby Speedline Airflow. "The longer and weirder the bicycle's tanks are, the more I want them." Also buys signs and shop fixtures, including old brake parts cabinets, literature, and advertising. He does not want middleweight bikes with 1.75" tires or plain bikes with no tanks. Send a photo with description.
>
> Alan Kinsey
> 1035 68th Street #1
> West Des Moines, IA 50266
> (515) 226-8352   <geswhosbac@aol.com>

◆ **Antique motorbikes** from before 1941. Parts and manuals from early motorized bicycles as well. Please leave your phone number and postal address clearly and slowly on his answering machine.
>
> Dale Ericson
> PO Box 442
> Kimball, MN 55353
> (320) 398-8285   <docoinbob@yahoo.com>

◆ **Stingray bikes and parts.** Stingrays he wants have banana seats, high handlebars and stick shifters. Send a photo with your description.
>
> Alan Kinsey
> 1035 68th Street #1
> West Des Moines, IA 50266
> (515) 226-8352   <geswhosbac@aol.com>

◆ **Bicycle license tags,** often called "sidepath licenses," from any state as long as they are dated before 1930. Value ranges from $20-$100 depending on the age, condition and place of issue.

> James Case
> 10189 Crane Road
> Lindley, NY 14858
> (607) 524-6606   <hftlicense@aol.com>

SHIPS & BOATS

◆ **Fine marine antiques of all types** including but not limited to:
- **Paintings and prints of boats,** ships and the sea, 1700-1900;
- **Navigational instruments from the 19th century,** sextants, telescopes on tripods, marine clocks, compasses, etc.;
- **Photographs of whaling, yachting,** ship launchings, and identified parts in the 19th or early 20th century;
- **Journals, logs and out-of-print books about whaling, yachting,** clippers, "but only in resellable condition";
- **Wood carvings** such as figureheads, pilot house eagles, name boards, and tail boards;
- **Scrimshaw** teeth and sailor's whimsies, inlaid boxes, crimpers, bone swifts, and tools, but only genuine quality old pieces;
- Paper and other ephemera including deck plans, broadsides, ship's china...anything rare, interesting and in fine condition;
- Artifacts related to **lighthouses** and the **Life Saving Service**.

Generally buys only 19th century items. He does not want fakes, altered items, modern scrimshaw, boxed compasses, or ship's telegraphs unless they are small, very early, or historically important. Description should include dimensions, note of repairs or restoration, history and price ("if you can"). He specializes in forming and liquidating collections and issues interesting catalogs of items for sale.

> Andrew Jacobson's Marine Antiques
> PO Box 437
> Ipswitch, MA 01938
> (978) 356-5583   fax (978) 356-8705
> <andrew@marineantiques.com>

◆ **Model sailboats.** "I'll buy wooden models that are at least 18" long, made of wood, with rigged canvas sails. May be up to 8' high. I prefer them to have stands. I'm looking for their decorative value so am not particularly looking for famous boats, ship builder's models, and other high ticket items. Send a picture of what you have, please." Should be in fine or readily restorable condition.

> Joan Brady
> 834 Central Avenue
> Pawtucket, RI 02861

◆ **Ship models,** particularly identified 19th century American, English or French vessels. "I also deal in 20th century high quality models of all types: sail, steam, liners, yachts, and pond models." Also buys builder's half models, including 19th century American or British hulls, exceptional 20th century hulls, and all yacht models. Does not want reproductions, or items which have been heavily "restored" or otherwise altered. Please give the dimensions, age, condition, history, and price. "If you want an appraisal, I must examine the object personally, and there is a fee, although I will give 'ball park' verbal estimates on routine items, with the understanding there is no legal responsibility or liability for accuracy."

> Andrew Jacobson's Marine Antiques
> PO Box 437
> Ipswitch, MA 01938
>> (978) 356-5583   fax (978) 356-8705
>> <andrew@marineantiques.com>

◆ **Whaling industry artifacts.** "I'm looking for anything related to the American whaling industry, including scrimshaw, tools, and early copies of *Moby Dick*, especially the 1851 first edition."

> Greg "Dr. Z" Zemenick
> 1350 Kirts Blvd. #160
> Troy, MI 48084
> (248) 642-8129   fax (248) 244-9495   <drzzeezz@aol.com>

◆ **Steamship memorabilia** including china, silver, ashtrays, whistles, locks, lanterns, badges, signs, uniforms and caps, calendars, posters, route maps, and numerous similar items. He does not want paper ephemera after 1910, low value paper goods, fake or altered items or big heavy tools. He does not buy items that are shabby or missing important parts.

> Scott Arden
> 20457 Highway 126
> Noti, OR 97461
>> (541) 935-1619 from 9 to 9 Pacific time

◆ **Ocean liner memorabilia** from all companies, especially paper items such as deck plans, menus, booklets, and passenger lists from Cunard, French, German, White Star, Italian, Canadian, Dutch, and all others. "We do not buy reproductions or items that are strictly 'travel' interest, such as brochures describing Paris. You may send items on approval as we cannot make offers based only on your description."

> Alan Taksler
> New Steamship Consultants
> PO Box 30088
> Mesa, AZ 85275
>> <ships@pobox.com>

◆ **Ocean liner memorabilia,** deck plans, postcards, paintings, posters, and anything relating to passenger ship travel especially from "disaster ships" such as the Titanic, Lusitania, Normandie or Andrea Doria. After 1945, only maiden voyage items wanted. Ken produces a large illustrated catalog for $15.
> Ken Schultz
> PO Box M-753
> Hoboken, NJ 07030
> (201) 656-0966   fax (201) 418-8640   <kencschultz@aol.com>

◆ **Canadian steamship ephemera** before 1950 such as deck plans, calendars, stock certificates, bonds, fancy letterheads, envelopes, etc. Seeks Canadian Pacific steamships, BC Coast steamships, and others.
> Michael Rice
> PO Box 286
> Saanichton, BC   V8M 2C5   CANADA
> (250) 652-9412 eves only   <mrice@pacificcoast.net>

◆ **Steamship ephemera** collections dating pre-1960, including menus, programs, deck plans, posters, etc., from either American or European lines. Promises a quick answer to all inquiries.
> George Theofilies, The Miscellaneous Man
> PO Box 1776
> New Freedom, PA 17349
> (717) 235-4766 days   fax (717) 235-2853

◆ **Licenses for ship masters, mates, pilots, and engineers.** Wants those issued by the U.S. Coast Guard and the Steamboat Inspection Service. Please photocopy. Also wants boat license stickers and decals from any state or agency.
> Bill Smiley
> PO Box 361
> Portage, WI 53901
> (608) 742-3714 eves   <wsmiley@chorus.net>

◆ **Lighthouses, U.S. Coast Guard, and sea rescue services,** pre-1940. Wants all types of ephemera.
> Rhonda Halloran, Columbia Trading Co.
> 1 Barnstable Road
> Hyannis, MA 02601
> (508) 778-2929   fax (508) 778-2922   <nautical@capecod.net>

◆ **Hardhat diving gear and old two hose scuba regulators.**
> Thomas Szymanski
> 5 Stoney Brook Lane
> Stratham, NH 03885
> (603) 772-6372   <tomski@nh.ultranet.com>

◆ **Chris Craft boats and ephemera.** "I buy vintage Chris Craft runabouts and utility boats, as well as owner's manuals, engine manuals, and other literature including sales catalogs, service bulletins, and advertising. Artwork, photos and factory models of Chris Craft are may also be of interest. We don't want reproductions, copies, or kid's models." When describing a boat, give the year of manufacture, the model, length, power, condition, and degree of originality. For other items, the age and condition. Wilson is Executive Director of the Chris Craft Antique Boat Club and editor of its newsletter, *The Brass Bell*, available with club membership of $25/year.

> Wilson Wright
> 217 South Adams Street
> Tallahassee, FL 32301
> (850) 224-5169 days   fax (850) 224-1033
> <wwright@nettally.com>

◆ **Boating memorabilia** especially items related to Gar Wood, the man and his boats, 1923-47, but also Chris Craft, Century, Lyman and Truscott. Buys sales literature, catalogs, boating magazines, photographs, and parts, like spot lights, dash board instruments, steering wheels, windshield brackets, etc., made before 1950.

> Tony Mollica
> 110 Cherry Hill
> Dewitt, NY 13214
> (315) 446-5654   <asmollica@aol.com>

◆ **Outboard motors, 1940-1960.** "I'm especially interested in motors by Flambeau, Neptune, Martin 200 and any racing outboards made in the United States, such as Mercury and Champion. If you send me a photo of your old outboard motor along with an SASE, I'll identify it for you, and if it's something I can use, I'll make an offer." Peter is the author of *The Old Outboard Book*.

> Peter Hunn, Antique Boat Museum
> 750 Mary Street
> Clayton, NY 13624
> <melodyfm@dreamscape.com>

TONY'S TIP: Almost any item marked with the name of a railroad, airline, shipping company, bus, etc., has a market if in good condition. Describe what you have carefully, noting all names, numbers and dates which appear. Chips, cracks, tears and other damage should be described. Photos are helpful as are photocopies.

Don't forget your S.A.S.E.

AIRPLANE & AIRLINE ITEMS

◆ **Aviation equipment and history.** This 15 year dealer wants any authentic military and antique flying equipment, parts, props, engines, wheels, armaments, suits, helmets, goggles, overhaul manuals, jackets, survival gear, maps, photographs, histories, toys, artwork, jewelry, etc. If it's genuine, old, and aviation, they probably want it. They do not want reproductions or items that have been altered. Please supply data found on the manufacturer's ID tag, a condition statement, and what you know of the item's history. Photo suggested and will be returned. A sample of their interesting catalog is $1. They say, "a satisfied customer is our number one goal."

> Norm and Bev Smith
> Aviator's World
> PO Box 608
> San Juan Capistrano, CA 92693
> (949) 240-9606   <norm@aviatorsworld.com>

◆ **Airplanes and old airplane parts,** early flight equipment, books, magazines, photos, etc., are sought by the 6,000 members of The Antique Airplane Association. Write what you have for sale in the way of early air memorabilia, and President Taylor will forward your letter to a member who is looking for what you have to sell. The Association is the parent organization of the Air-Power Museum and Bob is empowered to accept tax deductible donations of significant and interesting items from the history of air flight.

> Bob Taylor
> Antique Airplane Association
> 22001 Bluegrass Road
> Ottumwa, IA 52501
> (641) 938-2773 days   <aaaapmhq@pcsia.net>

◆ **Pan Am's China Clipper** and all Chinese airline memorabilia, 1925-45, including caps, uniforms, medals, photos, diaries, badges, posters, and what have you.

> Gene Christian
> 3849 Bailey Avenue
> Bronx, NY 10463
> (718) 548-0243

◆ **Early aviation memorabilia of alltypes.**

> Christopher Lynch
> Velhalk Aerostation
> PO Box 24
> Glens Falls, NY 12801
> (518) 793-8262 voice/fax

◆ **Concorde and SST items.** "Everything related to the Concorde or SST is of interest, including newspaper reports, magazines articles, advertisements, autographs of people influential in building the planes, models larger than 24", jewelry, videotapes of commercials, china, silver, parts, old seats, gifts given away on flights and commemorative menus. No everyday menus, underarm portfolios, airline magazines, or duty free catalogs are wanted, nor is the *How They Fly the Concorde* video. Send a Xerox™ and "an honest description."
Everen T. Brown
PO Box 296
Salt Lake City, UT 84110
fax (801) 364-2646 <etbrown@everent.com>

◆ **Ford tri-motor airplane memorabilia.** Wants aviation sales brochures and literature as well as airline ads and timetables picturing the Ford Tri-Motor airplane from 1926-1930's. Also wants aviation engine and parts manufacture literature featuring Fords. "Will pay $200 for Ford Airplane Co. factory badge, $25 to $100 for most other items."
Tim O'Callaghan
PO Box 512
Northville, MI 48167
(248) 449-2652 <timothyo@ameritech.net>

◆ **Commercial airline memorabilia** including pilot and stewardess wings, hat emblems, display models, anniversary pins, playing cards, postcards, buttons, flight schedules, kiddie wings, and almost anything else old and unusual from the airlines. Especially ephemera from Northeast Airlines, Delta, Chicago and Southern and Western Airlines.
John Joiner
173 Green Tree Drive
Newnan, GA 30265
(770) 502-9565 <propjoiner@mindspring.com>

◆ **Pan-Am airlines and affiliates ephemera** wanted including toys, playsets, schedules, brochures, premiums, posters, photos, postcards, advertising, and other memorabilia. Other companies include Panagra, Panair de Brasil, C.N.A.C., Pacific Alaska, Aeromarine, and N.Y.R.B.A. Especially wants items from the Clipper ships of the 1930's. Does not want kiddie wings, pilot wings, swizzle sticks, uniforms, glasses, or china. Give a complete description including dimensions. Describe the logo or make a photocopy.
Robert Horn
345 East 73rd Street
New York, NY 10021
(212) 371-1511 fax (212) 223-4911

◆ **Commercial airline memorabilia** including:
- Insignia: pilot wings, pilot cap badges, stewardess wings, service
  pins, award pins, commemorative pins, badges, jewelry, and
  ground personnel cap badges, uniform patches, etc.
  No military or international pilot or stewardess insignia;
- Dining service items: glassware, silverware, serving pieces, cups,
  butter pat plates, nut dishes, salt and pepper shakers, etc., from
  before 1980. He does not want broken, chipped, cracked or
  damaged china and glassware, but "average wear is OK;"
- Airline kiddie items: junior pilot wings, junior stewardess wings,
  junior flight certificates, junior pilot and stewardess patches,
  junior log books, etc. He does not want plastic kiddie wings
  from Delta, Northwest, Northwest Orient, United, American,
  TWA, Continental, Alaska Air, Eastern, Midwest Express,
  PSA, Piedmont, RAA, Republic, Southwest, Sun Country, or
  the red on white Midway;
- Airline paper: inaugural flight certificates, commemorative art
  work, ticket jackets, seat back packets, first flight envelopes,
  inaugural flights covers, dinner menus, timetables, safety
  cards, seat occupied cards, annual reports, log books, photos,
  etc. He does not want items in poor condition, although
  lesser condition may be acceptable for 1930's items;
- Other items: lighters, plane models, advertising and marketing
  giveaways, etc. He buys complete decks of airline playing
  cards, but decks after 1960 must be sealed and unopened.

"If you wish to sell it, you have to describe it. A Xerox™ copy can
often answer a lot of questions and save you a lot of writing. You do
not need to list every defect but you should provide an estimate of the
condition. Sometimes I may need additional information concerning
markings, colors, condition, etc. I do and will make offers to amateurs.
I expect dealers to provide accurate information and the selling price."
William is the author of *Kiddie Wings and Other Things*, available from
him for $18 postpaid.

William Gawchik
88 Clarendon Avenue
Yonkers, NY 10701
(914) 965-3010   fax (914) 966-1055   <panam314@aol.com>

◆ **Airline and aviation collectibles.** "I want anything from the early
days of commercial aviation: pilot wings, hat emblems, airline watches,
jewelry, rings, etc. I'm not interested in reproductions, restrikes or
modern items. Please give an accurate description including size, color,
material, and condition." Seller must set the price wanted. Author of
Pilot Wings of the United States, available from him for $36 postpaid.

Philip Martin
PO Box 91051
Long Beach, CA 90809
       (562) 434-6701   <wingman@earthlink.net>

◆ **Airline pilot and stewardess wings and hat badges** pre-1970. Also stewardess uniforms pre-1965 if they are complete. Looking for pilot and stewardess wings from the 1940's and 50's from Mohawk, Inland, Northeast, Pioneer, Empire, Colonial, Chicago and Southern Airlines, Mid-Continent, others. **Also metal desk models of airliners** (travel agent type) from 1940-70. No military items. Photocopies helpful.

  Charles Quarles
  204 Reservation Drive
  Spindale, NC 28160
 (828) 286-2962 (828) 245-7803 eves fax (828) 286-3224
  <airliner@rfci.net> <www.rfci.net/airliner>

◆ **Aviation models and toys** including **desk models, travel agency and airline promotional display models, wind tunnel and manufacturer display models, ID and recognition models,** and **aviation toys** of all types, including friction floor toys and battery operated toy airplanes. Seeks airplanes, helicopters, missiles and **rockets,** with civilian or military markings. No plastic or wood kid's model kits or homemade items. Tell him the material from which it's made, the size, the type of stand and all markings. Indicate any missing or broken parts.

  Larry McLaughlin
  17 Seventh Avenue
  Smithtown, NY 11787
  (631) 265-9224 <larrymak@erols.com>

★ **Zeppelin, blimp and dirigible memorabilia** including anything shaped like, or about, the giant gas bags such as photos, paper ephemera, postcards, china marked "LZ," stereocards, timetables, books, souvenirs, stamps and covers, training films, toys, games, and Christmas ornaments. Especially wants pieces and parts of zeppelins. No repros, repainted or restored items, homemades, or fakes. "I am a historian not a dealer."

  Art Bink, Airship Historian
  609 Hamilton Drive
  Cinnaminson, NJ 08077
  (856) 829-3959

◆ **Balloons, airships and zeppelin** memorabilia, relics, and historical ephemera. "Anything from 18th century to WWII, including books, prints, miniatures, flight manuals, uniforms, pieces, photos, etc., even pre 1940 children's toys. Early American ballooning is our specialty and we pay top dollar for porcelain, jewelry, snuff boxes, etc. with representations of early ballooning. We do not buy magazines or newspapers. Please give a full description or standard bibliographic info.

  Christopher Lynch, Velhalk Aerostation
  PO Box 24
  Glens Falls, NY 12801
  (518) 793-8262 voice/ fax <ltabooks@capital.net>

Continued from page 337

Their press releases rarely point out that a third of the items didn't sell, or, as with the case of a recent heavily promoted auction, that nearly everything in the sale brought less than the auction house estimated. It is in the best interests of auction houses for you to believe you will get the most money by selling through them, so they never tell you that a typical audience is made up of antique dealers who will take the item back to their shop and raise the price.

The price you get at auction depends upon *the quality of your item, its history, what is being auctioned with it, when and where the auction is held, and, most important of all, who will be attracted to bid in the auction. Prices range from a typical 15% to 60% of retail value. Only rare goods under perfect conditions in important auctions will sell for 75% - 100% of value, or more.*

Auctioneers are paid for their services. *Before counting your money, remember the auction house will charge you from 15% to 25% of the hammer price for selling your items. Auction houses can also charge fees for picking your items up, for storage, for photographing them, for advertising them, or for cataloging them, so make certain you understand all fees before the signing a contract. When dealing with an entire household make certain the contract specifies what is to be sold and when you are to be paid. If there are minimum amounts you want for an item, that's called a reserve and you must make that clear to the auctioneer in writing. I've known people who have signed auction agreements to handle the estate of a spouse and then found themselves unable to go back into the house and withdraw personal items from the sale.*

Local general household auctioneers can be found across the country. They are a handy way to get rid of small estates in a hurry. Be very careful about using them for mid to high range collectibles. Items that might bring $100 or more from private collectors or specialty dealers, will often bring pennies when sold by local household auctioneers.

The antiques press has been filled lately with scandals involving auction houses including slow payment, non payment, bankruptcy, and rigged bidding. Be certain at all times that you know whom you're dealing with.

Continued on page 363

Continued from previous page

IS EBAY FOR YOU?

The answer is yes and no. Yes, ebay is usually better than a yard sale. No, it is usually not better than selling directly to the buyers in **Trash or Treasure Guide to the Best Buyers**.

One drawback is that, like all auctions, what happens on ebay is a matter of public record. Your government knows, your ex-wife knows, your relatives know. Everything that happens on the internet is open to everyone who wants the information. If that is of concern, don't use the internet.

Another drawback is that to hold a successfull auction on ebay it is essential that you know exactly what you have and a general idea of its value before you begin. If you don't, then you won't describe it correctly. Unlike a local estate auction, the responsibility for identifying the item on ebay falls on you. If you don't use the exactly correct words and provide the right information, the people who might want your item won't be able to find you.

Most sellers think of the world of collecting as a gigantic mass of people. It isn't. There may be 20,000,000 people who think of themselves as "collectors" but many of the 2,000+ different hobbies have less than a dozen active "high end" buyers who drive prices up. If a half dozen examples of a particular rarity show up on ebay, the value can drop 30-50%. A spectacular tin sign advertising Campbell's Soup brought $93,000 at auction. The second one brought $57,000. The third one to appear brought $34,000. The lesson is to sell now. In most cases, the first one to sell gets the most.

The internet, in general, is driving prices down, not up. I interviewed hundreds of collectors in preparation for this book. Expert after expert report that ebay was "driving goodies out of the woodwork" and causing prices to drop for rarities and mid range items alike. Good things still bring the highest prices but "low end junk" struggles to find a bid at any price in any auction..

An email in January of 2002 from one of my recommended buyers said "I just scored a great bottle cheap. I would have paid one of your readers $100+ for it, but won the ebay bid for $7.40."

Continued on page 459

RAILROAD MEMORABILIA

◆ **Railroad and Express Company memorabilia** including dining car china, silverware, ashtrays, playing cards, paperweights, brass lamps and lanterns (including unmarked ones), locks, badges, switch keys, builder plates, steam whistles, caps pre-1960, uniforms pre-1920, railroad pocket watches if in perfect condition, pre-1916 timetables, posters, and calendars. Also *RR Cyclopedia*, dictionaries or other reference books published by RY Gazette, Simmons-Boardman, Moody, or Poors pre-1950. No large tools, large oil cans, spikes, low value paper, junky or damaged items, or material other than U.S. or Canadian. No "overly cleaned" or replated items. Veteran 26 yea dealer.
    Scott Arden
    20457 Highway 126
    Noti, OR 97461
        (541) 935-1619 from 9 to 9 Pacific time

◆ **Almost anything related to American railroads** especially dining car china, silverware, glass, marked lanterns, and marked brass locks. Pays $20-$85 for sugar tongs or spoons marked with railroad names. Make certain your description includes dimensions and all marks and logos. Rick does not want date nails, books, or model trains. This 34 year veteran (president of railroad collector organization) answers questions from amateurs with or without things to sell. Info on clubs, railroad collectors shows, etc., sent on request. SASE appreciated.
    Richard Wright
    West Coast Rick's
    PO Box 4894
    Diamond Bar, CA 91765
        (909) 681-4647 eves

◆ **Railroad books of all types,** especially locomotive, car builders, maintenances of way, signal dictionaries, and Poor's Manual of Railroads, pre-1920. Also other items, especially from Central RR of New Jersey's Blue Comet, such as pre-1920 annual passes, uniform buttons and pins. Wants all brass RR padlocks with raised letters.
    Dan Allen
    PO Box 917
    Marlton, NJ 08053
        (609) 953-1387 eves   <dannyea@aol.com>

◆ **Chesapeake & Ohio Railroad memorabilia** of all sorts, as long as it features of of the two cats, "Chessie" and "Peake." A photocopy or photo is appreciated. No repros. SASE please. "I do not make offers."
    Charles Worman
    PO Box 292624
    Kettering, OH 45429
        (937) 299-7752   <oldguns@aol.com>

◆ **Canadian railroad memorabilia** from before 1950, especially White Pass and Yukon Railway, Grand Trunk Railway, and Canadian Pacific, among others. Cannot use lanterns or hardware items.

>Michael Rice
>PO Box 286
>Saanichton, BC   V8M 2C5   CANADA
>(250) 652-9412 eves (no daytime calls) <mrice@pacificcoast.net>

◆ **Railroad maps,** of the entire world, USA or the Southwestern US before 1920. Description should include the author or map maker, the title or area depicted, the latest date on the map, the size, whether or not it is colored, and the condition, especially noting anything missing.

>Murray Hudson
>Antiquarian Books & Maps
>109 South Church Street
>Halls, TN 38040
>(800) 748-9946   fax (731) 836-9017   <mapman@ecsis.net>

◆ **Railroad maps** from before 1900. Please send a Xerox™.

>Dario Dimare
>1 Elda Road
>Framingham, MA 01701
>(508) 877-0958 eves   fax (508) 877-4474

◆ **Railroad date nails** and other small railroad items such as lanterns, locks, and keys. Will buy almost any date nails (nails about 2.5" long with a date on the head). If you describe the shape of the head, the number, and whether it is incised or raised, he says he's glad to tell you what you have. Dick is a collector with limited storage so is interested only in small fine items.

>Dick Gartin
>619 Adams Drive
>Duncanville, TX 75137
>(972) 296-8742 anytime   <g.gartin@att.net>

◆ **Date nails used by railoads,** telephone, telegraph, and power companies to record when their ties or poles were placed in service. Most, but not all, have either round or square heads and have numbers (or other symbols) either raised or indented on the head. Nails may be steel, copper, or aluminum. Although there are many common nails, there are also nails worth $50 up so describe what you have and Jerry will make an offer. Jerry is editor of *Nailer News* a brief bimonthly newsletter for nail collectors.

>Jerry Waits
>501 West Horton
>Brenham, TX 77833
>(979) 830-1495   <oaks@vindy.edu>

SPACE MEMORABILIA

★ **Space shot memorabilia** including souvenirs such as magazines, buttons, autographs, etc. Especially wants "internal" souvenirs such as special medallions, mission patches, models, etc., produced for people directly involved with some space "event" such as a launching or completion of construction. Also internal documents such as manuals, flight plans, charts, and so on. Also hardware, pieces of spacecraft, and other items discarded as part of mission preparation or completion. Also video tapes of launchings or reports from space. Does not want recent items which NASA still sells such as slide sets, T-shirts, patches, etc. Mike is the author of "Distant Suns," a desktop planetarium program to teach the stars for ages 8 to 80 available for Mac and PC for only $40. More about it can be found at <www.distantsuns.com>.

Mike Smithwick
450 Navaro Way #109
San Jose, CA 95134
(408) 383-0627   fax (408) 954-1406
<mike@distantsuns.com>

◆ **NASA and Soviet space artifacts.** Wants to buy hardware of all sorts (both flown and not flown) including space suit gloves, helmets, and other items. Badges, letters, documents, and autographs of spacemen are also interest. He does not want items sold in the souvenir shop (patches, pins, toys, and the like), autopen autographs, or photos with printed signatures. Please send an exact detailed description of what you have and how you came to own it.

Leslie Singer
7 Shackleford Plaza #C
Little Rock, AR 72211
(501) 221-2885 voice/fax days
<zenmotel@aol.com>

◆ **Space memorabilia.** "Anything and everything, with special emphasis on the U.S. space program. I prefer items issued by NASA, larger items, autographs, models, spacesuits, and objects that have been in space and would like to find unopened box of Pillsbury's space food sticks. No newspapers. Please Xerox© and give accurate description."

Everen T. Brown
PO Box 296
Salt Lake City, UT 84110
fax (801) 364-2646   <etbrown@everent.com>

TONY'S TIP ABOUT YOUR 'SPACE STUFF': *Collectors of space related items DO NOT WANT newspapers. They also DO NOT WANT items sold in NASA gift shops*

GOVERNMENT SERVICES

◆ **School, teacher, and student memorabilia** from before 1920, especially diaries, postcards, photographs, teaching certificates, teacher souvenirs, rewards of merit, report cards, letters, student assignments, and books having to do with teaching or operating schools. No student textbooks except those from before 1860. Has particular interest in ephemera associated with New England educator Samuel Read Hall (1795-1877), a prominent early textbook author.

Tedd Levy
PO Box 20
Old Saybrook, CT 06475
<teddlevy@aol.com>

◆ **Civilian Conservation Corps (CCC) memorabilia** such as belt buckles, scarves, uniforms, sweetheart pillows, china, etc., which run $15 and up. Items marked with the unit camp number are the most desirable, especially the sleeve unit patches designed by the individual camps, worth $25 up. Honor awards will bring $150 each, more if found complete with original ribbon in good condition. Send photo, sketch or photocopy of what you have, along with your asking price.

Tom Pooler
PO Box 1861
Grass Valley, CA 95945
(530) 268-1338

◆ **Civilian Conservation Corps (CCC) memorabilia** including uniforms, awards, footlockers, tools, photos, art, crafts, manuals, camp scrip, official records, diaries. "I'll buy just about anything you find at prices ranging from $10 to $5,000." Please, no WPA or other agencies.

Ken Kipp
PO Box 116
Allenwood, PA 17810
(570) 538-1440   <allenwoodantique@aol.com>

◆ **U.S. Post Office memorabilia** including steel postmarking devices, locks and keys, uniform badges and buttons, scales, marked handguns, and postcards depicting post offices. Many other items are also wanted, but not postage stamps. If you have a postmarking device to sell, make an imprint. His large illustrated wants list can be had if you send first class postage on a large self addressed envelope. "Please, only offer me obsolete items no longer in use."

Frank Scheer
12 East Rosemont Avenue
Alexandria, VA 22301
(703) 549-4095 eves   fax (703) 836-1955
<fscheer@erols.com>

FIRE FIGHTING EPHEMERA

◆ **Fire fighting antiques** such as early leather fire helmets, leather fire buckets with paintings on them, speaking trumpets with fancy en-graving, early fire nozzles from hand operated pumpers, fire department lanterns that burn kerosene or whale oil and have two color glass globes, gold or silver presentation badges, etc. Anything from the Chicago Fire Department from before 1940. Very old fire alarm boxes, wood cased fire gongs, fire alarm registers, and other old equipment marked Gamewell, Star, Moses Crane, American, or U.S. Police & Fire is wanted by this 33 veteran fire chief.

Larry Meyer
4001 South Elmwood Ave.
Stickney, IL 60402
(708) 749-1564   <lmeyer1212@aol.com>

◆ **Wood cased fire station gongs.** "I'll buy any wood cased fire station gong, working condition or not, made by Gamewell Fire Alarm Telegraph Co., Star Co., Moses Crane Co., or other manufacturer. Gongs have wooden cases, glass doors, and key wind movements." Also wants literature describing gongs or photos of fire station watch desks showing a wall gong.

Gary Carino
805 West 3rd Street
Duluth, MN 55806
(218) 722-0964   <gcarino@pawcom.com>

◆ **Fire and casualty insurance company memorabilia,** especially reverse on glass signs and automobile bumper and grill tags that have an insurance company's name. Your description should include the name of the insurance company, size, material, and condition. "Best to send a photo, along with the dimensions." If he doesn't want your item, he will give you the name of another collector who might be interested in what you have, whenever possible. No life insurance items.

Byron Gregerson
PO Box 713
Modesto, CA 95353
(209) 523-3300   fax (209) 523-3399
<byrongregerson@worldnet.att.com>

Check the index for other buyers of insurance items.

◆ **Badges, lanterns, helmets and other old fire department items.**
Have a special interest in fire items, including paper, from Cincinnati.
> Stan Willis
> 3029 Burning Tree Lane
> Cincinnati, OH 45237
> (513) 351-3441 days   <badges@isoc.net>

◆ **Fire Department antiques** and fire alarm equipment, especially fire
alarm boxes and wood cased gongs in any condition and quantity
(would like to buy entire systems or collections). Will also buy extinguishers, nozzles, bells, lanterns, helmets, badges, fire grenades, fire
related toys, and catalogs. Your description should give all markings,
dimensions, and any history of the piece you know. Make sure you
include your phone number and best time for him to call.
> Stan Zukowski
> 1867 Ellard Place
> Concord, CA 94521
> (925) 687-6426

◆ **Fire fighting and fire insurance ephemera** including, but not limited to, fire grenades, awards, helmets, buckets, axes, badges, toys, fire
marks, fire insurance signs, advertising items, nozzles, apparatus parts,
alarm equipment, photos, lanterns, extinguishers, postcards, books,
salesmen's samples, models, etc., especially from pre-1900. Nothing
made after 1940 is of interest.
> Ralph Jennings, Jr.
> 675 Forest Creek Drive
> Ambler, PA 19002
> (215) 646-7178 eves

◆ **Glass fire grenade bottles** in any color if embossed with a brand
name and "fire grenade." He is particularly interested in finding those
with the name of a railroad. List the color, size, and all defects, especially chips, cracks, or damage to any labels. He DOES NOT WANT
glass bulb grenades (shaped like a light bulb) from the 1940's that are
filled with carbon tetrachloride and have brand names like *Shur-Stop*
and *Red Comet*. Larry is a 33 year veteran fireman and chief.
> Larry Meyer
> 4001 South Elmwood Ave.
> Stickney, IL 60402
> (708) 749-1564   <lmeyer1212@aol.com>

DOCTORS & DRUG STORES

◆ **Unusual medicines and things claiming to act like medicines.**
"I'll buy pills, liquids, mixtures, devices and things promoted to cure ills or bring on better health. I'll consider items whether they work or not, whether scientific or crackpot, drab or colorful, sincere, absurd, or ridiculous. I'll even buy brand new items if they are odd or come with an interesting story."
• Bottles and containers, empty or full of pills and powders;
• Bottling and filling materials;
• Advertising flyers and trade cards of all sorts for medicines;
• Medical catalogs;
• Health devices, real or quack, such as vaporizers, electric gadgets, etc., the more unusual the better;
• Any product that makes a health claim such as tobacco, mineral water, etc.;
• Books and booklets, serious or humorous, on medicines;
• Medical teaching devices.
"I'd like as complete a description as possible, including the item's age, condition, price, and what you feel to be its unique characteristics."
August Maymudes
8356 West 4th Street
Los Angeles, CA 90048
(323) 653-7580   fax (323) 653-7546
<amaym@mediaone.net>

◆ **Medical instruments** such as monaural stethoscopes, ear trumpets and conversation tubes, brass anesthesia masks from the drop ether days, all bleeders, especially mechanical, and old dental instruments if made from wood or ivory.
Lucille Malitz, Lucid Antiques
PO Box KH
Scarsdale, NY 10583
(914) 636-7825   <lithophane@aol.com>

◆ **Medical, dental, and surgical instruments from before 1875** and other **scientific instruments** from before 1910 such as stethoscopes, **microscopes**, computing devices and precision clocks. Items preferred when in their original cases. Does not want items made after 1910, items in poor condition or common items. Xerox™ all written information accompanying the device, tell anything you know of the item's history, and include a photo and an SASE.
Dale Beeks
PO Box 117
Mt. Vernon, IA 52314
(319) 895-0506   (800) 880-5178   <dbeeksci@aol.com>

◆ **Medicine, dentistry, apothecary and quackery of all sorts:**
- Surgical tools with wood or bone handles or in boxed sets;
- Bleeding instruments, leech jars and cupping sets;
- Electric quackery, including belts, boxes, helmets, etc.;
- Stethoscopes with woven tubes and hard rubber bells;
- Ear trumpets;
- Homeopathic medicine cases;
- Apothecary cases, pill rollers, medicine bottles, mortars and pestles, and bottles with gold painted labels;
- Tooth extractors;
- **Phrenology** heads;
- **Eyeglasses** with telescoping ear pieces or wide loops;
- Hanging signs for opticians;
- Microscopes and microscope lamps;
- X-Ray tubes and other oddly shaped vacuum tubes;
- Medical books, 1600 to 1900, the earlier the better;
- Planetarium models.

Send photos or photocopies of what you have for sale. Make a Xerox™ of eyeglasses as he does not want 20th century eyeglasses (they have nosepads). Give standard bibliographic information on all books. Always include your phone number so he can phone you if he needs to ask questions before purchase.

Jon Lewin
622 Raleigh Avenue #3
Norfolk, VA 23507
(757) 625-6732

◆ **Microscopes and other medical or scientific instruments.** "I'll buy pre-1900 microscopes by the following makers: Zentmayer, Grunow, Bullock, McAllister, Gundlock, Tolles, Queen, Pike and Charles Spencer." Give the maker's name and serial number. Describe overall condition of the instrument, case, and accessories. "Don't clean or polish anything," he warns.

Dr. Allan Wissner
PO Box 102
Ardsley, NY 10502
(914) 693-4628   <wissner@bestweb.net>

◆ **Nursing memorabilia** of all types from hospital, military, missionary, Red Cross or school of nursing is desired. She DOES NOT WANT common items, reproductions, or items in poor condition. Please send a photograph and a clear description. The Nursing Museum is open to the public Monday through Friday and is free. Phone ahead for hours.

Rojann R. Alpers, Ph.D.
American Museum of Nursing
PO Box 873008
Tempe, AZ 85287
(480) 965-2195   fax (480) 965-0619   <rojann@asu.edu>

◆ **Medical, dental and apothecary antiques and curiosities** up to and including World War II, with a particular interest in nursing. Pre-sterilization instruments and sets before 1870 are most desirable and have wooden, bone, or ivory handles that make great hideaways for bacteria but have wonderful workmanship. Wanted ephemera includes:
  • Complete sets of **cased medical instruments**;
  • **Microscopes** before 1900;
  • **Quack medical devices** of all types, blood letting bowls,
      leech jars, electric devices such as belts and rejuvenators;
  • **Homeopathy**;
  • X-Ray tubes;
  • **Phrenology** heads and items;
  • Instruments, percussion hammers, hearing aids, stethoscopes, etc;
  • Posters and broadsides;
  • Photographs with medical, dental or apothecary themes;
  • Letters and manuscripts;
  • **Poison books**;
  • Medical school admission cards;
  • **Red Cross** items of all sorts;
  • Nursing items;
  • Drug store items, apothecary display pieces, show globes,
      pill rollers, medical files, etc.;
  • **Eye-glasses and lens testing sets** if before the Civil War ONLY;
  • Any relics of wartime medicine of the Civil War and before;
  • **Narcotics** related items before 1910;
  • **Dental** sets, tooth keys, etc.
The American Nursing Museum is interested in all types of nursing memorabilia. Generally, the earlier the item, the more desirable. To donate or to sell something, describe what you have, its measurements, maker, condition and history, if known and include a photograph.
        Rojann R. Alpers, Ph.D.
        American Museum of Nursing
        PO Box 873008
        Tempe, AZ 85287
(480) 965-2195   fax (480) 965-0619   <rojann@asu.edu>

◆ **Chiropractic equipment and books** especially electronic diagnostic gear or items from the Palmer College/School. Pre-1960 only.
        Mel Rosenthal
        RR #5 Box 5711
        Saylorsburg, PA 18353
                (570) 992-8282   <meljune10@yahoo.com>

◆ **Unusual or designer eye glasses from 1700 to 1980's.** "We sell mainly to people who want a great "look" from unique frames, whether far-out or conservative. The far-out, odd-ball and nerdy looks from the 1950's and 60's are some of our favorites. We can use older glasses, but only if they're wide enough for a normal man's face. We also buy glasses cases." Most frames bring $15-$20 if in good condition. Call before mailing. She DOES NOT WANT anything broken or reproduced.

> Gail Busche, Archangel Antiques
> 334 East Ninth Street
> New York, NY 10003
> (212) 260-9313   <richgail38@aol.com>

◆ **Old rare and unusual eyeglasses.** "I want only pre-1850 glasses with unusual lenses, frames or history. I don't want common looking glasses and don't buy frames for their gold content.

> W.H. Marshall
> PO Box 1339
> Melrose, FL 32666
> (352) 475-5990   fax (352) 475-5296
> <whmarshall@prodigy.net>

◆ **Antique eyeglasses and spectacles** are sought. Also would like to purchase early catalogs and trade cards featuring eyeglasses, unusual reading glasses, antique ophthalmoscopes, and any material from the McAllister Optical Co. He has some interest in textbooks on ophthalmology from before 1890. Please describe the condition thoroughly.

> Charles Letocha
> 444 Rathton Road
> York, PA 17403
> (717) 846-0428

◆ **Phrenology items** including heads showing trait lines, or numbered zones on the head, posters, and wall hangings. No books.

> Donald Gorlick
> PO Box 24541
> Seattle, WA 98124
> (206) 824-0508

◆ **Medical items and quackery.** Wants pre-1900 medical advertising, patent medicine ads and displays, and devices and ads related to medical quackery of any sort, except "I don't need any more violet ray machines." Send a good description; photocopy paper items.

> W.H. Marshall
> PO Box 1339
> Melrose, FL 32666
> (352) 475-5990   fax (352) 475-5296
> <whmarshall@prodigy.net>

◆ **Optical supplies and equipment.** The director of this popular Missouri tourist attraction buys old, rare and unusual testing devices, trade signs, **eyeglasses, eyeglass cases**, **quack devices, medicines for eye care**, and "anything optical." Give the maker's name, serial number, and description of the piece.

> Tom Baltrusaitis
> Optical Museum
> 214 North Main
> Hannibal, MO 63401
>   (573) 221-2020 voice/fax

◆ **All human glass eyes** in any size or color, rights or lefts.

> Donald Gorlick
> PO Box 24541
> Seattle, WA 98124
>   (206) 824-0508

◆ **Medical books and ephemera.** Wants quality items including books from before 1840, medical broadsides, pamphlets, hand colored illustrations, stereo views, letters, documents, and catalogs. "I'll pay well for quality material," he states.

> Ivan Gilbert
> Miran Arts & Books
> 2824 Elm Avenue
> Columbus, OH 43209
>   (614) 236-0002 voice/fax

◆ **Medical books and journals** published from 1850-1900, especially Lancet. Also a doctor's bag, medical and surgical instruments, including a professional quality microscope.

> Rev. Sherlock Holmes
> PO Box 3
> Worcester, MA 01613
> free (877) 306-4059   <antiques@sherlockholmes.com>
>   <www.sherlockholmes.com>

◆ **Medical books from before 1900.** Books should be in fine condition. Give standard bibliographic information. Note any illustrations.

> Michael Bell
> 7325 Quivira Road #238
> Shawnee, KS 66216
> (913) 962-8533   fax (913) 962-4418   <cjbell@msn.com>

TONY'S TIP: Standard Bibliographic Information:
Title, author, publisher, city where published,
date when published, and copyright date.
It's helpful if you also provide the number of pages
and the number and type of illustrations.

◆ **Twins, multiple births, and freak parasitic twin births.** This dedicated nurse archivist wants photos, newspaper clips, souvenirs, personal information, and anything statistical, scholarly, or informative. If you are one of a multiple birth, this is the lady who will preserve the experience. She always wants first hand information from multiples about their lives. She does not want undated clippings or items that have been damaged by pinning, pasting, or taping. When describing scrapbooks, make certain to note whether the clippings are dated. "My collection is not a hobby but a full time job in research, internationally recognized for its accuracy and extent,
a source of factual information for physicians, researchers, and news media of all types." She has been at it since 1939, but Miss Helen always appreciates help, especially people sending clippings from local papers and obscure magazines about twins (you must tell where it came from and the date). Especially wants photos and other Dionne quints items. This is a labor of love and scholarship, not profit, so keep your expectations reasonable and help this elderly researcher gather data.

"Miss Helen" Multiple Birth Museum
PO Box 254
Galveston, TX 77553
(409) 762-4792

◆ **Veterinary items of all types** from before 1930, including:
• Veterinary patent medicine bottles, tins and cardboard packages with original contents (colorful, pictorial items bring the most money usually);
• Veterinary signs, posters, calendars and display items;
• Store display cabinets by Dr. Daniels, Dr. Lesure, Pratts, Dr. Claris, Humphrey's, Columbia or Sergent's dog medicines or other over the counter purveyors of animal remedies;
• Paper ephemera including booklets, trade cards, letterheads, receipts, almanacs and other items of veterinary interest;
• Giveaways including celluloid mirrors, tip trays, decks of cards, pinback buttons, watch fobs and the like of particular interest with many items worth up to $300;
• Wooden packing crates for veterinary medicines;
• Photos of veterinarians, vet hospitals or vet colleges.

Among things he DOES NOT want are items from after 1930, screw top bottles, damaged or heavily stained items, or items that have been repaired. Reproductions are of no interest. Please send an accurate description, including size, color, and amount of damage. Include your phone number. This 15 year veteran collector is editor of *Veterinary Collectibles Roundtable* newsletter, published six times a year for $20.

Michael Smith, DVM
7431 Covington Highway
Lithonia, GA 30058
(770) 482-5100 days   fax (770) 484-1304
<petvetmike@mindspring.com>

DRUG STORE ITEMS

◆ **Patent medicine advertising.** "I'll buy 19th century advertising, trade cards, almanacs, booklets, postcards, posters, sheet music, tokens, pamphlets, cookbooks, and giveaway items related to any patent medicine. I have a particular interest in *Kilmer's Swamp Root* items. In trade cards, I am looking for 'private' cards, made for one manufacturer, not stock cards with overprints. Please send a photocopy or send the item itself on approval." Walker wrote *The Snake Oil Syndrome: Patent Medicine Advertising*, a colorful interesting 240 page book on patent medicine with emphasis on its advertising available from the author for $44 (a favorite book of Dr. Tony).
>   A. Walker Bingham
>   19 East 72nd Street
>   New York, NY 10021
>   (212) 628-5358   fax (212) 628-4936   <NickEnamel@aol.com>

◆ **Almanacs published by patent medicine companies,** between 1840-1920. Many of these pay $20-$30. If you have many of them to sell it is advisable to have his detailed wants list. There were dozens of almanac companies that are wanted. He does not want any of the three most common almanacs: *Swamp Root, Hostetters,* or *Ayers.* No foreign language editions, either. The only almanacs he wants are printed before 1920. Please don't offer medical booklets, pamphlets, cookbooks, or paper items other than almanacs.
>   Rodney Brunsell
>   55 Spring Street
>   Hanson, MA 02341
>   (781) 447-5384   <rodder781@aol.com>

MEDICINE & OTHER BOTTLES

◆ **Poison bottles.** Early poison bottles usually came in distinctive shapes and colors, so they could be readily identified, even in the dark. Many are marked with skull and crossbones, and others will say use with caution. Those with original labels and contents are of particular interest, and a blue bottle shaped like a skull with the word poison on the forehead could bring you $1,000 or more. This veteran collector notes that there is a ceramic reproduction of the skull bottle which is of no interest. Condition is of "extreme importance" to bottle collectors. Chips, cracks, bruises, stains, weak or faint embossing can all affect the value of a bottle. Please give the height of your bottle after examining it carefully for any damage. Bottles with screw tops are not wanted.
>   Tim Denton
>   113 St. James Street South
>   Waterford, ON   N0E 1Y0 CANADA
>   (519) 443-4162   <oldcollectables.msn@attcanada.net>

MISCELLANEOUS BOTTLES

◆ **Bottles from California and the old West.** "I'll buy whiskey, medicine, food and other bottles from the days of miners, loggers, and cowboys in the West. I especially like bottles with the names of California towns and companies on them." He wants whiskey bottles with pictures embedded in the glass, which bring from $100 to as much as $2,500 for a *California Club* bottle. "Bottles without names or designs embossed in the glass are generally valueless to collectors as are most cracked or chipped ones." Tell him what it says on your bottle, what color it is and what condition it is in, particularly regarding neck chips.

> John Goetz
> PO Box 1570
> Cedar Ridge, CA 95924
> (530) 272-4644 <btlguy@hotmail.com>

◆ **Flaccus, Hunter and Exwaco bottles and jars with colorful labels.** All West Virginia food companies from before 1910 are wanted. Has special interest in food jars, bottles, and crocks from the above, but buys any jars marked as made or used in Wheeling or Wellsburg, WV. Give the color of the glass and its size. Report exactly what is written on the jar or crock, and note any cracks, chips, or unwashable stains. They will pay $200 for a Flaccus stoneware water cooler.

> Tom and Deena Caniff
> 1223 Oak Grove Avenue
> Steubenville, OH 43952
> (740) 282-8918 <tomcaniff@aol.com>

TONY'S TIP: "If your bottle says federal law forbids the resale... it isn't old enough to be of interest to collectors."

◆ **Early U.S. and Canadian medicine and beer bottles,** both glass and pottery. Has a particular interest in the **patent medicine** bottles of G. W. Merchant of Lockport, NY. Also wants mineral waters, poisons, **barber shop bottles,** pottery mini jugs, and some sodas. Buys **trade cards, advertising, billheads, and other items associated with makers or users of bottles in Western New York state.** No cracks, chips, scratches or bad stains are acceptable. Offers made only on bottles shipped for inspection. If offer is refused, it's the seller's responsibility to pay return postage.

> Sven Stau
> 181 Crestmount Court #3
> Tonawanda, NY 14150
> (716) 693-4011 <svenstau@cs.com>

◆ **Bottles.** "I'll buy American bottles from before 1900 which have complete labels or interesting embossing. I prefer bitters, historical flasks, and barber bottles, but will consider cures, ink, patent medicine, figures, liquors, beer, soda, bar decanters, fruit jars, poisons, and miniatures. They may be clear, aqua, green, amber, blue, or milk glass in color." Bottles are not wanted if there is a side seam which goes from the base of the bottle to the top of the lip, or if they have screw tops (except canning jars). Bottles which do not have seams or which have seams that end before the neck of the bottle are usually old enough to be worth an inquiry. Age alone does not make value, though. Combinations of color, shape, embossing, and rarity are what makes a bottle worth money. Because color of bottles is so important in determining value, a clear accurate photo is essential when selling bottles. A rubbing of the embossing is advised. Dimensions should be included. Do not offer bottles which have cracks or chips. He will make offers to amateurs only. Dealers must set their price. Steve's one-page *Guide to Bottle Dating* is yours for only $1 and an SASE.

> Steve Ketcham
> PO Box 24114
> Minneapolis, MN 55424
> (952) 920-4205   <s.ketcham@unique-software.com>

◆ **Bottles.** "I buy antique bitters, figurals, historical flasks, poisons, cures, inks, sodas and mineral waters, **fruit jars,** whiskeys, free blown and pattern molded bottles, three mold bottles, decanters, and other forms. I'm looking for unusual colors and rarities, and will pay very well for them. I also want **advertising, trade cards, posters, boxes, display cases, tokens, tins, signs,** etc., related to antique bottles, or picturing old medicines and whiskey bottles." Nothing made after 1910 or marked "Wheaton NJ." **NO *Jim Beam*** type collectible ceramics. Please send a sharp color photo. Note the size and all chips and cracks, no matter how tiny. If you know the item's history, please share it. Dealers price your goods. Amateurs may ask for an offer.

> Mike Waters
> PO Box 2097
> Westerville, OH 43086
> (800) 894-8095 eves   <marblemike@veriomail.com.>

◆ **Bottles and bottle company ephemera** of all types such as calendars, brochures, and signs. Gayner Glass Co. is of special interest, as are Salem squats, a type of New Jersey soda bottle.

> Charles McDonald's Bottle Museum
> 4 Friendship Drive
> Salem, NJ 08079
>   (856) 935-5631

◆ **Fruit jars in unusual colors or with odd closures.** It is important that the jar be complete with its original closure. He DOES NOT WANT common jars such as most Atlas, Drey, Kerr and Ball-type mason jars. When offering your jar for sale, look for and describe the tiniest imperfections in the glass, including chips, cracks, open bubbles, potstones and/or bruises, as they are critical to pricing. Color is the most subjective part of a description, and the reason why a good color photo is so important in getting an evaluation. "I will buy entire collections if necessary to get the one or two good jars it might contain." Phil is a member of numerous bottle organizations and maintains a website devoted to fruit jars.

> Phil Murphy
> 322 Brown Ave.
> Collinsville, IL 62234
> (618) 345-3511   <pmurfe@intertek.net>
> <http://www.intertek.net/~pmurfe/fruitjars/main.html>

◆ **Early American bottles.** Buys a wide range of glass bottles, including bitters, campaign bottles, figurals, whiskey flasks and glass jugs with handles. Wants glass bottles with agricultural symbols, flags, sunbursts, portraits of national heroes, and the like, or bottles in the shape of log cabins, cannons, lighthouses, pigs, etc. Many of these items are worth in excess of $1,000. Pottery pig bottles are also wanted, but no *Jim Beam* type whiskey bottles.

> Robert Daly
> 10341 Jewell Lake Court
> Fenton, MI 48430
> (810) 629-4934   <ldaly1@aol.com>

◆ **Bottling equipment that is hand or foot powered.** Buys pre-1910 bottling tables, syrup gauges, gas (carbonation) generators, bottle washers, labelers and other equipment used by 19th century bottlers. Also interested in any bottling supply catalogs or convention materials prior to 1910. This 10 year veteran collector/restorer will consider items in any condition (for parts) so give him a call if you think you have what he wants. "I do not buy bench mount or table top bottle cappers of any type. The only cappers I buy are floor model industrial machines." Provide a thorough description concerning size, condition, missing parts, availability of manuals and specialized maintenance tools. Include all writing on the equipment, including serial numbers and patent numbers. Any history is particularly welcome. "I will always pay two or three times scrap value, and more if the machine and condition warrant."

> Steve Krispin
> 135 Whippoorwill Drive
> Oak Ridge, TN 37830
> (423) 481-0407   <skrispin@earthlink.net>

LAW ENFORCEMENT MEMORABILIA

◆ **Paper related to law enforcement before 1920** including wanted posters, warrants, subpoenas, letters, court documents, complaints, etc. Will consider anything signed by sheriffs, U.S. Marshals, or judges.
Warren Anderson
America West Archives
PO Box 100
Cedar City, UT 84721
(435) 586-9497 fax (435) 867-8078 <awa@netutah.com>

◆ **Fingerprinting equipment.** "I'll buy old police fingerprinting equipment including Bertillon equipment and especially books and magazines concerning fingerprinting."
Kathy Saviers
1230 Hoyt Street SE
Salem, OR 97302
(800) 852-0300 fax (503) 588-0398
<75464.20543@compuserve.com>

◆ **Leftovers and other stuff.** "Do you have items that are not listed in this book? Did you write someone and not get an answer? Did other buyers say they didn't want your stuff? Do you have items you don't know where to sell? **Sell your leftovers to me.** If you have a box of odd items of no apparent interest, don't throw them out! I want to buy ALL your small leftovers, **as long as you remember you're selling the stuff no one wants, so I may do nothing but reimburse your postage if it is indeed that worthless to collectors.** Items must be unbroken. I will look at it all. I won't pay top dollar, but I will pay wholesale prices for things that are re marketable. For my top offer, please ship anything complete and undamaged that might have value. Call if in doubt.
Rich Hartzog
PO Box 4143 CGX
Rockford, IL 61110
(815) 226-0771 <hartzog@exonumia.com>

◆ **Northwest Mounted Police items from before 1950.** Also the Royal Northwest Mounted Police, the Royal Canadian Mounted Police, the BC Provincial Police, or the Alberta Provincial Police. Especially awards and medals, cap badges, collar badges, uniforms, and law enforcement items marked with the initials of one of these agencies. He does not want tourist "Mountie" items.
Michael Rice
PO Box 286
Saanichton, BC
V8M 2C5 CANADA
(250) 652-9412 eves only <mrice@pacificcoast.net>

◆ **Law enforcement memorabilia such as badges, patches, night-sticks, handcuffs, and restraints** from all types of law enforcement officers including fish and game, railroad security, sheriffs, marshals, constables, Indian police, city police, and other. Also likes studio portraits of law enforcement officers. Make a photocopy of the front and rear of your badge or photo and give its history if you can. No security company, college police, or "gun show" brass badges. Include any wording or numbers you find on handcuffs or leg irons.

> Gene Matzke
> Gene's Badges
> 455 Big Horn Court
> Hancock, WI 54943
> (715) 249-5695   <badgeone@wirural.net>

◆ **All items related to imprisonment, locking and restraint** including handcuffs, shackles, ball & chains, leather restraints, straight- jackets, prison uniforms and antique or unusual padlocks. Also wants magician's escape locks, lock picks and books about lock picking. Well known dealers in magic and escape devices offer their catalog for $2.

> Joe and Pam Tanner
> Wheeler-Tanner Escapes
> 6442 Canyon Creek Way
> Elk Grove, CA 95758
> (916) 684-4006 voice/ fax   <jnpwlrtnr@aol.com>

◆ **Law enforcement badges, handcuffs, and leg irons** from anywhere in the U.S., the older the better. Also police department photos and histories, especially from Ohio. Mention whether your item works and has a key.

> Stan Willis
> 3029 Burning Tree Lane
> Cincinnati, OH 45237
> (513) 351-3441 days   <badges@isoc.net>

◆ **Handcuffs, leg irons, torture and execution devices,** and electric chairs, both authentic and reproduction. Also wants photos of these devices in use. Please photocopy any photographs you want to sell.

> Harvey Lee Boswell
> Palace of Wonders
> PO Box 446
> Elm City, NC 27822
> (919) 291-7181

382 LAW ENFORCEMENT & PRISONS

◆ **Anything related to the Pennsylvania State Police, Penna. Highway Patrol or the Penna. Motor Police.** This includes but is not limited to uniforms, badges, firearms, books, postcards, photographs, etc. This 20 year veteran will make offers if you give a good description. Photo helpful but not essential.

> Dave Stitt
> RD2 Box 748
> Altoona, PA 16601
> (814) 944-3278   <dbs4808@aol.com>

◆ **Convict memoirs and other prisoner memorabilia** from any era from any American prison. This retired prison psychologist is interested in staff, convicts, and the prisons themselves. He'll buy letters from prisoners, prison script and tokens, prison newspapers, photos and postcards depicting the inside or outside of prisons (with women's prisons especially rare and desirable), sheet music about prisons or prisoners, and prisoner folk art. Prisoners of special note are many, including men like Ed Morrell (Folsom and San Quentin at the turn of the century), Donald Lowrie (wrote *My Life in Prison* for the *San Francisco Call Bulletin*), Jake Oppenheimer (2nd longest death row prisoner), Sir Harry Westwood Cooper (widow swindler and famous forger who created his own prison passes), Jack Black (highwayman, skilled burglar and hard core convict), and Christopher Evans and George Sontag (who together ran a gang of train robbers in the 1890's). Books, writings, and other items related to wardens Thomas Mott Osborne and Lewis Lawes at Sing Sing is another special interest. Do you know or have anything about these people, or anyone else in prison or running a prison? If so, Jack wants to hear from you.

> Jack Fleming
> 1825 Vine #2
> Berkeley, CA 94703
> (510) 526-4565

◆ **Jail, prison, and law enforcement memorabilia,** with emphasis on all types of restraints, including U.S. or foreign military, third world, and Eastern European. Wants **handcuffs, ball and chains, manacles, leg irons, thumb screws, nippers, iron claws, and comealongs**. Also wants literature from manufacturers, copies of *Detective* (a peace officer trade magazine), and patent information on locks and restraints. Wants to find **magician's key rings** as well as restraint keys marked with the maker's name. He says now is a particularly good time to sell.

> Larry Franklin
> 2557 Westwood Blvd.
> Los Angeles, CA 90064

TIPS ON SELLING CARDS, ADS & OTHER PAPER

Because I have been the historian of the cigar industry for fifty years I can appreciate just how important business paper is.

Business paper refers to all the paper handled in the routine course of business. I mean letters, bills, invoices, business cards, catalogs, trade cards, flyers, brochures , banners, posters, handbills, blotters, matchcovers, envelopes, product announcements, instructions, and anything else printed on paper whether created by the manufacturer, the distributor, the retailer or as a response by the customer. **Collectors use a single word to describe all this paper. That word is "ephemera." It means paper meant to be used then throw away.**

Ephemera is often single pages, sometimes scraps, but it can provide vital information about how a product was made, marketed, used or priced...information that historians and serious collectors can obtain no other way. Illustrated paper is considered particularly important.

To give you an idea of how important paper can be, I recently paid $5,000 for five large cartons of paper that were the business records of a 1920 cigar company. I paid $1,200 for one carton from another late 1920's firm. In both, I found information I did not previously know... information that enabled me to better understand and someday better write about my field.

The following three pages will introduce you to people who care about business paper. **Be aware that buyers of business paper are found on nearly every page of this book because those who are serious collectors frequently also buy the paper associated with their hobbies.**

If you find cigar company paper, come to me first. If you find paper about turn-of-the-century bicycles, go to a specialist in bicycles. Paper about guns, try the appropriate gun buyer. And so on.

You'll be surprised how valuable the right piece of paper can be. It's money to you...and information to a collector. Of course, not all ephemera is worth a fortune. But all ephemera is worth checking out.

BUSINESS CARDS & OTHER PAPER

◆ **Business cards.** "I'll consider buying business cards that are unique, unusual, or have an interesting story. Cards from exotic or unlikely materials such as stainless steel, plastic, papyrus, tin, etc., and cards from celebrities. Looks for creativity, which is "timeless," so will consider anything imaginative in shape, color, message, or material. "I love cards that make you laugh." Photocopy what you have if possible, otherwise describe as best you can. Some trade card collections will be considered if they are suitable for resale or auction. Avery is president of the American Business Card Club. SASE a must.

> Avery N. Pitzak
> PO Box 460297
> Aurora, CO 80046
> (303) 690-6496

◆ **Business cards of all types.** "We buy business cards before 1960. We even buy cards that are damaged or written upon if they are rare ones. We also buy paper items such as bill heads that are directly related to business cards. We will pay postage on items sent to us on approval, but you must write first." Some business cards have high value like Mathew Brady, Benjamin Franklin, and some other famous people. He emphasizes that chromolith (color printed) cards were stock items issued in large quantities. Photocopies are the best description. Jack edits *The Business Card Journal*.

> Jack Gurner
> 116 Dupuy Street
> Water Valley, MS 38965
> (662) 473-1154   <jgurner@watervalley.net>

◆ **Illustrated commercial paper** from before 1950: envelopes, bills, invoices, posters, letterheads, booklets from any companies as long as they're in good condition and picture the product, company headquarters or some other illustration. Also buys similar paper with military and patriotic illustrations. Quality of the illustration, its rarity, colors and the condition of the paper all play a part in determining value. Prices range from a dollar or two up to $25. Jeff has no interest in paper related to hotels, but "I will consider other common categories." He does not buy anything removed from magazines or newspapers. A Xerox™ is the best description. Inquire about sending on approval.

> Jeffrey Meyer
> Turn-of-the-Century Enterprises
> 425 North B Street
> Arkansas City, KS 67005
> (620) 442-7024   fax (620) 442-2340   <totce955@aol.com>

◆ **Trade catalogs and piles of business letters and other illustrated commercial paper,** pre-1920, from manufacturers, wholesalers, and retailers. "The earlier the better," says Jim. Most common catalogs bring from $5-$10, but "we have paid as high as $400 for some." Please check that all pages are present as you list the company name, the type of products, size and number of pages, and the type and number of illustrations. Photocopies are helpful. Mention *Trash or Treasure* for a free copy of Jim's catalog of catalogs.

Jim Presgraves
Bookworm & Silverfish
PO Box 639
Wytheville, VA 24382
(276) 686-5813   fax (276) 686-6636   <bookworm@naxs.com>

◆ **Trade catalogs for consumer products.** "These are exciting peeks into their time, giving the unvarnished truth about their era. Prices vary from two figures (most catalogs are $10-$90) to over $10,000 for rare and desirable ones."

Ivan Gilbert
Miran Arts & Books
2824 Elm Avenue
Columbus, OH 43209
(614) 236-0002 voice and fax

◆ **Catalogs from Sears, Montgomery Wards and other mail order companies.** "The older the better," but will buy through the 1960's. Prefers toy and Christmas catalogs to all others.

Douglas Cowles
2966 West Talara Lane
Tucson, AZ 85742
(520) 297-9062

TONY'S TIP ABOUT YOUR SEARS CATALOG
If you have what you think is an old cata-
log, make certain to check the © date in
the front, as many of these (especially
Sears and Wards) have been repro-
duced. If the book has a Forward it is a
reproduction. Flip through the catalog to
see if all the pages are there. Missing
pages are also a sign of a reproduction.:

◆ **Trade cards,** especially better quality and specialized collections. Especially interested in clipper ships, mechanical banks, Currier & Ives, metamorphic and mechanical, and other better items. Will pay $300 up for fine cards depicting mechanical banks, and $150+ for clipper ships. No interest in damaged, common cards, or stock cards with no company name. Must actually see an item in person before making offers. No phone appraisals or evaluations of items not for sale.

Russell Mascieri
PO Box 284
Marlton, NJ 08053
(609) 953-7711   Fax: (609) 953-7768   <rmascieri@aol.com>

◆ **Advertising trade cards for chewing gum and insert cards issued by candy, gum, bakery, beverage, cereal or tobacco companies.** "Photocopy your cards and tell me what you want for them, or I welcome approvals, pay all postage, and respond within 48 hours of receipt. Condition is important as I do not collect trimmed cards, badly creased or otherwise battered items."

William Nielsen
PO Box 1413
East Dennis, MA 02641
(508) 385-9247

◆ **Employee photo ID passes.** All photo ID badges are wanted, especially celluloid buttons with pin backs. Rich pays $3 each except for older ones. Don't bother to inquire, just drop your badge in the mail.

Rich Hartzog
PO Box 4143 BVT
Rockford, IL 61110

TONY'S TIP: When selling trade cards and other commercial paper, it might prove profitable to offer your items to specialists in the particular topic being advertised in or on your item. Cigars, insurance, tobacco, jewelry, toys, soft drinks are among many specialties with collectors eager for commercial paper

TYPEWRITERS & OTHER OFFICE MACHINES

◆ **Typewriters** from before 1920 that are not normal are sought, such as those with three rows of keys, curved keyboards, no keyboard, etc. They don't want standard typewriters of any type, green colored Olivers, Remingtons past model #2, Underwoods, Coronas, LC Smiths. Please describe what you have in as much detail as you can, including the condition of any plated metal, paint, decals or decorations. Is the machine working, frozen, sluggish? List any accessories. Rare machines are acceptable in any condition. They are the producers of *ETCetera,* the Journal of the Early Typewriter Collector's Assn <http://typewriter.rydia.net/etcetera.htm>

> Chuck Dilts & Rich Cincotta
> PO Box 286
> Southboro, MA 01772
> > (508) 229-2064   <etcetera@writeme.com>
> > <www.typewriter.rydia.net/etcetera.htm>

◆ **Unusual antique typewriters and adding devices.** Wants items dating between 1870 and 1920. Look for typewriters with odd designs, curved keyboards, no keyboards, pointers, or more or less than the standard four rows of keys. The most desired machine is a *Sholes & Glidden,* worth as much as $5,000 in outstanding condition. Give the make and model number if it can be found on the machine, the serial number, and "an in-focus photo." Rehr will provide you with a free checklist to help you describe your typewriter to him. Buys **ribbon tins** and early literature and catalogs of typewriters. Darryl is also interested in small early hand-held adding machines, calculators and calculating devices. "I'll send you an evaluation of your typewriter if you send me a good sharp photo, or tell me the make, model, and serial number and include a long SASE." Darryl is the author of the excellent *Antique Typewriters and Office Collectibles.*

> Darryl Rehr
> 2591 Military Avenue
> Los Angeles, CA 90064
> (310) 477-5229   fax (310) 268-8420   <dcrehr@earthlink.net>

TONY'S TIP ON WHETHER YOUR TYPEWRITER HAS VALUE.
When looking at a typewriter ask four questions:
> *(1) Does it have four rows of keys?*
> *(2) Does it have or take a ribbon?*
> *(3) Can you see the key hit the paper?*
> *(4) Are the keys in the English alphabet?*
If you answer yes to all four of these questions it is almost certain that a typewriter collector doesn't want your machine.

★ **Typewriters and adding devices before 1920** that are odd in appearance, with unusual printing mechanisms or keyboards. This includes typewriters with no keyboards, but with a pointing device which typed letters one at a time. **Adding machines with slide levers and rotary hand cranks** to perform calculations are preferred. Also want sales literature for office machines before 1920. "I do not want *Remington, Underwood, Royal, Oliver, LC Smith, Corona* or other machines made after 1920. A photo is a must. If we agree on a price, I'll have the machine picked up at your home so you don't have to worry about shipping." A long SASE will bring you a wants list.

Anthony Casillo
325 Nassau Blvd.
Garden City South, NY 11530
(516) 489-8300 (516) 742-4919 eves fax (516) 489-6501
<typebar@aol.com> <www.typewritercollector.com>

◆ **Typewriters made before 1910,** especially those with fancy or strange mechanisms, such as the *Sholes & Glidden* from the 1870's which strikes from below so the typist can't see her work. "I'm always willing to give you an opinion about a machine if you send a picture or good description."

Joseph Weber
604 Centre Street
Ashland, PA 17921
(570) 875-4401 from 3 to 5 p.m.

◆ **Computer manuals** and literature from the 1940's to 1980. Wants software on diskettes, cassette tapes, reel to reel tape, paper tape, etc. Also computer books, magazines, manuals and papers, as well as trade show t-shirts, posters, and ephemera. "I'm not interested in "garden variety" IBM PC clones or anything less than ten years old. I'm not interested in the most common microcomputers from the 1980's as I already own most. However, I AM still buying software, books, manazines and manuals for these machines, but says he doesn't want Xerox™ copies of software. Ismail is the founder of the annual Vintage Computer Festival. "More than anything I have a passion for learning the stories behind the machines, and having the opportunity to meet the people who lived the stories."

Sellam Ismail
4275 Rosewood Drive PMB #29-161
Pleasanton, CA 94588
(925) 294-5900 eves (888) 742-6642 x300 fax (925) 294-5656
<sellam@vintage.org> <www.vintage.org>

◆ **Calculating devices before 1915** and associated ephemera including catalogs and advertising. Wants mechanical calculators such as arithmometers, generally in wooden cases. Brand names to look for include *Autarith, Baldwin, Calculmeter, Grant, Madas, Spalding, Thomas,* but interested in anything odd. Also rotary machine, heavy devices operated by a crank, and other types of calculators including slide rules (if they don't have patent numbers). He buys comptometers with wooden cases as well as planimeters, devices for measuring area on maps. Give a photo or sketch of what you have plus describe markings, serial numbers, etc. Weight and dimensions helpful. Photocopy your paper goods.

> Robert Otnes
> 2160 Middlefield Road
> Palo Alto, CA 94301
>   (650) 324-1821 eves   <botnes@pacbell.com>

◆ **Cash registers made of brass or wood,** especially early wooden registers with inlaid cabinets, dial registers, or multiple drawers. Also registers that ring only to $1. He also buys brass or glass amount purchased signs that were on top of registers, including electrified ones. **Clocks marked "NCR" on the face are also of interest, as is literature about registers.** Machines can be in any condition since he uses damaged machines for parts. Give both the brand name and model number of your machine and include the serial number. Provide your phone number so Ken can make arrangements to pick up your machine. Nothing after 1917, or with a serial number higher than 1,700,000.

> Ken Konet
> 4 Hortense Place
> St. Louis, MO 63108
>   (314) 361-7975   fax (314) 361-7982

◆ **Decorative resellable things found in the offices of doctors, dentists, undertakers, blacksmiths, watchmakers, gunsmiths, locksmiths, opticians, jewelers, mines, hotels, brothels, police stations, prisons, firehouses, asylums, saloons, roadhouses, arcades, breweries, boat wrights, etc.,** including furniture, cash registers, display counters, tools, and the like. He requests a complete description indicating all wear or broken parts. If you know the item's history, it is helpful. Photos of larger items and photocopies of smaller ones are recommended. **"I'd rather buy an entire store or business than a single item.** No lot is too large. I will respond to any honest inquiry for help to evaluate an item that is actually for sale."

> Larry Franklin
> 2557 Westwood Blvd.
> Los Angeles, CA 90064

◆ **Stock market tickers, books, and other memorabilia having to do with speculation, panics, commodities,** cycles, and other activities pre-1940. Also turn of the century prints depicting the stock market, and stock market magazines pre-1935.

> R.G. Klein
> PO Box 24A06
> Los Angeles, CA 90024
> (310) 476-6732 <rgk90024@hotmail.com>

◆ **Banking relics, bank safes, money bags, bullion and stage coach boxes,** Wells Fargo and Co. or Railway Express locks, assay office items, scales, and three fingered lock boxes (which cut off your fingers if you put them in the wrong holes to open the box). Wants things before 1900. Not interested in paper items of any type.

> Larry Franklin
> 2557 Westwood Blvd.
> Los Angeles, CA 90064

◆ **Safes.** "I'll buy small house type, pre-1910, black, cream or Burgundy colored safes, usually decorated with gold pinstriping and small painted vignettes. I also want early catalogs, photos, and other paper ephemera related to the use of safes, and would love to find a salesman's sample safe. I'll pay the cost of shipping safes via UPS."

> Greg "Dr. Z" Zemenick
> 1350 Kirts Blvd. #160
> Troy, MI 48084
> (248) 642-8129 fax (248) 244-9495
> <drzzezz@aol.com>

◆ **Embossers and company seals** in interesting forms or made of less common material such as whalebone. Special interest in unusual companies and occupations. "I'll pay $25 to $250 for figural examples."

> Greg "Dr. Z" Zemenick
> 1350 Kirts Blvd. #160
> Troy, MI 48084
> (248) 642-8129 fax (248) 244-9495
> <drzzezz@aol.com>

◆ **Mimeograph memorabilia.** Advertising, instructions, service manuals, etc. If it's very old and about mimeos, he may be interested.

> Walley Francis
> PO Box 6941
> Syracuse, NY 13217
> (315) 478-5671

★ **Portable electronic calculators** are wanted. Wants to buy battery or nicad powered items with "non-modern" LCD displays or with "displays that light up (LED, nixie tube, fluorescent digits) from about 1970 to 1978." He especially wants manufacturers like *M.I.T.S., Busicom, Adler, Decimo, Sinclair, Melcor* and *Omron* and calculators that were not marketed in the United States. He does not wamt machines powered exclusively by being plugged into the wall. Tell him the maker, model number, type of display if you can, some of the functions included, the power source and the condition. Most calculators from this period are worth from $10 to $20. Guy produces the newsletter for the International Association of Calculator Collectors, available from him for just $16 a year. You may request a sample for three 32¢ stamps. He is co-author of *The Complete Collector's Guide to Pocket Calculators.*

> Guy "Mr. Calculator" Ball
> PO Box 345
> Tustin, CA 92780
>   fax (947) 730-6140   <mrcalc@usa.net>

◆ **Calculators and adding machines.** They want to buy almost anything that calculates except models made in the past 15 years. Pocket calculators from the 1970's sell for pennies at yard sales but may be worth $10 to $50. You can tell these from new models because these calculators typically are fairly thick, more than a half inch, and have a hole in the side for a wall power adapter. These are wanted even if the adapters are missing. Desk-top calculators are also wanted, but NOT the kind that prints on paper tape. **Early microcomputers such as those made by *MITS-Altair* and *Scelbi* are also wanted.** Please send the maker and model number along with a self addressed stamped envelope. Bruce and Jan claim they'll try to beat any offer you have. Bruce is co-author of *The Complete Collector's Guide to Pocket Calculators.*

> Bruce and Jan Flamm
> 10445 Victoria Avenue
> Riverside, CA 92503
>   fax (909) 353-5625

◆ **Computers** including pre-1980 machines, parts from microcomputers, mainframes and punch card machines. Also original computer software on diskette, cassette, tape, reel to reel tape, paper tape, etc. Also computer books, magazines, manuals and papers before 1990 and advertising ephemera like t-shirts and give-aways from Comdex and other trade shows. "I'm primarily a historian of the industry, and not interested in common IBM PC clones or machines from the 80's, though would like to hear about software and manuals from the 80's. Not interested in those that are photocopied."

> Sellam Ismail
> 4275 Rosewood Drive PMB #29-161
> Pleasanton, CA 94588
(888) 742-6642 ext300   fax (925) 294-5656   <sellam@vintage.org>

◆ **Slide rules.** Seeking early and unusual rules used for general calculation, carpentry, logging estimates, tax calculations on alcoholic beverages, chemical analysis, mechanical and electrical engineering, cement calculations, etc. Generally does not want simple slide rules with white painted surfaces and numbers printed over them although there are a few specialty ones such as musical scales that would be desirable. Please send manufacturer, model number, condition and whether it has a case or not. A Xerox™ would be very helpful. Dealers set your price, but genuine amateurs may request an offer. SASE.

> Dr. Wayne Feely
> 1172 Lindsay Lane
> Rydal, PA 19046
> (215) 884-5640   fax (215) 884-8660   <wef@comcast.net>

◆ **Scientific and technical devices** from before 1910 such as microscopes, surveying instruments, computing devices, stock tickers, planetariums, typewriters, precision clocks, mining and mineralogical instruments, medical and surgical instruments (before 1875), devices used in physics demonstrations and precision instruments related to telegraphy, navigation, and watch making. Items preferred when in their original cases. Does not want items made after 1910, items in poor condition or common items. Xerox™ all written information with the device, tell what you know of the item's history, and include a photo and an SASE.

> Dale Beeks
> PO Box 117
> Mt. Vernon, IA 52314
> (319) 895-0506   (800) 880-5178   <dbeeksci@aol.com>

◆ **Scientific instruments and microphones.** Please send a picture and give a good description. List all writing and marks that might identify the manufacturer. Has been buying these items for 40 years.

> Dr. Tom Perera
> 11 Squire Hill Road
> North Caldwell, NJ 07006
> (973) 226-9185   (802) 767-3265 July/August
> <perarat@alpha.montclair.edu>

◆ **Antique surveying instruments** including compasses, transits, levels, wire link measuring chains, circumferentors, semi-circumferentors, railroad compasses, and solar compasses. Items may be wood, brass, or wood and brass. "**Also have interest in mathematical and philosophical instruments of the past.**" Give all names and numbers found on the body or lens.

> Michael Manier
> PO Box 110
> Houston, MO 65483
> (417) 967-2777 anytime   Fax: (417) 967-3026

◆ **Scientific and scholarly instruments and devices of the more ordinary 19th century nature** such as barometers, world globes, scales, periodic tables chart, chemical bottles, test tubes, flasks, stands, other chemistry equipment, chemical balance, spirit lamps, microscope, syringe, magnifying glass, etc. "Yes, it's my real name"
>Rev. Sherlock Holmes
>PO Box 3
>Worcester, MA 01613
>free (877) 306-4059 <antiques@sherlockholmes.com>
><www.sherlockholmes.com>

◆ **Microscopes.** "I buy antique microscopes, old microscopes, old toy microscopes, microscope parts, microscope books and any microscope accessories. American made early microscopes are my favorite, but I collect absolutely all microscopes from ancient to modern and never met a microscope I didn't like. I have over 1,500 microscopes but still want yours. Even if it's incomplete or a duplicate, I guarantee to buy it for a reasonable price." There is one exception. "I usually do not want small black toy microscopes marked "Japan" unless they are unusual." Please give the maker's name and serial number. It is helpful is you send a photo.
>Randy Watson, MD
>545 SE Oak Street #D
>Hillsboro, OR 97123
>(503) 297-7424 eve   fax (503) 681-0925
><antiquescience@hotmail.com>

◆ **Record cutting machines** by *Presto, Rek-o-Kut, Westrex, Scully, Neumann* and others. Describe what you have fully, including all information on the ID plate. Note if any tubes are missing or if anything seems damaged. Also **professional studio broadcast turntables and tonearms** by *Technics, Fairchild, SME* and others. Please give all model and serial numbers along with a statement of condition. He DOES NOT WANT home record players, no matter how good.
>Mr. Kim Gutzke
>7134 15th Avenue S
>Minneapolis, MN 55423
>(612) 866-6183   fax (612) 798-4169   <kgutzke@mn.rr.com>

*TONY'S TIP: the people in this book are often very busy professionals, working with no staff to help them answer letters. Many of them travel a great deal.
One important buyer sets up at more than 50 antique shows each year.*

TELEPHONES

◆ **Telephones and phone company memorabilia** including:
- Pay phones with 3 coin slots;
- Candlestick and cradle phones;
- Bakelite phones, especially in colors;
- Wood wall phones;
- Character phones of the 70's;
- Parts for any of the above;
- Signs and advertising;
- Literature of all sorts before 1920;
- Magazines from before 1900 with phone ads.

No modern or electronic phones. They offer *History and Identification of Old Telephones* with 6,000 pictures of old phones for $58.

> Ron and Mary Knappen,   Phoneco
> 19813 East Mill Road
> Galesville, WI 54630
> (608) 582-4124   fax (608) 582-4593   <Phonecoinc@aol.com>
> <http://www.phonecoinc.com>

◆ **Telephones made before 1905,** many types of coin phones, nickel plated candlestick phones, porcelain signs featuring phones, telephone watch fobs, pocket mirrors, and similar phone related items. Also Gamewell fire alarms. No paper. "A photo is worth 1,000 words."

> Paul Engelke
> Key Telephone Company
> 23399 Rio Del Mar Drive
> Boca Raton, FL 33486
> (407) 338-3332   <keytelco@bellsouth.net>

◆ **Telephones made before 1930.** His wants list and parts catalog's handy numbered illustrations will help you describe what you want to sell. Also buys **telephone directories pre-1950**, "the earlier the better."

> Gerry Billard
> Old Telephones
> 21710 Regnart Road
> Cupertino, CA 95014
> (408) 252-2104

◆ **Rare glass insulators.** Best colors are cobalt blue, amber, purple or various shades of green. All insulators that do not have threads where they attach to the pole may be of interest. Charlie answers letters accompanied by a long SASE. See page 395 for how to describe.

> Charlie Allmon
> 1200 West 76th Street
> Kansas City, MO 64114
> (816) 333-6727

◆ **Glass insulators.** Even though most threaded insulators have little value, a few can put thousands of dollars in your pocket. Certain brand names are more valuable than others, so photos and a good description are essential. Make sure to include all names or numbers on the insulator. His colored wants list will help you decide what you have. He also buys pre-1900 insulator or telegraph books, maps, or catalogs.

> Dario Dimare
> 1 Elda Road
> Framingham, MA 01701
> (508) 877-0958 eves   fax   (508) 877-4474

> *TONY'S TIP for describing ALL insulators: When writing, please describe the material from which it's made, all embossed words or numbers, color and whether the base is smooth, corrugated or has sharp or round drip points (if not embossed, give height, width, the number of skirts and an overall description). Describe whether it has threads, and its condition (any cracks or chips?).* **Color is particularly important.** *Blue is like a Milk of Magnesia bottle. Green is like a 7-Up bottle. Any other shades are described as "aqua" or "greenish aqua." White is milk color; If it has no color it is "clear."*

◆ **Rare glass insulators**. No damaged insulators. Color is particularly important. For information send a long SASE.

> Jacqueline Linscott
> 3557 Nicklaus Drive
> Titusville, FL 32780
> (407) 267-9170   <bluebellwt@aol.com>

◆ **Insulators.** Secretary of the National Insulator Association wants
• Glass insulators, especially in colors other than clear or aqua.
• Porcelain insulators in colors other than brown, orange and white;
• Unusual electrical insulators including knob and tube, composition, radio strains, high-voltage suspensions and lightening rod insulators.
• **Catalogs or ashtrays which advertise insulator companies.**
He DOES NOT WANT clear or aquainsulators embossed Hemingway numbers 10, 12, 16, 19, 20, 40, 42, 43. Make sure to include all embossing and to mention chips, cracks and BB dings.

> Rick Soller
> 4086 Blackstone Ave.
> Gurnee, IL 60031
> (847) 543-2958 days   (847) 855-9136 eves
> <com574@clc.cc.il.us>

TELEGRAPH

◆ **Telegraph keys.** "I prefer old and unusual but I will buy any telegraph keys. Send an SASE for an illustrated wants list showing prices I pay for keys, up to $500+ for keys from the Civil War era. Please send a picture and give a good description. List all writing and marks that might identify the manufacturer. I may buy any other telegraph items you might have as well." Has been buying telegraph keys for 40 years.

> Dr. Tom Perera
> 11 Squire Hill Road
> North Caldwell, NJ 07006
>   (973) 226-9185 (802) 767-3265 Jul/A
>   <pererat@alpha.montclair.edu>

◆ **Telegraph instruments and ephemera before 1900** such as keys, sounders, relays, and wood or porcelain signs. Of special interest are lineman's sets, clockwork driven registers, and stock tickers with or without glass domes. Toy instruments marked *Signal* or *Menominee* are not desired. Likes early telegrams sent on companies other than Western Union and Postal. A photo or sketch is appreciated but "a call to our 800 number may be all that's needed to identify your item."

> Roger Reinke, Brasspounder
> 5301 Neville Court
> Alexandria, VA 22310
>   (703) 971-4095   (800) 348-0294
>   <brspndr@capcity.com>

◆ **Telegraph instruments** if old, complete, and professional quality, especially from railroads.

> Scott Arden
> 20457 Highway 126
> Noti, OR 97461
>   (541) 935-1619

TONY'S TIP: WHAT IS A "COMPLETE DESCRIPTION"?
When a buyer asks for a complete description, it means (1) what your item is, (2) the title if it has one, (3) the maker, marketer, artist or author if known, (4) all marks or other identifiers including © dates, (5) what it is made of, (6) its dimensions, (7) its condition, (8) any special features and (9) tell what you know of its history. Make sure to include all dates, patent numbers, and other info printed on your item.

PRINTING

◆ **Letterpress printing items** including:
  • **Printing presses,** but only unusual presses before 1900; has particular interest in an *Akorn* hand press for which he'll pay $2,000 and a *Lowe* table top press for which he'll pay $300.
  • Printer's **wooden or metal type,** borders, cuts and dingbats from before 1900; has interest in ornate metal type from Ryan Type Foundry and wooden type from Wm. Page.
  • **Catalogs of printer's type** (called type founder's specimen books) from before 1918; pays $300+ for catalogs from California Type Foundry and Johnson Type Foundry.
  • Equipment for molding or making antique type.
Describe the condition well. Estimate the date whenever possible. Give information on the title page of catalogs, information on the name plates. If you have type, make a proof printing if you can. Dave is not interested in 20th century lead type, large newspaper presses, *Chandler & Price* platen presses, or any *Linotype* machines and mats. Dave is Director of the Amalgamated Printers Association and has collected printing related items for 35 years.
  David Peat
  Peat's Press
  1225 Carroll White
  Indianapolis, IN 46219

◆ **Table top printing presses.** "I'll buy table top and other small, amateur and toy printing presses, used by boys, businesses and tradesmen for do-it-yourself printing between 1865 and 1910." Brands to look for are *Lowe, Home, Novelty, Bonanza, Giant* and others. Those that print 3x5 or smaller are preferred, but unusual other presses will be considered. He also buys **catalogs, folders, instruction books, etc. for printers** before 1900. He does not want *Kelsey* presses. Send a picture which shows detail if at all possible. The name, model, dimensions, condition, and size of area it can print should be included in your letter. Jim has collected for 35 years and prints limited editions as a hobby.
  James Weygand
  852 East Marian Street
  Nappanee, IN 46550
      (219) 773-4832

ARCHITECTURE & BUILDING ITEMS

◆ **Architectural antiques, including fireplace mantles, doors, stair railings and posts, large chandeliers, wall sconces, garden statuary, gargoyles, gates, large quantities of iron fencing, leaded and stained glass windows and doors, ecclesiastical items (benches, pulpits, etc.), bathroom fixtures, toilets and the like.** Please send complete details and measurements along with a photo. They do not buy jewelry, china, small figurines, appliances, or reproductions. These folks have 20 years experience helping people find unusual items for remodeling older buildings
  Architectural Antiques
  607 Washington Avenue South
  Minneapolis, MN 55415
    (612) 332-8344 fax (612) 332-8967

◆ **Architectural antiques.** If you have mantles, stained glass windows, chandeliers, iron fencing or gates, garden statuary, and other architectural relics, it may be profitable to give this giant dealer a call.
  United House Wrecking
  535 Hope Street
  Stamford, CT 06906
  (203) 348-5371 <unitedhouse.wrecking@snet.net>
    <www.unitedhousewrecking.com>

◆ **Stained or beveled glass windows.** Send photos of the window, note all cracks or missing pieces, and include your phone number.
  Carl Heck
  PO Box 8416
  Aspen, CO 81612
    (970) 925-8011 voice/fax <www.carlheck.com>

◆ **Blueprints for buildings or machines** before 1920.
  Jim Presgraves
  Bookworm & Silverfish
  PO Box 639
  Wytheville, VA 24382
    (276) 686-5813 <bookworm@naxs.com>

◆ **Architect's renderings and other paintings of skyscrapers, houses, and other buildings.**
  Charles Martignette
  PO Box 293
  Hallandale, FL 33008
    (954) 454-3474

◆ **Architectural hardware, sets of doorknobs, decorative hinges** and other antique items, the more decorative the better. Sets preferred. Also buys **stained glass windows, columns, mantles, wall fixtures, doors, tubs and other dcorative pieces** from Victorian, Edwardian, Craftsman and other stylish homes. Give a good description, including the location, time frame for removal, etc. Buys loose or in place pieces.
>   Rick Padrone
>   1005 E. Idlewild Ave.
>   Tampa, FL 33604
>   (800) 991-0165   fax (800) 991-0166
>   <ricpadron@webtv.net>

◆ **Ornate doorknobs and other builder's hardware from 1870 to 1940. Ornate lock sets, hinges, doorbells, knockers, door handles, bin pulls, mail boxes, mail slots, etc.** May be brass, iron, wood, porcelain, glass, or other material, but must be ornately decorated. No plain porcelain or common octagonal glass knobs are wanted, but colored glass may bring a premium. "The decoration is the thing. I like state seals, railroads, Indians, and knobs that can be attributed to a particular building. Sets of knobs routinely bring $20-$30, but get my offer before you sell, as some can bring $300 each. Send SASE for my illustrated wants list. Photocopies speed offers. I need a photo, Xerox™ or rubbing. Don't clean them. Paint and corrosion are not a problem for me."
>   Charles Wardell
>   PO Box 195
>   Trinity, NC 27370
>   (336) 434-1145

◆ **Antique doorknobs.** "I am looking for antique doorknobs, escutcheon plates and old catalogs published by hardware companies. I co-edit the club's newsletter and can locate door hardware, lock sets, hinges, knockers, doorbells, etc., for restoring period homes, or put you in touch with dealers in your area. I will give you an honest appraisal of your hardware if you send photos/photocopy along with an SASE."
>   Loretta Nemec
>   Antique Doorknob Collectors of America
>   PO Box 126
>   Eola, IL 60519
>   (630) 357-2381   fax (630) 357-2391
>   <dornoblady@aol.com>

TONY'S TIP ABOUT ANTIQUE HARDWARE:
Charles Wardell said it best: "The decoration is the thing." In other words, the quality of the design and execution of decoration is what gives old hardware value.

OLD TOOLS

★ **Old tools of the trades and crafts especially wooden and metallic planes, folding rulers, chisels, levels, saws, plumb bobs, scribes, spokeshaves, hammers, squares, axes, trammel points, measuring devices, drills, bit braces, marking gauges, wrenches, fancy tool boxes, and hand or foot powered machinery.** Also wants advertising items and hardware store displays, catalogs ($200+ for pre 1900), and documents. Does not want car mechanics' tools, electric tools, agricultural and farm tools, or any "reconditioned" ones. Give all markings. Look for an ivory plow plane made in Ohio, because "I'll pay $10,000 for one." John accepts select auction consignments at 10% commission. John produced *Antique & Collectible Stanley Tools: A Guide to Identity and Value*, a detailed 455 page illustrated guide (obtainable from him for $25) and publishes *The Stanley Tool Collector News*.

    John Walter, The Old Tool Shop
    208 Front Street
    Marietta, OH 45750
(740) 373-9973   Fax: (740)373-9059   <toolmerchant@sprynet.com>

◆ **Joiner's planes and other tools.** "I'll buy planes or any pre-1900 paper ephemera about them. I'll also buy, and pay retail prices for, fancy old woodworking hand tools."
    Richard Wood
    PO Box 22165
    Juneau, AK 99802
(907) 789-8450 voice and fax   < dick@alaskawanted.com>

◆ **Blow torches.** Both foreign and American torches from the 19th and 20th century are sought, but condition is important. Wanted makers include Acme, Baum & Bender, Best, Boston Globe, Brookins, Climax, Dangler, Dixon, Doan & Wellington, Hull, Peerblow, Quick Meal, Sun Vapor, Union Heater and Wellington among others. Prices from $10 to $250. Include good photos along with a detailed description of condition. Ron is President of the blow torch collectors club and editor of its newsletter. You can join for $10.
    Ron Carr
    3328 258th Avenue SE
    Issaquah, WA 98029
             (425) 557-0634 eves   <roncarr@prodigy.net>

TONY'S TIP: As a rule, it's a good idea not to plug in any early electric device. Insulation breaks down over time and could cause a short, hurting you or damaging the equipment. Damage could make it worthless.
Let the experts deal with it.

◆ **Universal trimmers or cutters**, also called **miter trimmers.** These are giant hand planes which were initially produced for patternmakers. These hand-powered woodworking machines resemble a double bladed horizontal guillotine. Brands include American, Bauer, Diamond, Dosch, Fox, Leland & Faulconer, Lion, Oliver, Perkins and Pootatuck. "I'll pay from $250 to $1,500 depending on the brand and condition."
> Jeff McVey
> 1810 West State Street #427
> Boise, ID 83702
> (208) 342-8447

◆ **Electrical apparatus, tubes, test equipment, open frame motors, generators, switch board meters, knife switches, neon signs, fans, Tesla coils, quack medical devices (***Violet Ray***, etc.), unusual clocks, etc.,** as well as books on radio and electrical theory and practice. Give info from the item's ID plate. If possible, email him a photo. If not, call with a complete description, preferably with the item(s) in front of you.
> Hank Andreoni
> California
> (909) 849-7539   <hankjoy@webtv.net>

◆ **Early electrical meters, gauges, and other apparatus** made by *Thompson-Houston,* or of the 133 cycle type. Also early direct current watthour meters, type CS, manufactured by *G.E.* Any very old unusual electrical items will be considered by this veteran collector and electrical museum owner. Give him the information found on the item's ID plate, measurements and weight. "I prefer the seller to set the price. I may need to see the item before buying."
> Tommy Bolack
> Electric Museum
> 3901 Bloomfield Highway
> Farminton, NM 87401
> (505) 325-7873

◆ **Motors (1880-1920).** "I'm seeking very old 'open frame' motors with everything exposed, nothing enclosed. Names to look for include *Crocker-Wheeler, Holtzer-Cabot, C&C, Roth & Eck*, and others. I also buy old toy electric motors with names like *Ajax, Lil Hustler, Voltamp, Knott, Elbridge*, and **catalogs of electric motors** printed before 1905. I no longer make offers. You must price what you have."
> Steve Cunningham
> 3200 Ashland Drive
> Bedford, TX 76021
> (800) 991-0165   fax (800) 991-0166
> <sacunningham@attbi.com>

PACKAGING & ADVERTISING

◆ **Advertising signs, calendars, posters, display pieces, packaging, and small giveaway items.** "We prefer food, soda, coffee, hunting and fishing, veterinary, medicines, sporting goods, gasoline and autos with nice color pictures, especially those featuring celebrities. Items related to Planters peanuts are especially sought, with some bringing $1,000+. Condition is vital in advertising items, so please don't offer items in only fair condition. We prefer to see photos of the items along with accurate description of size, flaws, blemishes, etc." This large regional auctioneer issues semi-annual catalogs for absentee auctions.

    William Morford
    Wm. Morford Auctions
    RD #2
    Cazenovia, NY 13035
        (315) 662-7625   fax (315) 662-3570
        <morf2bid@aol.com>

◆ **Advertising signs and gaming machines.** Signs on paper, cardboard, and especially tin, advertising whiskey, beer, tobacco, and other home and personal products. Items must be old and in very fine condition to be of interest to this well known auctioneer.

    James D. Julia Auctions
    PO Box 830
    Fairfield, ME 04937
        (207) 453-7904   fax (207) 453-2502
        <jjulia@juliaauctions.com>

◆ **Advertising signs, posters, trays, calendars and other items including tip trays, die cut cardboard signs, trade cards, match holders, etched glasses, and tin or glass advertising display pieces.** Things must be interesting, colorful, old, original, and in perfect or near perfect condition. "Although I will consider any products, I am particularly interested in beer, whiskey, soda, patent medicine, food, and tobacco items which feature colorful pictures of pretty girls, children, sporting scenes, animals, or products. I do not buy signs without interesting pictures nor do I buy reproductions." Send a good quality photo, dimensions, and a statement of condition. Steve will make offers to amateur sellers only. Dealers must set their price. Include an SASE.

    Steve Ketcham
    PO Box 24114
    Minneapolis, MN 55424
        (952) 920-4205
        <s.ketcham@unique-software.com>

◆ **Trade signs from various businesses** including pawn shops, watch makers, jewelers, etc. "I'll pay large sums of money for American wooden carved trade signs." His interest is in genuine, old, three dimensional signs with interesting form and content, especially those which depict something to do with the business, such as a sign shaped like a fish made for a fish market. Condition is very important. Items should be in original paint, or old repaint. A sharp clear photograph should be accompanied by the dimensions, and your note about any damage which doesn't show up in the photo. Most of these signs tend to be in the thousands of dollars and must be handled carefully.

> Greg "Dr. Z" Zemenick
> 1350 Kirts Blvd. #160
> Troy, MI 48084
>   (248) 642-8129   (248) 244-9426
>   <drzzeezz@aol.com>

◆ **Three-dimensional advertising trademarked character displays** from stores. "I buy plaster, composition, plastic, vinyl and wooden store figures depicting cartoonish advertising characters. Items wanted are store displays and statuettes, promotional banks, figural ash trays, and bobbing head dolls. I'm particularly interested in items of the 1940's through the 1970's. Some character examples include *Speedy Alka Seltzer, Reddy Kilowatt, Elsie the Cow, Philip Morris's Johnny,* the *Esquire* man and the *Pep Boys* figures. Please provide a good description, paying close attention to damage. I prefer dealers to price goods, but will make offers to amateur sellers." Warren's *Advertising Character Collectibles* and *What a Character!* are available in stores.

> Warren Dotz
> 2999 Regent Street #300
> Berkeley, CA 94705
> (510) 652-1159   Fax: (510) 540-0325   <wellipsis@aol.com>

TONY'S TIP: WHAT IS A "COMPLETE DESCRIPTION"?

When a buyer asks for a complete description, it means (1) what your item is, (2) the title if it has one, (3) the maker, marketer, artist or author if known, (4) all marks or other identifiers including © dates, (5) what it is made of, (6) its dimensions, (7) its condition, (8) any special fea tures and (9) tell what you know of its history. Make sure to include all dates, patent numbers, and other info printed on your item.

◆ **Motion display advertising** by Baranger and others. These are small pieces, under 3' high, usually with animated people advertising watches from the 1930's and 40's, but other products are also found.

> Frank Novak, Modernica
> 7366 Beverly Blvd.
> Los Angeles, CA 90036
>   (213) 683-1963   (323) 933-0383
>   <rey@modernica.net>

◆ **Neon advertising clocks and signs,** 1920-50. Buys those entirely of neon as well as those with "reverse painting on glass" that are lit by neon. Prefers smaller sizes that can be safely shipped via UPS. His favorite clocks and signs are "point of purchase" which sit on counter tops, although he buys wall models, too. He is particularly interested in signs with neon glow tubes made by amglo. Also buys signs that bubble, create optical illusions, or are animated. Value is based on visual appeal so a photo is essential. Does not want new neon beer signs, plastic signs of any sort, or signs lit by fluorescent tubes.

> Roark Vane
> 6839 Havenside Drive
> Sacramento, CA 95831
>   (916) 392-3864
>   <NeonClock@aol.com> <roark@aol.com>

★ **Colorful tin cans, signs, trays, match holders and pocket mirrors advertising beer, whiskey, soda pop, medicines, tobacco, and food** such as peanuts, peanut butter, tea, coffee, and the like. Especially likes rare peanut butter pails and 1 lb. coffee cans from New York sate companies. Nothing rusty or damaged, please. Describe colors. Photocopy please. All items must date before 1930.

> Burton Spiller
> 49 Palmerston Road
> Rochester, NY 14618
>   (716) 244-2229   <bottlebug@aol.com>

TONY'S TIP ABOUT RETURN ENVELOPES:

If you do not include an SASE, you are telling buyers not to bother answering your letter if they are not interested in what you have to sell. Postcards and letters that arrive at my home without an SASE go immediately into the trash unless they are offering an exceptional item that I wish to buy personally.

◆ **Porcelain enamel signs, 1880-1950, advertising any U.S. bicycles, automobiles, motorcycles, gasoline, oil, soda pop, food, soap, clothing, telephones, telegraph, money orders, etc.** Likes all types of porcelain signs, including those with neon trim, thermometers, and the like, especially interesting figurals. Pays most for multiple color signs depicting animals, people, products, or fancy logos. Condition is very important. He is not interested in repros (look for brass grommets in the hanging holes). No signs bigger than 8 feet long or high. "I want a close up photo, dimensions, and any information the seller has on the item's background. Make certain to include your home phone."

> Robert Newman
> 17220 Silver Lane
> Encino, CA 91316
> (818) 461-9229

◆ **Porcelain signs advertising Canadian products.** Wants porcelain enamel signs, but warns that those with brass grommets in the corners are reproductions and not wanted. Will consider some U.S. products.

> Don Schneider
> PO Box 1570
> Merritt, BC
> V1K 1B8 CANADA
> (250) 378-6421

◆ **Food packages from 1960's and 70's especially cereal and snack cracker boxes and colorful empty TV Dinner cartons.** If you have old unused boxes from a grocery or drug store, email, or give him a call. The more colorful the better. Send an SASE and a clear photo or Xerox© copy.

> Paul Scharfman
> Chic-a-Boom
> 6817 Melrose Avenue
> Los Angeles, CA 90038
> <chickaboom@earthlink.net> (323) 931-7441

★ **String cracker boxes for children's crackers made by** *Sunshine, Loose-Wiles* **and other companies.** "We buy from any companies as long as the boxes are pictorially interesting and in fine condition before 1960. Boxes should have Disney characters, *Andy Gump, Popeye, The Katzenjammer Kids*, goldfish, animals, etc. If someone could find us **one with the Dionne quints on it, it would set a record price**."

> Liz and Dick Wilmes
> 38W 567 Brindlewood
> Elgin, IL 60123
> (847) 697-9679   fax (847) 742-1054   <bblocks@cris.com>

◆ **Pet food packages** including tins, boxes and bottles which held food for any dog, cat, bird, turtle from 1910 to 1950. Nothing newer. Describe condition by making a good Xerox© copy.

> Paul Scharfman
> Chic-a-Boom
> 6817 Melrose Avenue
> Los Angeles, CA 90038
> <chickaboom@earthlink.net> (323) 931-7441

◆ **Counter display cards filled with sunglasses from 1920-70.**

> Paul Scharfman
> 6817 Melrose Avenue
> Los Angeles, CA 90038
> <chickaboom@earthlink.net> (323) 931-7441

◆ **Tin plates from the turn of the century depicting women and/or advertising.** Plates were usually printed by Meek, Beech or Shonk. Plates must be in fine condition. Photos are almost essential.

> Lisa Van Hook
> PO Box 2666
> Spring Valley, CA 91979
> fax (619) 470-3430 <Badbluzz@aol.com>

★ **Typewriter ribbon tins.** "I'm interested in any typewriter tin in good condition. I especially want tins made to hold ribbon wider than 1/2" and boxed sets of tins. Large quantities eagerly accepted, but no cardboard boxes of any type." Please send a photocopy.

> Darryl Rehr
> 2591 Military Avenue
> Los Angeles, CA 90064
> (310) 477-5229 fax (310) 268-8420 <dcrehr@earthlink.net>

◆ **Salesmen's samples and other well-made miniatures of real objects.** "If your item is in miniature, all parts to scale, and complete, it can be well worth your while to contact me. A sample barber's chair, for example, is worth $10,000 to me. So is a Wooten desk sample. Other samples are worth from $300 to $5,000. I'm not interested in doll house miniatures, but want to hear about just about any other small well-crafted items. Since I am writing a book on salesmen's samples, I would like to hear from you even if your piece is not for sale." A photo is almost essential. Include dimensions. Note all repairs. Describe any marks or labels. Describe the case and its condition.

> John Everett
> PO Box 126
> Bodega, CA 94922
> (707) 876-3513 <jbe@sonic.net>

◆ **Tin can and box making and labeling.** "I buy items having to do with the history and processes of making cans, boxes, and labels of any kind before World War One. I want label collections, printer's proofs, artist's sketch books, and salesmen's samples of cans, boxes, and labels used to sell tobacco, food, cosmetics, or pharmaceuticals before 1920. Information, photos, and other ephemera from the people who created cans, boxes and labels, and those who made them, sold them, and used them." Xerox™ what you have whenever possible. Trade directories, instruction manuals, procedures books, job descriptions, and the like are sought. Unusual original photos of factories are always wanted."

> Tony Hyman
> PO Box 3028
> Pismo Beach, CA 93448
> (805) 773-6777   fax (805) 773-8436   <thyman@fix.net>

◆ **Canning machinery, catalogs and tools of the Ferracute Machine Company of Bridgeton, NJ,** are sought by this researcher who also wants anything related to company founder Oberlin Smith. The Oberlin Smith Society is particularly interested in advertising, catalogs, small presses, medals and tokens, but will consider anything related to FMCo or Smith himself. The OSS is a 501(c)(3) organization and seeks donations, too.

> James Gandy
> Oberlin Smith Society
> 336 Woodruff Road
> Bridgeton, NJ 08302
> (609) 451-8580   <jgandy8580@aol.com>

◆ **Advertising paperweights made of cast iron.** Must advertise a product or service. "I am primarily interested in figural items, but will purchase some non-figurals. Must be in excellent condition, preferably will all original paint. I am also interested in other cast iron items: shooting gallery targets, water sprinklers, and advertising. I do not buy reproductions. Nor to I want damaged items, even if they have been repaired." Photo is important, along with dimensions. "All inquiries answered and photos returned."

> Richard Tucker
> PO Box 262
> Argyle, TX 76226
> (940) 464-3752   fax (940) 464-7293   <rtucker@jw.com>

◆ **Advertising hand fans.**

> Robert Newman
> 17220 Silver Lane
> Encino, CA 91316
> (818) 461-9229

ADVERTISING FOR VARIOUS INDUSTRIES

★ **Coffee cans with pictures printed onto the tin** are wanted, especially tall one pound cans with slip tops. No vacuum (key open) cans are wanted. $500 to $1,000 each will be paid for *Army & Navy, Blue Parrot, College Town, Convention Hall* (green or yellow only), *Festall Hall, Mayflower* or *Town Crier*. Most paper label cans are not as desirable and bring a substantially smaller selling price. Send the name of the tin, height and diameter, and state whether the condition is like new or scratched and worn. The *Luzianne* can is common, worth about $15.

> Tim Schweighart
> 1123 Santa Luisa Drive
> Solana Beach, CA 92075
> (858) 481-8315

◆ **Cigar advertising boxes, labels and tins,** especially boxes featuring nudes, sports, gambling, comic characters, racism and other colorful scenes. **Also gambling devices, trade figures, or signs related to cigars.** Also pre 1910 tin tobacco cans and boxes. Photocopy the inside lid of boxes you'd like to sell and give the factory number, state and tax district as printed on the bottom of the box. Buys only US, Canadian and Cuban items normally, but exceptionally interesting European boxes will be considered. DOES NOT WANT items covered with cigar bands except as a gift. Nothing in poor condition. Will pay $500 for *Asthma Cure, Cheez It* or for any xxx rated box. A very few copies of his hardcover *Handbook of American Cigar Boxes*, an illustrated limited edition with Price Guide is available for $55 postpaid. Visit his Museum at <www.cigarnexus.com/nationalcigarmuseum>.

> Tony Hyman
> PO Box 3028
> Pismo Beach, CA 93448
>   (805) 773-6777   fax (805) 773-8436
>   <thyman@tobacciana.com>

◆ **Gun company and other ads picturing cowboys, cowgirls or cattle.** Wants tin or cardboard signs, posters, boxes with a Western theme. Also original art for gun and ammunition company ads. Please send a color photo and make certain to mention the dimensions of your item.

> Johnny Spellman
> 10806 North Lamar Blvd.
> Austin, TX 78753
>   (512) 836-2889 days   (512) 258-6910 eves
>   <dvm69@swbell.net>

◆ **Monarch Stove Company sample.** "I'm looking for a 32" tall miniature Monarch kitchen stove finished in porcelain enamel. Will consider in any condition."

> Marilyn Wren
> 9189 Sunrise Road
> Custer, WA 98240
>   (360) 366-4095   <corkyjo@earthlink.net>

◆ **Round Oak Stove Company and Simmons Hardware Company items,** especially the *Keen Kutter* brand items put out by Simmons. "I will buy just about anything put out by these companies, such as calendars, tools, postcards, store displays, advertising and the like. **Would love to find the Indian figure that stood atop the Round Oak stoves.**" He does not buy stoves, razors, or axe heads. SASE a must.

> Dennis Schulte
> 8th Avenue NW
> Waukon, IA 52172
>   (563) 568-3628

TONY'S TIP ON COLLECTING ADVERTISING:
Advertising for various products is very popular with today's collectors. What most collectors seek is ads that are colorful and well designed so they can be hung on the wall as art, or placed somewhere as a form of sculpture. As a general rule, the more colorful the better. Advertising collectors want pretty girls, cowboys, Indians, children, animals, and other time honored advertising themes. The category "advertising" includes signs, posters, packages, neon, and three dimensional figures. NEVER get rid of it without checking its value. I've found items worth hundreds of dollars sitting atop trash cans. The record price for a single piece of advertising goes to a Campbell's soup sign which brought $93,000.

◆ **Salmon cans and labels from Alaska, Canada, or the lower 48.** Also buys postcards, letterheads, and views of canneries, fish traps, etc. Only items dating from before 1960 are wanted. Send Xerox™ for offer. You have his authorization to send items on approval.

> W.E. "Nick" Nickell
> 710 North 102nd Street
> Seattle, WA 98133
>   (206) 789-7901

★ **Fruit and vegetable labels from Washington, Oregon, California and Florida.** Buys and sells singles, bulk quantities, and collections of can, crate and barrel labels having to do with agri-business. Will buy fruit crate labels still attached to boxes! Will buy all companies, but has a particular interest in *Sunkist*™ and will buy reamers and other items marked with that company, including postcards, trade cards, and other paper ephemera. Pat's informative *Collector's Guide to Fruit Crate Labels* and *International Price Guide to Fruit Crate Labels* are available for $42 each, or both for $75.

> Pat Jacobsen
> PO Box 791
> Weimar, CA 95736
> (530) 637-5923   <pjacobsen@neworld.com>

◆ **Florida citrus labels.** Also wants advertisements and other paper related to the Florida citrus industry. Jerry is co-author of the lovely and informative *Florida Citrus Crate Labels: An Illustrated History*, available from him for $39.

> Jerry Chicone
> PO Box 547636
> Orlando, FL 32854
> (407) 872-1171   fax (407) 877-1137
> <thegrove@worldramp.net>

◆ **Popcorn memorabilia including boxes, cans, crates, brochures, catalogs, old machines, parts of machines, Creator's steam engines, and everything else** related to popcorn.

> Jack Cory
> 7733 Spanish Bay Drive
> Las Vegas, NV 89113
> (702) 364-1645   <kernelcory@earthlink.net>

◆ **Advertising for medicine and whiskey companies.**

> Robert Daly
> 10341 Jewell Lake Court
> Fenton, MI 48430
> (810) 629-4934

◆ **Glass candy and other product jars with company names printed or embossed on the jars.** Typical companies include Necco, Life Savers, Sunshine, Lays, Toms, and many others. Must have lids. Your description should include a photo.

> Richard and Barbara Reddock
> 914 Ilse Court
> North Bellmore, NY 11710
> (516) 826-2032 eves   <pnutfanclb@aol.com>

◆ **Chewing gum related items** from before 1970 (wrappers, display boxes, signs, advertising) from companies such as *Wrigley's, Adams, Beechnut, Clark* and others. "I have special interest in pre WWII items. Gum packs from that period can be recognized because they do not have an ingredient list on the pack. Rare packs of gum, such as *Wrigley's* licorice are worth $50 and up.

David Welch
PO Box 714
Murphysboro, IL 62966
(618) 687-2282   fax (618) 684-2243
<pezdude1@aol.com>

◆ **Veterinary advertising of all types** from before 1930, including patent medicine bottles, tins cardboard packages, signs, posters, store display cabinets, calendars, display items, booklets, trade cards, letterheads, receipts, almanacs, mirrors, tip trays, decks of cards, pinback buttons, watch fobs, wooden packing crates for veterinary medicines and photos of veterinarians, vet hospitals or vet colleges. Among things he DOES NOT want are items from after 1930, screw top bottles, damaged or heavily stained items, or items that have been repaired. Reproductions are of no interest. Please send an accurate description, including size, color, and amount of damage. Include your phone number. This 15 year veteran collector is editor of *Veterinary Collectibles Roundtable newsletter*, published six times a year for $20.

Michael Smith, DVM
7431 Covington Highway
Lithonia, GA 30058
(770) 482-5100 days   fax (770) 484-1304
<petvetmike@mindspring.com>

◆ **Gun, ammunition or trapping related advertising.** "I buy and ammunition related advertising and memorabilia **that was put out by the manufacturers:** calendars, counter stand-ups, catalogs, shotshell boxes, gunpowder tins, pinback buttons and other small advertising items. I DO NOT WANT reproductions, NRA items, or any collectible that would grade less than 8 on a scale of 10. I am an advanced collector, buy fine items and will pay up to $12,000 for posters and calendars, $15,000 for shotshell boxes, to $3,000 for tins, $2,000 for pins. I will pay top dollar and will pay you in cash if you wish. All transactions confidential. Describe the condition including every bit of damage. I prefer sellers to set the price they would like but I will help amateurs who aren't just playing games, but are serious about selling."

Ron Willoughby
2281 Lime Kiln Road
North Haverhill, NH 03774
(603) 787-2060   <swillo@together.net>

ADVERTISING FOR SPECIFIC COMPANIES

◆ **Junk food character premiums and boxes that advertise them from 1950-1980 kid's junk food such as cookies, candy, cereal, ice cream, drink mixes, and snacks.** "Characters I buy in include Choo Choo Charlie, Quisp, Quake, Cap'n Crunch, Milton the Toaster, Mr. Bubble, Frankenberry, Count Chocula, Marky Maypo, Twinkles, Trix Rabbit, Mr. Wiggle, King Vitamin, Freakies, Farfel and other cartoon ad trademarks. Products include *Jiffy Pop, Mr. Chips, Fizzies, Funny Face, Cocoa Marsh, Bosco, Scooter Pies, Bugs Bunny Cookies, Nestle's Chiller, Kool Aid, Otter Pops, Kool Pops, Royal Pudding, Keds, P.F. Flyers, Big Shot Syrup* and especially discontinued oddball products. Will buy watches, toys, puppets, figures, banks, fan club kits, T-shirts, and especially store displays such as posters, stand-ups, animated displays and large 3-D figures. **I don't want fast food, generic products with no premium or character.**" Give condition, your phone number and best hours to call.

> Roland Coover, Jr.
> 1537 East Strasburg Road
> West Chester, PA 19380
> (610) 692-3112   <rlcoover@aol.com>

◆ *Cracker Jack* **products, packaging, prizes, point of sale advertising, etc.,** from before 1940. Not interested in plastic prizes from the late 1940's to the present, or anything marked "Borden Co." Also items associated with *Angelus Marshmallows, Chums, Checkers, Reuckheim and Eckstein* and *Reliable* candies. Wes prefers you to Xerox™ what you have, or simply mail him your prizes for his offer. SASE required. Do not call at home.

> Wes Johnson, Sr.
> 106 Bauer Avenue
> Louisville, KY 40207
> (502) 899-3030 extension 228 days only

◆ *Cracker Jack* **prizes, advertising and related items,** including tins, jars, store advertising, point of sale, and dealer items from any of the following companies: *Checkers Confections, Angelus Marshmallows, Chums Confections, Shotwell Mfg. Co., Rueckheim Bros.* and *Eckstein Co.* He does not want anything marked "Borden Co." Note any obvious signs of wear. Price if you can.

> Edwin Snyder
> PO Box 156
> Lancaster, KY 40444
> (606) 792-4816

◆ *Planter's Peanut* **memorabilia.** "I'll buy all rare or unusual items" with particular interest in any and all figural, 3-D *Mr. Peanuts* such as:
- Wooden jointed doll;
- "Blinker" with lighted eye;
- "Tapper" which taps on a window;
- Scale made of cast iron and aluminum, 4' high;
- Rubber squeeze toy about 8" tall;
- *Mr. Peanut* hand puppet;
- Fence sitter, cast iron, 42" high;
- Parade costume and anything papier maché;
- Any tin displays and 5# and 10# peanut tins;
- Unopened key wind tins of peanuts;
- Cardboard display boxes peanuts came in;
- Wooden shipping boxes;
- Old jars with peanut finials.

Does not want reproductions or anything made after 1970 or any cardboard boxes that candy bars came in. No broken or incomplete items. Send a photo and complete description, including condition of the surface and paint. Enclose an SASE for picture return. Richard is author of *Planter's Peanut Advertising and Collectibles.*

> Richard and Barbara Reddock
> 914 Ilse Court
> North Bellmore, NY 11710
> (516) 826-2032 eves <pnutfanclb@aol.com>

◆ *Planter's Peanut* **memorabilia** from before 1970 including:
- Unopened key wind tins;
- Display items, statues, signs, and jars;
- Banks and other giveaways.

"I'm interested in anything rare or unusual. Send a description and the price wanted."

> Glenn Grush
> 5344 North Collingwood Circle
> Calabasas, CA 91302
> (818) 880-6200   fax (818) 880-6500 <awallstguy@aol.com>

◆ *Reddy Kilowatt, Mr. Peanut,* **the** *Campbell Kids, Elsie the Cow,* **and** *Borden's* **ephemera** including games, toys, cookbooks, comic books, cups, glasses, Xmas cards, employee magazines, neon signs, trade cards and paper ephemera of all types. Describe carefully, noting damage. Dealers price your goods, but amateurs may request offers if the item is for sale. Marty buys primarily for resale.

> Marty Blank
> PO Box 636
> East Meadow, NY 11554
> (516) 485-8071 <martysbengalcats@aol.com>

◆ **California Raisin anything:** figures, videos, records, paper products, fan club items, etc. Buys singles, multiples or collections. Wants only licensed calrab items. He DOES NOT WANT the small vinyl figures given away by Hardee's (they're worth about a dime each).

>Ken Clee
>PO Box 11412
>Philadelphia, PA 19111
>(215) 722-1979

◆ *Arbuckle Coffee* **Company** items such as trade cards, advertising, receipts, coffee cans, and other ephemera. Send a Xerox™ if you'd like an offer. You have his permission to send items on approval.

>W.E. "Nick" Nickell
>710 102nd Street
>Seattle, WA 98133
>(206) 789-7901

◆ *Sunshine Biscuits* **and Loose-Wiles ephemera** including tins, boxes, signs, display racks, novelties, games, calendars, pin back buttons, trade cards, invoices, stationery and "things we have yet to imagine." Buys items from all brands produced by Sunshine or its predecessor, Loose-Wiles Company. These companies made potato chips, cookies, crackers, marshmallows, pretzels, candy, and several cereals. "We especially want uncut sheets of stuffed animal toys (worth $150 each), Ann Hathaway cookie tins ($250) and neckties advertising their products ($25 up)." Complete descriptions include size, shape, condition, what is pictured, and a photograph or photocopy of the best and worst side. "I will discuss an item with a seller on the phone but prefer a letter with pictures and SASE. I will not agree to purchase nor can I make an offer to buy or appraise an item without seeing it in person. I pay or reimburse postage on anything I request be sent for inspection."

>Liz and Dick Wilmes
>38W 567 Brindlewood
>Elgin, IL 60123
>(847) 697-9679   Fax: (847) 742-1054   <bblocks@cris.com>

◆ **M & M candy advertising items more than ten years old** that say M&M or Mars on them. Ken is the author of the book on M&M collectibles and DOES NOT WANT "any of the newer items produced by M&M for collectors such as toppers, dispensers, plush toys, or NASCAR items (there are too many of these items to have any value). Please contact me ONLY with older items not made for collectors." A good description includes dimensions, damage, a photo and an SASE.

>Ken Clee
>PO Box 11412
>Philadelphia, PA 19111
>(215) 722-1979   <waxntoys@aol.com>

◆ **Walgreens Drug Store products and ephemera.** "I'll buy a wide range of products marketed by this national chain between 1901 and 1960, including non-prescription drug and health aids, candy, tobacco, coffee, toys and what have you. Items were sold under many different brand names including: *Walgreens, Myers, Union Drug, Keller, Glide, Valentine, Carrel, Amoray, Ladonna, Olafsen, Orlis, Triomphe, Hill Rose, CRW,* and others. I'm especially interested in finding Walgreens tin cans for coffee and other products. I do not want any product marked with the words AGENCY or WALGREEN AGENCY, nor do I want heating pads, water bottles, or ice caps." To sell to this 15 year veteran collector, you need to tell him what you have, and its size, color, and condition. Indicate whether you have the original box or not, and give the original selling price, if it's marked on the container. Ask about his great new book on the history and collectibles of Walgreens.

Gordon Addington
260 East Chestnut #2801
Chicago, IL 60611
(312) 943-4085

GORDON SAYS: "*There are only a few collectors of Walgreens so there isn't a lot of competition. But some items are quite rare and I'd love to hear from you if you have one.*"

◆ *Beech-Nut* **items including any glass container with excellent paper labels, especially catsup, mustard, chili sauce, sliced beef, bacon, ginger ale, sarsaparilla, peanut butter, and jams.** Also wants spaghetti cans, gum or candy store display racks, tin or cardboard advertising, biscuit or cookie containers, souvenirs, Christmas boxes, postcards of factories, and anything else. Describe the condition. Include photo when possible. Dealers, price your goods; amateurs may ask for an offer if they don't know an item's value.

Bruce Van Evera
94 Montgomery Street
Canajoharie, NY 13317
(518) 673-3522   <vanevera@telenet.net>

◆ **Larkin Soap Company items.** "I'll buy items made by or relating to the Larkin Company, including products, trade cards, catalogs, advertising, calendars and other paper items. If the item says larkin, I'm interested.   I want info about the Larkin administration building designed by Frank Lloyd Wright and would love to find dedication programs, etc." Please make sure you describe condition.

Jerome Puma
78 Brinton Street
Buffalo, NY 14214
(716) 838-5674   <jpp@buffnet.net>

◆ **Coleman products,** either U.S. or Canadian made, such as lamps, lanterns, irons, heaters, torches, parts, parts racks, tools, shipping boxes, advertising literature, salesmen's samples, hats and shirts with Coleman logo, repair manuals and what have you. He does not want clippings from old magazines or camping products other than Coleman. Pictures are helpful if you don't know the item's proper name or catalog number. Describe condition. Dealers price your goods. Amateurs may request offers.

> Ernest Hiatt, S.T.A. Shop
> 3404 West 450 North
> Rochester, IN 46975
> (574) 223-3232 fax (574) 223-2842

◆ *Arm & Hammer* and *Cow Brand* **Baking Soda ephemera** including advertising cards, posters, tins, jars, premiums and give-aways, invoices, company correspondences and anything historical or unusual marked with those brand names. Soda and Saleratus tins and pre-1950 packages are wanted. Soda box cards are worth from $1 to $10, point-of-sale advertising up to $200 and posters with dowels or metal strips are worth from $100 to $500. He does not want magazine ads and soda boxes made after 1950. Photos or photocopies are preferred. Give the size, material and condition. John is author of *Church & Dwight Advertising and Soda Box Cards* available from him for $22.50

> John Hodge
> 4032 Lawngate Drive
> Dallas, TX 75287
> (972) 380-8539 <jdhodge@onramp.net>

◆ *Big Jo Flour* and **Wabasha Roller Mill items.** "I'll buy anything *Big Jo*, and will consider any other advertising, large or small, related to Wabasha, MN." She does not want flour items other than that one brand and mill.

> Carla Schuth
> Route 3 Box 6
> Wabasha, MN 55981
> (651) 565-4251

◆ **Blue bell paperweights** used as promotional items by the phone company. Values range from $30 to $1,500 so it's worth getting yours checked out. Also buys bell weights by the TPA (Telephone Pioneers of America). Give the color, embossing, and condition. She wrote *Blue Bell Paperweights* available with update and addendum for $17.

> Jacqueline Linscott
> 3557 Nicklaus Drive
> Titusville, FL 32780
> (407) 267-9170 <bluebellwt@aol.com>

◆ **RCA Victor's Nipper the dog items** of all sorts made before 1960. Please includedimensions for dog figures. Inquire about any fine condition old Nipper item you might have.
>
> Rick Padrone
> 1005 E. Idlewild Ave.
> Tampa, FL 33604
> (800) 991-0165   fax (800) 991-0166   <ricpadron@webtv.net>

◆ **Prudential Insurance Company ephemera,** especially pre-1920 calendars. Also wants postcards, pens, key rings, paperweights, policies, advertising material, and other ephemera from other life and casualty companies. Make a Xerox™ of your item.
>
> Mike Sawrie
> 1010 Midland
> LaMonte, MO 65337
>   (660) 584-6262 days

◆ **Fire service and fire insurance items** such as badges, histories of insurance companies, pre-1900 fire insurance policies, firemarks, signs, advertising, and postcards. Doesn't want anything except fire related items, and nothing modern. Fire department badges are a special favorite. Please also quote books that are fire related. Glenn is an officer in the Fire Mark Circle of the Americas.
>
> Glenn Hartley
> Smokey's Fire Museum
> 2859 Marlin Drive
> Chamblee, GA 30341
>   (770) 451-2651   <ghartleysr@aol.com>
>   <www.firemarkcircle.org>

◆ **Anything relating to fire insurance companies before 1940.** Wants firemarks, illustrated policies, advertising, signs, and giveaways. Does not make offers, so price what you have.
>
> Ralph Jennings
> 675 Forest Creek Drive
> Ambler, PA 19002
>   (215) 646-7178

◆ **Farn equipment advertising and memorabilia** such as calendars, catalogs, brochures, jewelry, watch fobs, pocket mirrors, yardsticks, and the like. Please include a Xerox™ copy with your SASE.
>
> Dave Nolt
> PO Box 553
> Gap, PA 17527
>   (717) 768-3554   <nolt@dnolt.com>

SOFT DRINKS

★ *Coca-Cola* **advertising of all type before 1940.** Buys cardboard cut-outs, festoons, and calendars, but has most interest in small items such as watch fobs, openers, pocket knives, pocket mirrors, coupons, letter heads, and the like. "I'll pay premium prices for all advertising for *Coca-Cola* **chewing gum.**" Thom says he "will be glad to help you evaluate the worth of your *Coca-Cola* items."

Thom Thompson
1389 Alexandria Drive #7
Lexington, KY 40504
(859) 255-2727 voice/ fax   (859) 873-8787 eves
<thomt@iglou.com>

◆ *Coca-Cola* **advertising.** "I'll buy pre-1969 calendars, trays, small signs, syrup bottles, clocks, thermometers, menu boards, ashtrays, playing cards, lighters, and just about anything else free of rust or wrinkles that says *Coca-Cola.*" Loves to find salesman's sample coolers and dispensers. Describe condition carefully and include a photo. Does not want magazine ads, reproduction trays, or commemorative bottles. He wants a straight sided bottle from Buchheit Bottling Company in New Decatur, but it must have *Coca-Cola* written in script.

Terry Buchheit
214 South Moulton Street
Perryville, MO 63775
(573) 547-5628   <terrydotti@ldd.net>

◆ *Coca-Cola* **memorabilia from before 1945,** including fancier *Coke* items with pretty girls and lots of color especially cardboard cutout signs and back bar decorations. He will pay up to $5,000 for pre-1900 calendars. Pays well for metal tins, trays, and signs. Magazine ads are wanted only if before 1932. No commemorative bottles, please.

Randy Schaeffer, C-C Trayders
611 North 5th Street
Reading, PA 19601
(610) 373-3333   fax (610) 683-4633
<schaeffe@kutztown.edu>

TONY'S TIP: Coca-Cola collectors want items that read "Drink *Coca-Cola.*" Those that read "Enjoy *Coca-Cola*" are new and not wanted.

◆ *Dr. Pepper* **memorabilia** including signs, fountain items, pinback buttons, serving trays, calendars, jewelry, clocks, toys, clothing, games, and what have you. Especially wants very early bottles with "blob tops or bowling pin shapes, and embossed bottles with dr. pepper written in script on the bottom of the bottle. I don't buy new stuff such as found at flea markets, but if you're not sure, send an SASE and your description of the item." Give him the colors, dimensions, and condition.

Bob Thiele
620 Tinker Avenue
Pawhuska, OK 74056
　　(918) 287-3845 eves　　<rthiele@mmind.net>

◆ **Advertising for** *Coca-Cola, Pepsi Cola, Dr. Pepper, 7-Up, Hires, Crush* **and** *Cherry Smash*. Advertising for other brands will be considered if the item is of high quality and has strong visual interest. The value of these items is in "the look" more than in rarity. Advertising includes three dimensional items like neon signs, syrup dispensers, clocks, fountain handles, trays, thermometers, signs that light up, tin toy trucks, straw boxes, calendars, tin cans, postcards, posters, decorations, playing cards and employee pins. Items may be of tin, porcelain, glass, cardboard, paper or mixed media. Paper and cardboard items must be attractive not just old. Signs must have pictures, the fancier and more attractive the better. Pretty girls, children, movie stars, men in uniform, animals, automobiles, and the like make advertising interesting and collectible. Few items are interesting without pictures. The original artwork, sketches, and proofs for these signs is also wanted. Condition is very important, the closer to as new, the better. HE DOES NOT WANT anything, no matter how good, that was made after 1965. HE DOES NOT WANT bottles, bottle caps, wooden bottle cases, commemorative pins, or magazine ads from any period, nor does he buy anything with severe damage. Every single stain, scratch, tear, fold, dent, faded spot, rust speck or marks from water damage makes an item less desireable to collectors. It does not matter how old a piece is, damage is damage. I need to know exactly where the damage is. Please describe your item well, giving dates, names, dimensions along with photos.

Robert Newman
17220 Silver Lane
Encino, CA 91316
　　(818) 461-9229

◆ **Ice chests and advertising from off-brand soda pops.** Send description, photo, and price desired as he won't make offers to anyone.

Andy Fulks
PO Box 92
Whitestown, IN 46075

★ **Soda pop bottles with painted labels** (called ACL's or applied color labels) are wanted. "I'm buying bottles from minor bottling companies anywhere in North America. Would love to find a **three colored** *Uncle Tom's Root Beer* from California. Please describe the color of the glass, all colors that are on the label and the exact wording "so I can make the best offer."

> Gary Brent Kincade
> 226 Ridgeway Drive
> Bridgeport, WV 26330
> (304) 842-3773 eves

◆ **Soda pop cans pre-1965, especially small local brands.** Will buy quantities of rare cans, but no rusty cans are wanted by this 10 year veteran collector-dealer. "Some light spotting and aging is natural. I require cans be sent before a final purchase offer is made because condition so greatly affects the value and I need to examine cans closely."

> Tony Steffen
> 14 N 679 Route 25 #A
> East Dundee, IL 60118
> (800) 498-3215 (847) 428-3150 eves <steinland@aol.com>

◆ *Hires Root Beer* **memorabilia** pre-1930 in fine to mint condition. Wants trays, dispensers, and signs. No syrup extract bottles or reproductions of any Hires items.

> Steve Sourapas
> 1212 9th Avenue West, Unit #2
> Seattle, WA 98119
> (206) 282-9922 fax (206) 782-1039 <sandswt@foxcomm.net>

◆ *Moxie* **memorabilia.** Wants signs, fans, toys, advertising posters, metal trays, and other pre-1940 items associated with this old time soft drink. Will buy *Moxie* bottles only if the name of a town is part of the inscription. Bowers is the author of *The Moxie Encyclopedia*, a 760 page illustrated history available for $19.95.

> Q. David Bowers
> PO Box 1224
> Wolfeboro, NH 03894
> (603) 569-5095 <bowersmerena@conknet.com>

◆ **Bottle caps from soda pop.** The world's largest collector of them still seeks early collections. Not interested in singles, unless you have something unusual like a prototype, error, etc.

> Danny Ginsberg
> 26753 Basswood Avenue
> Rancho Palos Verdes, CA 90275
> (310) 378-1821 <danny@realsoda.com>

◆ **Embossed Pepsi Cola bottle**s in unusual styles and colors, proto-type bottles, experimental bottles, transitional bottles with applied color labels. Bottles marked as having come from small towns are also sought. He DOES NOT WANT reproductions, common bottles after 1940 with applied color labeling rather than embossing. You must give an accurate description of the bottle and its condition, including where you found the bottle. He is especially looking for bottles which are not listed in the two Pepsi Bottle Books, or that have a 4 or 5 rarity rating in those books. The Pepsi Cola Bottle Guides to rarity and value are in full color and contain an amazing array of Pepsi and Mountain Dew bottles. These useful Guides sell for $30 (Vol. 1) and $35 (Vol.2) with a $6 discount if you buy both. Shipping these heavy books is $4 additional. "If your item is of interest, I prefer to look at it before sending a check as hundreds of dollars are involved for many of these bottles. I will pay return shipping charges it if I don't buy it. Write first, before shipping.
James Ayers
5186 Claudville Highway
Claudville, VA24076
(276) 251-8015   <jaayers@neocomm.net>

◆ **Soda pop advertising items from all companies** before 1975. Items wanted include signs, thermometers, clocks, cardboard displays, toys, a few types of cooler, and some cloth and paper items. Everything must be in good condition. Send a color photo along with dimensions. If you are a dealer, price your items. Amatuers may request an offer.
Mike Waters
PO Box 2097
Westerville, OH 43086
(800) 894-8095   <marblemike@veriomail.com>

◆ *Coca-Cola* **ephemera.** Wants pre-1960 signs, clocks, calendars, bottles and carriers, dispensers, machines, uniforms, etc. Will consider any item you have that reads "Drink *Coca-Cola*." Those that read "Enjoy *Coca-Cola*" are new and not wanted. Please include your phone number when you write.
Marion Lathan
PO Box 833
Chester, SC 29706
(803) 377-4455   <cccc@chestertel.com>

TONY'S TIP: Coca-Cola collectors want items that read "Drink Coca-Cola." Those that read "Enjoy Coca-Cola" are new and usually not of interest.

◆ **Soda Pop collectibles from both national and regional brands.** "I am really interested in Howel's brand flavors as a relative once distributed Howel's. Many other brands are soughtr: *Dr. Pepper, Pepsi Cola, Nehi, Orange Crush, Lemon Crush, Lime Crush, Chocolate Crush, NuGrape, Royal Crown, Double Cola, Grapette, Cherry Smash, Green River, Frostie Root Beer, Hires, Dad's Old Fashioned Root Beer, Lime Cola, Squirt, Dr. Swett's Root Beer, Mountain Dew, Rummy, Richardson's Root Beer, Whistle* and many more. The items I want vary widely. I like cardboard signs and cut-outs best, **especially pictorial signs** with lots of color and pretty people rather than signs that simply show the brand name. Signs are better when the bottle, cup, or carton of bottles or case of bottles is also pictured. I would very much like to buy bottle toppers or **displays** like cardboard signs and cut-outs that have a bottle of soda as part of the display. Toppers usually have a cut out hole to slip over the top of a soda bottle. Displays usually fold at the bottom to sit on a shelf. A bottle is ataached to give the sign a 3D effect. I DO NOT WANT magazine ads or pieces of heavy stock paper which was inserted into a carton or hung on a bottle to advertise special prices or deals. **I do not collect bottles or cans except as part of a display.** But I do buy **calendars, themometers, small tin signs, clocks, menu sheets, bottle bags, matchbooks and miniature items** like cartons, cases, and bottles. I have a nice collection of **wax paper cups** of various brands and sizes that I am always glad to add to. I'll buy quantities of cups for trading. I also buy **soda glasses with advertising** on them if old and in perfect condition. I ONLY BUY ITEMS MADE BEFORE 1970. NOTHING NEWER. Items must have no rust, fading cracks, or water damage and be in very very good condition. A good clear photo is needed. I prefer contact by email or mail with SASE. Please understand that I do not buy everything that comes my way.

Terry Buchheit
214 South Moulton Street
Perryville, MO 63775
<terrydotti@ldd.net>

TONY'S TIP: *Collectibles of fast food are part of "Pop Culture" and have become popular. Things you got free may find a buyer.*

McDonald's is the most popular, but other restaurant collectibles are on the rise.

RESTAURANT & FAST FOOD MEMORABILIA

◆ *McDonald's* **restaurant memorabilia** including *Happy Meal* toys, boxes, sacks, advertising pieces, postcards, paper items, uniforms, cups, glasses, mugs, pins, buttons, jewelry, foreign items, clocks, watches, displays, rings, retail items, games, clothes, shoes, special convention items, letters, newsletters, and other public and company items. Not interested in "common items which appear in *Happy Meals* nation-wide." Your description should include what it is, the color, size, any trademarks, dates, and condition. Meredith wrote *Price Guide to McDonald's Happy Meal Collectibles*, available from the author for $31 postpaid. The McDonald's Collectors Club offers a 10 page monthly newsletter on collecting *McDonald's* items available for $25.

>Mr. Meredith Williams
>PO Box 633
>Joplin, MO 64802
>(417) 781-3855   fax (417) 624-0090

◆ *McDonald's* **memorabilia** including:
- Employee uniforms with the M logo;
- Paper goods including boxes, place mats, napkins, flyers;
- Displays and promotions such as signs, decals, posters;
- Anything in foreign languages;
- Not for public items such as ID cards, newsletters, bulletins, sales and procedures manuals, and worksheets;
- Fixtures, signs, and lights.

Does not want items currently available in all restaurants. Take a photo of larger items please. Matt does not buy for resale, but hopes to build a *McDonald's* museum and put them on public display. Offers free appraisals if you send an SASE.

>Matt Welch
>PO Box 30444
>Tucson, AZ 85751
>(520) 886-0505   fax (520) 722-3607
><matwelch@aol.com>

◆ **Ephemera from** *Burger King, Carl's Jr., Wendy's, Hardees, Bob's Big Boy, What-a-Burger, Sonic Drive-In, Arby's, Roy Rogers* **and other fast food chains** including kid's meal toys and boxes from before 1988. Also crew pins, displays, and other fast-food related items that are odd or unusual.

>Ken Clee
>PO Box 11412
>Philadelphia, PA 19111
>(215) 722-1979   <waxntoys@aol.com>

TONY'S TIP: *Don't assume that what you have is common. Many fast food chain collectibles had limited distribution, and may in fact have been given away in only a few restaurants.*
Rare doesn't always translate into great value, but it can! Uniforms and other "Insider items" used by staff or management, or designed to decorate restaurants (like counter displays) can be worth the most to many collectors.

◆ *Bob's Big Boy* **and** *Coon Chicken Inn* **restaurant memorabilia,** ceramic ashtrays and salt and peppers, cups or dishes with logos, lunch boxes, game boards, toys, comics, figurines, and other unusual pieces. Please write or fax with a description, noting all repairs. Dealers must set the price they want; amateurs may request offers. Bob's vinyl plastic doll banks are NOT wanted.
Glenn Grush
5344 North Collingwood Circle
Calabasas, CA 91302
(818) 880-6200   fax (818) 880-6500   <awallstguy@aol.com>

◆ *Bob's Big Boy* **items,** especially menus, lamps, matches, ashtrays, salt and pepper shakers, and nodders. No plastic banks.
Steve Soelberg
29126 Laro Drive
Agoura Hills, CA 91301
(818) 889-9909   <opermatch65@earthlink.net>

◆ *Coon Chicken Inn* **memorabilia** of all kinds that features Blacks.
Diane Cauwels
3947 Old South Road
Murfreesboro, TN 37128
(615) 896-3614   (615) 896-3614   <colblackjack@msn.com>

◆ *Isaly's Dairy* **ephemera.** Wants badges, bibs, bottles, calendars, clocks, dishes, milk and ice cream cartons, mugs, signs, straw holders, and other advertising from this dairy/deli chain from PA and Ohio.
Brian Butke
2640 Sunset Drive
West Mifflin, PA 15122
<bsquared@bellatlantic.net>   <http://bbutko.tripod.com>

TONY'S TIP: *Glasses given away by restaurants are becoming collectible, with a few of them at $50 each. Look under "glasses" in the index for more buyers.*

◆ **Soda Fountain memorabilia** especially historical ephemera related to soda fountain operations such as photographs, trade catalogs, bills and letterheads, recipe and formula books, trade magazines (like Soda Dispenser and Soda Fountain), and the like. Also wants 19th century soda fountain items such as **hand crank milk shakers, crockery root beer mugs, straw dispensers with glass feet** or tops, pink ice cream soda glasses, and colored banana split dishes with feet. Especially interested in *True Fruit* and other advertising from the J. Hungerford Smith Co. of Rochester. The favorite find of this 20 year veteran collector would be an **equipment and supplies catalog** from before 1870. He does not want syrup well inserts for fountains, nor does he want match book covers, cup holders, trinkets, anything made of plastic, or anything related to the ice cream industry. "Please give as much reasonable detail as possible. A photo or photocopy is helpful." Dealers should price goods; amateurs may request offer. Appraisals of items not for sale require $25 and a clear photo. SASE a must.

> Harold Screen
> 2804 Munster Road
> Baltimore, MD 21234
> (410) 661-6765   <hscreen@home.com>

◆ **Ice cream and soda fountain memorabilia:**
- Postcards depicting ice cream or soda fountains, ice cream trucks, factories or any other ice cream topic (any year);
- Photographs of soda fountain interiors;
- Letterheads, envelopes and other paper with ice cream images;
- Magazines from soda fountain and ice cream trade, pre-1930;
- Trade cards with ice cream parlors, freezers, or soda fountains;
- Catalogs pre-1920 (except Mills #31);
- Advertising giveaways, fobs, buttons, tape measures, etc.

Allan buys a wide range of ice cream related items, but says his focus for the last few years has been on postcards with historical photos. He buys nothing damaged or made after 1945. He does not make offers, and requests you price what you have.

> Allan "Mr. Ice Cream" Mellis
> 1115 West Montana
> Chicago, IL 60614
> (773) 327-9123   Fax: (773) 327-9456   <mellis@enteract.com>

◆ *Dixie* **ice cream cup picture lids and other memorabilia** 1930-54 including premium pictures and offers, albums, scrapbook covers, ads, and company literature. Also buys some non-*Dixie* pictorial ice cream cup lids such as *Tarzan* or American Historical Shrines series.

> Stephen Leone
> 94 Pond Street
> Salem, NH 03079
> (603) 898-4900   <nhdixie@yahoo.com>

FARMS, HORSES & TRACTORS

◆ **Wagons, carriages and commercial horse drawn vehicles, in whole or in part.** Buys carriage lamps, dashboard clocks, wagon tools, nameplates, wheel making machines, coachman's and groom's clothing, jacks, tack room fixtures, whip racks, wagon odometers, hitching post statuary, rein clips, wagon seats, wagon poles, veterinary tools, lap robes, life size harness maker's horses, zinc animal heads, and anything else related to carriages and wagons. Offers from $500 to $2,500 for lamps marked *Studebaker, Brewster,* or *Healey.* Also buys goat and dog carts. If your item is old, genuine, and in good condition you may ship it on approval. No harnesses, please. Don will send you a thick illustrated wants list if you send him a long SASE with four stamps on the envelope.

    Don Sawyer, West Newbury Wagon Works
    40 Bachelor Street
    West Newbury, MA 01985

◆ **Horse bits.** "I buy old iron, brass or silver horse bits (mouthpieces) especially custom or unusual ones. I also want old decorative glass pictorial bridle rosettes. **Old catalogs that picture bridles,** bits, and other tack are also wanted."

    Jean Gayle
    Three Horses
    7403 Blaine Road
    Aberdeen, WA 98520
        (360) 533-3490   <jgayle@techline.com>

◆ **Horse bridle rosettes**, either singles or pairs, as long as they are decorated with letters or pictures.

    Dennis Schulte
    8th Avenue NW
    Waukon, IA 52172
        (563) 568-3628

◆ **Tractor, farm machinery, and gasoline engine paper ephemera including pre-1940 manuals, catalogs, parts books, in-house publications, and sales literature.** Also buys farm magazines such as *Implement Record, Farm Machinery & Hardware,* and *Farm Mechanics.* Also buys "giveaways" such as signs, ashtrays, buttons, etc. associated with any farm machinery. No textbooks or reprints are wanted. Please indicate the color of the item and the price you'd like.

    Alan C. King
    PO Box 86
    Radnor, OH 43066

◆ **Tractor memorabilia** including all sorts of paper ephemera and small trinkets given away as advertising promotion by tractor makers and dealers, such as watch fobs, pens, cigarette lighters, etc. You may ship on approval if it's old, original, and clean.

> Jay Ketelle
> 3721 Farwell
> Amarillo, TX 79109
> (806) 355-3456   fax (806) 355-5743   <jayk.lit@amaonline.com>

◆ *J.I. Case* **Tractor Company memorabilia** including tractors and implements, toy tractors, advertising signs, catalogs, books, and anything else marked *J.I. Case*. **If you want to sell an old *Case* tractor** make certain to tell them where it is presently located.

> Ed and Carla Schuth
> Route 3   Box 6
> Wabasha, MN 55981
> (651) 565-4251

◆ *John Deere* **items,** especially portable gasoline engines. He also buys corn shellers, watch fobs, advertising, pump jacks, or older farm equipment. "If you have anything *John Deere*, contact me."

> Gary Voigt
> 4010 Glendale Drive
> Excelsior, MN 55331
> (612) 474-3540 eves   <johndeereantique@uswest.net>

◆ **Ice Company memorabilia** including porcelain signs, delivery bags, tokens, badges, ice picks or axes, company records and handbills, photographs of any aspect of the business. He DOES NOT WANT ordinary wooden handled ice picks or plain metal tongs. Please give the size, color, and condition of what you have. Xerox™ or photo helpful.

> Joe Pedro
> 9 Whitcomb Ave.
> Ayer, MA 01432
> (978) 772-2971   <icetools2@ourweb.net>

◆ **Ice harvesting tools** are wanted, but "I have all the common ones." Buys crescent saws, house axes, and paper goods related to the history of ice. In general, most tongs, pikes, plows, and markers are not of interest, but some rare styles and makers are wanted, so you are encouraged to send a photo and maker's name. "Please, I don't need house signs which tell the ice man to stop." Phil lectures on ice harvesting and other 19th century practices, and heads the New England Tool Collectors Association, dues for which are $5/yr.

> Philip Whitney
> 303 Fisher Road
> Fitchburg, MA 01420
> (978) 342-1350 eves   <philhistor7@aol.com>

◆ **Windmill ephemera,** especially cast iron windmill weights, display model windmills and salesman's sample windmills. He does not want reproductions, damaged or repaired items, items with new paint, or "short tail horse" windmill weights. Also cast iron tractor hood ornaments. Please send a color photo, your phone number, and the price range you'd like to get.

Richard Tucker
Argyle Antiques
PO Box 262
Argyle, TX 76226
(940) 464-3752   fax (940) 464-7293   <rtucker@jw.com>

◆ **Poultry industry items** including, but not limited to, egg cartons from before 1955, egg scales ($25-$60), stoneware chick waterers and feeders ($40-$80), books before 1940, and egg shipping containers and carriers. Does not want cracked or chipped stoneware or tops with no bottoms, nor does he want rusted scales, plastic egg cartons, or wooden folding egg carriers. Identify all labels or marks, patent numbers, etc. "A nice close up photo would be helpful."

Roland Pautz
371 Lincoln Street
San Luis Obispo, CA 93405
(805) 543-2049   <rpautz@thegrid.net>

◆ **Round milk bottles with dairy names embossed or printed on them.** Square bottles OK if amber colored or from any Western states. Nothing worn, cracked, or chipped is wanted.

Leigh Giarde
PO Box 2243
Redlands, CA 92373
(909) 792-8681   <onlyleigh@cpl.net>

◆ **Dairy creamers made of glass with the names of dairies embossed or printed on** are sought. He does not want ceramic creamers or those without names. Also milk bottles with cop tops, baby tops, or war slogans, but only in excellent condition.

Ken Clee
PO Box 11412
Philadelphia, PA 19111
(215) 722-1979   <waxntoys@aol.com>

★ **Milk or dairy industry items marked with the name and address of a dairy** including old and unusual bottles, advertising, toys, and signs, especially from institutional bottlers such as prisons, colleges, railroads, hotels, and the like. Any bottles with character endorsements (sports, *Hopalong Cassidy*, etc.) are wanted with cartoon characters particularly desirable (Disney bottles bring $100+ each). Bottles and posters with WWII slogans are also sought. Unusually shaped bottles with faces or heads or those made of colored glass are always wanted, as are creamer size bottles marked with the name of a dairy, hotel, or restaurant. Bottles with glass lids, tin handles or lids and pour spouts can go as high as $300. **Just about anything related to *Borden's* or their *Elsie the Cow* trademark is wanted**, especially their ruby red bottles which bring from $700-$1,000 each. "I'll buy catalogs of bottle makers which show design variations offered." Large items like cream separators, churns, milk cans, and the like are not wanted. "If in doubt about the authenticity of what you own, feel free to call or send me a good photo. I will verify what you have and answer your questions about it, if you include a Self-Addressed Stamped Envelope."

Ralph Riovo
686 Franklin Street
Alburtis, PA 18011
(610) 966-2536   fax (610) 966-0368
<thepurplecow@erols.com>

◆ *Elsie the Cow* and other *Borden's* **ephemera** including games, toys, cookbooks, comic books, cups, glasses, Christmas cards, neon, postcards of milk plants, ads (especially from 1930's medical mags), bottles, trade cards and paper ephemera of all types. Also buys bottles from DuPage county, IL. Describe and price your items.

Ron Selcke
PO Box 237
Bloomingdale, IL 60108
(630) 543-4848 eve   <selckepoppy@aol.com>

◆ **Milk bottle caps of all kinds used on the old glass milk bottles.** The flat, plug type, caps that fit inside the top of the bottle are sought, especially those from Southern states and World War II. Other caps of note are special issue caps, those which name a college dairy, were made to advertise products, and those with holiday messages. Older collections or accumulations of caps are the most desirable, bringing $1 to $3 each. "I also want advertising and free samples from cap companies, but have no interest in pogs, nor do I want huge quantities of any one cap (I'll buy tubes, but not cases)." Photocopies are good.

David Wampler
1808 Hidden Harbor Road
Hixson, TN 37343
(423) 843-1693

MINING

◆ **Mining and blasting items,** including carbide lamps, candlesticks, safety lamps, tools, handbooks, tool catalogs, blasting cap tins, detonators, etc. He only wants items marked with a manufacturer's name, but warns "do not clean or wire brush your item, as I want them as is, not cleaned." Value depends on maker and condition, so give a good description including all names and marks. *Justrite* and *Autolite* lamps are not wanted if made after 1900. No repros. Photo suggested.
>
> Anthony Glab
> 407 East Wheel Road
> Belair, MD 21015

◆ **Mining items** including safety lamps, oil wick cap lamps, carbide lamps, blasting cap tins and blasting machines, candle holders, and hundreds of other small tools, photos, souvenirs, and advertising items related to mining. Will even buy ore carts and buckets. Also wants ribbons, banners, and badges from the United Mine Workers (UMWA) and the Western Federation of Miners (WFM). Dave says he's willing to pay you in cash if you prefer.
>
> David Crawford
> 3421 Fremont Street
> Rockford, IL 61103
>   (815) 637-6720   <dmcxls4u@aol.com>

◆ **Colorado mining memorabilia** 1859-1915 including photos, paper ephemera, stocks, maps, stereoviews, advertising, and small souvenirs, especially from towns of Cripple Creek, Victor, Central City, Leadville, Breckenridge, Idaho Springs, Telluride, etc. Also books about Colorado mining and any city directories pre-1915. No interest in "flatland cities" like Denver or Colorado Springs, nor in Colorado tourist attractions and parks. No photos unless a mine or mining town is featured.
>
> George Foott
> 120 West Park Avenue
> Salida, CO 81201
>   fax (775) 852-8666   <sfgfco@chaffee.net>

◆ **Mining collectibles of all types**: stock certificates, photographs, diaries, lteers, invoices, business records, maps, rare books, and some tools, etc., specially Nevada, California, Arizona and Colorado. This 25 year veteran says, "If it's related to the **California gold rush, the Comstock lode, the Pikes Peak gold rush,** I'm interested."
>
> Fred Holabird
> 3555 Airway Drive #308
> Reno, NV 89511
>   (775) 852-8822   fax (775) 852-8866
>   <fred@holabird.org>

◆ **Mining ephemera,** especially pre-1920 mining stock certificates, photographs of mining operations (but only if they are dated and identified), and postcards depicting mining. No coal mining is wanted. Buys books on mining and select other mining-related material.

>Russell Filer Mining
>13057 California Street
>Yucaipa, CA 92399
>(909) 797-1650   <rafiler@cybertime.net>

TONY'S TIP: When you have tools to sell, don't even consider cleaning them. Collectors do not want things that have been scrubbed with a wire brush or rust removing solvent. Some fossils can be destroyed by improper cleaning. Don't!

ROCKS, FOSSILS & CAVES

◆ **Meteorites.** Many types exist, and this wants them all, rough or smooth, large or small. Look for rocks that are especially heavy, or with signs of melting or with rust. A freshly fallen meteorite often has a thin black skin, called "fusion crust." If you have a rock that attracts a magnet, you may have a meteorite. "A strong magnet on a string will swing towards all meteorites, which makes this one of the best preliminary tests. Other excellent field tests for meteorites include checking for rust, and filing off a tiny corner to look inside for bright metal or metal flakes. If you think you have found a meteorite, please send a small, dime-sized piece for me to examine along with a description and photo of the entire specimen. If you wish to have the sample returned to you, you must enclose return postage. All non-meteorite samples without return postage are discarded. If I suspect your sample is a meteorite, I will contact you, so be sure to enclose your name, address and phone number along with all samples." Rare forms of meteorites can be surprisingly valuable. This buyer is convinced of his own importance so can be hard to do business with at times. Follow directions.

>Robert Haag
>PO Box 27527
>Tucson, AZ 85726
>(520) 882-8804   (520) 743-7225

◆ **Rock, mineral, and crystal collections** are wanted, as are samples of gold, silver, and copper, particularly samples associated with Western mining. Pays in any form you prefer.

>David Crawford
>3421 Fremont Street
>Rockford, IL 61103
>(815) 637-6720   <dmcxls4u@aol.com>

◆ **Fossils of fish, large trilobites or shark's teeth** such as those that are found on Florida's West coast beaches. "I prefer to buy in bulk, and want only those in near perfect condition. A photocopy (Xerox©) copy may do for starters, but eventually he'll want to see the actual item before making an evaluation and offer. Please indicate where you dug it or how you came about it.

> Sven Stau
> 181 Crestmount Court #3
> Tonawanda, NY 14150
> (716) 693-4011   <svenstau@cs.com>

◆ **Cave or cavern memorabilia before 1950,** including books, magazine articles, pamphlets, prints, postcards, and other ephemera. "Any items that would make a contribution to the history of a particular cave or area of the country such as journal entries, deeds, wills, maps, tickets, and advertising, are of interest." Common souvenirs and chrome postcards from after 1940 are not desired.

> Jack Speece
> 711 East Atlantic Avenue
> Altoona, PA 16602
> (814) 946-3155 eves

◆ **Caves or cavern memorabilia of all sorts.** "I'll buy anything old or unusual pertaining to caves or caverns worldwide" including photos, brochures, postcards, souvenirs, silver spoons, plates, etc. Does not want anything after 1940, and has a particular interest in items from before 1900. Make a Xerox© of paper goods to describe them.

> Gordon Smith
> PO Box 217
> Marengo, IN 47140
> (812) 945-5721   fax (812) 945-6891
> <glstis@aol.com>

◆ **Cave-related items from before 1950,** including post cards with real photos, souvenir plates and paperweights, signs, etc., related to either wild or show caves. Has particular interest in items related to the Floyd Collins rescue in Sand Cave, KY, including souvenirs sold at the event, books on the topic, songs recorded about it, etc. A good description should include dimensions and all names, numbers, and/or symbols on the item. Photograph or photocopy (Xerox©) is strongly suggested.

> Anthony Glab
> 407 East Wheel Road
> Belair, MD 21015

FRUIT, TREES & LUMBER

◆ **Canning machinery, catalogs and tools of the Ferracute Machine Company of Bridgeton, NJ,** are sought by this researcher who also wants anything related to company founder Oberlin Smith. The Oberlin Smith Society is particularly interested in advertising, catalogs, small presses, medals and tokens, but will consider anything related to FMCo or Smith himself. The OSS is a 501(c)(3) organization and seeks donations too.

> James Gandy
> Oberlin Smith Society
> 336 Woodruff Road
> Bridgeton, NJ   08302
>   (609) 451-8580   <jgandy8580@aol.com>

◆ **Everything about fruit and vegetable growing, packing and canning** is wanted, such as labels, photographs, postcards, magazines, buttons, ribbons and giveaway trinkets of all types. Wants all sorts of paper ephemera from various organizations and events promoting fruit and vegetable growing and packing. Buys orange juicers, reamers and extractors from major packers, if company name is impressed.

> Pat Jacobsen
> PO Box 791
> Weimar, CA 95736
>   (530) 637-5923   <pjacobsen@neworld.com>

◆ **Everything about fruit raising and varieties before 1900, including illustrated books, magazine articles, ceramic tiles depicting fruit, postcards, prints, folders, and greeting cards depicting apples.** Especially wants books and paper with color plates or descriptions of fruit varieties. May be in any language.   No tropical fruit, or anything later than 1940. This veteran horticulture experimenter wants cuttings from uncommon tree fruit varieties you have on your farm. He wants temperate climate fruits, especially apples, but also pears, plums, quinces and medlars. Also buys books on fruit propagation which were printed before 1920.

> Fred Janson
> 932 Glendale Court
> Burlington, Ontario L7R 4J3   CANADA

TONY'S TIP: Remember, dealers and collectors can't make offers on what they don't understand. Give clear complete descriptions.

OIL COMPANY MEMORABILIA

◆ **Gasoline and oil company advertising and promotional items from local, regional and independent oil companies and dealers only.** "I'll buy gas pump globes, banks shaped like oil cans or gas pumps, salt/pepper shaped like gas pumps, thermometers, transistor radios shaped like oil cans or gas pumps and small cans of oil. He is not interested in paper items, large signs, reproductions, or national brands like *Mobil, Shell, Esso, Phillips, Conoco, Amoco, Texaco* etc. Describe the condition, and include a description of decals or labels.
  Peter Capell
  1838 West Grace Street
  Chicago, IL 60613
      (773) 871-8735   <pcapell@intersurfer.com>

◆ **Gasoline and oil company signs in porcelain or enamel.** Also buys some other petroleum advertising.
  Gus Garton, Garton's Auto
  5th and Vine
  Millville, NJ 08332
      (609) 825-3618

◆ **Oil company advertising** of all types from all companies but from before 1960 only. Send a sharp color picture along with dimensions and a statement of condition, pointing out all flaws and damage.
  Mike Waters
  PO Box 2097
  Westerville, OH 43086
      (800) 894-8095   <marblemike@veriomail.com>

◆ *Gulf Oil Company* **items** including signs, globes, banners, cans, station giveaways, toys, maps and china. "I'm interested in anything made by or for *Gulf* except reproductions." Sent a detailed description of condition, along with a photo whenever possible.
  Buzz Houston
  PO Box 848
  Oxford, KS 67119
      (620) 455-2579

◆ **Oil company credit cards and pocket calendars** are purchased. You may send your items for his immediate offer and a return check.
  Noel Levy
  1109 Silent Glade Road
  Owings Mills, MD 21117
      (410) 363-9040

◆ **Adveritisng for gas, oil and auto companies** such as neon signs, clocks, and window display items. Seeking exceptional pieces, "no junk" or yard sale items. The older, rarer, and more colorful, the better. This well known Hollywood area dealer DOES NOT WANT reproductions, badly damage pieces, inexpensive items, or anything made in Asia. "We prefer the seller to set the price but will offer fair prices for sellers who have no idea what they have" if they give a good description and the item is actually for sale.

>Dennis Clark & Lisa Bosey
>Off The Wall Antiques
>7325 Melrose Ave.
>Los Angeles, CA 90046
>(323) 930-1185   fax (323) 930-1595   <weirdstuff@earthlink.net>

◆ **Oil cans from Canada,** especially British Columbia oil in tin cans, and any quart oil cans related to motorcycles.

>Don Schneider
>PO Box 1570
>Merritt, BC
>V1K 1B8   CANADA
>(250) 378-6421

◆ **Advertising for automobiles, motorcycles, gasoline stations and oil companies** is wanted. Major companies preferred but other brands will be considered if the item is high quality with strong visual interest. The value of these items is in "the look" more than in rarity. Advertising includes three dimensional items like porcelain signs, tin signs, neon signs, clocks, signs that light up, thermometers, calendars, oil cans, postcards, posters, decorations, playing cards, dealers models and employee pins. Items may be of tin, porcelain, glass, cardboard, paper or mixed media. Paper and cardboard items must be attractive not just old. The fancier and more attractive the better. Pretty girls, movie stars, men in uniform, animals, automobiles, and the like make advertising interesting and more valuable. Condition is very important, the closer to as new, the better. HE DOES NOT WANT anything, no matter how good, that was made after 1965. HE DOES NOT WANT magazine ads from any period, nor does he buy anything with severe damage. Every single stain, scratch, tear, fold, dent, faded spot, rust speck or marks from water damage makes an item less desireable to collectors. It does not matter how old a piece is, damage is damage. I need to know exactly where the damage is. Please describe your item well, giving dates, names, dimensions along with photos.

>Robert Newman
>17220 Silver Lane
>Encino, CA 91316
>(818) 461-9229

BARBERSHOP ITEMS

◆ **Decorated shaving mugs depicting the owner's occupation, trade, or hobby above or below his name.** Also hand painted personal occupational barber bottles. Since each was custom made, they must be evaluated individually. Also salesman's sample barber chairs made in porcelain or wood. No Japanese reproductions or "Sportsman's Series" mugs from the 1950's.

> Burton Handelsman
> 18 Hotel Drive
> White Plains, NY 10605
> (914) 428-4480

◆ **Barbershop memorabilia,** including:
• Decorated shaving mugs with original owner's name and picture of any occupation, vehicle, fraternal order, animal, etc.;
• Fancy barber bowls, bottles, and waste jars;
• **Catalogs of barber supplies** or equipment;
• **Salesmen's sample barber chairs,** and much more.

Powell both collects and deals so buys a wide range of fine items or accepts them on consignment. Include a tracing or close up photo. New shaving mugs are not wanted. This well known historian is the only member of the Barber's Hall of Fame who isn't a barber.

> Robert Powell
> 1333 Kathryn
> Hurst, TX 76053
> (817) 284-8145

◆ **Barber shop massagers and vibrators.** The earlier the better, but design, condition, attachments, etc., all figure into value. Give a complete description, including the brand name and model number if known. Does it work? Please don't clean things being offered for sale. Also wants **barber bottles and chairs** from before 1940. A photo and good description describing chips, cracks and pattern or color wear.

> Rick Padrone
> 1005 E. Idlewild Ave.
> Tampa, FL 33604
> (800) 991-0165   fax (800) 991-0166
> <ricpadron@webtv.net>

See also: razors and knives and advertising for buyers of this type of material.

TONY'S TIPS ON SELLING GUNS, WEAPONS & MILITARY ITEMS.

You're likely to own these items so I've supplied you premium experts to help you dispose of them properly. If your item is collectible, you'll find a buyer here.

To describe most military items, follow the basics: material(s) from which it is made, color(s), dimensions, serial numbers and other marks, what you know of its history, and the item's condition. If it's supposed to do something, does it do it? Are all parts and pieces there? Is it for sale or do you "just want a price"? It may be easier to photocopy small items.

When you offer a uniform for sale, you should describe all insignia and ribbons. They will decide the uniform's value. Your uniform should be in good condition. Buyers will forgive moth holes in a Revolutionary War outfit but not in most WWII uniforms.

When describing a sword, dagger or bayonet measure from end to end and from the tip of the blade to the handle guard. Measure the width of the blade where it attaches to the handle guard. List every word or number found on the blade, hilt, or handle. Trace or photocopy any decoration on the blade or sheath. Describe the condition of the scabbard or sheath. Treat knives and swords as fragile objects. Mishandling can be costly.

To sell a gun make sure it is not loaded before anything else. Gun buyers want to know the make, model, serial number, caliber or gauge, barrel length, type and percent of finish, type of stock or grips, mechanical condition and condition of the bore. List all marks inside and out and note dings, defects and alterations.

The buyer will tell you how to ship your items. When rare or valuable weapons are involved, the buyer may prefer to pick them up personally or arrange pick-up.

Buyers prefer to obtain military items from the veteran who owned them, or from a direct heir. **Counterfeits abound**...especially of leather jackets and Nazi items.

GUNS

◆ **Antique weapons of all types including guns, swords, uniforms and other high grade military goods.** Holds regular cataloged auctions of high grade guns.

> James D. Julia Auctioneers
> PO Box 830
> Fairfield, ME 04937
> (207) 453-7904   fax (207) 453-2502
> <jjulia@juliaauctions.com>

◆ **American percussion and early cartridge firearms, both long guns and revolvers, 1840-1920.** "I'll buy guns by any maker, but especially *Colt, Winchester, Remington, Marlin, Sharps, Smith & Wesson, Manhattan, Stevens,* and *Bacon.* I like to buy derringers of all types, especially those that are particularly small or short barreled, those that are very large caliber (.41 cal. up), or those which take metallic cartridges. I also like finding any pocket size pistols made by *Colt, Remington, Bacon, Marston, Moore, National, Reid, Terry, Warner,* and *Williamson,* among others." Pays $300 to $3,000 for these guns. Wants photos or photocopies of both sides of the weapon and all markings and numbers found anywhere on the gun.

> Steve Howard
> Past Tyme Pleasures
> 2491 San Ramon Valley Blvd. #1-204
> San Ramon, CA 94583
> (925) 484-4488   fax (925) 484-2551
> <pasttyme@attbi.com>

◆ **Guns and gun collections of all types.** "I'm always searching for Gattling guns."

> Ed Kukowski
> Ed's Gun House
> PO Box 62
> Minnesota City, MN 55959
> (507) 689-2925 voice/fax   <eek@hbci.com>

TONY'S TIP: Any gun buyer wants to know the make, model, serial number, caliber or gauge, barrel length, type and percent of finish, type of stock or grips, mechanical condition and condition of the bore. Describe all marks inside and out, list alterations, and note dings and defects.

◆ **Pinfire and other antique fire arms** are sought in any condition including cheap guns suitable only for parts. Provide a general description and all names, dates, and other numbers you find on the gun. If the parts of the gun have serial numbers, tell him whether the numbers match. This important 40 year historian says, "I'm retired now and don't buy many guns, but I own a big research library and am happy to answer questions, give free advice, and help you find a buyer."
> Larry Compeau
> 5262 Old Franklin Road
> Grand Blanc, MI 48439
> (810) 694-2705   <compeau@iavbbs.com>

◆ **American guns from before 1890, especially those with historic association.** No interest in reproductions. If possible, send a clear photo of the item and write down all markings found anywhere on it. If it is a pistol, please make a photocopy, or draw a pencil outline. Mention any broken or missing wood, metal that is pitted, parts missing, etc. Does it work? Worman wrote two books on firearms of the American West and was firearms editor of *Hobbies* magazine for sixteen years. SASE please. "I do not make offers."
> Charles Worman
> PO Box 292624
> Kettering, OH 45429
> (937) 299-7752   <oldguns@aol.com>

◆ **High grade shotguns, double rifles, and big bore rifles, whether English, Italian, or American made.** Guns must be in original condition. "I do not want broken or damaged guns, paramilitary weapons, clunkers or guns you can buy at your local gun shop. I will pay up to $100,000 for rare sporting guns, but a personal physical inspection is essential before any purchase." Your first contact by mail or phone should include the brand name, serial number, caliber or gauge, length of the barrel, a description of any markings stamped on the metal or wood parts, and a statement of condition. The history of the gun is useful. If writing, include your phone number.
> Francis Lombardi II
> PO Box 181-TH
> Syracuse, NY 13208
> (315) 685-9806   <francis@stellingtank.com>

TONY'S TIP: *If your rifle or pistol is in a wooden case or if it is heavily engraved, get expert advice NOW.*

◆ **Revolvers (pistols).** "I'll consider any antique or collectible firearms to build my dealer's inventory or to enhance my personal collection, but my special interests are:
- Serial number one guns, antique or modern;
- *Smith & Wesson* revolvers;
- Antique engraved revolvers;
- Old West firearms;
- Guns owned by famous individuals.

"I can travel if needed. Confidentiality assured. I try to be considerate and helpful in cases of divorce, bankruptcy, and estate liquidation. I can pay immediately or arrange auction or consignment sales. I'm interested in unusual or oddball older guns that many other collectors avoid. Honest wear and alterations from the period of use are OK, but do affect the value of the piece. I will consider heavily worn, broken, or refinished items only if they are rare or have documented historical connection. I am not interested in fakes, reproductions or modern guns. If offering an historic gun, quality of documentation is important. Send a copy of documentation and what you will swear to in a notarized affidavit. A personal inspection is required before final offer, especially on finely engraved guns. Please don't offer anything stolen or illegal. I won't buy it." Specific regulations govern shipment of firearms. Jim has the necessary licenses, but check for shipping instructions. Interesting catalog available. Jim is co-author of *Standard Catalog of Smith & Wesson.*

Jim Supica, Jr.
Old Town Station Ltd.
PO Box 14040
Lenexa, KS 66285
(913) 492-3000   fax (913) 492-3022   <OldTownSta@aol.com>
<http://www.armchairgunshow.com>

TONY'S TIP: Want to know what your pistol is worth?
Go to <www.armchairgunshow.com>
This is Jim Supica's web site and should answer
just about any question you might have.

TONY'S TIP: Any gun buyer wants to know the make, model, serial number, caliber or gauge, barrel length, type of finish on the metal, what percent of the original finish remains, type of stock or grips and its mechanical condition. The condition of the bore (the inside of the barrel) is important too. Describe all marks inside and out, list alterations, and note dings and defects.

◆ *Colt* **pistols with factory engraving.** "I'll buy single action *Colts* in 95% or better original condition, if they predate WWII and have factory engraving." Give the serial number when you write, and, if possible, a good close up photo of the artwork. Some newer single actions are also wanted. Also wants guns from outlaws and lawmen if they have proper documentation. All early memorabilia from the *Colt* company, including all advertising and literature are wanted, including *Coltrock* brand products and the boxes they came in.

> Johnny Spellman
> 10806 North Lamar
> Austin, TX 78753

(512) 836-2889 days   (512) 258-6910 eves   <dvm69@swbell.net>

◆ *Colt* **pistols and** *Colt* **Firearms Mfg Co. ephemera** including all correspondence on factory letterhead, pamphlets and brochures by *Colt,* empty black and maroon boxes that *Colt* guns were packed in, instruction sheets and manuals, and "anything else pertaining to *Colt* products." John wants *Colt* factory catalogs, 1888-1910, for which he pays from $40-$500+. 1910-1940 catalogs bring $20-$100. John also buys plastic and electrical items marked *Coltrock.*

> John Fischer
> PO Box 47
> Van Nuys, CA 91408
> (310) 474-2567   <jsfischer1@aol.com>

◆ *Newton* **Arms Co. guns and other memorabilia** from this progressive 1916-18 gunsmith. "I'll buy rifles, catalogs, loading tools, letters, stock certificates, cartridges, and any other paper or memorabilia from the Newton Arms Co. or the Buffalo Newton Rifle Corp. I will pay $5,000 for a .276 *Newton* rifle or a rifle in .280, .33 or .40 (.400) calibers if in mint condition, and look for unusual *Newton* cartridges. I will gladly pay a finder's fee for *Newton* guns I buy. I'll take anything signed by Chas. Newton but nothing marked "Buffalo Newton Rifle Co." Any items other than guns must be original condition."

> Bruce Jennings
> 70 Metz Road
> Sheridan, WY 82801
> (307) 674-6921

◆ **Junk guns and gun parts in any condition.** "I'm in the parts business and will travel to pick up large lots." Wants nothing having to do with current guns. Describe all markings and numbers. Bob is available for insurance appraisals of fire damaged gun collections.

> Robert Fay
> Box 24
> Star Route Box AF
> Whitmore, CA 96096
> (530) 472-3132   <yafer@shasta.com>

◆ **Old double barrel shotguns** are wanted in any condition. "I will buy any double barrel made before 1940, including parts guns and wall-hangers. Your trash is my treasure." Give the maker, model, condition, amount of bluing, rust, missing parts, engraving, etc." Charles has been in business since 1937.

> Charles Black, Gundoctor
> 512 Coman Street
> Athens, AL 35611
> (256) 230-3773

◆ *Iver Johnson* **products and memorabilia** including guns, bicycles, catalogs, etc. Special wants include engraved presentation guns and awards and any other unusual *Iver Johnson* item. This 30 year veteran collector does not want "common handguns in less than mint condition." Send a complete description, including a sketch or photo. Prefers seller to price, but will make offers.

> Charles Best
> 11523 Pinevalley Drive
> Franktown, CO 80116
> (303) 660-2318   <budbest@aol.com>

◆ **Brass military shell casings.** "I want to buy the casings for shells and projectiles in 37mm and larger sizes. Particularly wants an 8" Navy shell. I'll buy shell casings of all weapons, all nations."

> Charles Eberhart
> 3616 N.E. Seward
> Topeka, KS 66616
> (785) 235-1016

◆ **Ammunition and exploding devices including grenades, mines, bombs, and fuses of all type,** from the beginning of time to the present. "We buy everything from stone cannon balls to the smart weapons used in Operation Desert Storm. Also want books, films, reports, and videos about ordnance in any format or language." Schmitt's family has been making ammunition since 1849, so he particularly wants things marked with the Crittenden name. He is willing to pay $2,000 for a .69 caliber Crittenden and Tibbals Rimfire cartridge. He wants the measurements, condition, and all markings on what you have, preferring you also include a photo. He has no interest in store stock items. Schmitt is a contributing editor of two gun magazines and involved with cleaning up explosive ordnance from the Iraq/UN war.

> J. Randall Crittenden Schmitt
> Court House Station
> PO Box 4253
> Rockville, MD 20849
> (301) 946-2643

◆ **Machine guns made in Germany or Japan** for use in World War Two. Guns can be working or not. Also want machine gun parts such as firing pins, barrels, magazines, clips, tripods, bolts and all accessories such as scopes, flash hiders, covers, tools, cleaning kits and manuals. "I am a licensed gun dealer and member of the Automatic Weapons Collectors Assn., and all rules of The Bureau of Alcohol, Tobacco and Firearms apply. Contact me for more information." Dyke says there is a great deal of misinformation about this type of automatic weapon which results in people losing money rightfully theirs or in the destruction of valuable collectors items. He is not interested in pistols, rifles, assault rifles or other automatic weapons.

> Dyke Nagasaka
> PO Box 453
> Weiser, ID 83672
> (208) 550-0219   (208) 549-3841 eves   <kaznag@ruralnetwork.net>

◆ **Single shot target shooting rifles made between 1850 and 1915.** "I want only those rifles and no other guns. I do not want shotguns, skeet/trap guns, military or National Guard weapons, police guns, or rifles designed for hunting." If you have one to sell, include the maker and any information found on the barrel, sight or elsewhere on the rifle, including serial numbers. A photo of your item is helpful.

> Allen Hallock
> PO Box 7071
> Corte Madera, CA 94976
> (415) 924-1967   < arh@earthlink.net>

◆ **National Rifle Association (N.R.A.) shooting medals and literature showing or describing N.R.A. shooting matches and medals.**

> Charles Best
> 11523 Pine Valley Drive
> Franktown, CO 80116
> (303) 660-2318   <budbest@aol.com>

◆ **Target Shooting Organization memorabilia from Switzerland, Germany or the U.S.** Called SchuetzenVereins, they existed primarily from 1850 to 1915. He seeks medals, trophies, banners, painted targets, photographs, match programs, posters and other items. "I do not want military, National Guard, police, trap or skeet shooting, shotgun, hunting or recent (after 1915) material, nor does he want souvenir Swiss medals or coins" but if it says schuetzen on it send a full description, including any engraving or maker's marks, and the condition of the item. A Xerox™ or photo is helpful as most items are unique.

> Allen Hallock
> PO Box 7071
> Corte Madera, CA 94976
> (415) 924-1967   <arh@earthlink.ne>t

WAR & WEAPONS

★ **Anything military.** "My specialty is WWII paratrooper items from the U.S., Germany, and Japan, but I will buy **any military items from the Roman Empire to current issue Operation Desert Storm.** I buy small items like dog tags and big items like tanks, so look in the attic and give me a call." This 30 year veteran collector does not want reproductions or fakes but will consider anything you find in that trunk in your attic such as flags, uniforms, helmets, equipment, guns, daggers, hats, shoes, medals, jewelry, boats, jeeps, tanks. "I buy anything military." Take a photo if you can and tell him whatever history you know about the item(s) you have. "If you want to know what something is worth, but you can't take a photo, or find writing to be difficult," he says, "give me a call and I'll be happy to talk to you." If you write, make sure you include your phone number as I do 90% of my business over the phone.

> Michael Burke
> Kats Militaria
> PO Box 20519
> East York, PA 17402
>   (717) 699-4448   <katsmilita@aol.com>

◆ **Revolutionary War through the War of 1812 items** including:
  • Artillery shells and solid shot from 2" to 7" in diameter; •
  • **Cannon** or mortar barrels in any size, brass or iron;
  • **Tomahawks** or belt axe heads;
  • Triangular **bayonettes** or plug bayonettes;
  • **Trade beads or other Indian artifacts** of this period;
  • Flintlock military **muskets,** usually .50 caliber or larger;
  • Belt buckles, shoe buckles, plates, buttons, etc.;
  • Wooden canteens of all types;
  • Leather pouches for ammunition or personal items;
  • Swords, daggers, and belt knives;
  • Halberds, spontoons, pikes, and linstocks.
  • Anything similar to the above.

He is not interested in reproductions of these items, or in any books about the Revolutionary War era. "A photo is best, but a complete, accurate description is helpful. As much as possible, give the history of the item. Asking price is helpful but not necessary."

> Larry Jarvinen
> 313 Condon Road
> Manistee, MI 49660
>   (231) 723-5063

◆ **Museum qualit American Indian weapons.** Does not want arrow-heads, anything modern, or reproductions of early items.
   Daniel Brown
   PO Box 149
   Davenport, CA 95017
(800) 492-6786   (408) 426-0134   <green-garnet@sbcglobal.net>

◆ **Primitive weapons, trade beads and art from around the world.** Some items will be surprizingly valuable. Long respected dealer.
   David Boone Trading Company
   PO Box 669
   Brinnon, WA 98320
   (800) 423-1945   8 - 4 Pacific weekdays   fax (360) 796-4511
         <sales@boonetrading.com>

◆ **Mexican War (1846-48) photos and documents** are sought.
   Johnny Spellman
   10806 North Lamar
   Austin, TX 78753
(512) 836-2889 days   (512) 258-6910 eves   <dvm69@swbell.net>

◆ **Civil War artifacts, Union and Confederate** are wanted, including autographs of important military and civilian personalities, documents, photos, diaries, books, manuals, soldier's letters, personal items, campaign histories, regimental histories, G.A.R. or Confederate Veteran items. Has a particular interest in the battles of Gettysburg and Antietam. Provide a detailed description of items, especially condition.
   Stan Clark, Jr., Military Books
   915 Fairview Avenue
   Gettysburg, PA 17325
   (717) 337-1728   fax (717) 337-0581   <scmb@blazenet.net>

◆ **Civil War artifacts including guns, knives, documents, swords, and prisoner of war items.** No repros. It is important to indicate any markings. SASE requested. "I do not make offers."
   Charles Worman
   PO Box 292624
   Kettering, OH 45429
            (937) 299-7752   <oldguns@aol.com>

◆ **Civil War paper items** such as soldier's letters and diaries, documents, envelopes, stamps, maps, prisoner of war items, currency, script and photos. Specializes in Confederate items, especially stampless envelopes (covers). "I do not deal in reproductions."
   Gordon McHenry
   1615 Clower Creek Drive #T-177
   Sarasota, FL 34231
            (941) 966-5563

◆ **Civil War items, especially uniforms.** Buys muskets, pistols, swords, photographs and sundry items including bottles and excavated artifacts related to the war. Also buys other military items up through World War II. Nothing later.

    Will Gorges
    3910 U.S. Highway 70 East
    New Bern, NC 28560
(252) 636-3909 days (252) 514-5548 eves fax (252) 637-1862
    <rebel@civilwarantiques.com> <http://www.civilwarshop.com>

◆ **G.A.R. china, mugs, and spoons.** Any pieces marked G.A.R. (Grand Army of the Republic).

    Don McMahon
    567-R Higganum Road
    Durham, CT 06422
        (860) 349-4022 <dtmcmahon01@snet.net>

◆ **United Confederate Reunion (UCV)** badges, buttons, and ribbons.

    Peggy Dillard
    PO Box 210904
    Nashville, TN 37221
        (615) 646-1605 eves <pdill43795@aol.com>

◆ **Civil War regimental histories and first person narratives.**

    Jim Presgraves
    Bookworm & Silverfish
    PO Box 639
    Wytheville, VA 24382
(276) 686-5813 fax (276) 686-6636 <bookworm@naxs.com>

◆ **Indian War veterans material.** Anything from National Indian War Veterans, Order of Indian Wars of the United States and any similar organization: membership certificates or cards, medals, convention ribbons, photos, etc. Call or send complete details. Up to $5,000 paid.

    Thomas Pooler
    PO Box 1861
    Grass Valley, CA 95945
        (530) 268-1338

◆ **Military books of World War I, World War II and Korean War** on the air, land and sea. First editions in dust jackets preferred. Some rare titles will be purchased in lesser condition. Provide standard bibliographic information, including printing data found on the title page or reverse. No book club books and no paperbacks.

    Edward Conroy, SUMAC Books
    272 Smith Hill Road
    Troy, NY 12180
        (518) 279-9638 from 8 am to 4 pm EST

◆ **Afro-American militaria** especially unit photos in any condition, unit history books, holiday menus, unit insignia, shoulder patches, medals, scrapbooks, or what have you. "If you want an offer, send it for my examination. I pay all postage, both ways."

> Lt. Col. Wilfred Baumann
> PO Box 319
> Esperance, NY 12066
> (518) 875-6753 <wilfredc.baumann@att.net>

◆ **Black militaria.** "I will buy any and all items specific to African-American participation in wars from the Revolution through Vietnam, especially named medals, uniforms, equipment, documents, photos, and prints, as well as books dealing with Black military history; "I have a particular interest in the Buffalo Soldiers and the Tuskegee Airmen. Rare or one-of-a-kind items with strong provenance connected to a Black historical event are most desired. "I don't want books, sheet music, stereo cards or postcards, or any reproductions." Send a description, including the condition. You may set the price wanted or request offers. I buy, sell, and trade.

> Elizabeth Meaders
> 94 Mersereau Avenue
> Staten Island, NY 10303
> (718) 727-0703

◆ **Military items.** "I'll buy most military items, if original, especially WWI, WWII Airborne (paratroopers), military aviation and glider operations, and Vietnam. I do not want reproductions of WWII German items." Give the origin of your piece. Photograph expensive items.

> Robert Thomas, Jr.
> Thomas Militaria
> 931 Powell Drive
> Placentia, CA 92870
> (714) 572-1985   fax (714) 572-1986
> <robert@thomashouse.org>

◆ **Military souvenirs from WWI, WWII, Korea and Vietnam** from any country: books, documents, medals, uniforms, manuals, daggers, swords, guns, patches, hats, helmets, leather flight jackets, belt buckles, flags, and "any other war souvenirs you find." Can be U.S., German, Japanese, Korean, Italian or Vietnamese. Send a Photo or Xerox™ along with a description of all markings in your first letter. SASE.

> Gaal Long Jr.
> 22582 Highway 315
> Sardis, MS 38666
> (662) 487-2993   (662) 487-2457

◆ **Regimental and Battalion unit flags from all nations and periods** of history. "I'll also buy flag related items such as U.S. Army spear pole tops, color woven flag cords and tassels, engraved battle honor rings and battle streamers, canvas issue flag cover bags, and close up or parade photos showing unit flags." He DOES NOT WANT national flags or reenactment group flags. Please make a sketch of the flag, noting size and material. Ben can provide info about unit flags if you send an SASE.
> Ben Weed
> PO Box 4643
> Stockton, CA 95204
> <oldpatch@att.net>

◆ **Cloth shoulder insignia of divisions, regiments, brigades, and units from the Civil War to Vietnam.** WWI U.S. and German insignia are of special interest. Prefers to buy directly from the veteran or family. Condition is important. This 25 year veteran does not want repros.
> Hank McGonagle
> 26 Broad Street
> Newburyport, MA 01950
> (978) 462-2354   <saber12@attbi.com>

★ **Military medals and decorations** from all countries and periods. Also any documents or certificates related to military awards, medals and decorations. He prefers to buy directly from the vet or his family. Condition is important, and a photocopy is requested.
> Hank McGonagle
> 26 Broad Street
> Newburyport, MA 01950
> (978) 462-2354   <mcgonag@seacoast.net>

◆ **Medals, Decorations, and Orders** for military gallantry and other campaign medals of the U.S. and British Empire, 1780 to the present. Especially wants U.S. Medals of Honor and British Victoria Crosses and U.S. Purple Hearts for WWII officially named to the Navy and Marines. Does not want reproductions. Photocopy both sides.
> Alan Harrow
> 2292 Chelan Drive
> Los Angeles, CA 90068
> (323) 874-3474   <genoff@webtv.net>

◆ **U.S. Military medals** with the recipient's name engraved. Wants to buy the following: Purple Hearts, Distinguished Service Cross, Distinguished Flying Cross, Air medals, Silver Star, Navy Cross and Medals of Honor. Xerox® and give all printing.
> Gary Hullfish
> 16 Gordon Avenue
> Lawrenceville, NJ 08648
> (609) 896-0224   fax (609) 896-2040   <lawfuel@aol.com>

◆ **General Douglas MacArthur memorabilia of all types** is wanted. "I'll buy books, scrapbooks, autographed items, pictures, documents, toys, dolls, medals, coins, any item with 'I shall return' or 'I have returned' on it, buttons, statues, and any item documented as having belonged to MacArthur." Gaal also wants "letters or phone calls from anyone who knew MacArthur at any period of his life and can tell me stories about him. Please send a Xerox™ if you'd like an offer.

> Gaal Long Jr.
> 22582 Highway 315
> Sardis, MS   38666
> (662) 487-2993   (662) 487-2457

◆ **War crimes trial articles from Nurnberg or Japan** including jewelry, insignia, patches, etc. "Please give a ballpark price for your item."

> Jerry Keohane
> 16 Saint Margaret's Court
> Buffalo, NY 14216

◆ **Women's service uniforms from WWII,** plus any other items related to the women's military during that war. Wants photographs, orders, bulletins, medals, awards, certificates, flight instructions, training manuals, informative personal letters, and other items.

> Bruce Updegrove
> 52 Woodside Lane
> Boyertown, PA 19512
> (610) 369-1798

◆ **Military patches and other items from WWI and WWII.** "Premium items are patches, **pilot wings, painted leather jackets,** German ensignia, daggers, swords, **flags,** helmets and **medals.** Call or write me regarding what you want to sell. If you write, please include a photo with your description whenever possible." She says, "Being a female in this hobby is unusual, but you are encouraged to compare my prices with those of other buyers."

> Linda Canales
> PO Box 22
> Greendale, WI 53129
> (414) 529-7376   <ayli@wi.rr.com>

TONY'S TIP: Buyers agree that every single stain, scratch, tear, fold, crease, dent, chip, crack, fading, speck of rust, spatter of paint, or water damage makes an item less desirable to collectors. There is no such thing as "good for its age." It does not matter how old an item is. Damage is damage. A buyer needs to know what the damage is, where the damage is, and what is affected.

U.S. NAVY, MARINE CORPS & MARITIME SERVICES

◆ **Merchant Marine, Coast Guard and the U.S. Maritime Service with special emphasis on WWII** including photos, uniforms, medals, flags, discharge papers, etc.
>
> Harvey Lee Boswell, USMR Ret.
> PO Box 446
> Elm City, NC 27822

◆ **U.S. Navy memorabilia** including postcards, ship postmarks and documents, matchcovers, cruise books. Describe. Pricing appreciated.
>
> Frank Hoak III
> 59-541 Pueo Place
> Kohala Ranch
> Kamuela, HI 96743

◆ **U.S. Marine Corps everything.** Anything used and/or worn by Marines from 1776 to 1946, such as uniforms, medals, helmets and weapons. Also buys unit histories, documents and recruiting posters. Wants photos of Marines at war, work, or play, especially amateur photos. Also wants trench art created by Marines and souvenirs of war brought home by Marines. Tell what you can of the item's history.
>
> Bruce Updegrove
> 52 Woodside Lane
> Boyertown, PA 19512
> (610) 369-1798 eves

◆ **U.S. Marine Corps ephemera** including recruiting posters, other artwork, postcards, autographs, letters written by Marines, and "almost any" Marine related book, including signed books by or about Marines, personal memoirs, unit histories, campaign histories, biographies, fiction, juveniles, children's books and poetry. "I would especially like a set of monographs written by Marine Major Edwin McClellan in 1925, in book or mimeographed form." He is not interested in book club editions or in books "in questionable condition." To sell your Marine Corps books, give standard bibliographic information, including number of pages, size, and whether or not it has a dust jacket. This 10 year veteran distributes four catalogs a year of military books for sale. "If you are actually selling, give us a call, but we don't have time for casual inquiries or information seekers. Sorry."
>
> Stan Clark, Jr.
> Stan Clark Military Books
> 915 Fairview Avenue
> Gettysburg, PA 17325
> (717) 337-1728   fax (717) 337-0581
> <scmb@blazenet.net>

THE AIR WAR

◆ **Japanese and German pilots and planes.** "I buy all items related to Japanese and German wartime aviation and pilots including equipment, uniforms, float vests, boots, gloves, parachutes, etc. I'd especially like to find aircraft fuselage pieces with Japanese or German markings and airplane gauges, radios, and parts." Please don't contact him unless you are willing to sell what you have. This 20 year veteran collector pledges "a very nice purchase offer" if you're actually selling.

Stuart Tamaru
PO Box 1057
Huntington Beach, CA 92647
(800) 511-0583   (714) 846-0354   <dec_consulting@hotmail.com>

◆ **Army Air Force A2 flight jackets, AAF pocket insignia, sterling silver military aviation wings and WWI enlisted men's round collar discs.** Nothing later than the Korean War. "Please give a ballpark asking price for any item you offer."

Jerry Keohane
16 Saint Margaret's Court
Buffalo, NY 14216

TONY'S TIP: *"If the seller did not get the jacket from the veteran or his family, it is probably not old." In the world of military collecting, counterfeits abound. Patches, swords, knives, jackets and other items have all been faked.*

◆ **WWII aviation jackets, leather or cloth,** with squadron patch and or painted artwork on the back from any branch of the service. Needs all information on the jacket label, condition of both the jacket and the art, and what the art looks like. **All Flying Tigers information** is also wanted, including photos, diaries, nose art, patches, histories, etc.

Gary Hullfish
16 Gordon Avenue
Lawrenceville, NJ 08648
(609) 896-0224   fax (609) 896-2040   <lawfuel@aol.com>

◆ **Airplane identification models, 1940-1970.** Also promotional models, travel agency models, and squadron and bomb group unit histories. When writing, copy all info printed on the plane.

John Pochobradsky
1991 East Schodack Road
Castleton, NY 12033
(518) 477-9488

TANKS & HEAVY WEAPONS

◆ **Tanks, artillery, armored vehicles and machine guns and their parts and accessories.** "We are a Federally licensed machine gun manufacturer and dealer, and seek to buy registered operational machine guns and other military equipment, including muzzle loading cannon and *Gattling* guns. We buy machine gun parts and accessories including, but not limited to, barrels, buttstocks, magazines, clips, drums, bipods, tripods, mounts, loading machines, linkers, armorer's kits, etc. We are particularly interested in mounts for *Maxim* machine guns and will pay $150+ for them. We will buy most anything made in the 19th or 20th centuries. Parts and guns do not have to be in perfect condition. We will look at all items, but clear photos are a must. A VHS video is even better. Include dimensions and condition of accessories. Copies of any accompanying paperwork or manuals are helpful. If, after inspection, our offer is unacceptable, I will pay shipping both ways." I am not interested in toys, miniatures, stolen firearms or U.S. Army manuals about equipment or weapons.

 Greg Souchik
 T.M.P. Company
 PO Box 133
 Custer City, PA   16725
   (814) 362-2642   fax (814) 362-7356
   <director@armormuseum.com>

◆ **Half tracks, armored cars, tanks, *Gattling* guns, howitzers, and cannons,** especially a FT-17 *Renault* (M1917) tank in any condition. Larry will arrange for transporting what you have. Also wants:
- U.S. women's uniforms and accessories, WWI or WWII but only in fine condition;
- Hard hat diving equipment and related items including catalogs;
- *Mercedes Benz* 500K or 540K autos between 1930 and 1945;
- German military staff cars;
- Military aircraft from any country pre-1946.

Provide all the information printed on the machine's data plates. In most cases when you are trying to sell large equipment, a few photographs from different angles would be recommended.

 Larry Pitman
 Zanzibar War Museum
 5424 Bryan Station Road
 Paris, KY 40361
   (606) 299-5022   fax (606) 299-4522
   <zanzibar@qx.net>

THE HOME FRONT

◆ **MIA/POW bracelets stamped with the name and rank of a** soldier in Vietnam, and the date he was listed as missing in action or became a prisoner of war. Pays $8 each. Prefers to have the original certificate which came with the bracelet. Call or write before sending the bracelet.
> Judy Polk Harding
> 4347 Farm House Lane
> Fairfax, VA 22032
> (703) 503-7323   <thefivejs@aol.com>

◆ **Ration tokens.** Pays 2¢ each for red tokens, 3¢ each for blue. After the first 250, he pays 1¢ each. Pays "much more" for error tokens. Ship for his inspection and check.
> Rich Hartzog
> PO Box 4143 BVT
> Rockford, IL 61110

◆ **Patriotic embroidery.** "I want embroidered or hand stitched cotton or silk American or Confederate flags, patriotic or military themes, American eagles, and similar, especially turn of the century items with Marine Corps themes. Nothing made after 1960 is wanted, nor is anything with serious holes, tears, or insect damage." Photo is suggested.
> Stan Clark, Jr.
> 915 Fairview Avenue
> Gettysburg, PA 17325
> (717) 337-1728   fax (717) 337-0581   <scmb@blazenet.net>

◆ **Posters of WWI & WWII.** Include your phone number.
> George Theofiles, Miscellaneous Man
> PO Box 1776
> New Freedom, PA 17349
> (717) 235-4766 days

◆ **Posters from WWI and WWII.** Army recruiting posters by Christy or Flagg bring $500 to $1,500. No reproduction posters are wanted.
> George Dembo, The Poster Master
> PO Box 657
> Chatham, NJ 07928
> (973) 701-0713 voice/fax   <poster1776@aol.com>

◆ **American posters of WWI.** No foreign, repros, or damaged items. Give the main slogan, the size, the artist if known, and the condition.
> Ken Khuans
> 155 Harbor #4812
> Chicago, IL 60601
> (312) 642-0554

FOREIGN ARMIES

◆ **Napoleonic arms and armor.** This 30 year veteran collector/dealer in Western ephemera requires you to send a photo and complete description as well as your asking price. No fakes or reproductions of any kind are wanted.
>   Pierre Bovis
>   PO Box 5529
>   Santa Fe, NM 87502
>   (520) 318-9512   fax (520) 318-0023   <bovisp@hotmail.com>

◆ **Canadian military medals and cap badges.** "I'll buy all cap badges with the initials CEF on them, or badges with a number and the words overseas battalion and canada or canadian on them. I'll buy any war or period. Look for name, rank and military unit on the rims of medals as some are worth $1,000+." Answers all inquiries.
>   Michael Rice
>   PO Box 286
>   Saanichton, BC
>   V8M 2C5 CANADA
>   (604) 652-9412 evenings only. Please no day calls.
>   <mrice@pacificcoast.net>

◆ **Military items from the Coldstream Guards.** The museum wants to buy uniforms, equipment, badges, and miscellaneous items used by the British Coldstream Guards. Other British Army ephemera may be of interest. A full description includes dimensions, materials, and age. Indicate anything you believe to be unique. Donations acknowledged. No U.S. items are wanted.
>   Ernest Klapmeier
>   Coldstream Guards Living History Museum
>   83 South La Salle Street
>   Aurora, IL 60505
>   (630) 801-1696 voice/fax

◆ **WWII German militaria.** Buys a wide range of items, but has a special interest in swords, daggers, insignia, uniforms, etc. Less interest in paper items. Please describe what you have carefully and completely giving all dimensions and marks.
>   Ken Konet
>   4 Hortense Place
>   St. Louis, MO 63108
>   (314) 361-7975   fax (314) 361-7982

◆ **French or British military forces overseas, British Indian Native States forces, Spanish or French Foreign Legion, Abraham Lincoln Brigade, Camel Corps, Free French and Vichy forces, French forces in China, Devil's Island, White Russian forces, Chinese Customs Service, Chinese bandits or pirates, China Navigation Company, international settlements in China, Chinese airlines, and similar topics.** Wants badges, banners, medals, photos, certificates, souvenirs, etc. Material about American volunteers or famous soldiers of fortune of any nationality is particularly welcome. No repros of Devil's Island folk art or souvenirs produced by the Foreign Legion Veteran's Home.

> Gene Christian
> 3849 Bailey Avenue
> Bronx, NY 10463
> (718) 548-0243

◆ **Nazi notables especially Heinrich Himmler,** commander of the SS and Gestapo. Wants items given by or to Hitler, Goering, Goebbles, Hess, etc., including promotion and award documents, letters, trophies, uniforms or medals. "I am generally not interested in any item you or a member of your family did not personally bring back from overseas." He prefers you to write, describe what you have, make a photocopy, and include your phone number and an SASE.

> Thomas Pooler
> PO Box 1861
> Grass Valley, CA 95945
> (530) 268-1338

◆ **German war memorabilia from WW I and WW II.** Buys edged weapons and selected other quality items of German war memorabilia. He is not interested in reproductions or in "lesser condition" items. Please send a photo, sketch, or photocopy. He requests you set the price you have in mind, but will make offers to amateurs who are selling. Send $7 for one of his catalogs of items for sale. For $28 you can subscribe to his quarterly newsletter on military collecting. **Johnson is an internationally known appraiser and author of fourteen books** (send for his catalog). "Our firm offers the largest selection of Imperial and Third Reich swords and daggers in the world."

> LTC (ret) Thomas Johnson
> Johnson Reference Books
> Chatham Square Office Park #403
> Fredericksburg, VA 22405
> (540) 373-9150   fax (540) 373-0087
> <ww2daggers@aol.com>

◆ **German, Japanese, and Italian military wanted,** especially daggers and dagger parts, swords, medals, badges, spike helmets, flagpole tops, etc. Pays $50 up for German WWII helmets complete with liner. "I will also buy flags, but the bigger the flag, the less they're worth. You may write, giving me your phone number. Take a photo or send insured for cash offer." This is a hobby for Dick, so he says that he's happy to help people if they send him an SASE. Makes offers only on items for sale. Also interested in U.S. military patches.

     Dick Pankowski
     PO Box 22
     Greendale, WI 53129
     (414) 529-7376   fax (414) 529-7449   <warsouvenirs@wi.rr.com>

◆ **Japanese and German WWII military items** including swords, guns, daggers, medals, helmets, field caps, hats, field equipment, all uniforms and footwear, camouflage netting, diaries, insignia, maps, photos.,,you name it. If you intend to sell, send this 20 year veteran collector a brief description along with your phone number and address.

     Stuart Tamaru
     PO Box 1057
     Huntington Beach, CA 92647
     (800) 511-0583   (714) 846-0354 <dec_consulting@hotmail.com>

◆ **German and Italian WWII military items** including flags, swords, guns, daggers, medals, helmets, field caps, hats, insignia, uniforms and footwear, belt buckles, diaries, maps, photos, you name it. "**I also buy items from European collaborator countries such as Hungary, Slovakia, Croatia, etc.** I particularly enjoy buying from the family of the vet who brought the item back." If you intend to sell, send this 19 year veteran buyer a good description along with your phone number and address. Indicate how much of the original paint remains on painted surfaces. Describe whether blades show evidence of rust or sharpening? "I don't want reproductions but will sometimes buy items in poor condition if priced accordingly. Many items have been faked, and some fakes are quite good."

     John Telesmanich
     PO Box 62
     East White Plains, NY 10604
           (914) 949-5519   <militarybuyer@aol.com>

TONY'S TIP: As a general rule, don't clean your souvenirs. Amateur cleaning can turn a $300 item into scrap. Let the experts decide what they want to clean and not.

SWORDS & KNIVES

★ **Japanese swords and daggers, fighting issue or dress type.** He prefers to buy directly from the veteran or family, and wants information about your weapon's history. This 25 year expert appraiser offers free appraisals of all edged weapons to private parties.

> Hank McGonagle
> 26 Broad Street
> Newburyport, MA 01950
> (978) 462-2354   <saber12@attbi.com>

◆ **Japanese swords, daggers, spears, armor and other Samurai items,** especially fine swords and daggers, and sword and dagger parts. Ron will send you a checklist to help you describe a sword for sale. An SASE is appreciated. Please photograph your sword laying alongside its scabbard. Ron is an internationally known collector who has been studying Japanese swords for twenty years. He will be pleased to determine the quality of your sword and to make you an offer for it. No other guns, bayonets, or non-Japanese swords and daggers are wanted.

> Ron Hartmann
> 5907 Deerwood Drive
> St. Louis, MO 63123
> (314) 832-3477   <swords@usroute66.net>

◆ **Japanese swords.** A brief description is adequate. Give the length of the sword's blade as part of your description. "I am more than happy to discuss prices with people who contact me with items they intend to sell. I would like to avoid callers who are just trying to find out what something is worth. If you're actually selling, I'll make a very nice purchase offer."

> Stuart Tamaru
> PO Box 1057
> Huntington Beach, CA 92647
> (800) 511-0583   (714) 846-0354
> <dec_consulting@hotmail.com>

TONY'S TIP: If a Japanese sword has a 26 1/2" blade and has serial numbers it is probably an enlisted man's sword from WWII and worth around $100 or so.
One reader discovered that the sword on her rec room wall was from the 13th century and worth over $10,000. Another bought a sword at a yard sale for $100 and resold it to one of these buyers for $5,000.

★ **U.S. and German swords, bayonets and daggers, fighting issue or dress type.** Other countries also purchased. He prefers to buy directly from the veteran or family, and wants information about your weapon's history. This 25 year expert appraiser offers free appraisals of all military swords and edged weapons to private parties.
>
> Hank McGonagle
> 26 Broad Street
> Newburyport, MA 01950
> (978) 462-2354   \<saber12@attbi.com\>

◆ **American swords and large knives from before 1900.** Please describe thoroughly, including any numbers or writing found on the weapon. Photocopy the knife and of the sword handle if you can. Otherwise photograph it or make a good sketch. No fraternal, lodge or ceremonial swords, please. SASE requested. "I do not make offers."
>
> Charles Worman
> PO Box 292624)
> Kettering, OH 45429
> (937) 299-7752   \<oldguns@aol.com\>

◆ **British and American military knives from WWI and WWII** especially British Commando daggers, *Wilkinson Sword* fighting knives (marked FS FIGHTING KNIFE), and American special unit fighting knives. Value ranges from $50 to $1,500 depending on rarity, condition and its scabbard. It is very important for you to copy every word and symbol on the blade, handle, guard, and scabbard. John does not want bayonets that attach to the end of a rifle.
>
> John Fischer
> PO Box 47
> Van Nuys, CA 91408
> (310) 474-2567   (818) 902-1375   \<jsfischer1@aol.com\>

◆ **German swords, knives, daggers, and bayonets from WW I and WW II.** Also buys selected other quality items of German war memorabilia. He DOES NOT BUY reproductions or in "lesser condition" items. Please send a photo, sketch, or photocopy. He requests you set the price you have in mind, but will offer to amateurs who are selling. Send $7 if you'd like one of his catalogs of items for sale. For $28 you can subscribe to his quarterly newsletter on military collecting and collectibles worldwide. Johnson is an internationally known appraiser, author of eighteen books on edged weapons, and can provide you a catalog of available reference books. Visit him for a huge computerized selection of quality goods for sale.
>
> LTC (ret) Thomas Johnson
> Chatham Square Office Park #403
> Fredericksburg, VA 22405
> (540) 373-9150   fax (540) 373-0087   \<ww2daggers@aol.com\>

Continued from page 363

I have had similar experiences. Three different people sent Sell-A-Grams, offering me cigar boxes, my specialty. They each turned down offers of $40, $400 and $500 and listed the boxes on ebay. I won the three auctions for $5, $260, and $450, so all three lost money.

What is ebay best for? That's hard to say. Each field is very different. Each week is different. I bought an item on ebay in March of 2001 for $34. An identical item sold three months later on ebay for $1,700. What's it worth? Yesterday I bought an item on ebay for $16 to my absolute delight. Had the seller contacted me, I would have gladly sent my check for $75. In my opinion, ebay is best for the stuff you can't sell privately.

I LOVE EBAY. But I'm a buyer, not a seller. When I sell high quality items, I offer what I have to buyers in **Trash or Treasure Guide to the Best Buyers** or to other private parties.

In four years I've sorted through millions of one-sentence-long ebay descriptions, looked at around 25,000 of them, bid on about 3,000 and bought more than 1,000 items at auction on ebay, the vast majority of them at bargain prices far under what I would have paid someone who offered the item to me by mail.

As I nightly rush through ebay's "for sale" listings I am amazed at the number of sellers who shoot themselves in the foot, losing bidders and money because they don't understand what serious bidders need. Top value items in any hobby have only a small handful of people willing to bid strongly. If you lose them, you lose money.

Selling on ebay is actually quite simple as ebay leads newcomers through the process step-by-step. There are also companies and programs that can be a big help to the beginning seller. It isn't my goal here to teach you how to sell on ebay. There are entire books devoted to that topic. But because I've spent more than an hour a day for four and a half years buying on ebay, I do know, from the buyer's perspective, there are many things you can do to increase your odds of getting a decent price for what you have. Turn to page to page 517 for ten strategies to follow if you do decide to offer something on ebay.

Continued on page 517

TONY'S TIPS ON HOW TO FIND OUT IF YOUR OLD COINS AND BILLS ARE AS VALUABLE AS YOU HOPE

Everyone seems to have old coins or bills tucked away in a drawer. Now is the time to find out if you have something good to cash in. I've got some fine folks from the world of collectible money standing by to help you. These tips can help, too.

*Valuable coins and bills exist, and they do turn up in strange places on occasion, but **your bills and coins will probably not have collectors panting.** Since some unusual things do have value, including a few foreign bills, it might be worth your while to check out what you have.*

__Photocopying makes it possible to check the value of your money easily and quickly.__ If inquiring about modern currency, it is important to note the color of the Treasury seal to the right of the portrait on the face of each bill. Colors can be blue, green, red, brown, gold, or yellow. Value differs by color.

__If you want an idea of your coins' value without anyone knowing what you have, it's easy to do.__ Use "A Guide Book of United States Coins" by R.S. Yoeman. Called "The Red Book" it gives average selling prices of coins. Yoeman's "Handbook of U.S. Coins" ("The Blue Book") gives prices dealers pay for coins. These can be borrowed from most libraries. If you own anything that catalogs over $50, get expert advice. Coins valued under $10 will find few takers.

__Amateur sellers overestimate condition.__ Yoeman's books contain information you should read about coin grading, because amateurs over-estimate condition of coins and bills. Buyers will grade severely. A spot of wear at the tip of an eagle wing can cost 50% of a coin's value.

The coin world has attracted more than its share of shady characters. __Never sell coins, watches or jewelry to someone buying out of a motel room.__ You get much less than you would from well-established dealers. Deal with folks in here instead.

COINS & PAPER MONEY

◆ **Coins and antiquities,** especially Biblical, Greek, and Roman. Ancient artifacts including Egyptian, Greek, Roman, and Biblical pottery, glass and relics. Nothing made after 1000AD is wanted. This 20 year veteran collector wrote Guide to Ancient Jewish Coins and other books, and issues periodic catalogs of relics for sale. He does not buy prints, rugs, weavings, or drawings of Biblical topics. He does not want reproductions, pictures, or drawings. Ancient artifacts only.
David Hendin
Amphora
PO Box 805
Nyack, NY 10960   <amphoradh@aol.com>

◆ **Spanish pieces of eight.** Wants reales minted in Spanish or South American mints dated between 1732 and 1772. Seeks coins with globe and pillars on one side and shield and crown on the other. No pitted shipwreck coins. All coins must be shipped for examination before offers can be made as there are many reproductions. Postage both ways is the responsibility of the seller.
Sven Stau
181 Crestmount Court #3
Tonawanda, NY 14150
(716) 693-4011   <svenstau@cs.com>

◆ **Coins and currency** as well as other collectibles are handled by this well known auction firm. If you have large collections of any collectible to dispose of, give them a call. Ultimately, as will all coin buyers, you will be required to ship your items for inspection prior to any agreement for auction or purchase.
Kurt Krueger
Krueger Auctions
PO Box 275
Iola, WI 54945
(715) 445-3845   fax (715) 445-4100

◆ **Coins and currency.** This rare coin auctioneer holds auctions at major coin shows and holds internet auctions on your behalf. More interested in estates and collections than single coins. As with other coin dealers, you will be required to ship your items for inspection prior to any agreement for auction or purchase.
James Halperin
Heritage Rare Coin Galleries
Heritage Park
100 Highland Park Village, 2nd Floor
Dallas, TX 75205
(800) 872-6467   fax (214) 520-7108   <jim@heritagecoin.com>

◆ **Paper money.** "We'll buy any foreign and obsolete U.S. and Confederate banknotes. We will buy currency in any condition and quantity in order to supply fellow collectors in all parts of the world. We deal by mail only but telephone calls are welcomed. We will buy collections as well as single notes, but we do not want U.S. currency after 1928." A description should include the date, denomination, and the country of issue. A photocopy is the best way to describe currency. With his available research library, he is "able to identify and appraise any banknote ever issued."

> Josef Klaus
> World Wide Notaphilic Service
> PO Box 5427
> Vallejo, CA 94591
> free (877) 668-3988   (707) 644-3146   fax (707) 643-3806

◆ **Coins or paper currency from anywhere** especially silver or gold.

> Dr. Robert Hiett
> Maple City Coin
> PO Box 47
> Monmouth, IL 61462
> (309) 734-3212   fax (309) 734-8083   <hiett@gallatinriver.net>

◆ **Coin collections of all types,** "from pennies to gold." Also individual gold coins, medals, and artifacts. Also pre-1930 U.S. banknotes and commemorative coins. No pennies after 1955, nickels after 1939, dimes, quarters, and halves after 1964, or silver dollars after 1936.

> Ron Aldridge
> 250 Canyon Oaks Drive
> Argyle, TX 76226
> (940) 455-2519 eves   fax (940) 455-5094   <noacman@aol.com>

◆ **Paper money.** "I buy all U.S. paper money issued before 1929, all Confederate money and all broken bank notes from any state. I especially want **items made of ground up paper money,** and will pay 60% of retail. I recommend making photocopies of bills you'd like to sell."

> William Skelton, Highland's Vault
> PO Box 55448
> Birmingham, AL 35255
>   (205) 939-3166 ext 3   (205) 939-1178

◆ **All foreign paper money.** "I'll buy collections, accumulations, dealer's stock, hoards, rarities, German inflation currency, specimens, printer's proofs, banknote presentations, sample books and entire numismatic libraries." Will travel. Has been buying since 1964.

> AMCASE
> PO Box 5473
> Akron, OH 44334
>   (330) 867-6724   <eluck@neo.rr.com>

◆ **U.S. Coins and paper money.** Wants estates, collections and accumulations of early U.S. silver and gold coins, paper money, and all other U.S. coins from 1793-1900. This nationally known dealer has been around for 40 years, and will travel to see large lots and better collections. Send a list and description. Photocopy suggested.

> Littleton Coin Co., THCC
> 253 Union Street
> Littleton, NH 03561
> (603) 444-5386

◆ **Coins and paper money from the U.S.** from before 1965. Give the denomination, date and mint mark. This 30 year veteran especially seeks gold from rare mints. Dennis is a contributor to Yoeman's *Guidebook of United States Coins*, a highly recommended book for you to look up what you have and help you describe condition.

> Dennis Gillio, Gabelow & Albarian Rare Coins
> 10113 Riverside Drive
> Toluca Lake, CA 91602
> (818) 985-3900 days   (818) 563-9234 eves
> fax (818) 762-6717   <gilliocoin@aol.com>

◆ **Coin collections or single rarities.** This prestigious long time established auction firm seeks high quality coin collections. If you know of a large fine quality collection which is for sale, call them and they will pay you a fee if they obtain the collection.

> Harvey & Lawrence Stack, Stack's
> 123 West 57th Street
> New York, NY 10019
> (212) 582-2580   <info@stacks.com>

◆ **Rare currency (paper money), both foreign and U.S.** He is particularly expert in **California currency, national currency and Mexican currency.** He DOES NOT WANT items after 1935 or any kind of reproduction. A photocopy (Xerox©) of both sides of the bills will often do, but "I'll usually ask to see the item in person before making an offer."

> Lowell Horwedel
> PO Box 2395
> West Lafayette, IN 47996
> (765) 583-2748   fax (765) 583-4584
> <Lhorwedel@insightbb.com>   <horwedelscurrency.com>

◆ **Red coin books printed before 1954.**

> James Williams
> 342 South Garnet Lake Road
> Warrensburg, NY 12885
> (518) 623-2831

◆ **Items made from macerated (ground up) currency by the mint,** including statues, plaques, postcards, shoes, hats, etc., which have a small tag reading, this item made of us greenbacks redeemed and macerated by the us government. Describe damage carefully.

> Donald Gorlick
> PO Box 24541
> Seattle, WA 98124
> (206) 824-0508

ERROR COINS & ELONGATES

◆ **Mis-strike and error coins and currency** created by the U.S. Mint. Under most circumstances, it is best to send a good clear pencil rubbing or photocopy for evaluation if you wish an offer. Also paper currency issued before 1930. Include photocopy and SASE for free appraisal.

> Neil Osina
> Best Variety Coin Center
> 358 West Foothill Blvd.
> Glendora, CA 91741
> (626) 914-2273

◆ **Elongated coins dated before 1960.** Also buys the machines and the dies to make them. "I'll pay well for scarce items I want."

> C.J. "Gus" Meccarello
> Elongated Coin Museum
> 1572 Bowmans Trail
> Lakeland, FL 33809

◆ **Elongated coins.** If what you have is pre-1930, ship it for an offer, but do not ship COD. Hartzog pays $1-$5 and up for elongates before 1940. Large collections especially wanted.

> Rich Hartzog
> PO Box 4143 BVT
> Rockford, IL 61110
> <hartzog@exonumia.com>

COUNTERFEITING DEVICES

◆ **Coin scales and anything used to detect counterfeit money, coins or currency,** including coin detectors, scanners, grids, magnifiers, *Detectographs* and other devices to check weight, thickness or diameter of coins. Also any scale with markings in amounts, such as "20 dol., 10 dol., 5 dol." Names to look for: *Ewing, Herpers, Fairbanks, McNalley, MBT, Rice, Statler, Meyers* among many others.

> Donald Gorlick
> PO Box 24541
> Seattle, WA 98124
> (206) 824-0508

TONY'S TIP: Coin scales do not have pans or weights like a gold scale. They do have some method of weighing a coin, and another for testing thickness.

◆ **Coin scales, coin detectors, and counterfeit detectors.** Will buy the devices and/or books about them and the processes of counterfeiting and counterfeit detecting. Buys items outright or may accept on consignment for auction.
>Rich Hartzog
>PO Box 4143 BVT
>Rockford, IL 61110

(815) 226-0771   fax (815) 397-7662   <hartzog@exonumia.com>

CREDIT CARDS

◆ **Credit cards from any source, paper or plastic,** are desired. "Send items for immediate offer and check. I pay postage both ways."
>Noel Levy
>1109 Silentglade Road
>Owings Mills, MD 21117
>(410) 363-9040

◆ **Credit cards.** "I'll pay a flat $2 each for credit cards, charge plates, and charge coins made of celluloid, metal, paper or plastic, U.S. or foreign, as long as they are not abused. Ship the cards you have for my prompt payment." ATM and sample credit cards are worth very little, about 25¢ each, if that.
>Lin Overholt
>PO Box 8481
>Madeira Beach, FL 33738
>(727) 393-5397   <axvisamc@aol.com>

◆ **Credit cards.** "I've collected credit cards for over ten years and am seriously interested in buying both the older metal charge cards and modern plastic cards. Please ship any quantity of used or new cards. I pay $4 up for older metal charge cards and will pay at least $15 for any metal one I need for my own collection. Pre-1980 plastic cards bring $1 up, and those before 1970 average $2. More paid for local businesses, unusual types, etc. Post-1980 cards are worth 50¢ each, a few bring more. I also reimburse your postage if you ship for my check."
>Rich Hartzog
>PO Box 4143 BVT
>Rockford, IL 61110

(815) 226-0771   fax (815) 397-7662   <hartzog@exonumia.com>

STOCKS, BONDS & FISCAL PAPER

★ **Stocks and bonds of all types and in any quantity.** Especially interested in railroad, mining, telegraph, and circus but buy other topics as well. They don't need important autographs to be purchased. Prices range from zero to hundreds of dollars. "I'm not interested in modern stocks and don't buy items that are widely available in the trade. Tell me the date and place of issue and describe any pictures on the stock. Condition is important. Photocopy very helpful." Author of *Treasury of Mining Stocks from the Nevada Territory, 1861-64* ($27 postpaid) and *Mining Stocks & Bonds*, a 16 page pamphlet for $3.
>   Frank Hammelbacher
>   Norrico Inc.
>   PO Box 660077
>   Flushing, NY 11366
> (718) 380-4009   fax (718) 380-9793   <norrico@nyc.rr.com>

◆ **Stocks and bonds from around the world issued before 1930,** especially ornate 19th century transportation or mining certificates. Please send a Xerox© copy of what you wish to sell. This 30 year veteran stock expert cautions, "It is important that you not sell uncancelled certificates issued in your own name or in a family member's name without first having us check their value. These certificates could be worth much more if the company has changed names or left assets when it was liquidated. There are billions of dollars waiting to be claimed by people who believe their stocks are worthless."
>   Pierre Bonneau
>   Stock Search International
>   4761 West Waterbuck Drive
>   Tucson, AZ 85742
>   (800) 537-4523   fax (520) 579-5639
>   <ssi@stocksearchintl.com>

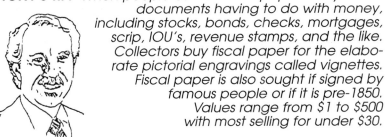

TONY'S TIP: *When people ask for "fiscal paper" they mean documents having to do with money, including stocks, bonds, checks, mortgages, scrip, IOU's, revenue stamps, and the like. Collectors buy fiscal paper for the elaborate pictorial engravings called vignettes. Fiscal paper is also sought if signed by famous people or if it is pre-1850. Values range from $1 to $500 with most selling for under $30.*

◆ **Elaborately illustrated stocks and bonds.** All are wanted but have particular need for pre-1920 railroads, mining, telegraph, aviation, oil, and automobiles. Also stocks from unusual companies like a maker of life rafts. Items pre-1870 given special consideration. Especially want Western paper with autographs of important people like Rockefeller, Carnegie, Gould, James Hill, U.S. Presidents, and other recognizable people. "Send a photocopy and an SASE for fast payment."
David Beach's Paper Americana
PO Box 471356
Lake Monroe, FL 32747
      (407) 657-7403   fax (407) 688-7495
      <dbeach@cigarboxlabels.com>

◆ **Stocks and bonds,** especially decorative stocks from pre-1900 railroads and gold mines. "Although these are our main areas of interest, we would like to see photocopies of any and all stocks and bonds that you might have, and will promptly give you a free appraisal/offer." Generally, nothing after 1940 unless you have 5,000 or more of them.
Richard Urmston
Centennial Documents
PO Box 5262
Clinton, NJ 08809
      (908) 730-6009   <centdocs@ptd.net>

◆ **Stocks and bonds issued in the United States before 1910,** especially mining, railroads, or unusual companies. "I am not interested in stocks that were never issued and are unsigned. Stocks and bonds must have an original company seal."
Phyllis Barrella
Buttonwood Galleries
3082 Eger Place
New York, NY 10465
      (718) 828-0649   <chickigram@aol.com>

◆ **Printed or manuscript items relating to coins, currency, medals, tokens, or counterfeiting.** Especially scholarly **books** on coins from any period or language. Also numismatic periodicals and catalogs of coin auctions pre-1940 in any language. Also **counterfeit detectors** and bank note reporters issued in the U.S., 1820 - 1900. No modern works or general surveys of numismatics. Makes offers on better items. **George Kolbe DOES NOT buy coins.**
George Frederick Kolbe
PO Drawer 3100
Crestline, CA 92325
      (909) 338-6527   fax (909) 338-6980
<numislit@compuserve.com>   <www.numislit.com>

◆ **Fiscal paper including checks, stocks and bonds, certificates of deposit, books on money, and other fiscal paper.** He also buys rare **currency (paper money)**, both foreign and U.S. He is particularly expert in California currency, national currency and Mexican currency. He DOES NOT WANT items after 1935 or any kind of reproduction. A photocopy (Xerox©) will often do, but "I'll usually ask to see the item in person before making an offer.

Lowell Horwedel
PO Box 2395
West Lafayette, IN 47996
(765) 583-2748   fax (765) 583-4584
<Lhorwedel@insightbb.com>   <horwedelscurrency.com>

◆ **U.S. stocks and bonds, issued before 1930,** especially mining, railroads, energy and automobiles. Signed, illustrated, used documents are desired, with premium paid for Western items before the Civil War with interesting vignettes. Plain items are not of interest unless before 1850 or signed by someone famous. Send Xerox™ of what you have. His six sales catalogs he issues each year cost $15.

Warren Anderson
America West Archives
PO Box 100
Cedar City, UT 84720
(435) 586-9497   (435) 867-8078
<awa@netutah.com>

◆ **U.S. and Canadian stocks and bonds,** especially railroads, mining, oil, shipping, automotive, aviation, expositions, and others. Also stocks or bonds signed or owned by someone famous. Also seeks documents with a printed revenue stamp. This past president of the Bond & Share Society also wants all pre-1800 certificates from any company.

Bob Kluge
American Vignettes
PO Box 155
Roselle Park, NJ 07204
(908) 241-4209 voice/fax

◆ **Fiscal paper from South Carolina before 1910,** especially from the city of Charleston.

Bob Karrer
17 Wentworth Street
Charleston, SC 29401
(843) 577-7876   <bkarrer@awod.com>

TONY'S TIPS ON SELLING TOKENS & MEDALS

Collecting tokens is popular because they are inexpensive. Most retail for 25¢ to $3. **Have an expert look at your tokens as a few are worth $500.** *Tokens are difficult to evaluate on your own because more than 300 books are in print about tokens and tiny differences can mean a lot. The following definitions should help you describe "a little round thing" to a potential buyer.*

Coins *are money issued by governments. Most modern coins contain the name of the issuing country, the denomination, and the date of issue.*

Exonumia *means all coin-like objects that aren't money. It refers primarily to tokens, but has come to include medals, orders, decorations, plaques, awards, ribbons, and the like. Dealers of exonumia often sell advertising mirrors (they were frequently trade tokens) and other small collectibles as well.*

Tokens *are money substitutes, often marked with a value, such as "Good for 5¢ in trade." Tokens were issued by local businesses usually for advertising. Sometimes they were issued because no legal coinage was available.*

Medals *are "any piece of metal marked with a design or inscription, made to honor a person, place or event," according to one of our buyers. Medals vary in size and shape, although most are round. Medals larger than 3" in diameter are usually called* **medallions.** *Small rectangular medals are called* **plaquettes** *and larger ones, meant to hang on the wall, are* **plaques.**

Orders *and decorations are an important separate category, generally related to diplomacy and the military. They are often worn around the neck or on sashes across the wearer's breast.*

Military medals *are emblems of honor normally made with ribbons so they can be worn.* **Badges** *have a top pin or device, with or without a ribbon, so they too can be worn. Both usually have a medallic device hanging from them (what amateurs think of when someone says "medals").*

Ribbons *are commemorative items, printed with information about the event commemorated. They are usually associated with lodges, fraternal organizations, conventions, and the like.*

Whichever one of these you have, make a pencil rubbing or a photocopy and let the buyers tell you exactly what you own and what they'll pay. Buyers of just about anything will also be interested in medals and tokens related to their specialty.

TOKENS & MEDALS

◆ **All types and quantities of tokens, medals, ribbons, badges, and related items.** Some old tokens are common, but others can be worth $1,500+ each if they picture a ship, trolley, horse car, ferry, or stage coach. Look for the words Depotel, Baggage, Hotel, Omnibus, Drayage, Depot to hotel, and similar wordings. He buys trade tokens, medals of all sort, hard times tokens, Civil War tokens, transportation and toll tokens especially with pictures on them, amusement tokens, telephone tokens, sales tax tokens, any token or medal made from another item, medals related to medicine or the arts and humanities, love tokens, World's Fair medals and elongated coins, G.A.R. badges and tokens, Indian peace medals ($1,500 up), slave tags, Canadian tokens and medals, military awards and medals, counterstamped coins, and just about everything similar to the above including advertising mirrors and Franklin Mint token sets. There are millions of varieties, and condition plays an important role in value. If what you have is pre-1930, simply ship it to him for an offer, but do not ship COD. Hartzog will send you a check for the lot. "We cannot make individual offers on a long list of material. Our offers are for the entire lot as we want to purchase everything. We are not interested in pricing your material for you to sell to others, sorry!" He claims to pay higher prices than anyone else. If your collection is very early, very large, or very valuable, phone collect and Hartzog will make arrangements to see what you have. Hartzog can auction your materials for you if you prefer. A sample of his auction catalog is available for $3. Hartzog's lengthy wants list shows prices and is recommended.

Also Franklin Mint and other private mint issues. "I will purchase all bronze, silver and gold singles, sets and other items such as plates, bronzes, etc., in any quantity. Many silver or gold pieces are worth substantially above issue price. Bronze tokens and medals are worth less than their issue price, most of them under 25¢ apiece. I pay reasonable prices for all modern mint items. Since I do not specialize in Franklin Mint items, do not ship them without inquiring first. State the price you want, or request my offer. If my offer is not accepted, I do not pay return postage on modern mint medals that have been shipped." **There is little market for Franklin Mint** items, so it's best to contact Rich first by phone or letter so you fully understand their value or lack of it.

Rich Hartzog
World Exonumia
PO Box 4143 BVT
Rockford, IL 61110
(815) 226-0771   <hartzog@exonumia.com>

◆ **Tokens and medals of all kinds and countries** including transportation tokens, advertising tokens, gambling tokens, merchants' good for tokens and the like. All old coin-like items are purchased as well as related items such as elongated or encased coins, engraved coins, pre-1900 dog licenses, advertising pocket mirrors, political buttons, and stage or movie money. Steve pays $10 to $250 for old original hobo nickels (buffalo nickels with the Indian head reengraved into another face). Award and commemorative medals from Fairs are also wanted. Photocopies are usually the best way to describe what you have. No large modern fantasy tokens are wanted. No Franklin Mint medals. No modern arcade tokens. Steve runs mail auctions of tokens and medals and has written books on amusement tokens, U.S.A. tokens, Scouting tokens and lucky souvenir coins, all available from the author at very reasonable prices.

Stephen Alpert
PO Box 66331
Los Angeles, CA 90066
(310) 836-2482   fax (3120) 836-5691   <quadra@pacbell.net>

◆ **Transportation or toll tokens for bridges, toll roads, ferries, horsecars, depot hacks, and early streetcars.** Tokens must be made of metal or plastic. Cardboard tokens are wanted only if round, not square or rectangular. Hotel to depot or transfer line tokens are worth $25-$100, more if pictorial. A token reading "I Gibbs Belleville & New York USM stage//Good for one ride to the bearer" would be worth $1,500 in nice condition.

Rev. John Coffee
PO Box 1204
Boston, MA 02104
(617) 277-8111

◆ **Medals and medallions from Canada, Britain, and other English speaking countries issued for coronations, jubilees, town celebrations, victories, fraternal groups, achievement, athletics, and especially military valor medals awarded to Canadians.** Also love tokens engraved with names, initials, dates, pledges, and the like from around the world especially pre-1900. Also merchant's good for trade tokens from Canada, Britain and English speaking countries. Also buys Canadian paper money dating before 1937, singles or collections.

Michael Rice
PO Box 286
Saanichton, BC
V8M 2C5 CANADA
(250) 652-9412 eves and weekends only
<mrice@pacificcoast.net>

★ **U.S. medals of all kinds particularly historical, art and award medals** of the 19th and early 20th century. This 25 year veteran offers $4,000 for the Teddy Roosevelt inaugural medal by Saint Gaudens and $2,000 up for silver Indian peace medals. Bronze Indian Peace medals are also purchased but are worth substantially less in most cases.

> H. Joseph Levine
> Presidential Coin & Antique Co.
> 6550-I Little River Turnpike
> Alexandria, VA 22312
>> (703) 354-5454   (703) 914-0547
>> <jlevine962@aol.com>

◆ **U.S., British, and Soviet valor decorations and war medals.** Foreign awards given to Americans are of great interest, especially Soviet World War II orders and decorations. All items must have supporting documentation of the award to U.S. personnel. Hlinka also buys all letters, certificates, or documents pertaining to valor awards. He asks you to photocopy both sides of medals and supporting paperwork. Hlinka has been dealing in medals for 40 years.

> Peter Hlinka
> PO Box 310
> New York, NY 10028
>> (727) 217-4823

◆ **Medals, decorations, and orders, especially military gallantry awards from U.S. and England,** but will consider all governmental awards from any Western nation. No Asian awards, please.

> Alan Harrow
> 2292 Chelan Drive
> Los Angeles, CA 90068
>> (323) 874-3474   <genoff@webtv.net>

◆ **Indian War medals, badges and awards issued by the U.S. government, states, or veteran's groups.** An Indian scout's Medal of Honor can be worth $20,000. Other items from $100 to $10,000. "No offers based on phone calls or photos. Items must be seen. Ship insured with record of delivery. Your postage will be reimbursed."

> Thomas Pooler
> PO Box 1861
> Grass Valley, CA 95949
>> (530) 268-1338

◆ **Medals commemorating or depicting Black Americans.** "I'll buy medals, medallions, badges, or tokens relating to, or depicting, Afro-Americans or including the words "negro," "colored" or "Black-American." Items may be positive or negative in tone. I'll pay $1,200 for the Franklin Mint set of 70 American Negro Commemorative Society medals." Tell him the material (silver, bronze, or aluminum), the size in millimeters, and inscriptions on both sides.

Elijah Singley
2301 Noble Avenue
Springfield, IL 62704
(217) 546-5143 eve   (217) 786-2251   <greenriver1899@yahoo.com>

◆ **Animal rescue, heroism, school attendance or truant officer's medals, badges and certificates.**

Gene Christian
3849 Bailey Avenue
Bronx, NY 10463
(718) 548-0243

◆ **Tokens, medals, and exonumia (non-money coinage) from Georgia** including "good for" tokens, encased and elongated coins, advertising and commemorative medals and tokens, including those issued for the 1895 Atlanta Cotton States Exposition, and any agriculture awards and medals from Georgia state fairs, the earlier the better.

R.W. Colbert
4156 Livsey Road
Tucker, GA 30084
(770) 938-2596   <rwc391@yahoo.com>

◆ **Wooden money.** First used in 1931, it comes in two forms, flat like bills and round like coins. Round pieces from civic celebrations bring 10¢ to $5. *Sambo's* and *McDonald's* bring 25¢ to $1.50 (but only if they have the city printed on the coin). Flat money from Tenino, WA, is $35 to $50, while other flat pieces bring $1 to $35. Please send a photocopy of your money and SASE for an appraisal. Boughton is the author of two books on wooden money of NY state (both for $7).

Norm Boughton
PO Box 1
Macedon, NY 14502
(315) 986-3851   <nbought1@rochester.rr.com>

◆ **Wooden money and exonumia.** "I buy medals, plaques, political tokens, advertising tokens checkers, badges and other money-like items made from stamped and printed wood. Please send a Xerox© copy."

Donald Tritt
81 Donald Ross Drive
Granville, OH 43023
(740) 587-0213   <tritt@denison.edu

TONY'S TIPS ON SELLING STAMPS

Only a few 20th century U.S. stamps have substantial value, but stamped and unstamped envelopes and letters dating before 1910 may be worth hundreds of dollars! Value is affected by the stamp, the cancellation, the carriers, and where it was mailed from and to.

Buyers of early letters are often interested in postmarks. Examine them with an eye toward historic places, vanished cities, and unusual cancellations as on board a riverboat, airplane, or military ship. Canadian buyer Mike Rice tells of a U.S. antique dealer who sent him two items and a bill for only $4. "If that dealer had taken your advice and asked me to make an offer, I'd have paid $300 for them. The postcard she sent me has the only known cancellation from a post office that was only open for a few months in 1912."

Empty envelopes sell, but an enclosed letter with interesting contents will add to the value. Decorated stamped envelopes sell too. Condition is crucial, although envelopes that have been opened messily can still find a buyer if the postmark and stamp are undamaged.

Letters about travel, Indians, mining, colorful people, disasters, famous events, business, military service, personal history, and the like, especially those which give details. are best. Someone looking for stamps paid $20 for a box of envelopes at a Beverly Hills yard sale. Letters in those envelopes were resold to experts for $267,000!

Don't be surprised if most foreign stamps turn out to have little value. Enough valuable ones do exist, however, to make it worth your while to check them, especially when they are on interesting envelopes. If you own a few foreign stamps you can look them up in "Scott's Standard Postage Stamp Catalogue." U.S. stamps are in "Scott's Specialized Catalogue of United States Stamps." Both are available at most public libraries. If you own many stamps, you are facing a tedious chore. Finding a buyer in Trash or Treasure will be faster and more efficient.

STAMPS

◆ **U.S. and foreign stamp collections and accumulations** are wanted by this 35 year veteran dealer who buys:
- Albums from any country or from mixed countries;
- Stockbooks and unsorted boxfuls of duplicate stamps;
- Old envelopes with stamps from any country;
- Mint sheets and blocks;
- Old revenue (tax) stamps on documents of all kinds;
- Duck hunting and fishing permit stamps, mint or used, especially on licenses;
- Stamp-like labels and seals of all kinds;
- Postal related souvenirs including booklets, cards, and stamp announcements;
- Philatelic reference books from any period or country in any language;
- Stamp magazines pre-1945;
- Worldwide stamp catalogs pre-1925;
- Philatelic (stamp) auction catalogs pre-1945;
- Photos or real photo postcards of mail carriers, mail trucks, post offices, and mail delivery.

"If in doubt, include it! I must be one of the last people who collect everything in stamps and stamp-related items." **Doug says stamp collecting has many variations and specialties, and that even the most common looking items (especially envelopes with unusual markings) may have value.** "Because of their nature and sheer numbers, stamps must be sent for my inspection. You must call first, because I can give you clear shipping instructions and help you eliminate heavy items that have no value, such as newer stamp catalogs, 3-ring notebooks, and empty albums. I can give you guidance on how to ship stamps to prevent damage and preserve value. Return postage must be included with your shipment. Never send things UPS or FedEx. Inquiries should include an SASE if you wish an answer." Mail inquiries preferred.

Douglas Swisher
PO Box 11766
Jacksonville, FL 32239
(904) 744-5493   <doug7777@attbi.com>

TONY'S TIP: Three serious mistakes made by amateurs:
(1) Cutting stamps off envelopes and documents;
(2) Improperly storing and handling mint stamps;
(3) Forgetting that labor costs of preparing stamps for resale will affect how much money you are paid. It's very costly to make your piles into attractive packages."

★ **Envelopes with stamps mailed in the Orient.** Buys nearly all envelopes with stamps mailed in China, Tibet, Korea, Hong Kong, Nepal, Mongolia and Japan. Advisable to first phone or send a Xerox© by mail or fax. Pledges to pay post on items sent on approval. Some of these can be very valuable, so it's important you contact him.

> Bruce Lewin
> Bridgewater Onvelopes Collectibles
> 680 Route 206 North
> Bridgewater, NJ 08807
> (908) 725-0022   fax (908) 707-4647

◆ **U.S. or foreign stamp collections** from before 1960.

> Ron Aldridge
> 250 Canyon Oaks Drive
> Argyle, TX 76226
> (940) 455-2519 eves   fax (940)455-5094   <noacman@aol.com>

◆ **Stamps from any country in any quantity.** "We'll buy everything you have," says Harvey, who has been dealing by the mail since 1934. He wants collections of singles, plate blocks, sheets, covers and rarities. If you have a large or valuable collection, Harvey Dolin & Company will come to your home. Smaller collections may be shipped to them for their cash offer. "Your satisfaction is always guaranteed," say their ads. Dolin buys stampless letters (dating before the first U.S. stamps in 1843, or after), Confederate stamps and envelopes, Wells Fargo envelopes, and Duck Hunting stamps.

> Harvey Dolin & Company
> 111 Fulton Street, Mezzanine Floor
> New York, NY 10038
> (212) 267-0216

◆ **Stamp collections, United States and foreign** in complete or partial collections. No collection is too large or too small. Also interested in stamped covers (pre 1900 envelopes). "Contact me for a free appraisal." David has 50 years of experience.

> David Quintin
> PO Box 800861
> Dallas, TX 75380
> (972) 625-7189   <dqtexas@aol.com>

TONY'S TIP: Always check inside envelopes. Letters or documents contained in them could be worth more than the stamps. A Beverly Hills yardsale sold $500,000 worth of letters for $20 because they didn't look inside.

REVENUE & SPECIAL TAX STAMPS

◆ **Federal and state revenue and special tax stamps including document stamps and all stamps used to show that taxes had been paid on a product.** Special tax stamps are large and look like licenses to engage in various occupations, such as liquor dealer, cigar salesman, wine maker, etc. Some of these issues, notably 1875, 1877, 1879, 1883, and 1885, are available in large quantities and sell for very little. Photocopies are strongly urged by this 30 year veteran buyer.

Hermann Ivester
5 Leslie Circle
Little Rock, AR 72205
(501) 688-8820 days   (501) 225-8565 eve   fax (501) 688-8807
<ivesters@aol.com>

◆ **U.S. Internal Revenue special tax stamps, licenses and permits for making and selling beer, liquor, wine, tobacco, cigars, margarine, firearms, opium and marijuana.** Also for businesses such as brokers, pawnbrokers, dentists, lawyers, etc. No stamps from between 1873 and 1885 with punched holes are wanted. Also wants state stamps and licenses for any business, activity, or product including hunting and fishing. USDA export stamps and certificates for meat products are also sought.   Ration coupons for gas, fuel oil and sugar are wanted, but no war books (1,2,3, or 4) or any red or blue tokens. "Photocopies are very helpful," he says.

Bill Smiley
PO Box 361
Portage, WI 53901
(608) 742-5336   (608) 742-3714   <wsmiley@chorus.net>

◆ **U.S. Internal Revenue (tax) stamps on documents of all kinds.**
Douglas Swisher
PO Box 11766
Jacksonville, FL 32239
(904) 744-5493   <doug7777@attbi.com>

TONY'S TIP: Three serious mistakes made by amateurs:
(1) Cutting stamps off envelopes and documents;
(2) Improperly storing and handling mint stamps;
(3) Forgetting that labor costs of preparing stamps for resale will affect how much money you are paid. It's very costly to make your piles into attractive packages."

TONY'S TIPS ON SELLING PAINTINGS & PRINTS

Paintings and prints that look sloppy, amateurish or depressing to you may be snapped up for big dollars. Each year, a few turn up in private hands that end up being worth $10,000 or more and $1,000,000 finds do happen. **If a painting has been passed down in your family for more than 60 years,** check the current value of that artist's work. Some painters whose work cost $50 in the 1930's are worth 100 times that today. **Using experts to evaluate and sell your art is smart.**

Researching art is work. So many paintings were created by unknowns, the vast majority of what you own will not be listed, cataloged or pictured. **Unsigned works or those by unknown artists seldom sell for more than $200, but you want to be very careful that it is indeed not signed.   Check the back too for dates or stickers.**

To sell a print, give the dimensions of the entire sheet and of the printed area. List all signatures, dates, and other information. Photocopy whenever practical. **Prints signed and numbered in pencil are more likely to have value.** Some prints like Currier & Ives have developed cult status and sell for $100 to $5,000 up! Photocopy if possible. **Reproductions of famous paintings are not sellable.**

To sell paintings, sculpture, or folk art, a good 35mm photo is essential, along with dimensions. Take a close-up of the signature if possible.   Folk art includes items made by untrained amateurs, done with style, vigor, form and color. Anything hand-crafted in decorative ways may qualify. Quality pieces bring thousands of dollars.

Art from places other than the U.S. and Europe is doing well. Prices are rising fast for South Pacific masks, bowls and shields. Mexican and South American paintings and folk arts have hit record prices within the last year and Oriental items remain strong.

WARNING: If you have a painting you think valuable, showing it to many dealers and auctioneers in hopes of getting ever higher prices is likely to do the opposite. Paintings often diminish in value in proportion to the number of people to whom they are offered. **The more people who see them, the LESS valuable they become.**

ART BY COMMERCIAL ILLUSTRATORS

◆ **Original illustration art for mystery, detective, horror, science fiction, adventure and fantasy magazines, pulps, and paperbacks.** "I want the original paintings created to illustrate these covers as well as black and white pen and ink illustrations for the stories inside." Seeks artists like Roy Kuenkel, J. Allen St. John, Paul, Frank Frazetta, Stromberg, Olson, and others, especially those that depict known characters like *The Shadow, The Spider, Doc Savage, Tarzan,* etc. Does not want covers, prints, or reproductions. Send a photo, including the dimensions, and the name of the artist if you can read the signature.
> Jim Gerlack
> 1621 Boundbrook Lane
> Irving, TX 75060
> (972) 790-0922   <j.gerlach@attbi.com>

◆ **Original paintings for American magazine covers and story illustrations, 1900 to date.** "I'll buy art for magazines and stories in the following genres: aviation, western, fantasy, science fiction, adventure, erotica, detective, mystery, and movie." Also buys art for pin-up calendars, advertising campaigns, and paperback book covers with similar themes. These covers were generally vividly painted on 24" x 30" canvas. Rough sketches for cover or story art can also have value. Sellers should send a photo of the art, the dimensions and an accurate description of the condition (any soil, holes, dents, scratches). Note the signature, in the unlikely event there is one. Check the back of the painting for exhibit or publishing history. Most pulp paintings are worth $500 to $2,000, depending upon the artist, subject and condition, although a few covers bring up to $10,000. Jim is a popular artist and comic book illustrator who wrote two books on the history of comics.
> Jim Steranko
> Supergraphics
> PO Box 974
> Reading, PA 19603

◆ **Original paintings by American illustrators for magazine covers, magazine story illustrations, or advertising, 1910-1980,** including artists such as Norman Rockwell and all his contemporaries. Also original art for magazine or calendar pin-ups. Has special interest in sexual or sentimental themes (children, dogs, families, patriotism, etc.).
> Charles Martignette
> PO Box 293
> Hallandale, FL 33008
> (954) 454-3474

◆ **Printed illustrations by well known 20th century artists** such as Maxfield Parrish, the Leyendecker Bros., Norman Rockwell, Mucha, Rolf Armstrong, Vargas, Petty, Rose O'Neill, Erte, Grace Drayton, Will Bradley, and Coles Phillips. Wants original art, prints, posters, advertising, calendars, magazines, and books, 1895-1930. Especially Maxfield Parrish and pin-up calendars, 1920-1960. Give dimensions and condition of your print, and tell what book, magazine, calendar, etc., it came from. Denis does not want "free appraisals, pen pals, or time wasters." He is the author of price guides for print artists and edits *The Illustrator Collector's News*, available for $17 a year.
Denis Jackson
PO Box 1958
Sequim, WA 98382
<ticn@olypen.com>

◆ **Maxfield Parrish paintings, watercolors, pen and ink sketches, letters, and 1st printings including art prints, Edison Mazda calendars, Brown & Biglow prints and calendars, posters, books, playing cards, games, novelty items, and other advertising.** She emphasizes she is not interested in "new prints" or reproductions of the first printings. This 18 year veteran dealer says she will pay $20,000 and up for paintings, $1,500 for a Mother Goose in Prose 1st edition from 1897, and from $800 to $3,500 for some posters and calendars, especially 1918, 1919, and 1920. "I need to know the size, color, and if there is any damage to the piece such as brown spots or water stains. It is helpful if you call with the piece in front of you."
Michelle Ferretta, Maxfield Parrish Collectables
1314 Oak Street
Alameda, CA 94501
(510) 522-1823   <mpferretta@aol.com>

◆ **Maxfield Parrish paintings, calendars (all years), complete books, full decks of playing cards, original prints, autographs and unusual advertising items.** Not interested in book fragments or modern reproductions. Describe condition.
Debra Buonaguidi
883 Lighthouse
Monterey, CA 93940
(408) 375-7345   <sportmsm@redshift.com>

◆ **Original art and prints by F. Earl Christy** who specialized in beautiful society women. Wants his work on covers from movie and women's magazines, advertising, fans, blotters, calendars, postcards, and anything else illustrated by Christy.
Audrey Buffington
Box 386
South Thomaston, ME 04858
(207) 594-2683

◆ **Paintings and prints by R. Atkinson Fox, Maxfield Parrish, and Icart.** Claims she'll pay "top cash" for Parrish art prints and Edison Mazda calendars illustrated by Parrish. She emphasizes that she has no interest in Icart reproductions, "only original etchings." Please state size and condition and if possible send a photo. Dealers price your goods. Amateurs may request an offer.
>Christine Daniels
>135 East Shiloh Road
>Santa Rosa, CA 95403
>   (707) 838-6083   <ctiques@aol.com>

◆ **Artwork by Joan Walsh Anglund.** Anglund is a prolific illustrator of children's books (1958-date). Also calendars, cards, and figurines. She had a Holiday page in *Good Housekeeping* magazine. This Anglund authority wants original art, Ebeling and Reuss music boxes, figurines and her Little Gallery spoons for Hallmark. Please send a Xerox©.
>Ann Bergin
>PO Box 105
>Amherst, NH 03031
>   <acbergin@aol.com>   fax (978) 649-6807

◆ **Illustration art by Philip Goodwin on trays, calendars, posters, and advertising.** He can provide a detailed wants list of magazines, illustrations, books, and other items to dealers who send an SASE.
>Jim Combs
>417 27th Street NW
>Great Falls, MT 59404
>   (406) 761-3320   <jifraco@montana.com>

◆ **Sketches, drawings, and paintings by Philip Boileau and Robert Robinson,** American 20th century illustrators. Boileau is known for his 1900-1917 paintings of attractive women done for private customers, magazine covers, and other commercial purposes. Robinson worked commercially from 1907-1952 also on magazine covers and other work. Provide a close up photo and as much info about the work as you can.
>Q. David Bowers
>PO Box 1224
>Wolfeboro, NH 03894
>(603) 569-5095   fax (603) 569-5319 <bowersmerena@conknet.com>

◆ **Commercial art by J.G. Scott** who drew cute round faced children. His work is signed JG SCOTT and can be found on the covers of women's magazines, blotters and calendars from the 1920's and 30's. His unsigned work appears on Valentine's Day cards printed by Gibson Co.
>Robert Stauffer
>3235 Mudlick Road SW
>Roanoke, VA 24018
>   (540) 774-4319   <stauffer@roanoke.edu>

◆ **Charles M. Russell memorabilia.** "I'll buy just about anything illustrated by Russell: trays, posters, books, magazines, calendars, etc., as well as personal items, autographs, and other Russell memorabilia.
> Jim Combs
> 417 27th Street NW
> Great Falls, MT 59404
> (406) 761-3320   <jifraco@montana.com>

◆ **Original art for advertising and calendars** especially airlines, automobiles, gasoline, tires, soft drinks or whiskey. Especially likes paintings for ads for Coke, alcohol, movies, tobacco products, and other culturally significant items and events. If in doubt, call.
> Charles Martignette
> PO Box 293
> Hallandale, FL 33008
> (954) 454-3474

PAINTINGS & PRINTS BY SUBJECT MATTER

◆ **Paintings of 18th and 19th century American political figures or historic events.** Please send a photo along with a copy of the painter's signature if there is one. Only fine condition original oils or watercolors are wanted. No paper prints, engravings or pictures torn from books.
> Rex Stark Americana
> PO Box 1029
> Gardner, MA 01440
> (978) 630-3237   <rexstark@yahoo.com>

◆ **Engraved portraits and photographs of famous people** in all walks of life. Will consider items loose or in books. Photocopies make the best descriptions.
> Kenneth Rendell
> 989 Madison Ave.
> New York, NY 10021
> (800) 447-1007   (212) 717-1776   fax (212) 717-1492
> <gallery@kwrendell.com>

◆ **Paintings and prints depicting smoking.** Buys selected prints and paintings depicting smoking, especially cigars or cigarettes before 1900. Prefers smaller paintings but all sizes, all media, and all nationalities considered. Buys pre-1900 only. Buying for resale and for his personal collection.
> Tony Hyman
> PO Box 3028
> Pismo Beach, CA 93448
> (805) 773-6777   <thyman@fix.net>

◆ **Paintings of Texas or by Texas artists.** If in doubt, call with the painting in hand. Will need to know the artist's name or signature.
> Johnny Spellman
>> 10806 North Lamar Blvd.
>> Austin, TX 78753
> (512) 836-2889 days   (512) 258-6910 eves   (512) 750-2838 cel
>> fax (512) 832-0242   <dvm69@swbell.net>

◆ **Paintings of cowboys, Indians or Eskimos.** Please send a photo for a prompt response. It's helpful if you can read the signature. Dealers, price your goods; amateur sellers may request an offer.
> Barry Friedman
> PO Box 55492
> Valencia, CA 91385
>> (661) 255-2365   <barryf@thevine.net>

◆ **Paintings of early California.** Claims she'll pay "top cash." Please state size, condition and name of the artist. If possible send a photo. Dealers price your goods. Amateurs may request an offer.
> Christine Daniels
> 135 East Shiloh Road
> Santa Rosa, CA 95403
>> (707) 838-6083   <ctiques@aol.com>

◆ **Paintings and prints depicting boats** including whaling, yachting, racing, working, etc., are sought by this well known dealer in marine antiques. Give the dimensions, history, and a careful account of any damage or restoration. Photo suggested. Will give "ball park" estimates of value on ordinary items, but appraisals are for a fee.
> Andrew Jacobson
> PO Box 437
> Ipswitch, MA 01938
(978) 356-5583   fax (978) 356-8705   <andrew@marineantiques.com>

◆ **Paintings and prints depicting automobiles before 1930.** Also photos from before 1930. He does not want magazine ads of any type. "A Xerox™ or photo is a must."
> David Bausch
> 252 North 7th Street
> Allentown, PA 18102
> (610) 432-3355   fax (610) 820-9368   <oldtoy@aol.com>

◆ **Prints and illustrations of flowers, children & beautiful women** including calendars, yard-longs, and books before 1919.
> Linda Gibbs, Heirloom Keepsakes
> 10380 Miranda
> Buena Park, CA 90620

PAINTINGS & PRINTS

◆ **Paintings, limited edition graphics and 3-D (sculptural) art by listed artists, folk artists old and new, both American and Oriental.** Give the size in inches, condition, and the medium (oil, watercolor, wood, marble, etc.). Include a photo, and if possible, a close-up photo of the signature.

> Ivan Gilbert
> Miran Arts & Books
> 2824 Elm Avenue
> Columbus, OH 43209

◆ **Paintings by listed artists of all types and periods, including 20th century.** This first rate auction house regularly handles works of art from $1,000 to $100,000 and may be the perfect outlet for your better quality paintings. Send a photo, give the dimensions, describe any damage and note any signature.

> James D. Julia Auctions
> PO Box 830
> Fairfield, ME 04937
> (207) 453-7904   fax (207) 453-2502
> <jjulia@juliaauctions.com>

◆ **Paintings, prints, and photographs made by artists listed in *Who Was Who in American Art.*** Although he's primarily interested in American Impressionism, Peter will consider a wide range of works from 1800-1950, as long as the artist is listed. Among the types of artwork in which he has a special interests are:

* Art depicting competitive rowing ($500-$1,500);
* Color woodblock prints, particularly the White Line prints of the Provincetown, MA, printmaker group ($500-$2,000);
* Paintings and prints by American women artists of any period ($500-$10,000+);
* Photos of Abraham Lincoln ($500-$10,000).

Does not want wood engravings from *Harper's, Leslie's,* and other newspapers or magazines. Send photograph and the dimensions. Falk's company, Sound View Press, publishes the *Art Price Index*, one of the basic reference books for the art world. This $199 book contains prices paid in the last year for more than 200,000 works of art.

> Peter Falk
> 859 Boston Post Road or PO Box 833
> Madison, CT 06443
> (203) 245-2246   fax (203) 245-5116   <info@falkart.com>
> <soundviewpress@worldnet.att.net>

◆ **Paintings by artists from Ohio, Kentucky, and Indiana with a special interest in Cincinnati artists who worked between 1850 and 1950.** Buys especially art by Blum, Twachtman, Hurley, Sawier, Weis, Vogt, Wessel, Selden, Casinelli, Duveneck, Sharp, Farney, Nourse, Potthast, Volkert, as well as selected other American and European artists. Please send a good clear photo of items for sale. If in doubt, telephone. Have your work in hand when you do.

> Riley Humler
> Cincinnati Art Galleries
> 225 East 6th Street
> Cincinnati, OH 45202
>   (513) 381-2128   fax (513) 381-7527
>   <info@cincinnatiartgalleries.com>

◆ **Artist's and designer's sketchbooks before 1970.** Has a particular interest in California artists, American art and artists, and creator's of modern decorative arts such as glass, furniture and ceramics before 1970. Alan writes monthly columns on art, and is author of *Art for All* ($17.95) and *Buy Art Smart* ($17.95), both available from him.

> Alan S. Bamberger
> 2510 Bush Street
> San Francisco, CA 94115
> (415) 931-7875   fax (415) 922-3580   <alanb@artbusiness.com>

◆ **Oil paintings of any size, particularly American before 1940.** Provide this veteran art dealer and appraiser with the name of the artist, the size, and a sharp photo of the painting, both front and back. He is not interested in newer paintings.

> Robert Anderson, Aaron's Fine Antiques
> 1217 Broadway
> Fort Wayne, IN 46802
>   (219) 422-5184   <iloverugs2@aol.com>

◆ **Damaged art of all kinds is wanted.** "If people send a good sharp photo I will make an offer on paintings, sculpture, and movie posters that have been damaged but are still in restorable condition." SASE will bring a free evaluation.

> Alan Voorhees' Art Restoration
> 450 Breesport Road
> Horseheads, NY 14845
>   (607) 739-7898 eves   fax (607) 739-3506
>   <avoorhees1@stny.rr.com>

TONY'S TIP: If you are not trained to recognize valuable art get expert advice. Mistakes can be costly.

PRINTS

◆ **Prints, American and European.** Buys a wide range of prints. topical prints are of more interest than scenics. Give a complete description, including size of image, size of sheet, colors, and any and all information printed or written at the bottom of the print. Newman operates the oldest and largest antique print source in NYC, a family business.

    Kenneth and Robert Newman
    The Old Print Shop
    150 Lexington Avenue at 30th Street
    New York, NY 10016
        (212) 683-3950

◆ **Prints, fine and decorative** are bought and sold by this veteran high quality bookseller. He particularly seeks:
- Prints signed by the artist, from any period, in b/w or color;
- Decorative color prints printed prior to 1900, including costume prints, botanicals, and other subjects;
- Scientific and scholarly prints prior to 1880;
- Decorative b/w prints in the fields of history, architecture, etc.
- Portraits of the famous and infamous.

Give them as much of the following information as you can: the title, artist, publisher, any dates, size of the paper and size of the print itself. If possible, make a Xerox™ if you can do so without damaging it. Open daily with 60,000 items in stock and 25 years of experience.

    James & Mary Laurie
    Booksellers
    921 Nicollet
    Minneapolis, MN 55402
  (800) 774-1114   (612) 338-1114   fax (612) 338-3665
        <lauriebk@winternet.com>

◆ **Prints, engravings, chromoliths, and woodcuts before 1900 on many topics** including city scenes of the U.S. and Canada, natural history (birds, bugs, fish, and animals), military uniforms, fashion, the old West, children, expositions and fairs, disasters, mining, Indians, and Oriental life in America. "These are very difficult to buy by mail, and must be examined under high magnification to set a fair price." If your print is framed, he believes "it is wise to remove the print from the frame in order to find the publisher and date of publication." Indicate the size of the image and the size of the paper on which it is printed. Include an SASE.

    John Rosenhoover
    100 Mandalay Road
    Chicopee, MA 01020
        (413) 536-5542

◆ **Chromoliths and hand colored prints** on topics of natural history (birds, bugs, fish and animals), military, medicine, old West, Indians, costumes and fashion, Negroes, sports, and Art Nouveau. Wants pre-1900 prints only, but does buy 19th and 20th century advertising art and labels on similar themes or with other attractive pictures. Describe fully for this major graphics dealer, known for paying high prices for quality items. Joe is author of two books on advertising labels.

> Joe & Sue Davidson
> 5185 Windfall Road
> Medina, OH 44256
>   (330) 723-7172   <artbroker@webtv.net>

◆ **Prints by artists listed in** *Who Was Who in American Art.*   Peter will consider a wide range of works from 1800-1950, as long as the artist is listed. He particularly wants color woodblock prints, especially the White Line prints of the Provincetown, MA, printmaker group and any prints by American women artists of any period. Does not want wood engravings from *Harper's, Leslie's,* and other newspapers or magazines. Send photograph and the dimensions. Falk's company, Sound View Press, publishes the *Art Price Index*, one of the basic reference books for the art world. This $199 book contains prices paid in the last year for more than 200,000 works of art.

> Peter Falk
> 859 Boston Post Road or PO Box 833
> Madison, CT 06443
> (203) 245-2246   fax (203) 245-5116   <info@falkart.com>
>   <<soundviewpress@worldnet.att.net>

TONY'S TIP: Prints of all types are also sought for their subject matter by historians in many fields. When looking for a buyer, make certain to check the buyers throughout the book.

Print buyers want to know the size of the image and the size of the paper on which it is printed. They also want to know everything that is printed at the bottom of the print. If there is a penciled signature, make a Xerox™ copy of it. Make certain to mention any damage, tears, stains, or little brown spots.

If you are not trained to recognize valuable art get expert advice. Mistakes can be costly.

◆ **Woodblock prints by European, American and Canadian artists (1895-1950) in color or black and white.** He buys only pencil signed prints created and signed by the artist whose work they are. Particular interests include:

- Landscapes and marinescapes by the widely traveled artist Arthur Wesley Dow of Ipswitch MA. His prints are signed but unnumbered, usually 5x7 inches or smaller, and can be worth $1,000 and more.
- Prints by Provincetown printers, especially "white line prints" characterized by blocks of color separated by white lines. These run in size from 3x4 inches to 16x20, but are mostly from 5x7 to 8x10 inches. Values run from $1,000 to $15,000.
- Prints with Oriental subjects, but only those by Western, often British, artists. People to look for include Bartlett, Hyde, Keith and Lum.

"I do not want Oriental prints from Japan and the Far East or wood engravings from *Harper's Weekly* or other magazines and newspapers. Nor do I generally buy woodblock illustrations from books." If your print is loose and unframed, a photocopy is quick and accurate. If you feel you have one of these valuable prints, the expense of a color copy may be justified. If your print is framed, try to get a good photograph by shooting outdoors in open shade. Thomas makes offers if your item is genuinely for sale, but is not interested in doing free appraisals. In business for 17 years, Thomas issues annual catalogs of art for sale and will send you an illustrated wants list if you send a #10 (long) envelope.

Steven Thomas, Inc.
PO Box 41
Woodstock, VT 05091
(802) 457-1764 fax (802) 457-1764 <stinc@sover.net>
<www.woodblock-prints.com>

◆ **Japanese woodblock prints.** "I buy woodblock prints by Paul Jacoulet, but I will also consider other artists. Send a clear color photo with dimensions and a general description of condition." Bob is a private collector.

Robert Block
PO Box 2321
Shelton, CT 06484
(203) 924-2802 <blockschip@aol.com>

TONY'S TIP: "Woodblocks are rectangular with sharply defined borders. When printed in color, a slight registration problem is often apparent. They are usually signed in pencil outside the image area."

WALLACE NUTTING

♦ **Wallace Nutting pictures, books, furniture and memorabilia.**
Among Nutting pictures, Mike particularly wants interiors, scenes with
people, animals, and houses. He does not want single pictures of common exteriors of apple blossoms, country lanes, trees, lakes, and ponds,
although he will take these as part of a large collection. Collections are
preferred, but single pieces will be considered. No size is too large.
Mike says he'll travel anywhere to view collections of considerable size
and diversity. When describing pictures, give the title, frame size, and
condition. When describing books give standard bibliographic information, including title, edition, color of the cover. Mike will either buy
outright or consider accepting your items on consignment for one of his
Nutting auctions. The 4th edition of Mike's *Price Guide to Wallace
Nutting Pictures* is available from him for $17 postpaid.
>   Michael Ivankovich
>   PO Box 1536
>   Doylestown, PA 18901
>   (215) 345-6094   <ivankovich@wnutting.com>

♦ **Wallace Nutting pictures, books and other ephemera,** including
furniture, lamps, wooden dishes, postcards, calendars, and greeting
cards designed, built, or used by him. "Especially interested in pictures
with indoor scenes and those which include people or animals. Not
interested in recent items, or things that are damaged or otherwise in
less than very good condition," says this 7 year veteran Nutting dealer.
>   James Buskirk
>   Eleanor's Hand Tinted Photos
>   3009 Oleander Avenue
>   San Marcos, CA 92069
>   (760) 599-1054   <toygun@earthlink.net>

*TONY'S TIP: High prices are being paid for good items
in today's art world, even though the market is
somewhat depressed. This is a very volatile time,
and tastes are changing as a result of the movement
of baby boomers into the market.*

*Personally, I believe their impact will be felt for
a long time, so I'm selling any piece of art that I
consider surplus that I don't feel has boomer-appeal.*

*If you get a good offer for something, **remember,
prices do not always go up over time**. Artists and
styles fall in and out of favor.*

PACIFIC ART

◆ **Hawaiian, Philippine, Indonesian and Vietnamese paintings** are wanted. Hawaiian artists whose work is wanted are Tavernier, Hitchcock, Walden, Farneaux, Bartlett, Coulter, Wores and Kelly. Indonesian artists whose work is sought are: Maurice Sterne, Lee Man Fong, Willem Hofker, Rudolf Bonnet, Roland Strasser, Willem Dooijewaard, Auke Sonnega, Isaac Israels, J. Le Meyeur, Theo Meier, Miguel Covarrubius, Walter Spies, Affandi, Bustman, and Hubert Vos. Philippine artists whose work is wanted are: Miranda, F. De la Rosa, Luna, Hidalgo, Martinez, Zobel, Magsaysay-Ho, Celis, Saragoza, Lagaspi, Tabuena, Edadas, Teodoro Buenaventura and Ocampo. Vienamese painters whose work is wanted are: Pham Chanh, Lo Pho, Vu Cau Dam, Le Van Mien, To Ngoc Van, Tran Van Can and Mai Trung Thu. If you have work signed by any of these artists, and these artists alone, please send a sharp photograph along with the dimensions and anything you know of the work's history.

> Geringer Art, Ltd.
> 98-360 Koauka Loop #221
> Aiea, HI 96701
> (800) 654-2017   <geringerart@yahoo.com>

FOLK ART

◆ **American folk art** such as:
- **Wood carvings, whirligigs, and decoys;**
- Old **weathervanes** of any and all materials;
- **Quilts** in fine, unworn condition;
- **Hooked rugs** with pictorials rather than patterns;
- **Handmade dolls** of wood and/or cloth;
- **Folk paintings** of children and animals;
- Figural **19th century pottery;**
- **Fishing decoys** in fine condition and good provenance;
- **Architectural figurals** such as cherubs and gargoyles;
- **Game boards** in original finish;
- **Indian art, rugs, baskets, pottery, pipes,** and other artifacts.

No damaged or repaired pieces. Send a photo and SASE. Include complete description, dimensions, and condition.

> Louis Picek
> Main Street Antiques
> PO Box 340
> West Branch, IA 52358
> (319) 643-2065   <msantiques@bigplanet.com>

◆ **Folk art including painting, sculpture, weaving, wood,** etc., including American Indian, Oriental, African, or Eskimo art. Provide the dimensions, condition, and photos. Condition critical. Special interest in current "outsider art." Contact Ivan only if your item is for sale.

> Ivan Gilbert
> Miran Arts & Books
> 2824 Elm Avenue
> Columbus, OH 43209
>> (614) 236-0002 voice/fax

◆ **Tramp art items made from cigar boxes or fruit crate wood which has been layered into edge-notched pyramids.** Typical items include boxes, picture frames, doll furniture, banks, and wall pockets. Collects interesting or unusual boxes, especially pedestal form, but will buy any good example for resale. Intact condition and original finish are important. Info about origin is a plus. He does not want items made from ice cream sticks, matches, wood burning or 'crown of thorns.' A photo is essential. Will also buy historical documents related to tramp art, such as old photos of makers with their work, patterns, etc.

> Michael Cornish
> 92 Florence Street
> Roslindale, MA 02131
>> (617) 323-6029

◆ **Prisoner of war straw figures woven or plaited by French prisoners during the early 1800's.** Other documented prisoner art from the 19th century, including ivory carvings, are sought.

> Lucille Malitz
> Lucid Antiques
> PO Box KH
> Scarsdale, NY 10583
>> (914) 636-7825   <lithophane@aol.com>

◆ **Fraktur birth and baptismal certificates dating before 1900.** These certificates are usually, but not always, printed with hand done watercolor decoration. Some are totally freehand drawn manuscripts. Most are written in German, but some are in English. Prefers colorful watercolor birds and flowers that are "folksy" rather than formal. These are wanted in any condition. Inquire by removing your fraktur from any frame and sending a photocopy, including the name of the printer. Do not make any repairs with tape or glue no matter how carefully. Make sure the copy is clear and readable.

> Louis Picek
> Main Street Antiques
> PO Box 340
> West Branch, IA 52358
>> (319) 643-2065   <msantiques@bigplanet.com>

◆ **American needlework samplers made before 1850.** "I prefer samplers, whether framed or unframed, to be in good condition with the name and date of the maker. I am particularly interested in those which contain poetry, but buy all types. These are valued between $300 and $3,000 depending on the nature of the work, quality of workmanship, and condition. I am not interested in those made after 1860 or those based on punchpaper mottoes." Give the name, date and condition, including a description of anything stitched other than the usual alphabets and numbers.

> Peter Cifelli
> PO Box 2160
> Los Gatos, CA 95031
> (408) 529-9797 voice/ fax days   (408) 395-4050 eves
> <samplerhi@aol.com>

◆ **Mourning pictures in watercolor or embroidery.** These are characterized by willow trees, tombstones, birth and death dates, weeping women, etc. These are often for famous people, presidents, generals, etc. Those honoring "nobodies" are more rare and desirable. Will pay at least $100 and as much as $300-$400 for better ones.

> Steve DeGenaro
> PO Box 5335
> Poland, OH 44514
> <sdgenaro@aol.com>

◆ **Samplers, both U.S. and English, from before 1850,** including mourning samplers and needlework pictures. Clear photo is essential, along with dimensions and the item's history as you understand it. **Books on American and/or British needlework** are also sought. Give standard bibliographic information.

> Donna Litwin
> PO Box 494
> Princeton Junction, NJ 08550
> (609) 275-0996   fax (609) 275-1427   <jsl58@comcast.net>

◆ **Quilts that are graphically artistic made before 1940** especially made before 1900. Cotton, wool, and silk quilts all have value if made well but children's size quilts are best if they do not have children's subject matter. Solid color materials and small calico patterns are most desirable. Large patterns cut into small pieces usually make the quilt of no interest. All quilts should be in mint condition, with at least six stitches per inch, preferably more. No holes, tears, stains, thin spots when held to light, fading, soft from too much washing, and no patched repairs. A photo is very desirable. Herb does not make offers.

> Herbert Wallerstein Jr., Calico Antiques
> 611 North Alta Drive
> Beverly Hills, CA 90210
> (310) 273-4192   fax (310) 273-1921

◆ **Patchwork quilts made by African-Americans,** especially unusual or improvisational quilts. Provide a full photo of the quilt, a statement of condition, and all information you can about its history. "I'll also buy fabric sample books, especially of printed cottons."

Eli Leon
5663 Dover Street
Oakland, CA 94609

◆ **Patchwork quilts of all types made before 1930,** including ones that have some damage. Please send a photo which shows the colors and pattern, along with a description of condition. Also buys ribbon pictures (small, usually framed, 8"x10" or so, patchwork pictures made from dimestore ribbons in the 1920's and 30's).

Vivian Temes
Bird In the Cage Antiques
110 King Street
Alexandria, VA 22314
(703) 549-5114 <bird_in_the_cage_antiques@compuserve.com>

◆ **Quilts made by hand before 1950 in any condition.** "I'm looking for rare patterns like U.S. Flag, albums, samples, and pictorials, but I also buy common patterns like starts, wedding rings, flower gardens, etc. Prices are from $200 to more than $1,000 for U.S. flag quilts. I do not buy quilts made with synthetic fabrics." He wants to know the pattern, size, condition, and age if you know it. A photo is needed.

Michael Council
130 Buttles Avenue
Columbus, OH 43215
(616) 299-9099 voice/ fax <equilt@columbus.rr.com>

◆ **Mexican weavings, including serapes, saltillos, rugs, and other pre-1940 items.** Excellent condition only. It is essential that you include a photo and the dimensions.

Barry Friedman
PO Box 55492
Valencia, CA 91385
(661) 255-2365 <barryf@thevine.net>

◆ **Pre-Columbian pottery from Mexico or Peru are sought,** but only if documented and authenticated. Collections preferred. A photograph is essential and Jones would like to know where the item was collected or obtained, and any other history of the piece.

Charles Jones
6716 Barren Inlet Road
Wilmington, NC 28405
(910) 794-3060 fax (910) 686-1313 <cjart@bellsouth.net>

TONY'S TIP: How do you tell ivory from bone from plastic from celluloid?
Bone has fine brown specks. Plastic sometimes has air bubbles or pits. Ivory has grain like fine wood. Celluloid is smooth and can be melted with a hot pin.

◆ **Ivory items of all sorts, including Eskimo and Oriental carvings, scrimshaw, ivory tusks (elephant, walrus, whale, hippo, etc.), dresser sets, poker chips, dice, and billiard balls.** Dave does not want ivory jewelry, letter openers, or sewing and crochet tools, nor does he buy bone or synthetic objects. If you are selling tusks, give the length around the outside curve, and the diameter at the large end. He asks you to use a flashlight to carefully inspect for cracks in the hollow end. Follow standard description form. A sample catalog is $1. Please list your phone number and best time to call.

> David Boone Trading Company
> PO Box 669
> Brinnon, WA 98320
> (800) 423-1945   8 - 4 Pacific weekdays   fax (360) 796-4511
> <sales@boonetrading.com>

◆ **Figures and native carvings made of ivory.** Ivory can be elephant, walrus, whale, hippo, wart hog, or narwhale, but he wants ivory art, not small useful items like pins, combs, spoons, brooches and toothpicks. Picture is a necessity, and he prefers you to set a price. Terry also buys primitive and pre-Columbian artifacts.

> Terry Cronin
> 1399 South Harbor City Blvd.
> Melbourne, FL 32901
>   (321) 726-1711   fax (321) 726-1715

◆ **African or South Pacific tribal art including masks, weapons, musical instruments, jewelry, household objects, bowls, furniture, feather work, textiles, and "almost anything else that was made for tribal use and not for the tourist trade."** Especially old collections including artifacts with elaborate decoration and animal, human, or spirit figures. High quality tribal art can bring as much as $100,000 so is worth inquiry. Does not want items made after 1970, ebony carvings, tourist items, or figures of natives holding spears. A photograph is essential and Jones would like to know where the item was collected.

> Charles Jones
> African Art
> 6716 Barren Inlet Road
> Wilmington, NC 28405
> (910) 794-3060   fax (910) 686-1313   <cjart@bellsouth.net>

TONY'S TIP: Buyers generally do not want any art from Mexico or South America without good provenance (history). The markets of that region have been flooded with modern imitations for nearly a century. Skill of the local artisans remains high, so it is hard for anyone but an expert to attest to the age of a piece...and they get fooled too, especially evaluating items made of clay. Objects made of precious metals and stones are harder to fake and less likely to come to you. Many art dealers are concerned about grave robbing and disruption of ancient sites.

◆ **Pre-Columbian art in all media: ceramic, stone, wood, textiles, and gold.** Requests photos of the front and back of each piece, measurements, a description of condition, and information on where you got it. This collector-dealer has been in business for seven years.
>   Jack Bond
>   Kent Bond Gallery
>   11301 North 56th Street #10
>   Tampa, FL 33617
>   (813) 988-2132   <kbgallery@cs.com>

ORIENTAL ART

◆ **Southeast Asian art** including bronze, wood, stone, china, ivory, porcelain and other materials. Oriental art objects of all types bought by travelers in genuine antique shops in the Orient, even recently, could be worth hundreds of dollars, though items purchased in tourist shops in major cities seldom have value. After 20 years collecting, buying and selling "I can usually evaluate condition and quality from good sharp photographs if good close-ups are included; a photo of the bottom is especially helpful, particularly with bronzes as it allows me to determine the casting technique." A description includes any and all markings (tracing, rubbing, or photo). Mention what the item is made of, its size, and any repairs, or defects. Everything you know about the figure, including where it was purchased is helpful. He DOES NOT WANT items from India cast in brass or anything which says "Made in Japan" or "Made in China."
>   Eric Matthies
>   PO Box 470965
>   San Francisco, CA 94147
>   (415) 921-6604   fax (415) 563-4957   <mattdebois@aol.com>

◆ **Fine quality Oriental antiques with special emphasis on Japanese netsuke, inro, lacquer, and fine Chinese porcelains.** Marsha buys, sells, and collects all types of Oriental antiques from early ceramics to late 19th century items including furniture, Japanese swords, sword fittings, jade carvings, and jewelry. Many small ivory and wood carvings are worth between $1,000 and $10,000. Modern or reproduction items are not wanted, nor are silk robes decorated with dragons brought back by WWII soldiers. Marsha is a senior member of the American Society of Appraisers, specializing in Oriental art, and will appraise for a fee. She will also help amateur sellers with fine items genuinely for sale if you take a good photo, give the measurements, and draw or photocopy all markings or signatures found on the bottom.

    Marsha Vargas
    Xanadu Gallery
    140 Maiden Lane
    San Francisco, CA 94108
        (415) 392-9999   fax (415) 984-5856
        <mvargas@theorientalcorner.com>

◆ **Antique Japanese netsuke, inro, and other art** including pouches, pipes and pipe cases, ivory and wooden statues, Japanese lacquer, metalwork, cloisonne, paintings, and ceramics. Will pay $10,000 up for ivory and wood 18th and 19th century netsuke and $1,000 for netsuke inlaid in various materials. No roughly carved pieces, man made materials, or factory pieces bought in hotel lobbies, airports, or gift shops. If you provide close-up photographs of your netsuke from all angles and an exact drawing of the signature, Denis will make an offer if interested. He has been president of the Netsuke Dealer's Association for 15 years, has written extensively on the topic, and is a member of the Appraisers Association of America. He does formal appraisals for a fee.

    Denis Szeszler
    Antique Oriental Art
    PO Box 714
    New York, NY 10028
        (212) 427-4682   fax (212) 860-4426

◆ **Japanese woodblock prints.** "I buy woodblock prints by Paul Jacoulet, but I will also consider other artists. Send a clear color photo with dimensions and a general description of condition." Bob is a private collector.

    Robert Block
    PO Box 2321
    Shelton, CT 06484
        (203) 924-2802   <blockschip@aol.com>

◆ **Modern Japanese woodblock prints on paper** with emphasis on pencil signed and numbered limited edition prints produced after 1945. Make a note of the signiture if it is in Western script (most are), the number in the series (such as "43/125"), and the date if given. All this information is usually located below the bottome of the printed image in the lower margin. Please send Xerox™ copy, dimensions, and a description of condition. This 20 year veteran collector DOES NOT WANT reproductions, calendar art or works on silk.

> Eric Matthies
> PO Box 470965
> San Francisco, CA 94147
> (415) 921-6604   fax (415) 563-4957   <mattdebois@aol.com>

◆ **Buddha images** in bronze, wood or stone. "I don't want tourist production items cast in brass, but ivory may be of interest if the piece is more than 8" tall. Images of the fat, happy, broadly smiling Chinese Hotai Buddhas are of no interest. Generally, items bought by tourists in tourist shops are not wanted, but items bought by travelers in genuine antique shops in the Orient could be worth hundreds of dollars. A well carved Buddha that is old and has traces of gilding or the original paint is usually a good bet to be of substantial value if it was purchased in a legitimate antique shop off the beaten path, even recently." To offer your figure for sale, good pictures are helpful. A description includes the material, height, any markings, repairs, or defects. Everything you know about the figure, including where it was purchased is helpful.

> Eric Matthies
> PO Box 470965
> San Francisco, CA 94147
> (415) 921-6604   fax (415) 563-4957   <mattdebois@aol.com>

SCULPTURE & FIGURINES

◆ **Sculpture and figurines.** "Since 1961 we have been buying and selling European and American **bronzes** and **porcelain figurines dating from before 1940.** We need you to tell us the dimensions and all signaturews and foundry marks along with sending a photo. Porcelain figurines include Snow Babies, bathing beauties, Kewpie dolls, Royal Doulton and Noritake Art Deco figures which show ladies' faces.

> Arnold Reamer, Timepiece Antiques
> PO Box 26416
> Baltimore, MD 21207
> (410) 486-8412   (410) 944-6414   cel (410) 336-1002
>   fax (410) 265-7877   <arnoldreamer@webtv.net>

◆ **Beautiful nude women in bronze, alabaster or marble.** Also any sculpture with romantic themes. Please send a photo, dimensions and your asking price.
> Charles Martignette
> PO Box 293
> Hallandale, FL 33008
> (954) 454-3474

◆ **Royal Doulton figurines and character jugs** are purchased by this well known dealer who has been in business for 20 years. "No collection is too large or too small. Call toll free as long as you have the name and HN number of the figurines and the name and size of the character jugs." Pascoe is especially interested in the rarest items, since they maintain a computer list of collectors worldwide who are looking for specific types of figure. Ed lectures frequently in the U.S. and England, and has edited price guides to these popular figures. He is not interested in buying dinnerware, and does not do pattern matching.
> Ed Pascoe
> Pascoe & Co.
> 101 Almeria Avenue
> Coral Gables, FL 33134
> (800) 872-0195   (305) 643-2550   <ed@pascoeandcompany.com>

◆ **John Rogers statuary.** If you have a gray or putty colored plaster grouping of figures, check for the signature john rogers, often accompanied by new york and a date. These Victorian figural groups can be from 12" to 48" high, with most just under 2' tall. Themes are Civil War, Americana, theater, etc., with a few comic. A few are made of material other than plaster, such as parian or bronze. Perfect condition is always best, but he will buy damaged pieces, as he is a restorer of Rogers' work. He needs to know the name of the piece (which is always found on the front of the base) and the condition of the putty colored paint. Prefers you to telephone him with your statue in front of you.
> Bruce Bleier
> 73 Riverdale Road
> Valley Stream, NY 11581
> (516) 791-4353 (call collect)   <emeralite@aol.com>

◆ **Kewpie figurines of German bisque.** These 3"-5" figures are most interesting in action poses with cats, toys, brooms, ducks, etc. Look for German figures to be marked o'neill on the back. Doesn't want figures made in Japan or elsewhere. Must be mint: no damage or repairs.
> Linda Vines
> 2911 4th Street #112
> Santa Monica, CA 90405
> (310) 314-0402   <lleigh2000@hotmail.com>

◆ **Bathing beauties and "naughties" figurines.** Wants small bisque or porcelain figurines, 1900-1940, which are nude, in bathing suits, in their underwear, stockings, or dressed in lace. They are finely modeled and in coy poses. Some had actual mohair wigs. Naughties were hollow figurines, often of children or women, intended to be filled with water so they peed or squirted out of their breasts. Other naughties appeared to be innocent figurines until lifted up or turned over, displaying a risque (often explicit) side. "I am especially interested in finding Black naughties or bathers with a wig, but I am interested in all fine examples of bathing beauties and naughties. I am also looking for old catalogs, advertisements, and other information about them. Bathing beauties and naughties can range anywhere from less than $100 to over $1,000 depending upon the rarity, pose, and quality of execution." She is also interested in fine quality mermaids, as well as original advertisements or catalogs featuring bathing beauty figurines or related items. No Japanese figures or reproductions. Generally does not want damaged pieces, but will consider extraordinary figures with minor damage. Size and pose is important so accurate measurements and a sketch or photo is almost essential. Include your phone number. Will buy only if you grant right of refusal after inspection. If you too collect these figures, please call. She'd love to meet you. Sharon has written *Naughties, Nudies and Bathing Beauties*, available from her for $20.

Sharon Hope Weintraub
3613-F Las Colinas Drive
Austin, TX 78731
(512) 323-9639   <bblady@onr.com>

◆ **Art Metal Works figures of humans or animals: ashtrays, bookends, incense burners, and the like,** especially those marked ART METAL WORKS, RONSON, or LVA. Send a sharp photo of what you have along with an SASE. In your description indicate the condition of the paint, including what percentage remains. No cracked or damaged items wanted. Will pay **premium price for Art Metal Works catalogs**. All brochures and advertising which pictures the line is wanted.

Urban Cummings
1231 Parkinson Avenue
Palo Alto, CA 94301
(650) 328-0329   <furryfeet@mindspring.com>

◆ **Noritake human and animal figures** are wanted by this well known glass auctioneer and porcelain collector.

Tom Burns
PO Box 608
Bath, NY 14810
(607) 776-7942

◆ **Snow Babies.** "I'll buy German 'Snow Babies' (china children in pebbly snow suits 1"-3" high), especially jointed Snow Babies and 'action' Babies with animals or engaged in some activity." Also buys small German bisque or papier mache Santas dressed in felt with fur beards. Doesn't want items from Japan or Taiwan, nor does she want damaged or faded items or anything newer than 1940. Give the size and markings, if any, and note all damage, no matter how minor. No offers or free appraisals. She expects you to look them up in price guides and says she pays "50%-75% of book value."

> Linda Vines
> 2911 4th Street #112
> Santa Monica, CA 90405
> (310) 314-0402   <lleigh2000@hotmail.com>

◆ **Hummel figurines with full bee and crown markings** preferred, though some later ones considered. Please give complete information concerning condition and an accurate drawing of all markings on the bottom. Price fishing is discouraged by this nationally known dealer who cautions that dealers can seldom use more common items, so can pay little if they buy them at all. "When you are ready to buy or sell Hummels, contact me, especially with rare items!" He is available to restore glass and porcelain, including your damaged Hummels.

> Donald Hardisty
> 3020 East Majestic Ridge
> Las Cruces, NM 88001
> (505) 522-3721   fax (505) 522-7909   <don@donsbossons.com>

◆ **Hummel-look-alike figures designed by Erich Stauffer.** Please give a detailed description of the figure's activity and props. Especially wanted are nuns, angels, two piece perfume girls, animals, and wall plaques. Height is important, as is the style number and complete mark found on the base. These are usually marked either designed by Erich Stauffer, ARNART or ROYAL CROWN. Does not make offers.

> Joan Oates
> 685 South Washington
> Constantine, MI 49042
> (616) 435-8353   <koates@remc12.k12.mi.us>

◆ **Hallmark Merry Miniatures and Kiddie Car Classics** are very different but early versions of both are sought by this well known Hallmark dealer. Kiddie cars from the 1940's and 50's hold the most interest. Among the 600 Hallmark miniatures, she has most for sale, but would love to find some from the 1974 offerings. You are encouraged to order her giant 60 page catalog for $5.

> Kathy Parrott
> 51 Jalbert Road
> Barre, VT 05641
> (802) 479-2024   <katparrott@aol.com>

◆ **Lladro Spanish porcelain figurines no longer available through retail stores.** Please note that some figures have been in continuous production for more than 20 years so the age is not important. "We are particularly interested in pieces created exclusively for the Lladro Collector's Society since 1985 and in the 21 "special event" figures created since 1991. There are approximately 100 other popular figures for which we will make offers." All Lladro figures are marked on the bottom with the Lladro trademark. Original boxes are important and the value of your piece is less if you do not have it. If you have the original box, the identification number will be on the box and "this tells me everything." If you do not have the box, the height in inches is a very important part of your description, as is the number and sex of the figures and any damage. "Lladro has produced a less expensive, lower quality, line of porcelain called NAO. We do not buy these at all." Write for their current catalog of Lladro and other fine items for sale.

Clark and Charlotte Sanchez
Sanchez Collectibles
1555 East Glendale Avenue
Phoenix, AZ 85020
(602) 395-9974   fax (602) 241-0702
<info@sanchezcollectibles.com>

◆ **Goebel figurines of cats.** "I don't want cats other than Goebel or Goebels other than cats." Include marks and numbers on the bottom.

Linda Nothnagel
Route 3 Box 30
Shelbina, MO 63468
(573) 588-4958   <katzen630@hotmail.com>

◆ **Osborne Ivorex plaques.** These 3-D plaster wall plaques were made between 1899 and 1968. In addition to plaques, the company made statuary of people and buildings, jewelry boxes, and other small items. Subject matter of the plaques includes individual characters to large cathedrals. Sizes range from a few inches to over a foot, with 3"x5" and 6.5"x9" being two popular sizes. Some premium items are factory framed in wood. Some poor quality repros exist. Most, but not all, Ivorex plaques are marked A/O (Arthur Osborne) on the lower right or left corner. In the 1930's they began marking them on the back with a three line ink stamp with the company name and copyright. Small vertical oval and rectangular plaques sometimes have markings on the lower rim. Values range from $30 up, with a few reaching $200. Andy wants to hear from other collectors for purposes of starting a club.

Andy Jackson
501 Falcon Lane
West Chester, PA 19382
(610) 692-0269   fax (610) 272-7040   <mrivorex@aol.com>

◆ **Erphila German figurines, teapots and other ceramics,** which are usually marked. Size, color and form are needed. Photo a good idea.

> Denise Hamilton
> 575 Latta Brook Road
> Elmira, NY 14901
> (607) 732-2550

◆ **Pen Delfin rabbits.** This mail order dealer in Pen Delfin is always looking for rabbits, especially those retired before 1980. Quality is important. Please no damaged, chipped or smudged items. Asking price helpful, but not necessary. Note the figure's name on the bottom.

> George Sparacio
> PO Box 791
> Malaga, NJ 08328
> (856) 694-4167   fax (856) 694-4536   <mrvesta1@aol.com>

◆ **Angel figurines made of china,** generally 3" to 7" tall are wanted. Made by various companies including Lefton, Napco, Enesco, Norcrest and Kelvin among others, these 1950's and 60's angels have the days of the week, months of the year, or signs of the zodiac on them and the figures are usually holding something appropriate to that day, month or sign (October holding a pumpkin, for example). They may also have a flower or birthstone. Some of these angels are incorporated into bells, planters, salt and pepper shakers, and the like. These older angels are made of hard fired glossy china, not the softer bisque (which he does not want). Most are in the $15 to $20 range, but a handful will bring twice that. He does not want angels playing musical instruments or other angel figures except those described, nor does he want broken or glued items. Give the name of the maker and any numbers stamped on the bottom of the figure. If this info isn't available, a photo is a must.

> James Atkinson
> 555 East School Street
> Owatonna, MN 55060
> (507) 455-3340 eves

◆ **Swarovski Austrian crystal animals in the Collector's Club series:** lovebirds (1987), woodpeckers (1988), turtledoves (1989), dolphins (1990), seals (1991), whales (1992), elephant (1993), kudu (1994), lion (1995) and unicorn (1996). The more recent the piece, the more plentiful and the lower the price. The original box and certificate is "almost a must" with Swarovski crystal. Write for their catalog of Swarovski and other fine items for sale.

> Clark and Charlotte Sanchez
> 1555 East Glendale Avenue
> Phoenix, AZ 85020
> (602) 395-9974   fax (602) 241-0702
> <info@sanchezcollectibles.com>

★ **Bossons artware including heads, wall plaques and figures.** These are made of plaster or Stonite, a vinyl/stone mix marketed as Fraser-Art. "We buy figures that are still available, but mostly seek discontinued figures, worth $85 up." There are Bossons look-alikes, but only figures marked BOSSONS CONGLETON ENGLAND are wanted. Slightly damaged figures will be considered by this authorized Bossons dealer and repairman. "If you want to buy or sell Bossons, contact me."

    Donald Hardisty
    Don's Collectibles
    3020 East Majestic Ridge
    Las Cruces, NM 88011
(505) 522-3721   fax (505) 522-7909   <don@donsbossons.com>

◆ **Sebastian miniatures by P.W. Baston** including commercial issues, limited editions and private commissions. "Ask me about any Sebastian miniatures because some common ones have rare variations." Give the title of the piece, the color of the label (if any), and the condition. Jim buys and sells miniatures and can help you obtain custom made miniatures for promotions or fund raising purposes.

    Jim Waite, Blossom Shop Collectibles
    112 North Main
    Farmer City, IL 61842
    (309) 928-3222   (800) 842-2593   <bigjim@farmwagon.com>

◆ **Collector's plates.** The Ernst family is one of the nation's larger dealers in collector's plates. If you have plates to sell, they will help you in one of two ways, (1) by outright purchase of those they can sell promptly or (2) by selling your plates on consignment (in the more likely event you own plates in less demand). They charge 20% of the item's selling price for this valuable service. When you call or write, they will send you complete information plus specific instructions on how to pack and ship your plates safely. The Ernsts have been in business since the late 60's and are listed in Dun & Bradstreet.

    Ross and Ruth Ernst
    Collectors Plates
    7311 Izard
    Omaha, NE 68114
        (402) 932-9525   <collectorsplatesernst@cox.net>

◆ **Bossons artware including heads, wall plaques and figures.** "We're only looking for the discontinued ones. They need not be perfect as I am a restorer of Bossons. Almost all are signed on the back in the plaster. The name of the piece is frequently inscribed on the bottom at the cross-section of the neck.

    Bruce Bleier
    73 Riverdale Road
    Valley Stream, NY 11581
(516) 791-4353   fax (516) 792-0519   <emeralite@aol.com>

TONY'S TIPS ON SELLING PAPER ITEMS

If you are handling an estate, closing a business, or have piles of family papers and photos, read this section carefully. **Piles of papers can be piles of dollars.**

Paper is bought for one of two reasons:
(1) It is pretty, and collectible because it is, or
(2) it is historically interesting and informative.
Some paper is bought for both reasons.

Popular papers are postcards, photographs, catalogs, bills and letters, autographs, posters, and advertising. Minor types include menus, blueprints, scrapbooks, maps, labels, etc. Values of these range from a few cents to a few thousand dollars. Some photos bring even more. A $50,000 photo was sold at a Hudson River yard sale for $5. The dealer who bought it, resold it for $15 to someone who decided to ask an expert what he had... and got $50,000 for being smart enough to do so.

Historical data is not often worth a lot of money, *but Trash or Treasure buyers will preserve what you have. Please, never to throw away paper with prices, formulas, processes, or descriptions of people or travels.*

Sports, movies, music, transportation, liquor, tobacco, business and Pop Culture paper is easiest to sell. You'll find buyers in the next few pages ready to buy a wide range of items. Don't give up if you don't find a buyer your first try.

Condition is critical for buyers of paper. *Don't clean paper yourself. It is easy to do more harm than good. Let the buyer do it.*

Describing paper is usually easy. *Photocopy it! If your item is too large to fit on a machine, take multiple copies and tape them together or go to a commercial copy center where larger machines are available. You don't need to get the entire item copied. Samples are fine.*

Important tip: *unless you are certain your item is both rare and desirable, do not go to a great deal of effort to make photocopies of big piles of paper. Write to the buyer first, expressing a willingness to make copies if desired. Cost of color copies is almost never justified.*

MISCELLANEOUS PAPER

◆ **Rare documents from the time of papyrus to the present.** Buys collections of letters, manuscript (hand written) material, land grants, photograph collections, diaries, hand colored maps, atlases, and "anything unusual in paper."

> Ivan Gilbert
> Miran Arts & Books
> 2824 Elm Avenue
> Columbus, OH 43209
> (614) 236-0002 voice/fax

◆ **Accumulations of paper items related to business, finance, mining, or transportation before 1920.** Buys stocks, bonds, billheads, advertising, land grants, maps, diaries, letters, photographs and other printed and manuscript items. Will consider all collections related to military, mining, railroads, energy, banking, express companies, law enforcement, and other topics generally associated with the old West.

> Warren Anderson
> America West Archives
> PO Box 100
> Cedar City, UT 84720
> (435) 586-9497   fax (435) 867-8078   <awa@netutah.com>

★ **Paper from The Old West.** Buys or accepts on consignment all types of rare paper **Americana related to Western history**, including the **Civil War**, also **maps, atlases, photographs,** railroad passes, Presidential autographs and other better quality historic paper. No junk, damaged items, or things after 1920. DOES NOT WANT reproductions, reprints made after 1920. Fred is a well established leading dealer and auctioneer capable of helping you buy or sell quality items.

> Fred Holabird
> 3555 Airway Drive #308
> Reno, NV 89511
> (775) 852-8822   fax (775) 852-8866   <fred@holabird.org>

◆ **Handwritten ephemera including diaries, ledgers, journals, day books, apprenticeship bonds, ships logs, deeds, wills, and family and estate papers of all sorts.** Especially interested in craftsmen's records. Condition is secondary to content. Not interested in recent items. Please indicate the dates covered in the journals, where from, contents in brief, etc.

> Dan Casavant
> Casavant's Rare Books
> PO Box 1830
> Waterville, ME 04903
> (207) 877-9097   fax (207) 872-6907   <casavant@qsilver.net>

◆ **Manuscripts and printed documents with interesting content.**
These need not be signed by anyone famous. "I particularly like colonial American documents from before the Revolutionary War, but will
consider material from all periods. Please describe the contents and
why you think the item is unusual." Photocopy advisable.

Chris Wilson
8101 Revatom Court
Dunn Loring, VA 22027
(703) 698-7073   <cmnzwilson@starpower.net>

◆ **Amateur poetry in autograph books, friendship books, sketchbooks, journals and diaries.** If what you have was written after 1870,
he is not interested at all. Please give any names, dates, and places mentioned, and mention any watercolor or other embellishment, including
fancy calligraphy. Making Xerox™ copies seems like a good idea. He
is author of *Early American Poetry: Voices of New England Youth*,
available from him for $19.

Peter Cifelli
PO Box 2160
Los Gatos, CA 95031
(408) 529-9797 voice/fax days   (408) 395-4050 eves
<samplerhi@aol.com>

★ **Pictorial wall calendars** (except those with the spiral binding in the
middle) **dating before 1959**. Especially interested in calendars illustrating horses, beautiful women, and women participating in outdoor
sports. Also wants Victorian die-cut (cut outs) and old advertising calendars before 1940. Calendars must have no handwriting and be in good
enough condition to frame. The value of calendars is based on the picture, the artist, condition of the paper and the product being advertised.
A description of a calendar should include its yearm iverakk size, the
size of the picture, and the artist, if known. Note any damage, including
missing months. "Sending a Xerox™ of the calendar is the best way to
get a quick sale at a fair price." Dealers must price their goods, but
amateurs may request an offer. Appraisals are for a fee. She DOES
NOT WANT spiral calendars or those with common or unattractive pictures, damage, writing, or religious themes.

Elizabeth Pensoneau
The Calendar Girl
427 Lexington Court
New Berlin, IL 62670
(217) 488-7709 eves and weekends   <calendargirl@wbsb.net>

*TONY'S TIP: Paper items are bought by many people.
Use the index to get the best deal possible.*

◆ **Scrapbooks with diecut embossed scrap from the Victorian era, trade cards and prints.** Also wants collections of loose die-cut, embossed Victorian paper, especially Santas, snow angels, and children. Also wants cards from any holiday, 1840 to 1910. Nothing later. Everything must be in suitable condition for resale. No postcards.

> Madalaine Selfridge
> 33710 Almond Street
> Wildomar, CA 92595
> (909) 674-9221 <ms@majornet.com>

◆ **Scrapbooks of Victorian era trade cards.**

> Russell Mascieri
> 9 North Sunset Drive
> Voorhees, NJ 08043
> (856) 354-2154 <rmascieri@aol.com>

◆ **Children's illustrators.** "I want prints, calendars, trade cards, magazine covers and books with color illustrations from 1920-1940 by children's illustrators like Frances Brundage, Maud Humphrey, Ida Waugh, Torres Bevins, Mabel Attwell, Rose O'Niell, Grace Drayton, Bessie Pease Gutmann and similar artists of that period."

> Madalaine Selfridge
> 33710 Almond Street
> Wildomar, CA 92595
> (909) 674-9221 <ms@majornet.com>

◆ **Collections of labels, stickers and poster stamps pre-1960.** Wants collections of colorful, smaller graphics of all types, even if many are duplicates. Immediate answer if you include your phone number.

> George Theofiles
> PO Box 1776
> New Freedom, PA 17349

◆ **Paper puzzles in any printed format.** "I'll buy crosswords, mathematical puzzles, rebuses, tangrams, brain teasers, picture puzzles, etc. The format can be a book, magazine, pamphlet, broadside, trade card, or newspaper, but I do not want 'hidden image' puzzles or those that are too juvenile, intended for small children." In general, he is most interested in items from before 1950, the earlier the better, although value depends on the quality of the puzzle and the rarity of the material. He also wants material about the history of puzzles, directories of puzzles, and anything with the byline 'Sam Loyd,' a famous turn of the century puzzlist. Give the date and condition, and describe the puzzle or state its objective. No jigsaw puzzles.

> Will Shortz
> 55 Great Oak Lane
> Pleasantville, NY 10570
> (914) 769-9128 voice/fax <wshortz@aol.com>

◆ **Pretty paper of all types:**
  • **Greeting cards from any event or holiday;**
  • **Calenders**;
  • **Valentines;**
  • Any **die cut people, animals, etc.**
  • **Advertising trade cards**;
  • **Prints** that are colorful and attractive;
  • **Early magazine covers**;
  • **Scrap books** of colorful paper, not news stories**;**
  • **Decorated crepe paper**, especially napkins;
  • **Bridge talleys**;
  • **Illustrated booklets**.
Especially likes beautiful women or children by **artists such a**s Francis Brundage, Maud Humphrey, Torres Bevins, M.L. Atwell, Grace Drayton, Rose O'Neill, and Becker. Buys all fine condition attractive items, generally from before 1930. Nothing later and no reproductions or modern reprints, calendars, etc. Please photocopy (Xerox™) what you have, or send a scan or photo.

> Madalaine Selfridge
> Hidden Valley Doll Museum
> 33710 Almond Street
> Wildomar, CA 92595
> (909) 674-9221   <ms@majornet.com>

◆ **Bookplates, primarily before 1930.** Bookplates are decorative printed ID plates which identify the owner of a book. Send a Xerox™ of the plate(s) you have and the price wanted. Does not make offers.

> Lewis Jaffe
> 1919 Chestnut Street #1117
> Philadelphia, PA 19103
> (215) 568-9253   fax (215) 568-6768

◆ **Passports and some other travel documents, pre-1940 American or foreign.** Documents must be complete: nothing missing, removed or torn. Photocopy the page with the owner's description and inside pages that have been used. "No overpriced passports owned by celebrities."

> Dan Jacobson
> PO Box 277101
> Sacramento, CA 95827

◆ "Dirty letters" written 1800-1975, ideally with the original envelope if mailed. May be hand written or typed. "Even better if photos or other items mailed with the letters are still there."

> Charles Martignette
> PO Box 293
> Hallandale, FL 33008
> (954) 454-3474

PAPER DOLLS

◆ **Paper dolls of all types.** Wants to buy antique paper dolls and toys, especially those by Tuck. Also wants books of paper dolls dating before 1960, magazine dolls from adult or children's publications and newspaper comic strip dolls from the 1930's and 40's such as *Flash Gordon* and *Brenda Starr*. May buy cut dolls if neatly done. Please give name, date if possible, book number and mention any writing on the front or back of the doll, the box, or the book. Can also use tinsel and antique crepe paper for making paper doll ornaments.

> Madalaine Selfridge
> Hidden Magic Doll Museum
> 33710 Almond Street
> Wildomar, CA 92595
> (909) 674-9221   <ms@majornet.com>

◆ **All types of paper dolls,** cut or uncut, one or a collection as long as they're pre-1960. Sellers should list paper dolls by name, if possible, and indicate whether they are cut or not. Photocopies of the doll are helpful. "I will identify your dolls for a reasonable fee."

> Fran Van Vynckt
> 7412 Monroe Avenue
> Hammond, IN 46324
> (219) 931-6813

◆ **Paper toys, figures, and buildings,** especially toys and models by Builtrite, but interested in any paper dolls and soldiers in good condition. In business for more than 20 years, The Paper Soldier publishes a large and informative catalog for $5.

> Barbara & Jonathan Newman, The Paper Soldier
> 8 McIntosh Lane
> Clifton Park, NY 12065
> (518) 371-9202

TONY'S TIP: HOW TO SELL PAPER DOLLS: When offering books of paper dolls for sale, it's helpful if you give the name of the book, the publisher, and the date. If it has one, give the Publishing Company's catalog number printed on the front or back.

"Dolls that have been cut out may be sellable if their arms and legs aren't bent. Do not mend with tape! It is absolutely essential you DO NOPT try to repair any tears, stains, creases. Don't tape dolls. Don't color paper dolls. Don't iron wrinkled dolls."

MAPS & GLOBES

★ **Maps and atlases before 1890** wanted, particularly those showing the present day United States. Maps and books that are damaged, torn, moldy, or bug eaten are worth a small fraction of those in fine condition. **Maps are worthless if laminated, dry mounted or glued to cardboard or Masonite.** Best to send your map on approval but description will suffice if you include the title, date, mapmaker, size and condition. No reproductions wanted.
>Charles Neuschafer
>New World Maps
>1123 South Broadway
>Lantana, FL 33462
>   (561) 586-8723
>   <maps@sover.net> <newworldmaps@prodigy.com>

◆ **Maps and globes.** Many different types of maps are wanted by this specialty dealer, especially U.S. areas pre-1920 and worldwide prior to 1900. Particular interests include:
- **Books with maps**: atlases, geographies, travel guides, gazeteers, land surveys and explorations prior to 1900;
- Wall maps before 1920;
- **Pocket maps with folding covers**, case maps which fit into cases, and other maps separately published (not as part of a book of maps) before 1920;
- **Hand drawn maps**, especially battlefields;
- City plat maps before 1900;
- Texas, the Southwest and Southeast maps before 1900;
- Decorative maps;
- Geologic maps;
- **Railroad maps**, especially of the entire world, USA or the US Southwest before 1920;
- **Bird's eye views of cities**;
- **Globes** of the world before WWII, especially those with unusual or decorative stands;
- **Games and puzzles** pre-1960, including jigsaw, based on maps.

Please do not offer atlases or geographies after 1900. Description should include the author or map maker, the title or area depicted, the latest date on the map, the size, whether or not it is colored, and the condition, especially noting anything missing.
>Murray Hudson
>Antiquarian Books & Maps
>109 South Church Street
>Halls, TN 38040
>(800) 748-9946   fax (731) 836-9017   <mapman@ecsis.net>

◆ **Atlases and maps before 1880 from anywhere in the world,** as long as they are in very good or better condition. When describing maps, give the topic of the map, publisher, date of publication and anything else written in the map's legend. Include the size of the paper and the size of the map itself. For atlases, give standard bibliographic information: author, title, place published, publisher, all dates of publication and a description of the cover, binding, pages, and dust jacket. Please, no book club books, textbooks, or anything in poor condition. Open daily with 60,000 items in stock and 25 years of experience.

James & Mary Laurie
Booksellers
921 Nicollet
Minneapolis, MN 55402
(800) 774-1114   (612) 338-1114   fax (612) 338-3665
<lauriebk@winternet.com>

◆ **U.S. maps and atlases before 1870.**
Joe Davidson
Antiquarian Graphic Society
5185 Windfall Road
Medina, OH 44256
(330) 723-7172   <artbroker@webtv.net>

◆ **U.S. maps and atlases before 1870.** When describing maps, give the topic of the map, publisher, date of publication and anything else written in the map's legend. Include the size of the paper and the size of the map itself.

Frank Klein,
The Bookseller
39 Westgate Circle
Akron, OH 44303
(330) 865-5831 10 - 6   fax (330) 865-5851
<thebooksellerinc@neo.rr.com>

◆ **Atlases with colored plates before 1870** as long as they deal in whole or in part with the United States. It is important that double page plates should not have a white area separating the plate into two sections. Also interested in commercial atlases prior to 1925 and books of all types with foldout maps in black and white or color, but they must be before 1870. Groups of loose color plate maps are also considered. Include dimensions with standard bibliographic information. Note tears, erasures, foxing, etc. If you have a book with many maps, give the number of maps in color and in b/w.

John Rosenhoover
100 Mandalay Road
Chicopee, MA 01020

◆ **London, England, and European maps, 1850 and 1900,** especially *Ordnance Survey Map.* Also a pull down wall map showing America from that same period. You must price.

> Rev. Sherlock Holmes
> PO Box 3
> Worcester, MA 01613
> free (877) 306-4059   <antiques@sherlockholmes.com>
> <www.sherlockholmes.com>

◆ **Maps of any Asian country:** Japan, China, Korea, Vietnam, Siam, Tonkin, Cambodia, Laos, Malaya, Singapore, Indonesia, Philippines, Burma, Formosa, Taiwan, Tibet, Mongolia, Manchuria, New Guinea, or anywhere else in Southeast Asia and the Far East. Maps before 1930 only, please. Photocopies are appreciated.

> Jerry Stanoff
> Rare Oriental Book Co.
> PO Box 1599
> Aptos, CA 95001
>   (831) 689-0203   fax (831) 689-0204
>   <jgs@rareorientalbooks.com>

TONY'S TIP: When describing an atlas or book of maps, use Standard Bibliographic Information consisting of: Title, author, publisher, city where published, date when published, number of pages, number of illustrations.

◆ **Globes of the world,** especially:
- globes made of glass (not plastic) covered with paper with interior lights that shine through;
- globes with black oceans;
- globes with revolving planets;
- globes that show the planetary system;
- globes with elaborate stands.

Anything unusual or before 1940 (map will show Palestine) considered. Identify the maker if possible. Send photo, including stand. Give height, circumference, and material. Condition critical.

> Murray Hudson
> Antiquarian Books & Maps
> 109 South Church Street
> Halls, TN 38040
> (800) 748-9946   fax (901) 836-9017   <mapman@usit.net>

ROAD MAPS

★ **Road maps given away by gas stations, state highway departments, automobile clubs, and various tourist offices.** Will consider all dates, but pre-1970 is preferred. Most maps are relatively low value, bringing $1 to $3 each if dated between 1930-1970, but a pile can add up, and some maps do bring more than those prices. Maps that are damaged, torn, moldy, or bug eaten are not wanted, although those with routes marked are "not a problem." He requests you send your maps on approval via 4th class book rate. Personal inspection is needed, since most maps are undated except for "secret codes" used by the printers.

> Charles Neuschafer
> New World Maps
> 1123 South Broadway
> Lantana, FL 33462
> (561) 586-8723
> <maps@sover.net> <newworldmaps@prodigy.com>

◆ **Road maps, particularly from the 1920's and 30's.** "I like city maps, state maps, and regional maps, foreign or domestic." Must be in good condition. Also will buy old official State Highway Department maps, the earlier the better. Noel says you may send your items for his immediate offer and a return check. Will buy large quantities, too.

> Noel Levy
> 1109 Silent Glade Road
> Owings Mills, MD 21117
> (410) 363-9040

PARTY PAPER

◆ **Greeting cards and other paper related to parties and celebrations before 1960 including Christmas, holidays, birthdays, etc:** gift wrap, ribbons, paper cups, napkins, plates, table covers, nut cups, place cards, party favors, paper costumes, decorations stickers, hats, noisemakers, confetti and the like. Special wants include **German valentines,** Hallmark story book character cards from the 1950's, and cards made of celluloid or with fringed silk. She does not want sympathy cards from any period. She will buy graduation and wedding announcements only if before 1925. Must be in perfect condition. When you contact her, include the nature of what you have, its approximate date and whether it is loose or in a scrapbook. Dealers must price their goods; amateurs may request an offer.

> Edie Rowe, Ye Olde Paper Shoppe
> 2838 Salamander Road SE
> Jefferson, OR 97352
> (541) 327-3265   <edierowe@proaxis.com>

AUTOGRAPHS

◆ **Letters, signed photos and signatures of famous people in any category:** Presidents, Hollywood, NASA, sports, Civil War, art, music, literary, scientific, historical, rock and roll, theater, aviation, old West. Also interested in old handwritten diaries, collections of letters from the not-so-famous, handwritten recipe books, and anything written while traveling across America. Wants California and New Orleans letters from 1800-1870. Offers $1,000 for signed Buddy Holly photo. Please photocopy what you have. No autopen or printed signatures.

> Michael Reese II
> PO Box 5704
> South San Francisco, CA 94083
> (415) 641-5920

*TONY'S TIP: The signatures of **politicians** other than U.S. Presidents are worth little. **Movie and TV stars** since 1960 are also of little value, with a few exceptions such as Marilyn Monroe and James Dean. The same is true for music. Only a few bands and individuals have value.*

The value of any autograph is highly influenced by the context. Handwritten letters are most desirable, especially when written concerning important events or personal thoughts of the famous.

Plain autographs on blank white cards are the least desirable but will still find some market, especially for important people.

◆ **Autographs, signed books, and rare documents in all fields.** Particularly wants U.S. Presidents and first ladies and "investment quality items." Wants handwritten letters of Presidents while in office, particularly of William Henry Harrison and James A. Garfield, whose letters could be worth as much as $50,000! No facsimile or secretary signatures. "It is usually necessary to see the actual item, particularly in order to make a firm offer." Their monthly catalog is free. Larry and Mike are authors of *From the President's Pen: an Illustrated Guide to Presidential Autographs*, available from them for $25.

> Michael Minor and Larry Vrzalik
> Lone Star Autographs
> PO Drawer 10
> Kaufman, TX 75142
> (972) 932-6050 from 10 to 10   Fax: (972) 932-6607
> <mail@lonestarautographs.com>

◆ **Autographed letters and documents from ancient times to modern day in all fields.** Significant medieval documents and manuscripts are always of interest. This 28 year veteran dealer does not want autographs obtained by writing celebrities, modern politicians, or movie stars. A photocopy is strongly suggested.

> Kenneth Rendell
> 989 Madison Ave.
> New York, NY 10021
> (800) 447-1007   (212) 717-1776   fax (212) 717-1492
> <gallery@kwrendell.com>

◆ **Handwritten documents and letters of famous Americans.** "We particularly want Washington, Adams, Jefferson, Franklin, Hancock, and Lincoln, and specialize in U.S. Presidents." Famous scientists, inventors, authors and musicians are sought. Note all imperfections.

> Steve and Linda Alsberg
> 9850 Kedvale Avenue
> Skokie, IL 60076
> (847) 676-9850   <lalsberg@earthlink.net>

◆ **Autographs in all fields with a particular emphasis on Presidents and political, military, and historical figures.** He does not want Hollywood or TV people after 1940. "The more information the better. Describe what it is written on, whether faded or bright, whether written in pen or pencil, and the wording of any inscription."

> Chris Wilson
> 8101 Revatom Court
> Dun Loring, VA 22027
> (703) 698-7073   <cmnzwilson@starpower.net>

◆ **Important autographs and manuscripts by Presidents or historical figures.** Wants the old, rare, and valuable only.

> Ivan Gilbert
> Miran Arts & Books
> 2824 Elm Avenue
> Columbus, OH 43209
> (614) 236-0002 voice and fax

◆ **American and foreign autographs in all fields throughout Western history, including politicians, Presidents, signers of the Declaration of Independence, music and the arts, literature, the military, and scientists.** Will buy one or collections. This 20+ year veteran is not interested in unsigned documents of any sort.

> Robert Batchelder
> 1 West Butler Avenue
> Ambler, PA 19002
> (215) 643-1430   or (484) 356-0484

◆ **Autographs of celebrities and newsmakers** on checks, letters, photos, etc. Want heads of state, Royalty, rock star signed albums, etc. "I can't tell from a photocopy whether your item is authentic. I must see your item in person." No printed signatures are wanted.
>Myron Ross
>PO Box 9088
>Calabasas, CA 91372
>>\<heroesross@aol.com\>

◆ **Greeting cards signed by famous people.** From Presidents to prisoners, if they're famous and signed a Christmas, birthday or other greetings card before 1960, this long time paper dealer will probably be interested. Make a photocopy of what you have.
>Edie Rowe, Ye Olde Paper Shoppe
>2838 Salamander Road SE
>Jefferson, OR 97352
>>(541) 327-3265   \<edierowe@proaxis.com\>

◆ **Composers, musicians and singers of classical music.** Buys signed photos, letters, musical notations, etc. No free appraisals.
>J.B. Muns Books & Fine Art
>1162 Shattuck Avenue
>Berkeley, CA 94707
>>(510) 525-2420   fax (510) 525-1126
>>\<jbmuns@aol.com\>

◆ **Composers, musicians, opera singers, and movie stars from the late 1800's to the 1950's.** Prefers to buy signed photos, letters with important content, or musical quotes. "We are not interested in the autographs of current performers, but will pay very well for first class older items. Condition is important. We request photocopies and prefer to see the item in person, especially when large collections are involved." Will make offers for amateurs. Dealers, price your goods.
>Bill Safka and Arbe Bareis
>PO Box 886
>Forest Hills, NY 11375
>>(718) 263-2276   fax (718) 263-2276
>>\<safkabareis@yahoo.com\>

◆ **Autographs of celebrities and "newsworthy persons" including photos, letters, checks, or other documents signed by mass murderers, assassins, spies, heads of state, royalty, rock stars, and other famous and infamous persons.** Xerox© a must if you want an offer.
>Sheldon Kamerman
>World Wide Auctioneering Group
>466 11th Street   Suite #F
>Lakewood, NJ 08701
>>(732) 363-6161 weekends   fax (732) 364-9292

Continued from page 459

TONY'S TEN TIPS WHEN LISTING ON EBAY

(1) Be smart about your title. You lose money when you neglect key words that buyers search on. Your title should include what you have and as much **relevant** information as you can jam in.

(2) Check out similar ebay listings. It doesn't make sense for you to list items that others have listed and that are not selling. See how people in that hobby describe things.

(3) List items in the most profitable category. Cross-over collectibles are items wanted in more than one hobby, and values may vary greatly.

(4) Get to the point. Assume bidders are in a hurry. Keep your offering simple, direct and thorough. Put a picture, a description and then, and only then, add anything else.

(5) When writing a description, give complete information in a logical order. Describe (1) what your item is, (2) the title if it has one, (3) the maker, marketer, artist or author if known, (4) all marks or other identifiers including © dates, (5) what it is made of, (6) its dimensions, (7) its condition, (8) any special features and (9) tell what you know of its history. Make sure to include all dates, patent numbers, and other information printed on your item. "See picture" is NOT a substitute for information.

(6) Spell key words correctly. Misspellings reduce the number of bidders who will find you. Every Power Buyer has a story about a misspelling which led to a bargain.

(7) Put your most informative photo first, above the description. Use a sharp overall view with important features clearly visible. Don't make bidders load six irrelevant views to get to one with the most important image. Post all other photos AFTER the description.

(8) Do not use animation and music. Just because you CAN do something, doesn't mean you SHOULD do something. Entertainment isn't your goal on ebay.

(9) Don't use color backgrounds. They're hard to read. Base your listing on the needs of bidders not your decorator.

(10) Avoid describing something as "awesome" or "rare." If an item is in my field and rare, I'll know it. The fact you've never seen something before does not make it rare.

TONY'S TIPS ON SELLING POSTCARDS

Postcards are bought for the photograph, message, artist, stamp, and the postmark. Real photo cards (black and white real photos of people, places or events) are among the most sought. If you have a card that pictures any business, occupation or vehicle, the folks interested in those topics will pay more for the card than will a postcard dealer or collector. **Scenics picturing rivers, trees, mountains, lakes and the like, are seldom wanted, and worth only a dime at best.**

If you want to sell postcards, you have two choices: (1)Send them on approval or (2) send photocopies. *Because most of my readers have postcards, and many buyers want them (all through the book), I'm giving you guidelines on how to identify the various types of cards, and how to evaluate their condition.*

TYPES OF POSTCARDS

EARLY "PIONEER ERA" CARDS: Cards from the mid 1870's to 1900. Until 1893 cards had no pictures other than advertising. These cards are wanted for the postmark as much as for the card.

POSTCARDS: In 1901, "real photo" cards were introduced. A black and white or sepia photo is on one side of the card and the address on the reverse. Messages were not allowed on the address side, so pictures were often defaced by messages.

DIVIDED BACK CARDS: Cards used between 1907 and 1914 are called "divided back" cards because the message was written on the left and address on the right, thus preserving the picture. Real photo cards often have divided backs. Very collectible.

WHITE BORDER CARDS: From around 1915 to 1930, most postcards had a white border around the picture. Desirable, but less so.

LINEN CARDS: During the Depression and WWII (1930-45), postcards had a textured surface, like linen. Inks from this period were usually bright. The colored printed photographs were usually of poor quality with little detail. Much less valuable.

CHROME CARDS: Modern brightly colored, slick surface postcards made since WWII. Their colors are vivid, the details are sharp, and the cards are of almost no interest to collectors.

Postcard buyers are fussy about condition. *Poor condition cards seldom have a buyer, and prices drop dramatically for anything less than "excellent" condition. That's why dealers and collectors want to see your cards before paying for them.*

If you have a large quantity of cards, my advice is to ship them on approval after first contacting the potential Trash or Treasure buyer. Check whether the postcard buyers wants you to contact them first. Most do!

HOW TO DESCRIBE CONDITION

MINT: A perfect card, as it comes from the press. No marks, bends or creases. No writing or postmarks. Rarely seen.

NEAR MINT: Like mint but very light aging or very slight discoloration from being in an album for many years. Not as fresh looking as mint.

EXCELLENT: Card looks like mint with sharply pointed corners (no blunt or rounded corners). It may not have any bends or creases. May be used or unused, but writing and postmark are only on address side, with clean fresh picture side.

VERY GOOD: Corners may be just a bit blunt or rounded, or it might have an almost undetectable crease or bend that does not detract from overall appearance of picture side. May have writing only on the address side.

GOOD: Corners may be noticeably blunt or rounded with noticeable but slight bends or creases. May be postally used or have writing, but only on the address side.

AVERAGE: Creases an bends more pronounced. Corners more rounded. Or it may have writing in margins on picture side, or the postmark may show through from address side but not on main portion of picture.

POOR: Card is intact, but has excess soil, stains, or heavy creases, or it is written on the picture side, or has a cancel that affects the picture. Salable only if a very rare and desirable card.

SPACE FILLER: Poor condition, perhaps with torn or missing corners or breaks in the picture surface. Cards in this condition are neither desirable nor valuable.

POSTCARDS

◆ **Postcards, American and foreign, all subjects, used or unused, if before 1950.** "I'll pay competitive prices for better single cards or will buy collections, box lots, accumulations, etc."
> Sheldon Dobres
> PO Box 1855
> Baltimore, MD 21203
(410) 486-6569 eves   (800) 342-5983 days   fax (410) 837-7430
> <sdpost@aol.com>

◆ **Postcard collections, pre-1930,** especially American street views, disasters, railroad stations, fire departments, and diners. He also buys cards depicting foreign royalty, expositions, snowmen, full length Santas, and pre-jet commercial aircraft. Does not want foreign views, scenery, parks, woods, mountains, lakes, and flowers. Does not want damaged cards or those which have been pasted in albums.   "If your cards are not for sale, or if my offer is not accepted, I will appraise your cards at a cost of only one postcard of my choice for each 100 cards I appraise." Cards must be shipped for inspection for purchase or appraisal. John runs auctions, postcard shows, and heads the Postcard History Society. **He can supply you with many interesting free or low cost items regarding postcard collecting.** For more information send a stamped return envelope for his "Postcard Opportunity" sheet.
> John McClintock
> PO Box 1765
> Manassas, VA 20108
> (703) 368-2757   10am to 10 pm Eastern

◆ **Postcard albums and collections,** the older the better, in very good condition only. Interested in all topics, but does not want damaged cards. Jo Ann conducts mail auctions and sells on approval. Wants to know the number of cards, condition, and types of subjects pictured. She's been a collector for nearly 50 years!
> Jo Ann Van Scotter
> 14709 NE 22nd Place
> Silver Springs, FL 34488
> <jvanscotte@aol.com>

◆ **Picture postcards, foreign or U.S., from before 1946.** Real photo views are especially wanted, but all in good condition, whether used or not, will be considered. "Please ship for our offer. We will gladly pay for your postage. On larger lots, please call for instructions on packing and shipping."
> Josef Klaus, World Wide Notaphilic Service
> PO Box 5427
> Vallejo, CA 94591
toll free (877) 668-3988   fax (707) 643-3806   (707) 644-3146 eves

◆ **Picture postcards before 1950** are sought by this paper dealer, who does not buy chrome cards of any type or subject matter.

> Mike Rasmussen
> PO Box 726
> Marina, CA 93933
> (831) 759-0259   fax   (831) 422-1529   <rasspapercol@thegrid.net>

◆ **Postcards worldwide, used or unused, before 1950,** from any country, but especially from the U.S. and Canada. Wants street scenes, buildings, occupationals, sports, transportation, and people. Doesn't want water, forests, trees, mountains, deserts, etc. Also buys some pictorial "greetings." Pays 25¢ to $5 for most postcards, but a few European cards drawn or painted by famous illustrators can bring $100 up. No quantity too large. "Prompt payment if you send your cards on approval; unwanted cards are returned." Neil makes payment in the currency of the seller.

> Neil Hayne
> PO Box 35005
> Ingston Centre
> Kingston, ON   K7L 1H2   CANADA
> (613) 531-3666   <postcard@kos.net>

◆ **Canadian and English postcards from before 1930, new or used.** "I'm particularly interested in real photo views of small towns and interesting social history. I'll pay excellent prices for real photo cards of British Columbia or Yukon street scenes. I can not use damaged cards or boring mountain scenery. You may send cards on approval for my offer, and I'll pay the postage." Will pay in U.S. funds.

> Michael Rice
> PO Box 286
> Saanichton, BC   V8M 2C5   CANADA
> (250) 652-9412 eves only. Please, no day calls.
> <mrice@pacificcoast.net>

◆ **Canadian postcards from Ontario, Saskatchewan, Alberta, and Newfoundland provinces.** Want small town views, events, railroad stations, politics, buildings, and transportation. No scenics. Nothing after 1930. "A photocopy of the item is almost essential."

> Peter Cox
> 480 Bois Street
> Espanola, ON   P5E 1A7   CANADA
> (705) 869-2441 winter   (705) 859-2410 July & August
> <pcox@accglobal.net>

**If you have postcards it is important
that you read pages 518 and 519.
Do it now.**

POSTERS

◆ **Posters of all types.** This 30 year veteran dealer says, "I'll pay top prices for any printed poster done before 1960, especially WWI and WWII, film, travel, theater, circus, and transportation (ocean liner, railroad, and air). Also buys poster books, periodicals, and photos of posters being printed or posted. Include your phone number.
George Theofiles, Miscellaneous Man
PO Box 1776
New Freedom, PA 17349
(717) 235-4766 days

◆ **Posters of all types,** 1880-1950, all countries and subjects, especially U.S. posters from WWI and II and 1890-1910 American advertising. Army recruiting posters by Christy and Flagg from WWI bring $500 to $1,500. No reproduction posters are wanted.
George Dembo, The Poster Master
PO Box 657
Chatham, NJ 07928
(973) 701-0713 voice/fax   <poster1776@aol.com>

◆ **American posters of WWI.** No foreign, repros, or damaged items. Give the main slogan, the size, the artist if known, and the condition.
Ken Khuans
155 Harbor   #4812
Chicago, IL 60601
(312) 642-0554

◆ **Rock and roll concert posters from the 1960's.** Must give the name of the bands, where they are performing, the date, and the price of admission. Send a photo.
Bill and Linda Montgomery
12111 SE River Road
Milwaukee, OR 97222
(503) 652-2992

◆ **Wild psychedelic black light fluorescent posters (1960's - 70's),** but only in perfect condition. Send photo along with your asking price.
Judy Polk Harding
4347 Farm House Lane
Fairfax, VA 22032
(703) 503-7323   <thefivejs@aol.com>

TONY'S TIP: Rock concert posters will be of interest to Rock & Roll buyers and Pop Culture dealers.
Movie posters may find a buyer on page 170.
European posters may find a buyer on page 181.

TONY'S TIPS ON SELLING PHOTOGRAPHS

Unidentified portraits typically have little value. *But those same portraits will find buyers quickly if the sitters are in uniform or holding tools or weapons. Photos of officials, workers, events, outdoor city scenes, parades, stores, vehicles and uniforms will always find a buyer among collectors trying to learn more about an industry or era.*

To sell a photo, *Xerox© what you have. Condition of the photo and its mat are both important to a buyer. Note banged corners, stains, and the like. If the photo is faded, make certain you indicate that fact, as photocopies tend to make photos look better than they are.*

TYPES OF PHOTOGRAPHS

DAGUERREOTYPES: 1839-1854, recognizable by a silvery image on glass. The leather and early plastic cases are often worth more than the photo. Outdoor and city views are rare. Large "Dags" can be valuable. Do not clean them and do not leave them exposed to sunlight.

AMBROTYPES: Photos on a glass negative backed with dark paper to make a positive image. Mid-19th century. Subject matter is the key to value. These often come in elaborate cases.

ALBUMEN PHOTOGRAPHS: Paper prints before 1890 usually used egg albumen in preparation of the image surface.

TINTYPES: Cheap popular portraits, 1858-1910, printed on sheets of black tin. Also called ferrotypes. Subject matter is the key to value. Pictures not taken in a studio are usually more valuable.

CARTES DE VISITE (CDV): Photos on card stock measuring 2.5" x 4" popular between 1860-1890, often found in albums.

CABINET CARDS: Photos on 4" x 7" cards, usually studio shots with the photographer's name at the bottom. These are found with pictures of celebrities, Presidents and generals.

STEREOVIEWS: Cards containing two shots of the same subject to give a 3-D effect seen through a viewer. Views before 1890 are larger, flat, have colored mounts (yellow, pink, etc.) and generally no printing on back. Later views have curved gray mounts (Underwood is common). Newest, and worthless, are colored printed stereoviews. Older views will often be curved as a result of being stored with newer cards.

SNAPSHOTS. Printed in b/w on thin paper, popular from 1920-1960, when color pictures and slides became the photo of choice.

PHOTOGRAPHS

◆ **Photographs,** especially signed 19th and 20th century images, also tintypes, Daguerreotypes, ambrotypes, cartes de visite, cabinet photos, albumen prints, stereoviews, silver prints, platinum prints, cyanotypes, and photo albums. His list of "fine subjects" includes: banjo players, Russians, kids playing marbles, Brooklyn, photographers, auto racing, nudes, military, Civil War, funny photos, Lincoln, John Wilkes Booth, unusual photos, WWII, mug shots, writers, artists, Philadelphia, famous people, Hawaii and Samoa in the 19th century, Indians, mining, Orientals, sports, aviation, people at work and pre-1915 images. No ordinary studio portraits, and no photo equipment is wanted. Photocopy both sides of your photo and price what you have for sale.

Richard Rosenthal
4718 Springfield Avenue
Philadelphia, PA 19143
(215) 726-5493   fax (215) 726-5926   <rtrphoto@philly.infi.net>

◆ **Rare old photographs, cased photos, stereoviews, etc.,** especially work by important Western photographers such as Jackson, Curtis, and others. Also buys books with actual photos tipped (pasted) in. Buys modern computer generated art photos also. Send Xerox™ copy.

Ivan Gilbert
Miran Arts & Books
2824 Elm Avenue
Columbus, OH 43209
(614) 236-0002 voice/fax

TONY'S TIP: If you have photos of events, businesses, industry, or sports, you might find it profitable to deal with specialists in those subjects as they are often your best buyers. It could put more $$$ in your pocket to read the chapter dealing with the subject matter of your photo.

◆ **Photographs, especially Daguerreotypes, ambrotypes, tintypes, stereoviews, and round *Kodak* snapshots.** Would love to find photos of photographers at work, kids with pets, early swimming photos, photos containing microscopes, photos related to speech and hearing and photos of Pittsburgh and Allegheny County, Pennsylvania. Buys complete unpicked photo albums. "I haven't had an offere refused in 32 years so I must be treating folks fairly." SASE requested.

Nicholas Graver
276 Brooklawn Drive
Rochester, NY 14618
(585) 244-4818   <ngraver@rochester.rr.com>

★ **Interesting photographs of all types including Daguerreotypes, ambrotypes, tintypes, cabinet cards, cdv's, albumen prints, real photo postcards and stereoviews.** Indicates a willingness to pay high prices for a wide range of photos including the following categories:
- Civil War soldiers and scenes;
- Presidents and famous 19th century persons, especially Lincoln;
- Street or riverfront scenes;
- Cowboys and Indians;
- Sports, circuses, and other amusements;
- Crime scene photographs;
- Photographers in the studio or in the field;
- Artists and sculptors;
- Nudes, both artistic and erotic;
- Portraits of ordinary people in CDV or Daguerreotype form that are very sharp and in fine condition;
- Travel albums with mounted albumen photos (America, Egypt, and the Far East are preferred), albums of black construction paper with snapshots of extraordinary subject matter;
- Extraordinary portraiture, strange people, people in costume, side show performers and early soft focus art photography;
- Children or adults posed with unusual objects;
- Bizarre and unusual subject matter including death portraits;
- Political or other public events.

Has special interest in the Civil War, Lincoln and fine Daguerreotypes. All photos must be undamaged and not faded. Do not ask about printed or halftone reproductions. Make a Xerox™ copy of your photo for this relatively new collector/dealer who pledges prompt answers and competitive prices.

Thomas Harris
223 East 4th Street #14
New York, NY 10009
(212) 420-9121   <saltprint@mindspring.com>

◆ **Daguerreotypes, ambrotypes and tintypes of children, families, animals, architecture, Indians, Civil War, military, or anything out of the ordinary.** "I will buy complete family albums with photos from the 1800's, but don't want loose individual ordinary portraits, unless the person sitting for the photo is identified." Indicate any inscriptions or markings as well as any damage.   Dealers must price their goods. Amateur sellers may ask for help. "Please, I do not want any empty albums or photos taken after 1900."

Ed Clark
Texas Photo Center
215 W. Camp Wisdom #6
Duncanville, TX 75116
(800) 327-1654   (972) 780-5735   fax (972) 780-0937
<edclark@texasphoto.com>

◆ **Stereoview cards "in nearly all categories"** are sought. He points out that there are two types of stereo cards, printed and photographic, and that he wants only photographic views of:

- Famous people;
- Ships, sailboats, riverboats, wharfs, etc.;
- Railroads, street cars, cable cars, etc.;
- Airplanes, blimps, balloons, etc.;
- Automobiles, fire engines, bicycles and other vehicles;
- Military, especially the Civil War;
- Western lore, cowboys, Indians, mining, etc.;
- Music, bands, theatrical scenes, etc.;
- Street scenes from any city or town;
- Occupationals - people at work, especially photographers.

"I want any cards that capture a bygone era, people at leisure, at home, children playing, costumes, furniture, and the like. In addition to U.S. views, I will buy fine condition photos of Canada and Europe. Please describe your cards briefly, telling the subject matter and condition."

Steve Jabloner
145 Kent Avenue #4
Kentfield, CA 94904
　　(415) 461-9541　　<jabloner@marin.cc.ca.us>

◆ **Stereoview cards,** particularly older Western scenes, transportation, mining, Mt. Lowe, fires, high wheel bicycles, famous people, Civil War, and early California. "But I buy most common stereos, too," but for a lot less. He particularly wants stereos of Lincoln published while Lincoln was alive. If you want to sell your cards, Chuck wants to know the subject of the card quite specifically, an accurate description of condition, and the publisher. If you have a price you want, say so. He does not want cards printed in color or in black and white.

Chuck Reincke
2141 Sweet Briar Road
Tustin, CA 92780
(714) 832-8563 eves　　fax (714) 832-8563　　<creincke@tumaros.com>

◆ **Stereoviews, U.S. and foreign, that are real photos pasted on cards,** not printed in color. Especially wants the odd and unusual, old West, occupations, photographers and their equipment, Indians, Civil War, nudes, ships, railroads, whaling, stores, factories, street vendors, circus, and many more topics. Send an SASE for his informative handout and wants list which gives much greater detail. Scenery is of interest only from Western states or exotic foreign countries. All views must be in fine condition to be considered for purchase. Send a Xerox™ of both sides of the card if writing is on the back.

Russell Norton
PO Box 1070
New Haven, CT 06504
　　(203) 281-0066　　<www.stereoview.com>

◆ **Bizarre photos, such as freaks, dwarfs, lynchings, slaves, public punishment** and what have you. Especially interested in photos of death, especially post-mortem photos, but also mourning photos, executions, lynchings, and embalming and medical photos with doctors and cadavers. Likes photos of the family gathered around the deceased. Worth from $10 to $100+ for the very early and unusual.

Steve DeGenaro
PO Box 5335
Poland, OH 44514
<sdegenaro@aol.com>

◆ **Stereoviews showing the development of the early West, 1860-1900:** expeditions, railroad construction, freighting in the Sierras, maritime scenes, Indian portraits and culture, mining, logging, and early small town scenes as well as San Francisco. Particular interest in Custer, Teddy Roosevelt, Mark Twain, Bret Harte, John Sutter, artist Albert Bierstadt, and all early photographers and their equipment. The latter will bring "hundreds of dollars" in excellent condition. Also wants paper advertising from early western photographers. Not interested in faded views or those with damaged mounts. No lithographed views, only real photos in excellent condition.

Jim Crain
131 Bennington Street
San Francisco, CA 94110
(415) 648-1092 eves

◆ **Daguerreotypes** of famous people, Negroes, outdoor scenes, military, freaks, animals, people working or with tools, nudes, ships, fire engines, railroads, old West, balloons and disasters. Premium paid for very large ones. Describe the picture, give the dimensions and describe the case and its condition.

Russell Norton
PO Box 1070
New Haven, CT 06504
(203) 281-0066 11 a.m. to 8 p.m. any day

◆ **Original photos of Lincoln.** "I'll buy photos of Lincoln taken from life and printed before 1866. Will also purchase the Ayers photos of Lincoln printed in the 1880's and 1890's. I'll also buy photos of Lincoln look-alikes." No photos of prints, statues, or Abe's house. Send a photocopy of what you have. "Serious sellers only, please."

Stuart Schneider
820 Kindermack Road
River Edge, NJ 07661
(201) 599-4250   fax (201) 599-4251
<stuart@wordcraft.net>

◆ **Photos of cowboys, Indians, and related subjects,** including cattle drives, early Texas towns, outlaws, lawmen, the Geronimo expedition (especially those taken by C.S. Fly), and the Mexican War. All types wanted, including stereo. Please send photocopies.

> Johnny Spellman
> 10806 North Lamar
> Austin, TX 78753
> (512) 258-6910 eves   (512) 836-2889 days   <dvm69@swbell.net>

◆ **Photos of old Western personalities,** Wild West Show characters, armed cowboys and cowgirls, trappers and scouts dressed in buckskin, famous lawmen, armed Indian braves, and death views of outlaws. This 25 year veteran pays from $200 to $2,500 depending on the subject and type of photo. Excellent condition items before 1920 only. He does not want postcards, Indian women, children, cattle drives, or general Western views. Must send a clear Xerox™ of what you have. Dealers, price your goods. Amateurs may request an offer.

> Emory Cantey, Jr.
> Our Turn Antiques
> 1405 Ems Road East
> Fort Worth, TX 76116
> (817) 737-0430 voice/fax   <ourturn@swbell.net>

◆ **Photos of famous people, outdoor scenes and "the odd and the unusual"** taken before 1910. Will buy Daguerreotypes, ambrotypes, tintypes and cartes de visite in fine condition. Send a photocopy.

> Chris Wilson
> 8101 Revatom Court
> Dunn Loring, VA 22027
> (703) 698-7073   <cmnzwilson@starpower.net>

◆ **Photographs and engravings of famous people** in all walks of life. Will consider items loose or in books. Please photocopy.

> Kenneth Rendell
> 989 Madison Ave.
> New York, NY 10021
> (800) 447-1007   (212) 717-1776   fax (212) 717-1492
> <gallery@kwrendell.com>

◆ **Photos of Indians and Eskimos,** especially the work of Edward S. Curtis. Also buys real photo postcards on the same theme. Please send photocopies for a prompt response. Dealers, price your goods, but amateur sellers may request an offer.

> Barry Friedman
> PO Box 55492
> Valencia, CA 91385
> (661) 255-2365   <barryf@thevine.net>

◆ **Photographs of people with guns.** Has a particular interest in Civil War and Western scenes but wants hunters, soldiers, sailors, Indians, and cowboys. All types of early images are considered, including cdv's, cabinet cards, tintypes, Daguerreotypes, etc. Send a photocopy of any image you want to sell, except those on Daguerreotypes, the cased photos with a mirror finish. SASE please. "I do not make offers."

    Charles Worman
    PO Box 292624
    Kettering, OH 45429
        (937) 299-7752   <oldguns@aol.com>

◆ **Photos in memorial matts** (ordinary portraits mounted in memorial matts after the person died). Memorial matts have printed or embossed angels, doves, Gates of Heaven, etc., and mottoes like "Free at Last."

    Steve DeGenaro
    PO Box 5335
    Poland, OH 44514
        <sdegenaro@aol.com>

◆ **Photos of the Dakotas, Minnesota, Wyoming, and Montana from before 1930 in any format,** including real photo postcards, especially those marked DT, Dakota Territory, DAK or South Dakota. Buys single items or collections. Is often as interested in the photographers as the subject matter of the photo. Photocopies are recommended. If your items are in fine condition, you may ship them on approval.

    Robert Kolbe
    1301 South Duluth
    Sioux Falls, SD 57105
        (605) 332-9662

TONY'S TIP: Watch for revenue stamps on the back of Civil War era cartes de visite and other photos. Most are common, but a few are valuable. Buyers of revenue stamps may be found on page 477.

TONY'S TIPS ON SELLING CAMERAS

You may find it hard to recognize the earliest Daguerreotype cameras because they look like wooden boxes without a lens. They are quite valuable.

So are hidden ("detective") cameras, popular in the late 1800's. Cameras were hidden in canes, shoe boxes and the like. Other cameras that will sell quickly include cameras with more than one lens, panorama cameras, and other early oddities.

If you want to sell a camera, provide the following information in your first letter:

(1) *Brand name, and model name if you know it;*

(2) *All numbers on the body of the camera;*

(3) *The name of the brand of lens, and any numbers and other information printed around the front circumference of the lens;*

(4) *Whether or not the camera works;*

(5) *Whether or not the camera seems to be complete;*

(6) *Whether the case and camera are covered with wood, metal, leather or cloth...and its condition;*

(7) *Whether or not the camera has a folding cloth or leather bellows; if it does, the bellows' color;*

(8) *A list of accessories with the camera, such as lenses, boxes, instructions, etc.*

Kodak cameras with built in flash are collectible but of such low value they're not worth your fuss. Brand name German and Japanese 35mm cameras from the 1930's, 40's and 50's are. Prices can top $1,000 and have actually hit ten times that. They are well worth your time.

Don't try to clean your camera or the lens. *You're not helping...and you may cost yourself money. If there is old film in the camera, do not remove it. Whenever selling any equipment or mechanical devices, the less you do, the better off you are.*

CAMERAS

◆ **Cameras.** "I'll buy complete camera collections or camera shops." Has a special interest in:
- 35mm rangefinder cameras by *Leica, Nikon* and *Canon*;
- 1940's-50's SLR cameras by *Nikon, Zeiss, Konica* and others;
- 16mm movie cameras by *Angenieux, Arriflex, Beaulieu, Bolex* and *Mitchell* only (no 8mm cameras are wanted);
- *Polaroid* models 180, 190, and 195 only;
- 3-D cameras and all accessories and advertising;
- Subminiature cameras.

Harry offers free appraisals of these, but does not want to hear about your *Brownies*, built-in flash cameras, plastic cameras, black box cameras, folding cameras with black bellows, or 16mm home movie cameras and projectors, please. These have no value to collectors.

Harry Poster
PO Box 1883
South Hackensack, NJ 07606
(201) 794-9606   fax (201) 794-9553   <hposter@worldnet.att.net>

◆ **Cameras of brass, chrome, or wood made before 1948.** Anything interesting photographic, be it camera, book, or what have you, will be considered, including **pre-1930 photo magazines, pre-1948 catalogs,** and other ephemera. No *Polaroids*. Provide any numbers or names anywhere on the object. Describe condition of wood, leather, or metal. Must include an SASE. Free evaluation if you include an SASE.

Alan Voorhees
Cameras & Such
450 Breesport Road
Horseheads, NY 14845
(607) 739-7898   fax (607) 739-3506   <avoorhees1@stny.rr.com>

◆ **Cameras and related equipment both old and modern.** This long time dealer buys, sells and trades cameras and dark room equipment from all periods and buys one item or an entire collection. Not interested in plastic cameras. Pledges to provide an hones evaluation of what you own, whether vintage or modern. Provide the information on the previous page if you have just a few cameras. Best to contact him by phone if you have a large collection of items to dispose of.

Eric Mehl
Columbia Camera
55 East Blake Ave.
Columbus, OH 43202
(614) 267-0686   fax (614) 267-5526   <colscamr@infinet.com>

◆ *Kodak* **cameras, advertising, and memorabilia.** "I'll buy only pre-1930 cameras in near mint condition, especially those with original cardboard or wooden cartons. I'll also buy just the empty cartons!" Frank's list of cameras he seeks is too long to print here, but if you deal in cameras or if you have an old *Kodak,* it might be worth picking up his wants list. He also wants a *Kodiopticon* slide projector, and cameras made by companies absorbed by *Kodak* including *Poco, Columbus, Ludigraph, Kameret* and Rochester Optical's *Empire State View* camera. *Kodak* newspaper and magazine advertising before 1930 may also find a buyer, as will counter top advertising, posters, signs, wood framed pictures of people using *Kodaks,* and any of the hundreds of items with the *Kodak* logo. "If it says '*Kodak*' on it, I want to know about it. That includes books which use *Kodak* as part of the title, advertising in foreign languages, instruction books, stock certificates from any camera company, *Kodak* annual reports, and anything else that is old, in fine condition and related to *Kodak.*"

> Frank Storey
> 194 School Lane
> Linthicum, MD 21090
> (410) 850-5728 eves/fax 24 hrs   <frankstorey@bigfoot.com>

◆ **Cameras** are wanted, but only the rare, unusual, or very early (pre-1880), especially stereo, multiple lens, and panoramic. Cameras hidden inside other objects are of great interest, as are the very small cameras called subminiatures. Not interested in *Kodak, Ansco,* or *Polaroid.* Give make, model, and names and numbers printed around the lens.

> Russell Norton
> PO Box 1070
> New Haven, CT 06504
> (203) 281-0066

TONY'S TIP: Most Kodak and Polaroid still cameras have little if any value, although commemorative, colored, and very early Kodak cameras are worth inquiry. 16mm home movie cameras and projectors have no collector value.

Whenever selling any equipment or mechanical devices, the less you clean, repair or adjust the better off you are.

VIEW-MASTER & 3-D EQUIPMENT

◆ *View-Master* **reels and equipment** made by Sawyers or GAF, the companies that owned *View-Master* before 1980. Will buy single reels, 3-pack reels, cameras and accessories, Stereomatic 500 projectors, and the blue Model B viewer (worth $100 to him). Also buys some *Tru-Vue* and other 3-D items. Pays from 25¢ to $50 per reel, with top money going to 3-D movie preview reels and reels of commercial advertising for popular products. The more obscure 3-reel packets (such as those for *The Munsters* or *The Addams Family*) can bring good money. Does not want any cartoon reels or any damaged, broken, or worn items. Give numbers on the reels and state their condition. If you have anything from *View-Master* that was intended for in-house or factory use and not for the public, make certain you inquire as it might be valuable.

Walter Sigg
PO Box 208
Swartswood, NJ 07877
<ws3dent@nac.net>

◆ **3-D cameras, reels, and other** *View-Master* **equipment,** including flash, close up lenses, cases, film cutters, 3-D projectors, library boxes, adjustable viewers, and old order lists from Sawyers or GAF, the manufacturers of *View-Master*. Wants early views with blue backs, view reels that look like they're hand printed, Belgian made scenic views, pre-1970 U.S., and scenics of other continents. "I don't want children's cartoon reels made after 1950 or any scratched or damaged reels." The reel number and copyright date are more important info than the title.

Robert Gill
PO Box 485
Allendale, NJ 07401
(201) 934-7754   fax (201) 934-7754

◆ *View-Master* **and 3-D (two lens) cameras and accessories** including viewers, projectors (2 lens), manuals, and books. Brands include *Airequipt, Realist, Kodak, Wollensak* and other makers. Stereo cameras are worth $200 to $2,000, and many viewers are $100 each, especially the focussing viewer and stereo projector. "I'll pay 20¢ to $20 for most *View-Master* reels and packets, and some are worth more."

Harry Poster
PO Box 1883
South Hackensack, NJ 07606
(201) 794-9606   fax (201) 794-9553   <hposter@worldnet.att.net>

SOUVENIRS ALONG THE HIGHWAY

◆ **Souvenirs from diners and drive-in theaters on the Lincoln Highway and other items related to that road.** He looks for films, photographs, maps, ashtrays, calendars, guidebooks, lapel pins, matchbooks, postcards, menus, and toys like miniature drive-ins. The Lincoln Highway was known as Route 30 to Wyoming and Route 40 or 50 from there to San Francisco.

      Brian Butko
      2640 Sunset Drive
      West Mifflin, PA 15122
    <bsquared@bellatlantic.net>   <http://bbutko.tripod.com>

◆ **Pennsylvania Turnpike, National Road (US 40), Lincoln Highway (US 30) and The Mother Road (US 66) memorabilia of all kinds** including maps before 1950 for my personal collection. What have you? Please photocopy or send a photo with your description.

      J.C. Keyser
      PO Box 937
      Powell, OH 43065
    fax (614) 436-4760 after 5 EST   <oilcheck@aol.com>

◆ **Trailer park memorabilia.** "If it moved down a highway and you could live in it, we're interested" including auto campers, mobile homes, motor homes, VW campers, and specialty vehicles designed for various professions. Everything about the vehicles, the gear and the parks they stayed in, 1900 to 1970, is wanted: **magazines, brochures, photos, film footage, personal reminiscences, stories, models, toys, salesmen's samples, matchbook covers, sheet music, postcards, articles, advertisements, signs, ID plates, license plates and hubcaps.** Please send a photo or Xerox™ of what you have. Todd & Kristin operate *Lost Highways*, a club, archive, and magazine filled with photos, reminisces, ads, etc. from the heyday of trailering and motor camping. Sample issue $6. Compete information for a long SASE.

      Todd & Kristin Kimmell
      Box 43737
      Philadelphia, PA 19106
    (215) 925-2568   fax (215) 925-5646   <www.losthighways.org>

Collectors of "places" want a wide range of items. Many of the buyers in the next 16 pages are historians of their region. They buy old photos and documents llike catalogs and maps. Most folks in this section will buy just about anything that's old, colorful, informative and in good condition ... doodads and novelties.

◆ **Souvenir travel decals** of the U.S., Canada and Mexico including but not limited to States, parks, cities, highways, attractions, landmarks, motels, hotels, and the like. They must be the water dip transfer type. Most decals bring $1 to $6 each in small quantities, and sometimes more for rare and desirable locations like Route 66 attractions such as Petrified Forest, Meramec Caverns, Gallup, etc. Earlier types by EMCO, ENCO, Goldfarb Novelty (always labeled on the back) and Mastercraft (catalog #'s begin with MD) bring more. Early decals from the 1940's in their original envelopes can bring as much as $12-$15 each. The more obscure and off beat the place the better. Large quantities of the same decal, often drops the price considerably. He DOES NOT WANT vinyl self stick decals, bumper stickers, postcards, or water decals from colleges, scools, etc. Call or email if in doubt.

Dick Schneider
Lost Highway Art Co.
PO Box 164
Bedford Hills, NY 10507
(914) 234-9029   <losthwyart@aol.com>

TONY'S TIPS: *The value of photos and documents depends on their content ... what is pictured or what is said ... and how well .* *Other factors which influence value are condition, scarcity, desirability and age. The value of photos and documents which tell the story of a region, state or town generally ranges from $5 to $50 but can go higher..*

Some collectors seek products made in or traditionally associated with the region of the country in which they live. Examples include: Great Lakes shipping, New England crabbing or oystering, Western mining. Florida citrus, and the like.

A few collectors want it "all,' from cheezy souvenirs to the fine art native to their area. Amost every collector or dealer likes to pick up paper associated with their hobby or business.

FROM AND ABOUT VARIOUS PLACES

◆ **Wooden Adirondack souvenirs.** "I buy the weird and wonderful! I want items made in the Adirondacks but sold all over America, usually stamped with the name of the place where they were sold." The distinguishing feature of these rustic wood souvenirs is the maker always left some bark on the piece. Barry buys lamps, mugs, tankards, picture frames, smoker's stands, clocks, plaques, inkwells, towel racks, wishing wells, and just about anything else EXCEPT nut bowls and salt and pepper shakers. Many of these items had decals of Indians on them and better pieces had carvings of big game animals like moose or bear. He also buyS miniature canoes other birch bark items, but only if in perfect condition. Price and describe fully in your first letter.

> Barry Friedman
> PO Box 55492
> Valencia, CA 91355
> (661) 255-2365   <barryf@thevine.net>

◆ **Great Barrington, Massachusetts, and Berkshire County souvenirs** including pictorial china, spoons, cups, postcards, photos and especially souvenir china from the years 1900-1930. Towns to look for are Stockbridge, Housatonic, Van Deusenville, Risingdale, Egremont, North Egremont, and Sheffield.

> Gary Leveille
> 5 Brook Lane
> Great Barrington, MA 01230
> <garyleve@aol.com>

◆ **Ocean Grove, New Jersey, memorabilia** including souvenirs, maps, photos, postcards, books, glass, porcelain, and anything else from this camp meeting seaside resort located south of Asbury Park. "I want everything, including beach, hotels, auditorium, etc."

> Norman B. Buckman
> PO Box 608
> Ocean Grove, NJ 07756
> (800) 533-6163   <buckman@monmouth.com>

◆ **Hoboken, New Jersey memorabilia** including paper, books, photographs, postcard, prints, maps, articles, letterheads, labels, and any manufactured item with the word hoboken molded or printed on it. "We buy almost everything, no matter how trivial, including personal reminiscences of early Hoboken residents for inclusion in various local histories we are writing." You have the Hans's permission to ship any early Hoboken item on approval. They pay postage both ways.

> Jim and Beverly Hans
> PO Box M-1220
> Hoboken, NJ 07030
> (201) 653-7392

◆ **Souvenir china from many New York State cities and towns** is sought, especially Rochester, LeRoy, Batavia and Thousand Islands. "I also buy quality pieces from Florida, California, New Mexico and all New England states." He seeks creamers, vases, toothpick holders and other forms with scenes from the cities and towns depicted in multicolors. This pre WWI German china is particularly desirable in cobalt blue. Nothing chipped or cracked, please.

> Burton Spiller
> 49 Palmerston Road
> Rochester, NY 14618
>   (716) 244-2229   <bottlebug@aol.com>

◆ **Coney Island souvenirs including Dreamland, Luna Park, and Steeplechase.** He particularly wants pitchers, glasses, dishes, and other cream colored diamond and peg pattern custard glass marked coney island. SASE appreciated.

> John Belinsky
> 84 Day Street
> Seymour, CT 06483
>   (203) 888-2225

◆ **Tennessee ephemera** wanted, including trade tokens, medals, pins, badges, real photo postcards of small towns, city business directories and phone books printed before 1950, Civil War tokens, city and county histories, and items from the Tennessee Centennial Expo of 1897. This major token collector asks that you describe your item well, including its condition. He is not interested in modern reproductions.

> Joe Copeland
> PO Box 4221
> Oak Ridge, TN 37831
>   (865) 482-4215   <joenatca@icx.net>

◆ **Southern souvenir china, glass or silver spoons from before 1920** with pictures of old buildings, streets, resorts or celebrations. Photo or description, the trademark, and exact condition required. SASE a must.

> Abbie Bush
> PO Box 503
> Elkader, IA 52043-0503
>   (319) 245-2128

◆ **Eureka Springs, Arkansas souvenirs and paper ephemera.** Wants informative or colorful paper, plates, cups, spoons, etc., from this resort capitol of the Ozarks. Only pre-1930 items in fine condition.

> Sheryl Baker
> Bank of Eureka Springs
> PO Box 309
> Eureka Springs, AR 72632
>   (501) 253-8241

◆ **Panoramic group photos taken in North or South Carolina.**
Lew Powell
700 East Park Avenue
Charlotte, NC 28203
(704) 358-5229   <lpowell@charlotteobserver.com>

◆ **Charleston, Georgetown and Kingstree South Carolina items** such as letters and envelopes, maps, tokens, medals, souvenir spoons, books, pamphlets, postcards, stock certificates and other fiscal paper. Also any South Carolina item related to the Confederacy, the SC Interstate, and the West Indian Expo of 1901-02.
Bob Karrer
17 Wentworth Street
Charleston, SC 29401
(843) 577-7876   <bkarrer@awod.com>

◆ **Georgia, South Carolina, and Florida paper pre-1870** that is related to slavery, the Civil War, indentures, King's grants, state grants, wills, or historically interesting topics. Georgia is of particular interest and documents can bring $100-$500 depending upon contents.
John Parks
203 Tanglewood Road
Savannah, GA 31419
(912) 925-6075   <historyman@earthlink.net>

◆ **Florida items.** Wants to buy everything about Florida history, but only items made before 1930. including: maps, postcards, stereoviews, souvenir china and spoons, paintings and prints, books, pamphlets, RR China, transportation schedules, license plates, stampless postal covers, etc. Please send a "detailed description including condition." Most souvenir china brings from $15 to $35, the same as real photo post cards.
Douglas Hendriksen
PO Box 21153
Kennedy Space Center, FL 32815
(321) 867-2551 day   (321) 452-0633 eve   <fl_collector@mpinet.net>

◆ **Orlando, Florida, memorabilia.**
Jerry Chicone
PO Box 547636
Orlando, FL 32854
(407) 872-1171   fax (407) 877-1137   <thegrove@worldramp.net>

◆ **Coral Gables, Florida, souvenirs** and advertising, especially items related to land sales in that area.
Sam LaRoue
5980 SW 35th Street
Miami, FL 33155
(305) 237-7478   fax (305) 237-7534   <slaroue@mdcc.edu>

39

NOTE ABOUT APPRAISALS

An appraisal is an evaluation and estimate of what your item is worth. The quality of the appraisal depends on the experience of the appraiser and how current his information is.

A formal appraisal includes a written description of your item and a reasonable retail selling price backed up with data about comparable sales when this information is available.

An informal appraisal provides the owner with a fair retail price and, sometimes, an offer of purchase. Selling or keeping is always the option of the owner.

The advantages of a formal appraisal include having it in writing, having a degree of accountability and having the work done by a person who is not involved in the purchase or sale of the material. If an insurance company or the courts are involved, they may require a formal appraisal, especially in areas of fine arts, or other items thought to be exceptionally valuable.

Any appraiser, whether it is someone you hire or someone who gives you a free estimate, is only as good as his or her experience. Do not rely on casual "appraisals" given by "experts" on television as having any bearing on something you might own, as they frequently appraise outside their area of real expertise. Folks who appraise on television are under great pressure to come up with high prices as TV producers feel they are more entertaining. They make lots of mistakes.

There is a national association of appraisers and you will frequently see recommendations that you should use only their members when you want something appraised. The problem with that is twofold. First, if you live anywhere outside a large metropolitan area, there are no members near you. Second, the organization is primarily concerned with painting, sculpture, silver and fine arts and lacks people qualified to appraise souvenirs, pop culture and the other middle class collectibles which fill most lives.

MIDWESTERN

◆ **Ohio memorabilia,** especially books, manuscripts, maps and photographs, from before 1900. Particularly interested in local history prior to the Civil War, especially in the Akron area.

> Frank Klein, The Bookseller
> 39 Westgate Circle
> Akron, OH 44303
> (330) 865-5831 10 - 6 fax (330) 865-5851
> <thebooksellerinc@neo.rr.com>

◆ **Wisconsin small town main street postcards.** "I have two lists: [1] 1,200 towns I have and [2] about 1,800 towns I don't have. I'll send one or both to anyone who is interested who sends a long SASE."

> Leo Smith
> 1831 Folsom Street
> Eau Claire, WI 54703
> (715) 832-6188

◆ **Waukesha and Slinger, WI.** Waukesha was noted for spring waters and a number of food products, so keep your eyes open for all sorts of things marked as being from Waukesha.

> W.E. Schwanz
> S. 45 W22339 Quinn Road
> Waukesha, WI 53189
> (262) 542-8586 <gschwanz@execpc.com>

◆ **Michigan and the Great Lakes ephemera** and historically interesting paper goods of all types from that region.

> Jay Platt, West Side Book Shop
> 113 West Liberty
> Ann Arbor, MI 48104
> (734) 995-1891 days <jplatt@provide.net>

◆ **Midwestern souvenir china** from before 1920, especially from Iowa. "All good items from all Iowa towns, especially Colfax, Clayton and Elkader are sought." Send a long SASE for her wants list.

> Abbie Bush
> PO Box 503
> Elkader, IA 52043
> (319) 245-2128

◆ **Humboldt or Rutland, Iowa,** pictorial postcards and advertising from those two towns.

> Don Olson
> PO Box 245
> Humboldt, IA 50548
> <donolson@goldfieldaccess.com>

◆ **Iowa trade tokens and dog licenses.**
Dennis Schulte
8th Avenue NW
Waukon, IA 52172
(563) 568-3628 before 10 p.m.

◆ **Rockford, Freeport, and Belvidere Illinois tokens, medals, buttons, badges, ribbons, and other small flat collectibles.** Also banks, early signs, coffee tins, bottles, etc. Loves to find larger items marked as being from Rockford. No paper or cardboard items.
Rich Hartzog
PO Box 4143 BVT
Rockford, IL 61110
(815) 226-0771 <hartzog@exonumia.com>

◆ **Dakota Territory, South Dakota, North Dakota, Minnesota, Wyoming, and Montana photographs and small ephemera** from before 1930 in any format, including real photo postcards. Wants all historically or pictorially interesting paper ephemera, advertising, letters, books, bottles, and small objects. Especially wants items marked DT, Dakota Territory, DAK or South Dakota. Buys single items or collections. Is often as interested in the photographers as the subject matter of the photo. Photocopies are recommended. If your items are in fine condition, you may ship them on approval.
Robert Kolbe
1301 South Duluth
Sioux Falls, SD 57105
(605) 332-9662

WESTERN EPHEMERA

◆ **Restaurant menues, postcards & matchcovers from Southern California.** Especially Los Angeles, Beverly Hills, Hollywood, Santa Monica, Malibu, Long Beach, San Diego and the San Fernando Valley. Other towns, especially Southern California coastal, will be considered. He ONLY wants menues from 1940 to 1990 from restaurants that no longer exist. Please Xerox™ the cover and give the year or the © date. All items must be fine condition.
Jerry Mezerow
442 Via Porto Ave.
Ahanheim, CA 92806
(714) 630-6198 <moviebuff35@webtv.net>

◆ **Western U.S. paper ephemera (1840-1920) related to the military, early forts, ghost towns, Mormons, railroads, mining, banking, cowboys, Indians, lawmen, cattle, courts, and financial matters.** Buys letters about the West, autographs of famous Westerners, and most illustrated pre-1920 Western documents such as checks, stocks, and the like. Holds regular auctions and sales by mail. Subscription to his 6 annual sales catalogs is $15.

> Warren Anderson
> America West Archives
> PO Box 100
> Cedar City, UT 84720
> (435) 586-9497   fax (435) 867-8078   <awa@netutah.com>

◆ **Western and Midwestern U.S. paper ephemera from before 1890.** Primarily wants pamphlets and broadsides dealing with emigration matters, travel, tourism, obscure town and county fairs, mining, railroads and "street scene" photographic images which must be identified. "I have been a serious collector in this field for many years, so please do not hesitate to get in touch with me." He DOES NOT WANT postcards, checks, letterheards or similar paper items or items from the Pacific Coast (California, Oregon or Washington).

> Ron Pearson
> 10620 Creekmere Drive
> Dallas, TX 75218
> (214) 321-9717   <rcpearson@webtv.net>

◆ **Colorado mining memorabilia, 1859-1915, especially Cripple Creek and all other mining towns and camps and the railroads that served them.** Wants photos, stereoviews, advertising, letterheads, billheads, brochures, pamphlets, mining papers, stock certificates, maps, badges, candlesticks, souvenirs, and other small items marked with the name of one of these towns. Photos should be of mining, railroad, or downtown activities, not people or scenery. Albums with numerous photos eagerly sought, as are business or mining directories and books on Colorado mining. Does not want anything from the flatland Colorado towns like Denver, Pueblo or Colorado Springs, nor anything from state or national parks. Give whatever info is printed or written on the backs of photos.

> George Foott
> 120 West Park Avenue
> Salida, CO 81201
> fax (775) 852-8666   <sfgfco@chaffee.net>

◆ **Las Vegas, Reno, and Nevada souvenirs and memorabilia from before 1970** with a special interest in gambling and casinos that are now closed. Buys gambling tokens and chips, playing cards, stock certificates, business directories, and collections of showroom programs, prints, photos, and maps. Will consider other ephemera from this desert playground if it has any historical significance, such as anything related to Nevada mining.

>Fred Holabird
>3555 Airway Drive #308
>Reno, NV 89511
>>(775) 852-8822   <fred@holabird.org>

◆ **Maps of Texas from before 1900.** Also trail driving maps.

>Johnny Spellman
>10806 North Lamar
>Austin, TX 78753

(512) 836-2889 days   (512) 258-6910 eves   <dum69@swbell.net>

◆ **Colorado and Wyoming memorabilia from 1860 to 1930.** Wants real photo and advertising postcards, souvenirs, "good for" trade tokens, stereoviews, envelopes and letterheads, fancy whiskey bottles, posters, calendars, trade cards, political buttons, ephemera from the Leadville Ice Palace, any item from the 1908 Democratic National Convention held in Denver, items from military forts, and items from fairs, rodeos, and Cheyenne Frontier Days. All items must be from Wyoming or Colorado within the 1860-1930 time frame. "I do not want items from National Parks, items after 1930, newspapers, or magazines. Please give a complete description." He emphasizes, "Please do not send unsolicited items."

>Edward Marriott
>9191 East Oxford Drive
>Denver, CO 80237
>>(303) 779-5237   fax (303) 733-2479

◆ **Nevada, Death Valley, and San Bernardino County ephemera** before 1930 is wanted including books, newspapers, magazines, diaries, letters, maps, promotional brochures, "and anything else printed or written on paper." Also stereoviews, merchant tokens, dog tags, hunting licenses, photos, postcards and what have you. He requests prices but will make offers.

>Gil Schmidtmann
>2346 Naples Avenue
>Mentone, CA 92359
>>(909) 794-1211

◆ **Dallas, Ft. Worth and Austin paper ephemera pre-1900,** including photographs, pamphlets, documents, and promotional materials. Also wants early Texas State Fair. He DOES NOT WANT Texas Centennial items or any postcards.

> Ron Pearson
> 10620 Creekmere Drive
> Dallas, TX 75218
>   (214) 321-9717   <rcpearson@webtv.net>

◆ **Montana memorabilia of all types,** with a particular interest in Great Falls, and its breweries and famous saloons like The Mint and the Silver Dollar. Among Montana items he wants are:
- Photos of saloons, cowboys, Indians, etc.;
- Tokens;
- Advertising from Montana companies, saloons and breweries;
- Books and paper ephemera from Montana Territory.

This 25 year veteran prefers you to set the price you want, but you may ask for offers if you provide a good description.

> Jim Combs
> 417 27th Street NW
> Great Falls, MT 59404
>   (406) 761-3320   <jifraco@montana.com>

◆ **Montana, New Mexico, Nevada, Utah and Wyoming souvenirs** are wanted including china, glass, sterling silver, postcards, pottery, and other small items originating in those states. SASE for wants list.

> Abbie Bush
> PO Box 503
> Elkader, IA 52043
>   (319) 245-2128

◆ **Idaho, Montana, and Washington items** including trade tokens, postcards, letterheads, calendars, buttons, ribbons, wooden nickels, stocks, match holders, calendar plates and other advertising china. Pays $1-$3 for postcards with postmarks from obscure post offices. Pays $2-$10 for cards of small towns he can use. Nothing after 1930.

> Mike Fritz
> PO Box 160
> Rathdrum, ID 83858
>   (208) 687-0159   <idahofritz@aol.com>

◆ **Oregon related items,** especially small items marked with the name(s) of Oregon cities or places. "A photo or good Xerox is a must."

> Fred Swindall
> 2219 SE Salmon
> Portland, OR 97214
>   (503) 224-0678 days   (503) 234-2454 eves

◆ **Yakima County, Washington, items.** "I buy pre-1950 photos, phone books, newspapers, directories, souvenirs, promotional booklets, and postcards, but no chrome faced postcards." Yakima HS yearbooks from pre-1910, 1933-34, and 1953-54 are also wanted. If in doubt, send for his wants list of 28 towns he seeks.

> Ron Ott
> 10 North 45th Avenue
> Yakima, WA 98908
> (509) 965-3385

◆ **San Francisco Bay area ephemera pre-1910,** especially related to the 1906 quake. Photos, diaries, letters, family mementos, and the like are wanted with emphasis on unusual. Ron has particular interest in items associated with schools and education before 1906 and in meal tickets and other items related to life in relief camps immediately after the disaster. No newspapers, postcards, or checks. Ron heads the S.F. History Ass'n and can accept tax deductible gifts from any period.

> Ron Ross
> 1076 Munich Street
> San Francisco, CA 94112
> (415) 333-5511   <ross1906@aol.com>

◆ **Pismo (Pizmu) Beach, Shell Beach, Avila Beach, Oceano, and Port San Luis, California.** Historian seek photos and stereoviews, but will consider anything interesting. Please Xerox™ what you have.

> Tony Hyman
> PO Box 3028
> Pismo Beach, CA 93448

◆ **San Gabriel Valley, California, items.** Wants pre-1930 items from any San Gabriel Valley towns: Arcadia, Temple City, El Monte, San Gabriel, Baldwin Park, Rosemead, Pasadena, Covina, San Marino, Monrovia, Duarte and Azusa. Also wants anything related to Emperor Norton and Lucky Baldwin. He suggests you ship your items to him via UPS at 650 West Duarte, #309, to get his offer.

> SC Coin & Stamp Co., Inc.
> PO Drawer 66180
> Arcadia, CA 91066
> (800) 367-0779   (818) 445-8277 in LA Co.   fax (818) 445-8278

◆ **San Diego, California, memorabilia** including postcards, pamphlets and photographs.

> Ralph Bowman's Paper Gallery
> 5349 Wheaton Street
> La Mesa, CA 91942
> (619) 462-6268 voice/fax   <ralph@thepapergallery.com>

ALASKAN ITEMS

◆ **Alaska and Yukon memorabilia.** Wants real photo postcards, salmon cans and labels, advertising mirrors, matchbook covers, trade tokens, ashtrays, cards, maps, dishes and brochures about Alaska, Alaskan industry and Alaskan steamshipping. "You name it and I want it." Will be happy to answer any questions about Alaska collectibles. Send a Xerox™ copy if you'd like an offer. You have his permission to send pre-1940 Alaska and Yukon items on approval.
> W.E. "Nick" Nickell
> 710 North 102nd Street
> Seattle, WA 98133
> (206) 789-7901

◆ **Alaskan memorabilia.** "I'll buy nearly anything old about Alaska, the Yukon, or the Polar Region including postcards, books, photographs, stereoviews, lantern slides, letters, maps, souvenirs, china, spoons, and miscellaneous ephemera. I buy for resale, and seldom buy items newer than 1945."
> Richard Wood, Alaska Heritage Bookshop
> PO Box 22165
> Juneau, AK 99802
> (907) 789-8450 voice/ fax   <dick@alaskawanted.com>

◆ **Alaska and Yukon historical items.** "I buy old photos, postcards, books, embossed bottles, magazines, artifacts, art prints, license plates, train and steamer brochures, Alaska Yukon Expo and items related to Klondike history. Give description, condition, date of origin, and what cities, towns, or regions are featured. Do not send items unsolicited.
> Reed Fitzpatrick
> PO Box 369
> Vashon, WA 98070
> (206) 567-055   <reed369@attno.com>

TONY'S TIP: When you ask someone for information or an offer, include a long business size #10 envelope, address it to yourself, and put a stamp in the corner. This is a Self-Addressed Stamped Envelope (SASE). Use a long envelope because many buyers will send you information which won't fit into smaller envelopes. If you do not include an SASE, you are telling buyers not to bother answering your letter if they are not interested in what you have to sell. "If my help isn't worth an envelope and stamp to the seller," said one expert, "it's not worth my time and money either."

HAWAIIAN ITEMS

★ **Hawaiian items for resale in specialty shop:** Wants to buy Hawaiian souvenirs, hand-tinted photos, Matson Line menus, Julene figurines, lithographs of Hawaii, airbrush paintings, hula lamps, Paradise of the Pacific Holiday Edition magazines, koa wood items, ukeleles. Mings Jewelry. Does not want other islands, items after 1960, vinyl hula girls, Hawaiian shirts, bolts of material or damaged paper items. Items must be in condition for resale. Description should include dimensions and a brief history. A few items, especially art, will have to be inspected before making payment. "Please don't ask about anything that is not for sale now."
     Susan Mast
     413 Western Drive #1
     Santa Cruz, CA 95060
(831) 423-9786   <sme@cruzio.com>   <www.hawaiiana-shop.com>

◆ **Hawaii, South Seas and Samoa ephemera.** Wants:
 • Books before 1920 about Hawaii, written by Hawaiians,
     or printed in Hawaii;
 • Magazines from 1940 or earlier with stories of Hawaii;
 • Paintings and prints of Hawaii, the South Pacific, or Asia;
 • Printed ephemera of any type before 1920 about these areas;
 • Oriental block prints, tapa cloth, ethnographic carvings from the
     South Pacific, and any other art of this region of the world;
 • Photographs of Hawaii, South Pacific or Asia before 1940;
 • Postcards mailed from, or depicting, this region;
 • Diaries or manuscripts about this area;
 • Whaling souvenirs;
 • Jewelry, pottery, and jade from these areas.
And other memorabilia from Hawaii or the South Pacific, as long as it's pre-1920. Send insured. No Hula dolls or Hawaiian shirts.
     Bernie Berman
     755 Isenberg Street #305
     Honolulu, HI 96826
         (808) 941-8639

◆ **Hawaiian items before 1970,** including art by Mundorff, Halepua, Tip Freeman, or Oda, usually in bamboo frames. Any 1960's or older surfing items, ukeleles, cruise line menus, paper leis, books, photos, hula girl figures, and tikis. "I am not a dealer. I'm decorating my house. What do you have that will fit in? Please call me."
     Wayne Babcock
     4846 Carpenteria Avenue
     Carpenteria, CA 93013
         (805) 684-8148

FOREIGN EPHEMERA

◆ **Canadian items:** calendars, stock certificates, bank notes, old letters in original envelopes, fancy letterheads, all Canadian railway, merchants' tokens from Western Canada, Canadian military or law enforcement, and postcards of BC, Yukon, NWT, AB, SK, and Newfoundland. Nothing after 1950, please. No road maps, tourist brochures, and postcards of tourist attractions or scenery. Prefers items be sent on approval or a photocopy made and included in your letter.
> Michael Rice
> PO Box 286
> Saanichton, BC
> V8M 2C5   CANADA
>> (250) 652-9412 eves & weekends only
>> <mrice@pacificcoast.net>

◆ **Panama Canal Zone and the Isthmus of Panama memorabilia** including postcards, letters, stamped envelopes, scrapbooks, tokens, medals, maps, coins, stamps, and everything else including souvenirs. Especially likes pre-1915 picture postcards with cancellations from obscure Canal Zone post offices. "I usually offer to buy anything Isthmus related."
> Bob Karrer
> 17 Wentworth Street
> Charleston, SC 29401
>> (843) 577-7876   <bkarrer@awod.com>

◆ **Cuban items before 1960:** cigar boxes, cigar labels, cigarette packs, photos, military decorations, stereoviews, tin advertising signs, etc. "I do NOT want junk souvenirs. I'm looking for items that give a glimpse of what life was like during the Spanish years and the Pre-Castro years of U.S. control. They are for illustrations in a book and website on Cuba before Castro. Please make Xerox copy and set your asking price whenever possible. Thank you for helping."
> Tony Hyman
> Box 3028
> Pismo Beach, CA 93448
>> <thyman@fix.net>

◆ **Philippines, Borneo, and nearby islands.** "I buy postcards, photos, books, magazines, maps, and other paper items, especially real photo postcards from Manila or elsewhere in the Philippines." Please make a Xerox© copy of what you have. He DOES NOT WANT coins, stamps, paper money, or books on the Spanish American War."
> Michael G. Price
> PO Box 468
> Michigan Center, MI 49254
> (517) 764-4517   <mgprice@acd.net>

◆ **Antarctic and Arctic ephemera** especially books but also diaries, posters, photographs, letters, pamphlets and other paper items associated with the expeditions. He will buy any clean copies of *Aurora Austrailis*, the Antarctic newspaper 1907-09.
> Jay Platt
> West Side Book Shop
> 113 West Liberty
> Ann Arbor, MI 48104
> (734) 995-1891 days   <jplatt@provide.net>

◆ **Arctic and Antarctic exploration items:** diaries, journals, articles, newspaper accounts, and memorabilia from expeditions. Send Xerox.
> Everen T. Brown
> PO Box 296
> Salt Lake City, UT 84110
> fax (801) 364-2646   <etbrown@everent.com>

◆ **Greenland, Pitcairn Island, Hudson's Bay, Canada, Mexico, and other countries' ephemera** especially tokens and medals, but other small items, especially before 1930 are likely to be of interest. Your best bet is to photocopy what you have.
> Rich Hartzog
> World Exonumia
> PO Box 4143 BVT
> Rockford, IL 61110
> (815) 226-0771   <hartzog@exonumia.com>

◆ **Australian Aborigine artifacts:** boomerangs, bull-roarers, shields, spear throwers and other artifacts. Pictures and complete description.
> Barry Friedman
> PO Box 55492
> Valencia, CA 91385
> (661) 255-2365   <barryf@thevine.net>

◆ **Switzerland ephemera** including books, medals, badges, emblems, postcards from before 1930, travel brochures, luggage labels, boxed stereoviews, trade cards, maps, prints posters and other collectibles. Please send Xerox© copy and SASE for offer.

    Donald Tritt
    81 Donald Ross Drive
    Granville, OH 43023
        (740) 587-0213   <tritt@denison.edu>

◆ **Lapland and Lapp/Sami culture from before WWII,** including maps, postcards, travel brochures, photographs, and some books. He requests a detailed description of the content and condition, a Xerox™ when practical or the item on approval. Contact before sending things.

    Mel Olsen
    8605 East Sage Road
    Wentworth, WI 54874
        <knut@discover-net.net>

◆ **Imperial Russian antiques and memorabilia whether civil, military, or religious.** Buys and sells pre-1917 Russian:
- Orders, decorations, badges, buttons, medals, and other militaria;
- Porcelains, bronzes, prints, icons, paintings and graphic arts;
- Coronation and other commemorative memorabilia.

Items are bought for cash or brokered. "Please send a clear photo or photocopy and price wanted." Mail order catalog and appraisal services available. ART Co DOES NOT WANT items made in the Soviet Union, nor do they want samovars or hammered brassware.

    Timothy Miller
    American Russian Trading Co.
    PO Box 4011
    Frederick, MD 21705
  (301) 668-6271 voice/ fax   <artco@mindspring.com>
        <www.artcoantiques.com>

◆ **Asian books and paper ephemera:** books, maps, photos, prints and paintings of Japan, China, Korea, Vietnam, Tonking, Siam, Cambodia, Laos, Burma, Malaya, Singapore, Indonesia, Philippines, Formosa, Taiwan, Tibet, Mongolia, Manchuria, New Guinea, South-East Asia and the Far East. A good description should include the dimensions, any signitures or marks, and how you came to own the piece.

    Jerry Stanoff
    Rare Oriental Book Co.
    PO Box 1599
    Aptos, CA 95001
        (831) 689-0203   fax (831) 689-0204
        <jgs@rareorientbooks.com>

TONY'S TIPS ON SELLING MAGAZINES

People are attracted to magazines for many reasons. Some buy for the covers and illustrations. Others look for early articles or advertising relevant to their hobby. Some folks just collect magazines!

To describe items for sale, give name and date of the magazines and note all tears, creases, address stickers, writing, or anything else affecting the cover or contents. If you have many issues, list them, counting only those with covers and pictures intact, no water damage, and no mildew smell. Describe the condition of a typical issue.

If you offer a magazine to someone because of an article contained in it, give the name and date of the magazine, the author of the article, and the number of illustrations. It's a good idea to photocopy the cover.

Collectors who buy books, magazines, photos, maps, postcards and other paper items tend to be fussy about condition. Don't overestimate the condition of a magazine. What you think of as "normal wear" can be "serious damage" to any paper collector. If you you find a magazine with pictures cut out, it's likely that others in the pile will also be cut.

DESCRIBING CONDITION OF MAGAZINES

VF (very fine) = fresh, bright copy without flaws except for minor aging of paper;

F (fine) = bright copy with very minor wear and only minute cover tears or creases;

VG (very good) = cover and spine wear, tiny tears and creases, minor chipping , browning of paper;

G (good) = obvious cover and spine wear, discoloration, water stains, pieces missing, tears up to 1" long;

FA (fair) = tight and complete, but longer creases, tears, rubbing, fading, and/or store stamps or dates;

P (poor) = many defects, serious damage, well worn; called a "reading copy," not as a collectible.

MAGAZINES

◆ **Volume 1, Number 1 (first issue) magazines, newspapers, comic books, or miscellaneous publications** including newsletters, catalogs, fan publications, etc. Also buys pre-publication issues, dummies, proofs and premier issues. "When I don't buy, I will try to help the seller find someone else who might."

> Stan Gold
> 7042 Dartbrook
> Dallas, TX 75240
> (972) 239-8621 fax (972) 239-9622
> < record@astimegoesby.com>

◆ **Most magazines in quantity if before 1950** and most newer movie, fashion and quality photography magazines. Has a particular interest in erotica, nudity, and spicier men's publications except *Playboy* and similar general newsstand magazines. Give quantity of each title and a description. They don't want *National Geographic* after 1910, *Reader's Digest* after 1930, *Life* after 1936, *Arizona Highways* after 1940, or *American Heritage* hardcovers. One of the largest magazine dealers, they will pick them up if you have a truckload.

> The Antiquarian Bookstore
> 1070 Lafayette Road
> Portsmouth, NH 03801
> (603) 436-7250

◆ **Women's, children's, theater, motorcycle, farm, and many other illustrated magazines, including pulps, 1895 to 1930.** Titles such as *Collier's, Esquire, Vogue, Saturday Evening Post, Vanity Fair, American* and others are wanted. Buys movie and men's adventure magazines up to 1960. Does not want magazines from 1970's or 80's. Give the date, condition, and price you'd like. Most of these magazines do not have extreme value. Denis publishes The *Illustrator Collector News* ($17/year), offers a large catalog of magazines for sale, and produces many reasonably priced price guides to magazines and magazine illustrators. Send SASE for info. Denis makes his information available in many different publications. He does not give free appraisals. "I'm happy to talk to you if you're seriously buying or selling, but I don't have time for pen pals or time wasters."

> Denis Jackson
> PO Box 1958
> Sequim, WA 98382
> (360) 683-2559 fax (360) 683-9708
> <ticn@olypen.com>

◆ **Movie magazines before 1960** in very good uncut condition.
>Claude Held
>PO Box 515
>Buffalo, NY 14225

◆ **Bound volumes of illustrated fashion and other magazines** including *Graham's, Godey's Ladies Magazine,* and others published before 1880. Wants *Craftsman* (1900-1915), *Ladies Home Journal, Delineator, Woman's Home Companion, Vogue* and *Saturday Evening Post* from 1910-1922. Condition is important. Note cracks, tears, foxing. Include SASE for answer.
>John Rosenhoover
>100 Mandalay Road
>Chicopee, MA 01020
>(413) 536-5542

◆ **Men's outdoor magazines** including *Field & Stream, Outdoor Life* pre-1920, and *Sports Afield* but only those published before 1932.
>Thomas McKinnon
>Twin Magnolia Farm
>8500 Odom Road
>Laurinburg, NC 28352
>(910) 268-1800

◆ **Hot Rod and custom car magazines from 1940-1964.** Wants the small 5" x 8" digest size. Must be complete with its original cover and have no pages removed.
>Don Schneider
>PO Box 1570
>Merritt, BC   VIK 1B8 CANADA

◆ *Sports Illustrated* **and other sports magazines** from before 1970.
>Gary Alderman
>PO Box 259164
>Madison, WI 53725
><gjazz@tds.net>

◆ **Old golf magazines, books and ephemera.** Wants fine condition complete magazines about gold. No paperback reprints or magazines published after 1950.
>George Lewis Golfiana
>PO Box 291
>Mamaroneck, NY 10543
>(914) 698-4579   <george@golfiana.com>

◆ *Billboard, Cashbox* and *Record World* magazines. **Negro magazines** such as *Sepia, Jive,* and *Tan* from the 1940's and 1950's. "I'll buy one or a truckload as long as they're fine clean complete issues with good covers between 1930 and 1979."

> Paul Scharfman, Chic-a-Boom
> 6817 Melrose Avenue
> Los Angeles, CA 90038
> (323) 931-7441   fax (323) 930-2990
> <chickaboom@earthlink.net>

◆ **Magazines about diving and underwater activities.** Buys foreign and domestic magazines such as *Skin Diver, Aquarius, Diver, Scuba Times, Sport Diver, Ocean Realm,* etc. No books, hardcover or soft. Also interested in old Mike Nelson *Sea Hunt* comic books and *Primus* comic books.

> Thomas Szymanski
> 5 Stoney Brook Lane
> Stratham, NH 03885
> (603) 772-6372   <tomski@nh.ultranet.com>

◆ *Esquire* magazine, 1933-1959. Also buys *Playboy* pre-1960 only, *True,* and complete years of *Cosmopolitan, McCalls, Vogue, Ladies Home Journal, Woman's Home Companion, Redbook, Saturday Evening Post, Country Gentlemen* and *Collier's.* List the years and the condition of the covers and magazines. Do they smell musty?

> Charles Martignette
> PO Box 293
> Hallandale, FL 33008

◆ *Architectural Digest* and similar architecture picture magazines. Please give the issue date or issue number and describe the condition. "I don't want magazines with no pictures or with pictures cut out."

> Gary Bart
> 620 Siena Way
> Los Angeles, CA 90077
> (310) 471-6980   fax (310) 471-1910

◆ *TV Guide* and other TV log magazines, 1948-1970. Selected U.S. issues from 1971-1996 and Canadian issues 1977-1996 are also purchased. Also wants early local editions, and all weekly newspaper TV supplement magazines from any period. Issues of NY City's *Television Guide* from 1948 are worth $25-$50 each. Note if there is a mailing label on the cover, and if it affects the picture.

> Jeffrey Kadet
> PO Box 20
> Macomb, IL 61455
> (309) 833-1809   <jkadet@macomb.com>

★ *National Geographic* **Society publications of all types.** Buys magazines, books, maps, article reprints, atlases, pictorials, school bulletins, advertising, invitations, slides, videos, postcards, and calendars produced by the NGS. Also buys materials published by other companies with articles about the NGS, which spoof the NGS, are funded by the NGS, or in any way refer to the NGS. He particularly wants pre-1913 magazines, NGS books such as *Machu Picchu* ($1,000) and the complete advertising brochure sent to prospective members in 1888. He'll pay $5,000 for a Vol. 1, No. 1 magazine. No magazines after 1959. He encourages buyers and sellers to call.

> Nick Koopman
> Collectors Exchange
> 10600 Lowery Drive
> Raleigh, NC 27615
> (919) 870-8407   fax (919) 870-8416
> <nick@geographicexchange.com>

◆ **Pulp magazines.** Buys nearly 1,000 titles: adventure, aviation, crime and detective, hero, mystery and menace, Western, science fiction and fantasy, romance, spicy, sports, confession, and others. Give the title, date, and condition of each magazine, with emphasis on the condition and graphic appearance of the cover.

> Jim Steranko
> PO Box 974
> Reading, PA 19603

◆ **Pulp magazines.** Buys mystery, detective, spicy, adventure, superhero and character pulps such as *The Shadow, The Spider, Gun Molls, Dime Detective, Doc Savage, Black Mask,* and similar crime and Terror pulps. Not interested in romance or Westerns. Give the title, date, and overall condition. Include your phone number. Offers $1,000 for the October 1912 *All Story* in very good condition.

> Claude Held
> PO Box 515
> Buffalo, NY 14225

◆ **Pulp magazines.** Buys magazines from the 1930's and 40's in the hero and horror genre like *The Spider, The Shadow, Doc Savage, The Whisperer,* etc. Will consider fine condition Western and detective pulps. Does not want magazines with missing covers or pages or with paper so brittle it breaks when you turn pages.

> Christopher Ticknor
> 3400 Eisenhower Road
> Columbus, OH 43224
> (614) 267-4560 eves   fax (614) 267-2013

◆ **Science Fiction magazines.** Give the name and publication date or issue number. Describe the condition. No books with missing pages or badly damaged covers. Value is highly dependent on condition.

> Jack Klodzinski & Rich Levy
> PO Box 470
> Geneva, FL 32732
> (407) 327-8223 days   <askdoctorjack@hotmail.com>
>   <cmitoys.com>

◆ **Science fiction and horror digests and magazines.** He'll consider all fine condition digests from before 1965, and pulp magazines before 1960. Has particular interest in Edgar Rice Burroughs and Steven King magazine stories.

> Dave Sheldon
> 9000 Williams Road
> North East, PA 16428
>   (814) 897-1894 days   (814) 725-1394
>   <drskull9@hotmail.com>

◆ **Crossword and other puzzle magazines** before 1970. "It doesn't matter if they're filled in." Give the name, date and condition. The first 18 issues of *The Eastern Enigma* are worth $1,000.

> Will Shortz
> 55 Great Oak Lane
> Pleasantville, NY 10570
>   (914) 769-9128 voice and fax   <wshortz.aol.com>

◆ **Magazines about the fruit or printing industry, 1860-1960,** such as *Modern Packaging, Better Fruit, Calif Citrograph, Blue Anchor, Modern Printing, Skookum News, Pacific Bottler, California Farmer* and other publications from the produce and printing industries.

> Pat Jacobsen
> PO Box 791
> Weimar, CA 95736
>   (530) 637-5923   <pjacobsen@neworld.net>

TONY'S TIP ABOUT PULP MAGAZINES: Pulp magazines are lurid fiction magazines popular in the teens, twenties, thirties, and forties. Pulp magazines came in many titles and genres. They were approximately 6 1/2" x 10", printed on newsprint, and had colorful covers. The paper and covers are very fragile today because they used such poor paper stock. Handle them with care, as some can be quite valuable.

TONY'S TIPS ON SELLING NEWSPAPERS

Newspapers seldom sell for much money, even if they're over 100 years old. *A whole year of the London Gazette from 1800 is only worth about $300. Some newer years are much more valuable as value is in part determined by what historic events happened that year.*

Some 19th and early 20th century publications are important, however, because they contain the first printing of stories by famous writers.

In some cases, it is artwork found in the papers which has itself become collectible. *The newspapers that are always welcome are illustrated weeklies like Harper's, Leslie's and Judge from 1855-1910.*

To describe a paper you wish to sell give the name, city, date, number and size of pages, and mention any significant stories.

If the newspapers are bound, *indicate the type and condition of the binding (leather or boards, loose, split, leather crumbling, etc.). If it is a small town 18th or 19th century paper, a photocopy of the masthead is suggested as some papers are available in very limited numbers and the masthead itself could be wanted.*

When offering 19th century illustrated papers, *make certain they are complete as the value drops significantly if important pictures are missing.*

Tell the buyer about tears, rips, stains, cut outs, and foxing (brown spots). *If the paper is dry, brown, or brittle, it is seldom of value unless it's before 1750 or the only known copy of a title.*

Both newspapers and magazines can be shipped "Special Fourth Class Book Rate," which is inexpensive. **You are smarter, however, to ship via** *First Class or, if more than 12 ounces, Priority Rate. It's faster and safer. Compare the latest rates at your post office.*

◆ **Newspapers covering any important event before 1945.** Also all half year bound runs of pre-1870 papers, especially from Southern U.S., Confederate states, early West, or anywhere in the U.S. pre-1800. Wants specialty papers covering the women's movement, labor, railroads, abolitionism, temperance, or the Civil War. Also illustrated newspapers like *Harper's, Leslie's, Ballou's, Southern Illustrated News, London Illustrated News,* etc. Also bound volumes of British newspapers and magazines pre-1700 (although he will buy later issues if historically significant). Also issues of any American magazine before 1800. Pays $100 each for newspapers before 1730 but notes that many reprints exist so they need to be authenticated. No 20th century items except mint condition reports of important events. No severely defective papers.

> Phil Barber
> PO Box 8694
> Boston, MA 02114
>   (617) 492-4653   fax (617) 868-1534
> <phil@historicpages.com>   <www.historicpages.com>

◆ **Bound volumes of American and European illustrated newspapers dated 1850-1910** including *Harper's Weekly, Leslie's, Illustrated London News, Judge, Vanity Fair, Das Plachate, Puck,* and the like. Prefers to buy in large quantities. Prepared to buy entire libraries.

> Joe and Susie Davidson
> 5185 Windfall Road
> Medina, OH 44256
>   (330) 723-7172   <artbroker@webtv.net>

◆ **Bound volumes of illustrated weekly newspapers** such as *Puck, Harper's, Scientific American* and others, but only if they are in fine condition and date before 1890 only. Loose stacksof magazines will be considered but single copies are not wanted.

> John Rosenhoover
> 100 Mandalay Road
> Chicopee, MA 01020
>   (413) 536-5542

◆ **Confederate newspapers.** Any paper printed in the South during the War. Give the name, place and date on the masthead. Please be aware that the newspapers printed on wallpaper have been forged so it must be examined to determine authenticity.

> Peggy Dillard
> PO Box 210904
> Nashville, TN 37221
>   (615) 646-1605   <pdill43795@aol.com>

★ **Newspapers related to the Lincoln assassination and other newspapers with historic content.** "I've been collecting for about 30 years and for the past dozen have been editor and publisher of *Collectible Newspapers,* the Journal of the Newspaper Collectors Society. I will make purchase offers on any Lincoln assassination related newspapers ("If you have an April 15, 1865 *New York Herald* it is almost certain to be a reprint. If you have other collectible newspapers, I will forward to other buyers (libraries or private parties) who specialize in the area of interest of your paper (most people specialize). When writing about newspapers, include the title of the paper, date, historic content in the paper, noting stains, tears and any defects. You are encouraged to send a long SASE for information about the Society. Rick is author of *Index of American Newspaper Editions known to have been Reprinted* ($8 ppd) and *New York Herald April 15th 1865 Lincoln Assassination Reprints* ($5 ppd).

>Rick Brown
>Newspaper Collectors Society
>6031 Winterset
>Lansing, MI 48911
>(517) 887-1255   <help@historybuff.com>

TONY'S TIP ON HOW YOU DESCRIBE A NEWSPAPER:

"Philadelphia Inquirer, April 28, 1865. Capture and death of John W. Booth, front page coverage, solid condition, no stains or tears. Folded, with some damage at fold.

◆ **London newspapers published 1850 to 1900.** You must price.

>Rev. Sherlock Holmes
>PO Box 3
>Worcester, MA 01613
>free (877) 306-4059   <antiques@sherlockholmes.com>
>   <www.sherlockholmes.com>

◆ **Newspapers of historical significance especially relative to Lincoln's speeches or death, George Washington, the Revolution, the Civil War, colonial America, early Illinois and the Chicago fire.** Buys individual issues of historical significance or bound volumes. Buys all *Harper's Weekly* and *Frank Leslie's Illustrated,* 1855-1916.

>Steve and Linda Alsberg
>9850 Kedvale Avenue
>Skokie, IL 60076
>   (847) 676-9850   <lalsberg@earthlink.net>

TONY'S TIPS ON SELLING OLD BOOKS

Hundreds of millions of books have been printed. Valuable ones exist, but most are destined for yard sales and thrift shops. There are some surprises, though, none greater than the astonishing value of detective first editions from 1920-1990.

Being old is not enough to make a book valuable. Buyers look for books on specific topics, by specific authors, published by certain publishers, illustrated in a particular manner, from a particular period or country, and of a specific type, like leather bound or first edition.

When writing to potential buyers about a book, provide what we call "Standard Bibliographic Information."
- Title as on the title page, not as on the spine;
- Author, publisher, and place of publication;
- **All** printing and copyright dates;
- Number of pages;
- Type and approximate number of illustrations.

A Xerox© machine can capture that in seconds; copy the title page, back of the title page and dust jacket.

Remember, a book has parts. Describe the condition of each part: (1) cover, (2) spine, (3) binding, (4) pages and (5) dust jacket. Tell the buyer about bookplates, writing, and all damage. Don't offer damaged books or books not in the buyer's specialty as listed in Trash or Treasure. Books with missing pages, covers off, bindings collapsing, or water stains simply aren't wanted unless before 1800.

The amount a dealer will pay for books depends upon his customers and present stock, the rarity of your offering, current market, and his cash flow at that moment. Read the next fifteen pages and try selling on your own. Many people report being pleasantly surprised by selling books local dealers told them were worthless.

Books can be shipped Special 4th Class Book Rate which permits three pounds for around two dollars. However, books are fragile and may be damaged in transit. **It only costs $1 or so more to send a book first class or Priority. Since the buyer is paying for shipping, use the faster, safer method.**

BOOKS

◆ **Fine quality books from all periods** are wanted. "My book buying is guided by the belief that the quality of a book comes from both the content and from the physical book itself. The books I seek are generally **first or early printings** or are examples of high quality hand made **private press bookmaking**. I am particularly interested in buying books in the fields of art, architecture, Americana and the West, science and medicine, literature and literary criticism, travel and exploration, philosophy and religion, and world history, but **will consider any high quality book.** I am always looking for examples of **fine binding, printing and illustration**, especially books signed by Zaehnsdorf, Sangorski and Sutcliffe, Riviere, and other fine binders. Some fine **private press books** to look for include Kelmscott Press, Ashendone Press, Doves Press, Cranach Press, Nonesuch Press, Arion Press, and Golden Cockerel Press, among others. Books **signed** by the author or illustrator are also of particular interest to me as are *Chagall's Illustrations for the Bible* and *Drawings for the Bible,* Harold Bell Wright's *To My Sons,* pre-1800 copies of *The Book of Common Prayer,* pre-1955 Alcoholics Anonymous books, and the Limited Editions Club books, especially *Lysistrata* and *Ulysses.* I do not want book club editions, *Reader's Digest* books, dictionaries or encyclopedia sets after 1850, Bibles after 1750, and incomplete sets of books. I generally prefer the seller to set the price, but if you want an offer, you should provide all information on the title page and copyright page. Make a photocopy of these two pages if you can do so without damaging the book. Describe the binding and format, and the condition of the cover, binding and pages." Don't forget your SASE.

Paul Melzer, Fine & Rare Books
12 East Vine Street
Redlands, CA 92373
(909) 792-7299 fax (909) 792-7218 <pm@pmbooks.com>

TONY'S TIP: Standard Bibliographic Information:
Title, author, publisher, city where published,
date when published, and copyright date.
It's helpful if you also provide the number of pages
and the number and type of illustrations.

◆ **Leather bound books.** "I'll buy decorator leather bound books in quantity for $3 to $5 each. Not interested in fine first editions, just old books with little other value. Must have good spines and covers, but can be in any language from any period, as I want them only for their decorator potential. Call if you've got a bunch of them."

Joan Brady
834 Central Avenue
Pawtucket, RI 02861

◆ **Large collections of good books**, especially:
  • **Collections of books on a single topic**, such as Michigan history, the Civil War, theology, golf, Indians, art, architecture, etc.;
  • Books with **color plates**;
  • **Leather bound** books;
  • **Autographed** books by famous authors.
Catalogs are issued periodically. If you want to sell, give standard bibliographic information. One of the nation's largest used and rare booksellers, John does not buy *Reader's Digest* books, *National Geographic magazines,* book club editions, textbooks of any kind, encyclopedia sets, or anything in poor condition.
> John K. King Books
> 901 West Lafayette Blvd.
> Detroit, MI 48226
> (313) 961-0622   Fax: (313) 963-9138   <kingbooks@aol.com>

◆ **Various fine and early books,** including:
  • Incunabula, **hand written books** before 1501;
  • European books before 1600;
  • English books and manuscripts from before 1700;
  • American books before 1800;
  • Books **published in Pennsylvania before 1810** in English or 1830 in German. Especially seeks items printed by Benjamin Franklin in Philadelphia, the Brotherhood in Ephrata, or the Saurs (Sower) in Germantown;
  • Fine **leather bound** books in sets;
  • Books **with fore edge paintings**; "Let us hear about all fore edge paintings, no matter what era;"
  • Books **illustrated in color**, especially chromoliths before 1900;
  • Books **on China or Japan** if scholarly and illustrated;
  • **African exploration** and development and materials devoted to problems faced by less developed countries today;
  • **Arabic studies** including material relating the spheres of Moslem influence, both ancient and modern. Buys important books in Arabic and related languages;
  • **Urban studies** including all aspects about any cities anywhere and in all eras;
  • **City view books** of buildings and streets of cities worldwide.
Make certain to include count of pages and photos in your description. Photocopy the title page. In business for 20 years, Ron offers a series of fine catalogs.
> Ron & Isabel Lieberman
> The Family Album
> 4887 Newport Road at the Old Mill
> Kinzers, PA 17535
> (717) 442-0220   fax (717) 442-7904
> <rarebooks@pobox.com>

◆ **Collectible and scholarly books and art in all fields.** Book and other items this high quality shop seeks include, but are not limited to:
- Books printed in Europe before 1600;
- Books printed in America before 1700;
- Important literary works in first, **limited or illustrated editions**;
- Illustrated books by noted artists;
- Modern **first editions**;
- Fine and **limited editions**;
- Scholarly, significant books in art, architecture, photography, travel, exploration, music, psychology, religion, history, science, and other fields.
- **Atlases** and individual maps;
- Prints signed by artists from any period;
- **Decorative prints** prior to 1900.

Please, no book club books, textbooks, or anything in poor condition. Give standard bibliographic information: author, title, place published, publisher, all dates of publication and a description of the cover, binding, pages, and dust jacket. Open daily with 60,000 items in stock. Will buy individual books and entire collections.
James & Mary Laurie, Booksellers
921 Nicollet
Minneapolis, MN 55402
(800) 774-1114   (612) 338-1114   fax (612) 338-3665
<lauriebk@winternet.com>

★ **Books.** A selection of books is sought, including:
- Books **signed** by U.S. Presidents, authors, sports celebrities stars;
- **Mystery first editions;**
- **Cookbooks** before 1920;
- **Children's books** (see page 520 for more detail);

Books must be in fine condition and complete with dust jackets if originally issued with them. Torn or missing pages, writing, water damage, missing covers or other damage is not acceptable as this specialty dealer buys these for resale to collectors. Give standard bibliographic information, including edition number.
Barbara Ruppert, Alcott Books
5909 Darnell
Houston, TX 77074
(713) 774-2202 before 6pm   <bruppert@earthlink.net>

◆ **Fine and antiquarian books, pamphlets, and original manuscripts,** especially illustrated books, including children's. Has a special interest in old **medical books and paper**.
Ivan Gilbert, Miran Arts & Books
2824 Elm Avenue
Columbus, OH 43209
(614) 818-3222 days   (614) 236-0002 eves
fax (614) 818-3223

TONY'S TIP ON OLD JEWELRY: One of the most confusing areas for sellers is old jewelry. It is also one of the potentially most profitable. I met a reader in Southern California that made a profit of $75,000 from a single box of jewelry she purchased at a yard sale for $10.

The most helpful book I've found is "How To Be a Jewelry Detective" by highly recommended buyer Jeanenne Bell (p.77) who supplied me with her favorite jewelry buyers, hopefully one near you.

Hand painted porcelain jewelry. Wants jewelry, pins, cuff links and collar buttons decorated with paintings on porcelain, especially unusual items with interesting subjects or patterns. Send a photocopy and list all marks or signatures. She DOES NOT WANT transfers (decals) or embellished transfers.

Dorothy Kamm
Box 7460
Port St. Lucie, FL 34985
(772) 465-4008 fax (772) 460-9050 <dorothykamm@usa.net>

Signed and unsigned costume jewelry, especially big, bold and ugly pieces in rhinestone, glass, sterling, or carved old plastic. Also wants jewelry with movement on springs or dangles. Signed pieces from some artists will bring premium prices. "I pay up to 50% of retail value. Some costume pieces can be worth from $200 to $1,000. If I cannot buy the piece, I can usually find a buyer and take a small (5%-10%) commission. I buy pieces outright or offer a 50/50 consignment split."

Rhinestone Rosie
606 West Crockett
Seattle, WA 98119
(206) 283-4605 <rhinestonerosie@yahoo.com>

High quality figural pins from the 1930's and 40's especially designer signed pieces by Trifari, Coro, Boucher, Mazer, Pennino, de Roisa, Reinad, Reja, and Staret. "I tend to sell the same types of jewelry I collect, including signed pieces, 30's and 40's pot metals, gaudy rhinestones, etc. I prefer pins, but also buy earrings, necklaces and bracelets. I also like the 1950's moonglow and pearlized thermoplastics if they are interesting."

Deborah Kosnett, Rhinestone Rainbow
Box 3609
Gaithersburg, MD 20878
(202) 293-2200 fax (801) 437-1909 <dkos@radix.net>

Cuff links. "We like well designed links in any material, especially unusual figurals and enamels of animals, sterling links from the 1920's and 30's, and designer links by Anderson, Jensen and others. We'll pay postage for collections send for our examination as long as you call first to make sure we're interested. We DO NOT WANT broken links but will buy sets with missing stones."
> Gal Busche & Richard Cullen, Archangel Antiques
> 334 East Ninth Street
> New York, NY 10003
> (212) 260-9313   <richgail38@aol.com>

Hat pins. Wants good quality, antique hatpins, especially over 7" long. "Top prices paid for collections or unusual pins."
> Debby Wolley, Favorite Past-Times Antiques
> 6 Main Street
> Bridgton, ME 04009
> <info@maine-antiques.com>

Hat pins from around 1900. Please include a description of the head of the pin, the material it's made from and the length. This president of the Hat Pin Ass'n does NOT WANT newly made pins.
> Virginia Woodbury
> (310) 326-2196   <hatpenginea@aol.com>

Costume jewlry tremblants (pieces that move), particularly Frank Buck "Bring 'em Back Alive" pieces.
> Denna Shgare
> 4349 Lavale Court
> Clemmons, NC 27012
> (336) 766-6579   <denarnc@aol.com>

Butterfly jewelry. Wants pendants, rings, necklaces, bracelets and pins made of sterling or white metal with a background made of butterfly wings. Scenes are painted or decals, usually of the beach, mountains, deserts, Dutch cottages, or the English countryside.
> Roberta Mullings
> 2624 North Louise Street
> Santa Ana, CA 92706
> (914) 543-7555   <oneslow1@pacbell.net>

Cameos made before 1920. Also **old powder boxes and other dresser items.** Describe thoroughly or send a Xerox© or photo.
> Carolyn De Koven
> 3600 Alabama Street
> San Diego, CA 92104
> (619) 574-0678   <9-chekoven@cox.net>

◆ **Books about art, architecture, photography and design written before 1970.** Has a particular interest in California artists, American art and artists, and modern decorative arts such as glass, furniture and ceramics (1890-1970). Alan writes the nationally syndicated "Art Talk" column, and is author of *Art for All* ($17.95) and *Buy Art Smart* ($17.95), both available from him or at your local bookstore.

    Alan S. Bamberger
    2510 Bush Street
    San Francisco, CA 94115
(415) 931-7875   fax (415) 922-3580   <alanb@artbusiness.com>
    <http://www.artbusiness.com>

TONY'S TIP: You are more likely to have valuable books when you own a private library of hundreds on a single topic. **Never break up a private library on a particular topic without help.** *All fiction, even if fairly recent, should be checked out if it is by a famous author and has its original dust jacket.*

◆ **Jewish and Hebrew books,** particularly illustrated material pre 1920. Anything printed or photographic related to Jewish history in the U.S. or Europe before WWII may be of interest including photo albums, cookbooks, diaries, scholarly books, and the like. This 25 year veteran buyer says that if your book is printed in any language you can't read, simply Xerox© the front and back of the title page. If your book is in English, provide a Xerox© or standard bibliographic information including the condition of cover, binding and pages.

    Elliot Brill
    505 8th Avenue
    New York, NY 10018
(212) 695-1996   (800) 562-9911   fax (212) 695-3860
    <Laceywig@aol.com>

◆ **Asian books, maps, photos, and prints on Japan, China, Korea, Vietnam, Tonkin, Siam, Cambodia, Laos, Burma, Malaya, Singapore, Indonesia, Philippines, Formosa, Taiwan, Tibet, Mongolia, Manchuria, New Guinea, South-East Asia and the Far East.** Has special interest in books illustrated by Japanese woodblocks.

    Jerry Stanoff
    Rare Oriental Book Co.
    PO Box 1599
    Aptos, CA 95001
        (831) 689-0203   fax (831) 689-0204
        <jgs@rareoritnbooks.com>

◆ **Reference books on any topic published in England, 1850-1900.**
Science, medicine, geology, electricity, geography, poisons, toxicology,
Great Britain, Law, criminal history, boxing, anatomy, bee-keeping, etc.
Special wants include *Lloyd's Register of British & Foreign Shipping,
History of British Birds*, Crockford's *Clerical Directory, Gazeteer of the
World*, Morris's *Directory,* Kelly's *Post Office Directory*, Whitaker's
Almanack, The Holy War, History of the Holy Warre. Also *King James
Bible* from that period. Any book that might be in the fictional Sherlock
Holmes' private library will be considered. Give title, author, date of
publication and condition.
> Rev. Sherlock Holmes
> PO Box 3
> Worcester, MA 01613
> free (877) 306-4059   <antiques@sherlockholmes.com>
> <www.sherlockholmes.com>

◆ **Books** on the following subjects:
- Russian and East European Royalty, especially Romanovs;
- Russian Revolution;
- World Wars I and II in Europe and in Asia;
- Aviation and air wars;
- Korean War;
- Tibet and environs;
- Soviet Union, Eastern Europe, Communism, Socialism.

First editions in dust jackets preferred. Some rare titles purchased in
lesser condition. Provide standard bibliographic information, including
printing data found on the title page or reverse. No book club books and
no paperbacks.
> Edward Conroy
> SUMAC Books
> 272 Smith Hill Road
> Troy, NY 12180
> (518) 279-9638 8 am - 4 pm

◆ **Books about reptiles and amphibians including snakes, turtles,
crocodiles, lizards, frogs, etc.** Prefers older, illustrated volumes as well
as scientific monographs. Would pay $1,000 for Holbrook's *North
American Herpetology* in fine condition. Not interested in books still in
print, biology textbooks, children's and juvenile titles published after
1960 (but will consider early ones) or Ditmar titles greater than $5.
Please send a photo of unusual items and give complete bibliographic
info. A computer bulletin board about reptiles is at (215) 698-1905.
> Mark Miller
> Herp-Net
> PO Box 52261
> Philadelphia, PA 19115
> (215) 464-3561 voice or fax   <70176.1153@compuserve.com>

TONY'S TIP: Publishers have many different ways of marking their first editions. *Some do it in code. Many make it easy buy listing the printing near the bottom on the front or back of the title page. Look for a string of numbers which usually start around 10 and count backwards. Whatever the lowest number is...that's the number of the printing you have.*

◆ **Books about wine.** "I'll buy hardcover books intended for resale to dealers and collectors. I prefer older, less well-known titles but will consider all offers of books in good shape. Give author, title, publisher, year of publication(s), edition, and a detailed description of condition. I do not buy paperbacks, price guides to bottles of wine, wine tasting notes, and travel guides of wine regions. I will buy some cookbooks which emphasize wine, especially those which are colorful and have eye appeal." He especially wants to find fine condition 19th Century wine books in very good condition.

> Warren R. Johnson
> Second Harvest Books
> PO Box 3306
> Florence, OR 97439
> (541) 902-0215   <2harvest@presys.com>
> <www.secondharvestbooks.net>

◆ **Books on gambling.** "We can give anyone information as to whether their book or gambling paraphernalia has value if they write, call, or preferably fax us." Not a bad bet, since Howard has been described elsewhere as the man who "knows more about gambling literature than anyone else alive."

> Howard Schwartz
> Gambler's Book Club
> 630 South 11th Street
> Las Vegas, NV 89101
> (702) 382-7555 (2 to 5pm)   (800) 522-1777   fax (702) 382-7594

◆ **Books about social etiquette (manners) books for adults, children, or teens,** especially first editions. Very good condition preferred, but unusual titles will be considered in lesser condition. Please do not inquire about cookbooks or health books. Give this 20 year veteran collector standard bibliographic information. Free appraisals.

> LuAnn Gavula
> 20 Barrington Bourne
> Barrington Hills, IL 60010
> (847) 658-1500

◆ **Hollywood biographies of all types** in hardcover with dust jacket.
Edward Conroy , SUMAC Books
272 Smith Hill Road
Troy, NY 12180
(518) 279-9638 8 am - 4 pm

◆ **Genealogy books.**
James Williams
342 South Garnet Lake Road
Warrensburg, NY 12885
(518) 623-2831

◆ **Alcoholics Anonymous books earlier than 1975.** Nothing later.
Will pay $50 to $100 each for 1939 to 1954 first editions. Does not
want 3rd editions, plain books or those in poor condition. Describe the
dust jacket, date, and printing number.
Clark Phelps
390 K Street
Salt Lake City, UT 84103
(801) 355 1394   <clark@aros.net>

◆ **Occult and mystic science, astrology, magic, numerology, alche-
my, palmistry, spiritualism, pyramids, tarot, Yoga, Atlantis, UFO's,
ESP, and anything else metaphysical.** "I'll also buy art, posters, cards,
games, antique crystal balls, and other mystical and occult ephemera.
I'll buy one or one thousand, if in fine condition."
Dennis Whelan
PO Box 609
Melrose, FL 32666
(352) 475-9520

◆ **Technical books and paper ephemera, pre-1910.** He wants books
on trades, machines, manufacturing and technical processes.
Jim Presgraves
Bookworm & Silverfish
PO Box 639
Wytheville, VA 24382
(276) 686-5813   fax (276) 686-6636   <bookworm@naxs.com>

◆ **Books on poultry, fancy chickens, pigeons, etc.** Nothing after
1930 please, or anything that's badly damaged. Please give standard
bibliographic information plus condition of cover, binding and pages.
Prices can start at $100 up for books with at least 10 color plates.
Clark Kidder
3219 East Country Road "N"
Milton, WI 53563
(608) 868-4185   fax (608) 868-6808   <ckidder@jvlnet.com>

◆ **Books about coins and currency.**
Lowell Horwedel
PO Box 2395
West Lafayette, IN 47996
(765) 583-2748   fax (765) 583-4584 <Lhorwedel@insightbb.com>

◆ **Books and magazines on weight lifting, body building, physical education, exercise, gymnastics, and calisthenics before 1980.** Has a special interest in books by or about Gustav Zander and his medico-mechanical system of gymnastics. This serious exercise historian also wants *Nautilus Bulletins #1* and *#2* by Arthur Jones as well as instruction manuals for various early brands of exercise equipment. He does not want sports magazines. Give issue and date info and describe the condition. Dealers price your goods. Amateurs may request offers.
David Landau
Ultimate Exercise Books
18151 N.E. 31st Court #1505
Aventura, FL 33160
(305) 932-9879   fax (305) 937-7809 <exarchives@aol.com>

◆ **Crossword puzzle books.** It doesn't matter if the puzzles are filled in, as long as the books are hardcover and before 1955. Give standard bibliographic information.
Will Shortz
55 Great Oak Lane
Pleasantville, NY 10570
(914) 769-9128 voice/fax   <wshortz@aol.com>

◆ **Pre-1970 crossword and other word puzzle books,** hard or soft cover, even if written in. Especially wants Simon and Schuster hardcover puzzle books 1924-60. Give the complete title, date, and series number, and how much of the book has been filled in. No crossword dictionaries, but does buy crossword magazines. Wants list sent for large SASE. Stan also buys pre-1970 board games if they are in good condition with no missing pieces. No common games, though.
Stanley Newman
American Crossword
PO Box 69
Massapequa Park, NY 11762
        <crosswordpuzzles@aol.com>

TONY'S TIP: Standard Bibliographic Information:
Title, author, publisher, city where published,
date when published, and copyright date.
It's helpful if you also provide the number of pages
and the number and type of illustrations.

BOOKS BY PARTICULAR PUBLISHERS

◆ **Books published by the Limited Editions Club.** "I'll buy all years, all titles, as long as they are in fine condition in a fine box. I'll also buy Club ephemera including monthly letters, prospectus, etc." Only *Lysistrata* and *Ulysses* are acceptable without original box. Also buys Heritage Press books. Please describe fully.
> Lee and Mike Temares
> 50 Heights Road
> Plandome, NY 11030
> (516) 627-8688   fax (516) 627-7822   <tembooks@aol.com>

◆ **Roycroft and other high quality small press books,** especially editions of less than 500 with hand tooled binding and/or hand painted illumination or illustration. Buys the books of 60 small hand presses of the 1890-1920 era (dealers are encouraged to send an SASE for his list). He does not want *Little Journeys to...,* Scrapbooks or Notebooks published by Roycroft. Give the title, date, material of binding, unusual characteristics, and the condition if you want an offer. A Xerox™ is a good idea.
> Richard Blacher
> 209 Plymouth Colony/Alps Road
> Branford, CT 06405
> (203) 481-3321   <dblacher@javanet.com>

◆ **Tower Publishing Company books and other books and printed ephemera related to the Watchtower Society from before 1930.** He'd like to hear from you if you have anything pertaining to the Watchtower Society, Tower Publishing, the International Bible Students Assn (IBSA), Pastor C.T. Russell, or George Storrs. Books of particular interest include N.H. Barbour's *Three Worlds,* 1877 ($200 "or a great deal more in fine condition"), J.H. Paton's *Day Dawn* (1880, $200+), C.T. Russell's *The Object & Manner of Our Lord's Return* (1877, $500+), J.F. Rutherford's *Man's Salvation from a Lawyer's Viewpoint* (1906, $500+), and various books by George Storrs. The special Watchtower Edition of *Human Linear Bible* (1902) is a $500 and up prize. Numerous magazines, Journals, and Reports from before 1930 are sought, including *Watchtower, Golden Age, Herald of the Morning, Bible Examiner,* and *Overland Monthly.* This 35 year veteran collector/researcher wants to hear about anything you have from before 1930, books between 1930 and 1940, and nothing after 1950. Dealers should price their goods. Amateurs may request an offer from this 35 year veteran collector/dealer.
> Jeffrey Neumann
> PO Box 171
> Wadsworth, OH 44282
> (330) 334-1784   <jneumann@neo.rr.com>

◆ **Books about kites** written before 1979 in any language. In the case of rare books, content is more important than condition. Children's books about kites are of little interest unless in fine condition before 1920. Writers to look for include G.T. Woglom who wrote *Parakites*, Charles Miller of the U.S. Weather Bureau, P.E. Garber of the Smithsonian, Joseph LeCornu, James Wagenvoord, Wyatt Brummitt and Will & Jane Yolen. Any book about S.F. Cody would be of interest as well. Give standard bibliographic information.

Valerie Govig
Kite Lines Bookstore
PO Box 1775
Millsboro, DE 19966
(302) 945-0449   fax (302) 945-0550   <kitelines@compuserve.com>

◆ **Fine quality small press books from all periods** are wanted. "My book buying is guided by the belief that the quality of a book comes from both the content and from the physical book itself. I seek high quality hand made private press bookmaking. Some fine private press books to look for include Kelmscott Press, Ashendone Press, Doves Press, Cranach Press, Nonesuch Press, Arion Press, and Golden Cockerel Press, among others. I do not want book club editions, *Reader's Digest* books, dictionaries or encyclopedia sets after 1850, Bibles after 1750, and incomplete sets of books. I generally prefer the seller to set the price, but if you want an offer, you should provide all information on the title page and copyright page. Make a photocopy of these two pages if you can do so without damaging the book. Describe the binding and format, and the condition of the cover, binding and pages." Don't forget your SASE.

Paul Melzer
Fine & Rare Books
12 East Vine Street
Redlands, CA 92373
(909) 792-7299   fax (909) 792-7218   <pm@pmbooks.com>

◆ **Fine quality limited editions from all periods** are wanted, especially important literary or scholarly works, or those illustrated by important artists. Please, no book club books, textbooks, or anything in poor condition. Give standard bibliographic information: author, title, place published, publisher, all dates of publication and a description of the cover, binding, pages, and dust jacket. Open daily with 60,000 items in stock. Will buy individual books and entire collections.

James & Mary Laurie
Booksellers
921 Nicollet
Minneapolis, MN 55402
(800) 774-1114   (612) 338-1114   Fax: (612) 338-3665
<lauriebk@winternet.com>

◆ **Books illustrated with color pictures before 1890** depicting plants, animals, birds, fish, Indians, sports, cowboys, medicine, military, buildings, costumes, fashion, or advertising. Standard bibliographic data is requested.

> Joe and Susie Davidson
> 5185 Windfall Road
> Medina, OH 44256
>   (330) 723-7172   <artbroker@webtv.net>

◆ **Books illustrated with full page b/w illustrations,** including steel engravings, etchings, copper plates, and woodblocks. Wants views of the U.S. and Canada, North American Indians, explorations and Western America, animals, art, railway surveys, pre-1880 fairs and Centennials, architecture, Civil War, and pre-1860 Hawaii (Sandwich Islands). Indicate size along with standard bibliographic information. Note tears, foxing, etc. Count the number of illustrations.

> John Rosenhoover
> 100 Mandalay Road
> Chicopee, MA 01020
>   (413) 536-5542

◆ **Books illustrated with color plates before 1899,** especially German before 1895, American natural history (plants and animals) before 1870, and Indians. Especially wants books illustrated by Kate Greenaway, Arthur Rackham, Jessie Smith, K. Nielson, Wyeth, W. Crane, Maxfield Parrish, Pogany, Dulac, Newell, Maud Humphrey, Remington, Erte, or Harrison Fisher. Books must date between 1890 and 1926. Give standard bibliographic information, noting tears, erasures, foxing, etc. Count and indicate the number of illustrations in color and in b/w.

> John Rosenhoover
> 100 Mandalay Road
> Chicopee, MA 01020
>   (413) 536-5542

◆ **Used and rare books, manuscripts and maps.** "We specialize in U.S. maps and atlases before 1870, books on the military, aviation, lighter-than-air craft and Ohio subjects. We also have interest in obtaining old bookbinding tools and equipment."

> Frank Klein,
> The Bookseller
> 39 Westgate Circle
> Akron, OH 44303
>   (330) 865-5831 10 - 6   fax (330) 865-5851
>   <thebooksellerinc@neo.rr.com>

FICTION

◆ **Detective and mystery 1st editions in hardcover or paperback.**
Also biography, reference, and bibliography related to the detective/
mystery genre. Wants Dashiell Hammett and Raymond Chandler and
other classics, and authors like **Tony Hillerman, Sue Grafton, Robert
Block, and other popular contemporary writers in 1st editions** with
dust jackets. Computerized for modem access.

> Richard West
> 116 Pleasant Street 2nd floor
> Easthampton, MA 01027
> <questions@periodyssey.com>

◆ **Large 20th century fiction collections.** If you have many hundreds
of hardback fiction books with their original dust jackets, give him a
call. Has strong interest in John Steinbeck, Wallace Stegner, Richard
Brautigan and Jack London signed limited editions, first editions, first
printings by subsequent publishers, appearances in anthologies, spoken
word records, tapes, film and theater memorabilia, and things owned by
him. Does not want book club editions or items in poor condition. If a
book had a dust jacket, slipcase, box, or wrap-around as originally
issued, these items should still be present. Be specific about what you
have for sale, giving complete bibliographic information and a full
description. No interest in paperbacks or contemporary remainders.

> James Dourgarian
> Bookman
> 1595-A Third Avenue
> Walnut Creek, CA 94596
> (510) 935-5033   <jimbooks@earthlink.net>

◆ **Books by Jules Verne are wanted in British, French and
American editions.** Most interested in buying first or other early editions, or editions of lesser known titles such as *Clovis Dardentor,
Mathias Sandorf* and *Foundling Mick*. Also interested in appearances of
Verne in the Seaside Library or Lakeside Library dime novels. "If you
find an old edition of any work in good shape, you might send a quote."
Give the full title, all copyright dates, publisher, the type and number of
illustrations and a complete statement of condition of the cover, binding, and pages.

> Dana Eales
> 2447 Delta Drive
> Uniontown, OH 44685
> (330) 699-5341   <deals@sssnet.com>

★ **Beat Generation poets and authors.** Wants first edition books and records by Allen Ginsberg, Jack Kerouac, Kenneth Rexroth, and others who symbolized "The Beat Generation" of the 1950's, especially in San Francisco. State condition, date, and how the item was stored.

> Richard Synchef
> 208 Summit Drive
> Corte Madera, CA 94925
> (415) 927-8844

◆ **Books by Harlan Ellison, U.S. or foreign.** Will consider mint condition paperbacks or fine hardcovers with dust jackets. Especially wants U.S. first editions, numbered editions, and autographed copies. Wants to find *Sex Gang* written under his Paul Merchant pseudonym.

> Edy Chandler
> PO Box 20664
> Houston, TX 77225
> (281) 531-9615

◆ **Books by Stephen King, Anne Rice or Larry McMurtry.** Want first editions, foreign editions, and uncorrected proofs. Books must be in fine condition and complete with dust jackets. Torn or missing pages, writing, water damage, missing covers or other damage is not acceptable as this specialty dealer buys these for resale to collectors.

> Barbara Ruppert, Alcott Books
> 5909 Darnell
> Houston, TX 77074
> (713) 774-2202 before 6pm   <bruppert@earthlink.net>

◆ **Science fiction hardcover 1st editions only, especially auto-graphed.** Also interested in trade paperbacks issued at the same time as the hardcover editions. "Please, no book club editions (these are usually marked on the dust jacket). No ex-library books and nothing in poor condition. Please note I am not interested in fantasy. Only science fiction. Fantasy involves witches, warlocks, wizards, dragons, magic and is usually set in a Pre-Industrial Revolution technology."

> David Kveragas
> 1943 Timberlane
> Clarks Summit, PA 18411
> <hiwind2000@aol.com>

◆ **Science fiction and horror hardcover novels.** Will consider hardcover first editions to the present. Especially wants Edgar Rice Burroughs and **Steven King** magazine stories and first editions.

> Dave Sheldon
> 9000 Williams Road
> North East, PA 16428
> (814) 897-1894 days   (814) 725-1394   <drskull9@hotmail.com>

◆ **Paperback books from before 1960,** but only in mint or near mint condition. Give title, publisher, catalog number (usually on the spine), cover price, and edition or printing number.

James Williams
342 South Garnet Lake Road
Warrensburg, NY‑12885
(518) 623-2831

TONY'S TIP ABOUT WHICH BOOKS ARE COLLECTIBLE: *Every book is collectible. Not every book is sellable.*

TONY'S TIP ABOUT SELLING CHILDREN'S BOOKS: *Children's book printed since 1970 are very common and have no resale value. Book dealers do not want them. Other kids do want them, so they're perfect to sell for 10¢ or 25¢ to kids (50¢ or a buck to adults) at yard sales.*

Children's books are a welcome donation in many places if they're in good condition. Day Cares want them. Women's shelters want them. Thrift shops want them. Some private schools may want them. They just don't have much money value to collectors, so you're best to give them away and perhaps be eligible to take a tax deduction.

TONY'S TIP ABOUT YOUR BOOKS: *Dealers want books to sell to collectors not readers. They must be in fine condition. Book dealers almost never want Book Club editions, though thrift shops and rummage sales are glad to have them.*

TONY'S TIP ABOUT BOOKS PRINTED AFTER 1920. *They were probably sold originally with a dust jacket. If they were, that's the way dealers want them today.*

TONY'S TIP: Book buyers want to know standard bibliographic information: *title, author, publisher and place of publication, all dates of printing or copyright, number of pages, the illustrator, and approximate number of illustrations. Describe condition of the cover, spine, binding, pages and dust jacket. Note bookplates, writing, and all other damage.*

TONY'S TIP ABOUT ILLUSTRATIONS: *Children's books are nearly always collected for their illustrations.*

CHILDREN'S BOOKS

◆ **First editions of children's books in very good condition.** Wants books illustrated by Mabel Lucie Atwell, Jessie Wilcox Smith, Charles Robinson, Maxfield Parrish, Charles Folkard, Maurice Sendak, Edward Gorey, and Ralph Steadman, among others. Can send you a wants list.
>Joel Birenbaum
>2765 Shellingham Drive
>Lisle, IL 60532
>(630) 637-8530   <birenbau@netwave.net>

★ **Children's books** including:
- *Dick and Jane* readers in all their forms, including flash cards;
- Boys' and girls' series books like Nancy Drew, Hardy Boys, Tom Swift, and many others as long as they are in fine condition and have original dust jackets;
- Judy Bolton and other modern children's books in fine condition with dust jackets;
- *Little Black Sambo, Nicodemus, Little Brown Kokos* and other stories about black/negro children;
- *Oz* books by Baum and others;
- *Uncle Wiggily;*
- *Uncle Remus;*
- Books with high quality illustrations, especially by Parrish, N.C. Wyeth, J.W. Smith, T. Tudor, Pogany, Rackham, Pyle, Potter, Lenski, Gruelle, Nielson, Dulac, Crane, Ward, and other prominent illustrators;
- Books that have won the Newbery or Caldecott Award;
- Children's pop-up books from before 1940;
- Old Mother Goose and Father Goose stories.

Books must be in fine condition and complete with dust jackets if originally issued with them. Torn pages, writing or crayoning, water damage, missing covers or other damage is not acceptable as this specialty dealer buys these for resale to collectors. Give standard bibliographic information, including edition number.
>Barbara Ruppert
>Alcott Books
>5909 Darnell
>Houston, TX 77074
>(713) 774-2202 before 6pm   <bruppert@earthlink.net>

◆ **Children's books, American or English,** from the 1400's to 1925, including **educational books such as McGuffey's readers.**
>Ron Graham
>8167 Park Avenue
>Forestville, CA 95436
>(707) 887-2856   <old78rpm@juno.com>

◆ **Children's series books.** Must be in dust jacket if issued that way. Especially seeking the last 3 or 4 titles in any series. Describe condition of dust jacket. Better if you Xerox™ both sides.

> Lee and Mike Temares
> 50 Heights Road
> Plandome, NY 11030
> (516) 627-8688   fax (516) 627-7822   <tembooks@aol.com>

TONY'S TIP: Book buyers want to know standard bibliographic information: title, author, publisher and place of publication, all dates of printing or copyright, number of pages, the illustrator, and approximate number of illustrations. Describe condition of the cover, spine, binding, pages and dust jacket. Note bookplates, writing, and all other damage.

Illustrators and illustrations are particularly important in the world of children's books, many of which are purchased only for their pictures.

◆ **Children's books.** Dealer with more than 30,000 children's books in stock still wants more. Buying for resale so condition is very important. Give standard bibliographic information and a photocopy of the cover if you can.

> Bob Matteson, RPM Books
> 104-29 Jamaica Avenue
> Richmond Hill, NY 11418
> (718) 441-6208   <rpmbooks@aol.com>

◆ **Thornton W. Burgess and Harrison Cady books and ephemera.** Does not want any of their books published by Grosset & Dunlap.

> Stephen Kruskall
> PO Box 418
> Dover, MA 02030
> (508) 785-1195   Fax: (508) 785-2621
> <steve418@aol.com>

◆ **Big Little Books** are wanted, but only if in fine condition with no missing pages, coloring, or trashed spines. Please give the title, catalog number, and a photocopy (Xerox™) when possible.

> Mike Rasmussen
> PO Box 726
> Marina, CA 93933
> (831) 759-0259   fax (831) 422-1529   <rasspapercol@thegrid.net>

A

Abbate, Jim 187
Ackerman, Donald 290
Addington, Gordon 415
Aikins, Larry 157
Albert, Gene 308
Alderman, Gary 213, 230, 231, 233, 236, 553
Aldrich, Shawn 345
Aldridge, Ron 307, 462, 476
Alexander, Diane 52
Allen, Bob 32
Allen, Dan 364
Allmon, Charlie 394
Almquist, Eldon 294
Alpers, Rojann 371, 372
Alpert, Stephen 471
Alsberg, Steve /Linda 515, 559
Altman, Seymour 50, 60
AMCASE 462
Amer-Russian Trade Co. 550
Anderson, Robert 7, 485
Anderson, Warren 310, 380, 468, 505, 542
Andreae, John 154
Andreoni, Hank 190, 401
Andrews, Leda 58, 103
Anthony, Hank 283
Antiquarian Bookstore 552
Architectural Antiques 398
Arden, Scott 355, 364, 396
Arendt, Helen 94
Armstrong, Rita 62, 68
Atkinson, James 502
Augsburger, Jeff 225
Austin, Bruce 4, 14
Axler, Bruce 23
Ayers, James 421

B

Babcock, Wayne 235, 547
Bagdade, Susan & Al 63
Bagnall, Gary 336
Bailey, David 71
Baker, Sheryl 537
Baldwin Leslie 332
Ball, Guy 84, 391
Baltrusaitis, Tom 374
Bamberger, Alan 485, 566
Bank of Eureka Springs 537
Barber, Phil 558

Bareis, Arbe 516
Barlow, Mark 258
Barnes, Richard 153
Baron, John 336
Barrella, Phyllis 467
Bart, Gary 169, 185, 554
Bartoli, Ann 175
Baseman, Marilyn 80, 148, 323, 333
Basore, Tom 87, 144
Basse, Cary 88, 89, 119
Bassett, Mark 59
Batchelder, Robert 515
Bates, Alan 202
Baum, Rod 212
Baumann, Wilfred 447
Bausch, David 127, 483
Bays, Carter 21
Beach, David 467, 505
Bearce, Doug 307
Becker, Jonathan 238
Beckwith, Sharlene 334
Beeks, Dale 370, 392
Belinsky, John 536
Bell, Jeanenne 77
Bell, Michael 374
Benedict, John 255
Bergin, Ann 104, 156, 308, 318, 325, 481
Berkey, Alice 157
Berman, Bernie 547
Berman, Robert 87
Berman, Ralph 112
Berman, Rita 94
Berman, Bob 3, 6, 11, 16, 55
Berning, Bill 85
Bernstein, Andy 347
Best, Charles 115, 442, 443
Bietz, Duane /Eunice 29, 328
Billard, Gerry 394
Bingham, A.Walker 376
Bink, Art 361
Bird In the Cage 51, 59, 66, 70, 92, 493
Birenbaum, Joel 156, 577
Blacher, Richard 17, 571
Black, Charles 442
Blank, Marty 413
Bleier, Bruce 11, 91, 498, 503
Block, Robert 67, 120, 488

Block, Stanley 18, 69, 120
Blue Ridge Knives 86
Bodnarchuk, Joe 129, 141
Bogart, Joan 3, 8
Bohenstengel, Jim 314
Bolack, Tommy 401
Bond, Jack 495
Bone Room, The 302
Bonneau, Pierre 466
Books, Dennis 137, 166
Boone, David 303, 445, 494
Bordelon, Marilyn 188
Bosey, Lisa 5, 435
Boswell, Harvey 302, 381,449
Botts, Rick 218
Boughton, Norm 239, 473
Bovis, Pierre 299, 454
Bowen, Glen 28
Bowers, Q. David 420, 481
Bowman, Ralph 171, 545
Brady, Joan 231, 235, 354, 561
Brady, Paul 263
Brand, Jay 310
Brasch, Walter 327
Breedlove, Michael 26
Bridges, Herb 176
Bridgewater Onvelopes 476
Brill, Elliot 566
Brill, Richard 192
Brinn, Richard 267
Brooks, Mike 194, 296
Brooks, Tim 205
Brosamer, R. C. 318
Brown, Daniel 80, 298, 445
Brown, Everen 154, 341, 359, 366, 549
Brown, Rev. Ken 309
Brown, Rick 559
Brown, WT 270
Browning, Jack 123
Broyles, Ken 56
Bruch, Larry 114, 126, 137
Brundage, Linda 101
Brunsell, Rodney 346, 376
Brunswick, Ms. 25, 72, 73
Bryson, Bobbie & Alan 22
Buchheit, Terry 418, 422
Buckman, Norman 536
Buffington, Audry 68, 156, 480
Bunnell, Wayland 206

Buonaguidi, Debra 480
Buonaguidi, John 228, 240
Burke, Michael 444
Burkett, Russ 38
Burla, Frank 276
Burns, John 125
Burns, Tom 66, 499
Busche, Gail 373
Bush, Abbie 537, 540, 544
Bushing, David 229
Buskirk, James 114, 115, 489
Butak, Jerry 242
Butke, Brian 424, 534

C
Cairo, Terry & Karen 268
Calendar Girl 506
Campesi, William 88
Canales, Linda 449
Caniff, Tom & Deena 34, 377
Cantey, Emory 186, 528
Capell, Peter 434
Carey, Larry 35
Carino, Gary 368
Carnegie Hall Corp 188
Carr, Ron 400
Carrandi, Mario 183
Carter, Tina 33
Casavant, Dan 505
Case, James 335, 348, 354
Casillo, Anthony 388
Castro, Mike 312
Cauble, Ronald 303
Cauwels, Diane 304, 424
Cauwels, Don 260
Cawthorn, Jim 273
Centennial Documents 462
Cerull, David 369
Cervon, Linda 187
Chandler, Edy 575
Chartrand, George 311, 333, 335, 346
Chase, Mark 158
Chicone, Jerry 410, 538
Chipps, Cindy 23, 314
Christian, Gene 358, 455, 473
Cifelli, Peter 492, 506
Cincinnati Art Glry 55, 64, 485
Cincotta, Rich 387
Clack, Tammy 224

Clark, Dennis 5, 435
Clark, Ed 81, 525
Clark, Hank 145
Clark, Stan 445, 450, 453
Clark, Tom 86
Classic Billiards 245
Clee, Ken 29, 69, 214, 414, 423, 428
Cleveland, Dwight 170
Coffee, John 471
Coffee, Sue 103
Colabuono, Gary 162
Colbert, R.W. 178, 473
Colclough, Don 5, 73
Cole, Barbara 234, 332
Combs, Jim 481, 482, 544
Comer, Patsy 81
Compeau, Larry 439
Condon, Jack 153
Conley, James 108, 219, 317
Conrad, Norman 184
Conroy, Edward 446, 567, 569
Cook, Grayson 171
Cooper, Reid 31
Coover, Roland 155, 412
Copeland, Joe 178, 236, 537
Cornish, Michael 491
Corwin, Ed & Carolyn 247
Cory, Jack 410
Cotting, Carl 11, 30, 49
Council, Michael 271, 493
Cowles, Douglas 385
Cox, Allison 121
Cox, Helen & Duncan 39
Cox, Peter 521
Crain, Jim 527
Crawford, David 430, 431
Cronin, Terry 494
Cummings, Urban 497
Cunningham, Steve 15, 19, 26, ˉ24, 401
Curran, Pamela 58

D

Daly, Robert 9, 379, 410
Daniel, Gwen 96, 98, 312, 324, 325
Daniels, Christine 481, 483
Davidson, Joe 487, 511, 558, 573
Davidson, Marl 100

Davis, Richard 169, 171
DeBolle, Frank 250
DeCesare, Roland 271
Deeks, Herb 125
DeGenaro, Steve 303, 492, 527, 529
Dembo, George 453, 522
Demont, Cary 291, 293, 326
Dennis and George 284
Denton, Tim 376
Dequaine, Lester 89
Deveny, Jack 557
Deweber, Don 118
DeWolfe, Scott 311
Dickar, Alan 181
Dillard, Peggy 178, 285, 292, 295, 446, 558
Dilts, Chuck 387
Dilworth Billiards 245
Dimare, Dario 365, 395
Dinner, Craig 30, 37
Dipboye, Marilyn 333
DiProspero, Art 239
DiRenzo, Mercedes 33
Dobres, Sheldon 520
Docks, Les 210
Dolin, Harvey 180, 185, 230, 296, 310, 476
Donachy, Gary 276
Dotz, Warren 403
Doucet, Larry 149
Dourgarian, James 328, 574
Dubas, Rita 173
Dudley, Richard 8
Duncan, Royal 232, 244, 350
Dunkin, Jim 124
Dunlop, Paul 69, 339
Dunn, Bob 234
Dunwoodie, Ralph 341
Durham, Ken 219
Dwyer, Lois 323

E

Eales, Dana 574
Eberhart, Charles 442
Edmisten, Rick 246
Eisenstadt, Robert 254, 257
Elford, David 175
Eliot, Drew 185
Elliott, Richard 267
Engel, Michael 286, 293

Engelke, Paul 394
English, Deric 287
Enter, David 133, 177
Eodice, Ralph 133, 221
Ericson, Dale 353
Ernst, Ross & Ruth 503
Escoe, Adrienne 34
Eslinger, Bob 192
Evarkiou, Charles 267
Everett, John 406
Exclusively Dogs! 334
Experienced Denim 72

F

Facey, David 342
Falk, Peter 484, 487
Farha, Eugene 349
Fawcett, John 144, 145, 148, 151, 166
Fay, Robert 350, 441
Feely, Wayne 392
Fendel, Cynthia 27
Ferguson, Karen 320
Ferretta, Michelle 480
Filer, Russell 431
Fink, Paul 116
Fischer, John 441, 458
Fisher, Bob 114
Fisher, L.C. 38
Fitzpatrick, Reed 237, 341, 347, 546
Flamm, Bruce & Jan 391
Fleming, Jack 184, 382
Florey, Ken 293
Flynn, Joe 213
Foott, George 430, 542
Forman, Dave 289
Forsko, Harold 284
Fougere, George 21, 115
France, Madeleine 91, 92, 498
Francis, Dave 113
Francis, Walley 353, 390, 325
Franklin, Larry 382, 389, 390
Freedman, Myron 274
Frei, Peter 24
Fresno State Univ 178
Friedman, Barry 6, 7, 21, 75, 105, 260, 297, 299, 301, 321, 483, 493, 528, 536, 549
Fritz, Mike 544

Fuchs, Danny 146
Fulks, Andy 419

G

Galt, Dave 255, 330
Gallacher, Greg 238
Gandy, James 407, 433
Gardner, Gary 311
Gartin, Dick 365
Garton, Gus 341, 342, 353, 434
Gatanis, Gary 230, 243
Gavula, LuAnn 568
Gawchik, William 360
Gayle, Jean 426
Geissman, Grant 149
George, Joan 40
Geringer Art, Ltd. 490
Gerlach, Jim 147, 329, 479
Geyer, Lynn 262, 264
Giarde, Leigh 428
Gibbs, Linda 74, 80, 81, 483
Gilbert, Ivan 282, 285, 374, 385, 484, 491, 505, 515, 524, 563
Gill, Robert 533
Gillio, Dennis 463
Ginsberg, Danny 420
Ginsberg, Sam 304
Glab, Anthony 112, 430, 432
Glass, Herb 351
Glickman, Sid 197
Godek, Matt 232
Goetz, Albert 25
Goetz, John 377
Gold, Stan 138, 552
Goldstein, Lee 233, 234, 236
Goodwin, Tom 200
Gordon, Steve 263
Gorges, Will 446
Gorlick, Don 108, 205, 302, 325, 373, 374, 464
Gotelli, Dolph 108, 313
Gottuso, Bob 225
Govig, Valerie 110, 572
Goyda, Michael 242
Graham, Ron 209, 577
Graver, Nicholas 524
Gregerson, Byron 368
Griffin, Mark 48

Gronowski, Richard 124, 129
Gronsky, Michael 146
Gross, David 138
Grush, Glenn 413, 424
Gumtow, Alan 52
Gurner, Jack 384
Gutzke Kim 193, 393

H

Haag, Robert 431
Hakal, Ed 202
Hake, Ted 132, 152, 292
Hall, George 168
Halloran, Rhonda 356, 357
Halperin, James 461
Hamburg, Bill 115, 127, 135
Hamer, Beverly 206
Hamilton, Denise 74, 334, 502
Hammelbacher, Frank 466
Hammerman, Jay 237
Handelsman, Burton 436
Hannan, Steve 72
Hanners, Doug 211
Hans, Jim & Beverly 536
Harding, Judy 19, 75, 78, 85, 221, 320, 453, 522
Hardisty, Donald 500, 503
Hardy, Art 188
Harper, Michael 350
Harris, Tom 525
Harris, Warren 24
Harrow, Alan 448, 472
Hartley, Glenn 417
Hartmann, Ron 457
Hartzog, Rich 24, 178, 239, 286, 288, 290, 294, 303, 335, 386, 453, 464, 465, 470, 541, 549
Hash, Ken 245
Hatscher, Dick 66
Hawes, Rhonda 254
Hayne, Neil 521
Hecht, Eli 29, 279
Heck, Carl 10, 398
Heckard, Alvin 192, 205, 217, 343
Heilmann, Bob 85
Held, Claude 165, 553, 555
Hendin, David 461
Hendriksen, Douglas 299, 538
Hersey, Marcia 111

Herz, Mike 128, 140, 141, 142, 147, 172
Hess, Robert 329
Hiatt, Ernest 416
Hiett, Robert 462
Hill, Joe 162
Hill, John C. 297
Hiller, Robert 280
Hiscox, Mimi 98
Historical Collections 292, 305
Hlinka, Peter 472
Hoak, Frank 450
Hodge, John 416
Hoffman, Barry 269, 289, 319
Holabird, Fred 430, 505, 543
Holden, Cal 306
Holmes, Rev Sherlock 22, 72, 173, 329, 374, 393, 512, 559, 567
Holms, Leslie 93
Horak, Carl 165
Horn, Robert 359
Horowitz, Joe 279
Horwedel, Lowell 463, 468, 570
Horwitz, Dennis 118, 173
Houston, Buzz 434
Howard, Steve 438
Hudson, Murray 118, 365, 510
Hullfish, Gary 448, 451
Hultzman, Don 139
Hume, Richard 60, 61
Humler, Riley 55, 485
Hunn, Peter 357
Hunter, Tim 159
Hyman, Tony 202, 268, 273-4, 281, 287, 327, 407-08, 482, 545, 548

I

Ingberman, Ned 201
Irons, Dave 21
Ismail, Sellam 388, 391
Ivankovich, Michael 489
Ives, Jacquelynn 44
Ivester, Hermann 477

J

Jabloner, Steve 220, 526
Jack London Bookstore 328
Jackson, Andy 501

Jackson, Denis 480, 552
Jacobs, Lee 272, 300
Jacobsen, Pat 129,410,433,556
Jacobson, Andrw 354, 355, 483
Jacobson, Dan 508
Jaffe, Lewis 508
Jamison, Carolyn 223
Jamison, Phillip 220
Janaczek, Gregory 339, 351
Janson, Frederic 327, 433
Jarvinen, Larry 444
Jay, Stan 198
Jennings, Bruce 441
Jennings, Ralph 369, 417
Jobe, Mike 83
Johnson, Joedi 104
Johnson, Thomas 455, 458
Johnson, Warren 568
Johnson, Wes 156, 412
Joiner, John 359
Jones, Charles 493, 494
Jones, David 199
Jones, Donald 241
Jones, Mark 200
Judson, Jack 168
Julia, James 3, 10, 64, 96, 108, 402, 438, 484
Jung, Paul 278
Jurich, Jeff 164

K

Kadet, Jeff 554
Kamerman, Sheldon 516
Kantrud, Hal 316
Kaplan, Michael 352
Karrer, Bob 468, 538, 548
Katz, Sheldon 50, 241, 336
Keefe, Thomas 187
Kegebein, Jim 59, 86
Keller, Leland 373
Kelley, Dan 72
Kelley, Steve 34, 51, 58, 127, 250
Kelly, Mike 158
Kenyon, Maggie 84
Keohane, Jerry 449, 451
Ketcham, Steve 378, 402
Ketelle, Jay 340, 349, 350, 427
Keyser, J.C. 534
Khuans, Ken 522, 453
Kidder, Clark 175, 569

Kimmell, Todd & Kristin 177, 183, 345, 534
Kincade, Gary 346, 420
King, Alan 192, 426
King, David 341
King, Jerry 307
King, John 562
King, Steve 336
Kingman, Winifred 328
Kinsey, Alan 353
Kipp, Ken 48, 367
Kirk, Miss Helen 375
Kirsner, Gary 265
Klapmeier, Ernest 454
Klaus, Josef 462, 520
Klein, Frank 511, 540, 573
Klein, Pat 52, 288
Klein, R.G. 390
Kline, Wayne 217
Klodzinski, Jack 111, 134, 137, 143, 147, 157, 163, 169, 556
Klompus, Gene 80
Kluge, Bob 468
Knappen, Ron & Mary 394
Knauer, Judy 68, 323
Knicely, Fay 70
Knopke, Thomas 5
Koenig, Walter 134, 160
Kolbe, George 467
Kolbe, Robert 529, 541
Konet, Ken 389, 454
Koopman, Nick 555
Korman, Alice 45
Korzun, Jonathan 200
Koyt, George 242
Kozloff, Ed 234
Kraker, Bernice 29
Krieg, Holly 46
Krispin, Steve 379
Kritzberg, Gary 149
Kroll, Peter 158, 266
Krueger, Kurt 461
Krug, Larry 290, 321
Krumholz, Phillip 89
Kruskall, Stephen 578
Kukowski, Ed 438
Kurella, Elizabeth 74
Kveragas, David 283, 575

L

Laaker, Ken 155

Lahammer, Rob 233
Lambert, John 30
Lambert, Lindsay 8, 169, 185
Landau, David 324, 570
Landgrebe, Lori 94
Larouche, Linda 105
LaRoue, Sam 349, 538
Lathar, Marion 421
Lau, Tammy 178
Laurie, James & Mary 486, 511, 563, 572
Lavin, Fred 179
Lawrence, Tim 245
Lazarus, Hillel 121
Le Poulaille 3, 16
Ledford, Gordon 12
Lee-Leff, Laura 174
Leon, Eli 493
Leone, Stephen 425
Leong, Howard 81
Letocha, Charles 373
Leveille, Gary 51, 289, 536
Levi, Charles 277
Levine, Alan 148, 151, 164, 172
Levine, H. Joseph 291, 472
Levy, H.M. 116
Levy, Noel 434, 465, 513
Levy, Tedd 367
Lewin, Bruce 310, 476
Lewin, Jon 371
Lewis, George 553
Lieberman, Ron 235, 310, 335, 562
Lincoln, Dave 347
Linn, Kier 63
Linscott, Jacqueline 395, 416
Lipschitz, Suzanne 154
Littleton Coin Co. 463
Litwin, Donna 492
Litwin, Jeffrey 118
Loehr, David 173
Lombardi, Francis 275, 439
Lone Star Autographs 514
Long, Gaal 447, 449
Lubliner, Larry 257
Lucente, Sue 333
Lukach, Joe 31
Lunzmann, Dan 31
Lyall, Holly 81

Lynch, Christopher 358, 361

M

Mackin, Bill 300
Magoon, Orville 328
Mahfuz, Geoffrey 162
Malitz, Lucille 32, 107, 370, 491
Malone, Michael 142
Mancina, Dean 187
Manier, Michael 392
Margolis, Sy & Ronnie 343
Marier, Vincent 324
Mark, James 236
Markley, Ken 13, 14
Marks, Jerome 33
Marriott, Edward 543
Marrone, Sandy 207
Marshall, Michael 325
Marshall, WH 373
Martignette, Charles 6, 7, 166, 175, 192, 282, 284, 398, 479, 482, 498, 508, 554
Martin, Frank 130, 216
Martin, Philip 360
Mascieri, Russell 48, 178, 386, 507
Mast, Susan 17, 547
Mastro, William 229
Matteson 578
Matthies, Eric 208, 495
Matzke, Gene 381
Mauck, Jeff 49
Maundy International 83
Maxwell, Lee 20
Maymudes, August 370
McCaw, Martin 156
mcClain, Craig 114, 117
McClintock, John 520
McDaniel, Buddy 171
McDonald, Charles 379
McGlothlin, Chris 41
McGonagle, Hank 448, 457, 458
McHenry, Gordon 445
McInroy, Rusty 241
McKeeby, Matthew 140
McKeon, Harry 110
McKinnon, Thomas 155, 246, 336, 553
McLaughlin, Larry 361
McMahon, Don 446
McVey, Jeff 344, 401

McWhorter, George 147
Meaders, Elzbth 286, 304, 447
Meccarello, Gus 464
Medeiros, Gary 243
Mehl, Eric 531
Melcher, Richard 9, 343
Mellis, Allan 425
Melzer, Paul 561, 572
Merline, Merlin 8, 10
Meyer, Jeffrey 384
Meyer, Larry 368, 369
Mezerow, Jerry 541
Mickolas, John 221
MidweSterling 38
Mihlheim, Rick 112
Miller, Hal 308
Miller, Jay 273
Miller, J. Ann 175
Miller, Mark 20, 302, 303, 331, 567
Miller, Mike / Sherry 18, 92, 93
Miller, Timothy 550
Miller, Walter 242, 340
Minor, Michael 514
Miran Arts and Books 385, 484
Miscellaneous Man 522
Mitchell, Ken 135, 163, 165-66
Moebius, Cliff 342, 345
Mogilner, Jeff 269
Mollica, Tony 357
Molloy, Scott 287
Monterey Bay Sport Mus 240
Montgomery, Bill & Linda 522
Moore, William 234, 239
Mordas, Al 186
Morford, William 402
Morrell, Stuart 267
Morris, Jack 249
Morris, Thomas 174, 186
Moses, Arthur 182
Mr. Condom 284
Mueller, Heinz 122
Muldavin, Peter 211
Muller, Jerry 165
Mullin, Alexander 264
Munger, Lynn 298
Muns, J.B. 327, 516
Munsell, Gloria 48
Murphy, Michael 241
Murphy, Phil 379

Murphy, Sue 91, 92
Murray Cards Intl. 270

N

Nackman, Joan 48
Nagasaka, Dyke 443
Natale, Art 177
Natale, Ed 267, 344, 351
National Cuff Link Society 80
Nauck, Kurt 204, 208
Nedry, Boyd 249
Negus, Doug 203
Neill, Nollie 20, 126, 186
Nelson, John 203
Nelson, Scott 56
Nemec, Loretta 399
Neumann, Jeffrey 312, 571
Neuschafer, Charles 510, 513
Newell, David 311
Newman, Jonathan 509
Newman, Kenneth 486
Newman, Robert 256, 270, 405, 419, 435
Newman, Stanley 570
Nickell, W.E. 179, 409, 414, 546
Nielsen, Bill 120, 148, 271, 386
Nolt, Dave 128, 417
Non-Sport Update 160
Norma's Jeans 318, 328
Norris, Bud 145
Norris, Chip 159
Norton, Russell 526, 527, 532
Nothnagel, Linda 501
Novak, Frank 403
Novak, Jay 5, 15
Novak, Marty 223
Nowicki, Peter 263
Nowlin, Kaaren 75
Nussbaum, Warren 282

O

O'Brien, Jim 262, 263
O'Brien, Trish 249
O'Callaghan, Tim 322, 342, 359
O'Key, Tom 269
O'Neill, David 102
Oates, Joan 49, 500
Oberlin Smith Society 433
October Farm 332
Oglesby, Dave 116

Okula, Richard 127
Old Bottle Museum 378
Old China Patterns Ltd 45, 68, 315
Old Print Shop, The 486
Old Timers 13, 14
Olins, Evan 71
Olsen, Mel 550
Olson, Don 244, 351, 540
Olson, Larry 344
Olson, Michael 261
Osina, Neil 464
Otnes, Robert 389
Ott, Ron 545
Over, Naomi 65
Overholt, Lin 465
Owen, Robert 123, 343

P

Padron, Richard 24, 26, 29, 40, 123, 219, 319, 335, 399 417
Page, Robert 44
Palicia, Joan 235
Palm, Phyllis 306
Pankow, Nadine 67
Pankowski, Dick 456
Pantozzi, John 244
Pardee, Elaine 102
Pardini, Dick 91
Parks, John 538
Parris, Jeane 90
Parrott, Kathy 315, 500
Pascoe, Ed 47, 259, 330, 498
Pasquino, Bill 256
Patterson, Donald 190, 195
Pattison, Lee 248, 277, 279
Paul, Les 266
Pautz, Roland 428
Pawlow, Nick 184
Payne, Carol 17, 40, 47, 330
Pearson, Ron 542, 544
Peat, David 397
Pecina, Dennis 275
Pedro, Joe 427
Pensoneau, Elizabeth 506
Perera, Tom 392, 396
Perkins, Danny 222, 350
Perry, Chris 172, 177, 319
Perzel, Bob & Nancy 57

Phelps, Clark 256, 569
Phelps, Jerry 15, 105, 370, 398
Phillips, Stan 130
Picek, Louis 36, 37, 61, 298, 314, 490, 491
Piecskowski, Ron 145
Pimenta, Gary 146, 152
Pitman, Larry 452
Pitzak, Avery 384
Platt, Jay 540, 549
Platt, Joel 228, 237, 240
Pochobradsky, John 451
Podley, Andrea 149
Polk, Jo Anne 73
Pooler, Tom 367, 446, 455, 472
Poppel, Seth 326
Portukalian, Robert 199
Posner, Judy 35, 305
Poster, Harry 191, 195, 531, 533
Potawatomi Museum 298
Powell, Lew 295, 538
Powell, Robert 436
Presgraves, Jim 32, 150, 207, 385, 398, 446, 569
Price, Michael 549
Prince, Eileen & Irwin 322
Pulati, Evalene 317
Pulvers, Marty 277
Puma, Jerome 415
Purkey, Cari 154
Purkey, Donna & Al 97, 101
Purtell, Jeffrey 67

Q

Quarles, Charles 361
Quesinberry, Robert 163
Quinn, Patrick 230
Quintin, David 291, 294, 476

R

Rago, David 4, 16, 56
Ramm, Steve 205, 220
Ramsay, Chet 204
Rann, Rick 180, 225
Rapaport, Ben 276
Rasmussen, Mike 163, 171, 521, 578
Raymond, Doris 71

Reamer, Arnold 77, 83, 90, 497
Redding, Doug 538
Reddock, Rich /Barb 410, 413
Reedy, Don 219
Reese, Michael 514
Regan, Richard 238
Rehr, Darryl 23, 49, 387, 406
Reighter, Frank 174
Reincke, Chuck 526
Reinke, Roger 396
Reiss, David 209
Rendell, Kenneth 482, 515, 528
Replacements, Ltd. 44
Retskin, Bill 280
Rice, Boris 28
Rice, Michael 229, 295, 356, 365, 380, 454, 471, 521, 548
Ridenour, Ron 289
Ries, Iwan & Co. 277
Riovo, Ralph 429
Ritch, Jerry & Marsha 11
Rivkind, Mark 278
Robinson, Jay 122, 126, 128
Robnett, Cliff 122, 214
Roderick, CW & Hilda 49
Roenigk, Martin 107, 204`, 216, 257
Rogers, Alan 6, 301
Roland, Scott 65
Rondeau, Rene 84
Rosaaen, Robin 224
Rosato, Geri 60, 372, 373
Rosen, Benton & Beverly 46
Rosenhoover, John 486, 511, 553, 558, 573
Rosenthal, Mel 335, 372
Rosenthal, Richard 524
Ross, Myron 516
Ross, Ron 545
Rowe, Edie 22, 513, 516
RPM Children's Books 578
Rudoff, Andy 179
Ruppert, Barbra 563, 575, 577
Rush, Herman 207, 221
Russ, William 248
Ryan, Fred 216, 240

S

Sabreen, Ed 281

Sachen, Bill 254
Safka, Bill 516
Safran, Mike 236
Sage, Ed 16, 191
Sager, Jamie 211
Salveson, Ted 217, 257
Samuelian, Sam/ Anna 12, 15
Sanchez, Clark / Charl 501-02
Santi, Federico 62
Saputo, Jana 105
Sargent, Lia 104
Sater, Denise 63
Saviers, Kathy 380
Savitt, Claire 275
Sawrie, Mike 417
Sawyer, Don 84, 426
SC Coin & Stamp Co. 545
Scales, William 317
Scarfone, Jay 176
Schaeffer, Randy 418
Scharfman, Paul 223, 405, 406, 554
Scheer, Frank 367
Scheiner, C.J. 282
Schenck, Marc 331
Scher, Arnold 27
Scheuch, Allen 234
Schmidtmann, Gil 543
Schmitt, JR Crittenden 442
Schmitt, Otti 214, 237
Schnatz, Stephanie 47, 323
Schneider, Dick 321, 535
Schneider, Don 129, 322, 340, 344, 345, 348, 351, 405, 435, 553
Schneider, Gary (Ohio) 190
Schneider, Gary (Calif) 67
Schneider, Stuart 25, 316, 317, 527
Schoenharl, Paul 20
Schreckinger, Sy 12, 113
Schulte, Dennis 348, 409, 541
Schultz, Ken 356
Schuth, Ed & Carla 416, 427
Schwanz, W.E. 540
Schwartz, Howard 256, 568
Schweighart, Tim 408
Schwimmer, Mike 275
Screen, Harold 421
Segel, Norman 232

Selcke, Ron 429
Selfridge, Madalaine 96, 314, 317, 507, 508, 509
Selman, Larry 69
Senerchia, Steve 198
September, Pahaka 70
Settembre, James 243
Seymour, Dale 255
Shanks, David 191
Shannon, Thomas 225
Sharpe, Kip 264
Sheeran, K. 285
Sheldor, Dave 133, 164, 556, 575
Shelley, Don 409
Sheridan, Jim 256
Sherlock's Haven 277
Shochet, Jerome 240
Shortz, Will 507, 556, 570
Shriner, Kim 221
Sigg, Walter 533
Simon, Richard 229
Singer, Leslie 142, 366
Singleton, Karen 64
Singley, Elijah 41, 260, 473
Skelton, William 462
Slocum, Jerry 119
Smiley, Bill 248, 356, 477
Smith, Catherine 99
Smith, Chris 170
Smith, David 36
Smith, Earl 48
Smith, Gordon 432
Smith, Jack 192, 270
Smith, Leo 540
Smith, Michael 375, 411
Smith, Norm & Bev 358
Smith, WH 210
Smithwick, Mike 366
Smurf Collector's Club 154
Snyder, Edwin 120, 299, 412
Snyder, Patricia 97
Soelberg, Steve 424
Soller, Rick 395
Sommer, William 59, 62, 305
Sorgenfrei, Jan 297
Souchik, Greg 307, 452
Sourapas, Steve 420
Sparacio, George 281, 502
Speck, David 314, 315, 316

Speece, Jack 432
Speezak, Judy 74
Spellman, Johnny 114, 240, 301, 408, 441, 445, 483, 528, 543
Spiess, Greg 288
Spiller, Burt 379, 404
Sports Immortals Musm 240
Spragins, M.B. 236
Spruce, George 242
Stack's 463
Stanley, John 258
Stanoff, J. 327, 512, 550, 566
Stapp, Charles 86, 88
Stark, Rex 52, 180, 293, 482
Stau, Sven 124, 264, 377, 432, 461
Stauffer, Robert 481
Steffen, Tony 262, 266, 420
Stephens, Michael 287
Steranko, Jim 479, 555
Stevenson, Ron 270
Stewart, Charlie 203, 352
Stidham, Rhett 87
Stillman, William 176
Stitt, Dave 382
Stock Search Intrnatl 466
Stock, Sue 116, 180
Stolz, Connie 46
Storey, Frank 532
Storino, Lou 272
Strauss, Mike 128
Strawser Auctions 45, 62
Struncius, Gary 4, 17, 57, 58
Suozzi, Mark 109
Supica, Jim 440
Sutton, Mark 296
Svacina, Larry 120
Swindall, Fred 320, 544
Swisher, Douglas 475, 477
Synchef, Richrd 285, 286, 575
Szeszler, Denis 496
Szymanski, Tom 235, 356, 554

T

Taksler, Alan 355
Tamaru, Stuart 451, 456, 457
Tanner, Joe /Pam 85, 183, 381
Tarrant, Jenny 313
Taylor, Billie 278

Taylor, Bob 358
Teixeira, Neil 174
Telesmanich, John 456
Temares, Lee / Mike 571, 578
Temes, Irv 83
Temes, Vivian 27, 51, 66, 70, 92, 493
Thalberg, Bruce 27, 151
Thalberg, Jan 305
Theofilis, George 170, 356, 453, 507
Thiele, Bob 419
Thomas, Robert 447
Thomas, Steven 488
Thompson, Kenna 182
Thompson, Steve 150
Thompson, Thom 263, 418
Thornton, Don 31
Tice, Warren 73
Ticknor, Chris 555
Tiftickjian, David 7
Timepiece Antiques 77
Tobacciana Res 268, 271, 272
Tompkins, Sylvia 39
Tonelli, Joe 249
Toohey, Marlena 64
Tori, Vicki 319
Toser, Roxanne 160
Tritt, Donald 473, 550
Trombly, Ken 182
Trautwein, Richard 109
Tucker, Richard 37, 407, 428
Tumbusch, Tom 134

U

Unerwood, Lisa 19
United House Wrecking 398
University of Louisville 147
Updegrove, Bruce 449, 450
Urmanic, Bob 223, 224
Urmston, Richard 467
Utley, Bill 25

V

Van Ausdall, Marci 104
Van Evera, Bruce 415
Van Hook, Lisa 272, 406
Van Scotter, Jo Ann 520
Van Trump, George 347
Van Vynckt, Fran 509

Vane, Roark 404
Vargas, Marsha 496
Vaughn, Gary 172, 220
Vent Haven Museum 184
Vines, Linda 325, 499
Viola, Jeff 193
Visakay, Stephen 260
Vogt, Vernon 193
Vohs, Sharon 58, 60
Voigt, Gary 427
Volker, Margarita 237
Voorhees, Alan 485, 531
Vrsalik, Larry 514

W

Wagner, Michael 111
Wagner, Joe 324
Wagner, Lowell 123
Waite, Jim 503
Waits, Jerry 365
Wallerstein, Herbert 492
Walter, John 400
Wampler, David 429
Warchol, Joe 143
Wardell, Charles 399
Warren, Jon 170
Warren, W.J. 66
Waters, Mlke 378, 421, 434
Watson, Randy 393
Way We Wore, The 71
Weaver, Jim 172
Weber, Joe 205, 218, 343, 388
Weed, Ben 448
Weintraub, Sharon 497
Welch, David 136, 138-9, 143, 144, 157, 212, 411
Welch, Matt 423
Weltman, Sandy 130
Werbin, Stan 197
West Newbury Wagn Wrk 426
West, Richard 574
Weygand, James 397
Whelan, Dennis 312, 569
Whipple, Tom 50
Whitaker, Robert 247
Whitehill, Bruce 117
Whitney, David 309
Whitney, Philip 427
Whitson, Sandra 18, 19, 39
Widmar, John 210, 214

Wiener, Ron   122
Wilch, Dale   339
Wiley, John   176
Wilhite, Ann   99
Williams, James   311, 463,
  569, 576
Williams, John   280
Williams, Meredith   423
Willis, Stan   369, 381
Willoughby, Ron   248, 250, 411
Wilmes, Liz/Dick   119, 405, 414
Wilson, Chris   506, 515, 528
Wilson, Mike   342
Wilson, Richard   173, 318, 326
Winningham, Henry   331, 348
Winther, Jo Ellen   50
Wissner, Allan   371
Wood, Barbara   79
Wood, Richard   400, 546
Woollard, Doug   179
Worman, Charles   364, 439,
  445, 458, 529
Wotring, Charles   349
Wren, Marilyn   409
Wright, Richard   364
Wright, Wilson   357
Wrobbel, Eric   194
Wyman, Ric   153, 174

Y
Yagoda, Marvin   183, 218
Young, Joe   30, 258
Young, Scott   299

Z
Zadra, Frank   239
Zakszewski, Valerie   98
Zanzibar Museum   452
Zarneski, Polly   98
Zecker, Barry   316
Zeder, Audrey   288
Zekley, Mickie   201
Zemenick, Greg   15, 108, 110,
  113, 275, 355, 390, 403
Zeppelin   362
Zimmerman, David   404
Zukowski, Stan   369
Zygmunt, Frank   218

A
Abbot and Costello items   174
abolitionist   326
action figures   132-141, 147
adding machine   23, 387-89, 391
addresses of celebrities   517
Advent calendars   308
**advertising   272-281, 340-376,
  394, 402-435**
  You'll find buyers of advertising
throughout this book. If you have
advertising use the index to look
under the product name, the type of
product and the subject of the illustration used to sell the product.
advertising (con't)
    ad campaign manuals   151
    by famous artists   507
    characters136, 138, 144, 412
    depicting
      Blacks   305
      card games   255, 257
      cats   333
      cigars   274
      cowboys   300
      farm equipment   417
      gambling   255, 257
      pool playing   245
African art & artifacts   491, 495
Afro-American history   304
agate, items made from   18
airplane items   358-362, 451-52
    overhaul manuals   358, 362
    parts, military   451
    pilot's handbooks   362
    company models   361-62
    toy   124-127, 130
alarm clocks   15
Alaska/Seattle Expo   180
Alaskan items   546
Alcoholics Anonymous   569
Alice in Wonderland, all   156
Alka-Seltzer figures   403
alligators, images of   331
almanacs   375, 376
aluminum jewelry   78
Alvin & the Chipmunks   221
Amazon River items   549

ambulance ephemera   349
ammunition   442
    advertising for   408
Amos and Andy   304
amplifiers, guitar   203
amusement park items   186, 187
ancient artifacts   461
angel figurines   502
    church size   312
Anglund, Joan, art by   481
animal collectibles   330-336,
    497, 499
    heads, zinc   426
    stuffed   302, 303
    toy   114
    freak animals   302
animation, Japanese   133, 169
animation art   132, 133, 136,
    137, 153, **165-166, 169**
Annie Oakley   186
Anti Saloon League   259
anti-war movement   286
antlers   **303**
apothecary equipment   370
apple growing, info about   433
apple parers   30
aquarium tanks   336
Arbuckle Coffee Co. items   414
arcade machines   **215, 217,
    218, 219, 255, 389**
architects' drawings   398, 399
Architectural Digest   554
arctic ephemera   357, 549
Ariquipa pottery   59
Arkansas ephemera   538
Arm & Hammer ephemera   416
armor   454, 457
armored cars   452
arrest warrants   380
arrowheads   **297-299, 461**
art, all types   **478-503**

    You'll find buyers of paintings, prints and figures throughout this book. If you have art to sell or wish appraised you should use the index to look under the type of artwork but also the subject/setting of the painting or print.If you know the name of the artist of your work, look up their name in the index too.

    African   491, 494
    Asian   484, 496, 550
    comic book   162, 165, 166
    commercial   487
    erotic   282
    Eskimo   491, 492, 494
    How to Sell Art   **478**
    Indian   297, 298, 490-492
    Oriental   484, 491, 495-496,
    547
    Peter Max   19
    pin-up   282, 283
    pre-Columbian   493, 495
    religious   308
    Russian   550
    sketchbooks   485
    South Pacific   490, 547
    trench (by soldiers)   450
    various artists   149, 367, 547,
Art Metal Works   497
artillery   444, 452
ashtrays   267, 268, 275, 344, 543
    cigar band   274
    rubber tire   267
Asian books & photos   566
assassins, autographs of   517
astrology   312, 569
atlases   505, 510, 511
atomizers   91
Aunt Jemima ephemera   305
Australian items   549
autograph albums   506
autographs   **514-517**
    criminals   289
    classical & opera   220
    country music   220
    financiers   467
    judges   380
    movie   172, 175
    musicians   224
    Protestant churchmen   308
    rock and roll   172, 222
    sheriffs   380
    spacemen   366
    spies   287
Automobile Club   346, 347

automobile parts, etc. 340-348
automobiles , 339
  Mercedes 500 452
  military 452
Autry, Gene 172
Autumn Leaf items 50
aviation items 358-362
  military 451
Avon bottles **94**

B

baby toys 111
Baccarat crystal 68
badges, all types **320**
  airline 358, 360, 361
  auto plant 340
  bus driver 349
  fire department 368, 369
  law enforcement 300, 381-83
  post office 367
  railroad 364, 365
  truant officer 473
bagpipes 201
Bakelite 79
Baldwin, Lucky, ephemera 545
Ball, Lucille, items 153, 154
balloons & blimps 361
balls, sports 228-29, 231-33, 236
banjos **197-199, 203**
banks, toy 109, **112, 113**
  oil can 351
baptismal certificate 491
barbershop items 377, 436, 490
Barbie **96, 97,100, 101**
barrettes, plastic 81
Bartholdi, Auguste, items 296
baseball **228-231**
baseball cards from tobacco 273
basketball 228-229, 231, 233
baskets, Indian 297, 298
bath tubs 398
batons, band conductor's 200
bayonets 444
BB guns **114**
beads, glass 80, 444, 445
beat generation items 285
Beatles **132, 223, 225**
beatnik figurines 155
bedspreads 75

Beech-Nut items 415
beer 262-266, 377-78, 402, 404
  glasses & mugs **158, 262**
  steins **265-266**
bells 318
belts 70
Benny, Jack 174
Berigan, Bunny 221
Bermuda 548
Betty Boop 148
Bewitched items 153
Bib-Lable Lithiated drinks 419
Bibles **308, 310, 311, 561, 572**
biblical coins and relics 461
bicycle licenses 353
bicycles **352, 353**
  Iver Johnson brand 442
  motor driven 353
big band anything 221
Big Jo Flour ephemera 416
Big Little Books 135, 148, 164
Billboard magazine 554
billiard ephemera **245, 257**
billiard balls, ivory 494
Billikens 323
Billy Possum ephemera 98
bingo ephemera 256
bird calls 249
bird's eye views of cities 510
birth certificates 491
Blacks, racist items **304-305**
Black history 285, 286, 304
Black magazines 554
black magic 302
Blacks, medals depicting 473
blacksmiths shops, entire 389
Blake, Eubie, ephemera 220
blankets, Indian **297, 298**
blasting cap tins 430
blimps 361
blocks 109, 116
blowtorches 400
blueprints **398, 399**
boars, wild, ephemera 331
boat building 357
boatwrights shops, entire 389
boats **354-357**
  military 444
  pond models 355

594 THINGS YOU CAN SELL

Bob Hope 175
bobbing head dolls **159, 160**
body building 244
Bogart, Humphrey 172, 173
bombs 442
Bond 007, James 138, 146
bonds **466-468, 505**
bones 302, 336
bookbinding equipment 573
bookends, Arts & Crafts 16, 17
bookplates 508
books **561-578**
You'll find buyers of books all through Trash or Treasure. For more buyers use the index to look up the subject of the book.
books (con't)
autographed 514, 562-64, 567
Bibles 308, 310, 561, 572
children's 108, 136, 148, 164, 313, 563, 576-578
city view books 562
erotic 282
first editions 561, 565, 574
geography 510
horse breeding 243
How to Sell Books **561**
illus by artists 480
illus with maps 510, 511
Jewish 566
leather bound 562
limited edition 561, 563, 572
medical 370, 371, 374
miniature 23
music, song books 207
nautical 357
paperback 576
Peanuts 149
Pogo 150
pop-up 108, 577
puzzles 507
Red Riding Hood 156
reference 567
religious 310, 311, 312
school **577, 578**
science fiction 575
Sherlock Holmes 329
stud books 332
Tarzan 147, 329

boomerangs 249, 550
boots
cowboy **299, 300**
fox hunt 249
women's 73
Borden's ephemera 413, 429
Bossons figures 503
bottle caps 420
items made from 490
bottle openers 37, 258
bottles **377-379**
barbershop 378, 379, 436
bitters 378, 379
Dakota, N & S, from 541
drug store 376
ginger beer 264
ink 378, 379
Jim Beam type 259
made in Italy 63
medicine 370, 377-379
milk 379, 413, 429
perfume 90
pig shaped 379
poison 377, 378, 379
Royal Doulton 52
soft drink 420
w/gold painted labels 371
w/things built in them 321
bottling plants 378, 379, 420
bowling shirts **72**
boxes
Bakelite 79
celluloid 18
cereal **136, 144, 145**
cigar **274**
food products 405
food w/characters 412
ivory 354
shotshell 408
tramp art, carved 491
Turnbridge 32
woodburned 81
boxing **228, 230, 240**
Boy Scout items 306, 307, 325
bracelets with compacts 94
brand books 301
Brazil 549
bread wrappers 409
Breen, Bobby, items 221

bridal gowns 70
bride & groom cake tops 325
bridle rosettes 426
British militaria 454
British royalty 288
bronzes 497
    depicting dogs 334 , 335
    Russian 550
Brosmer, Betty, items 284
brothel items 389
Brundage, Francis, art by 507
brushes 19
Buddha figures 497
Buddy Holly photo 514
Buddy Lee dolls 97
Buffalo Bill 186
Buffalo pottery and china 50, 60
Buffalo soldiers, Black 447
Buick ephemera 343
builder's hardware 399
buildings, parts of 398
buildings, small replicas of 289
bullets 442
Burger King items 423
Burial Society certificates 303
burlesque 177, 183, 284
bus ephemera 349
business 384-424
    How to Sell Business 337
business cards 384
busses, real full size 349
butter molds 30
butterfly collections 331
buttons, pin-back 132-135, 290,
    291-296, 320
    civil rights 285, 292
    fox hunt 249
    Horace Greeley 327
    I.D. badges 386
    labor union 287
    movie 169
    Pogo 150
    political 132, 286, 290-96
buttons, clothing 73

C

C.C.C. items 367
Cabbage Patch dolls 99
Cagney, James, items 172
cake tops, bride & groom 325

calculators 23, **387-391**
calendar plates 52
calendars 262, 282, 308, 402,
    435, 480, 481, 483, **506,** 507
California
    beach towns 545
    Southern Cal souvenirs 541
California Perfume Company 91
California Raisin items 414
cameos 565
cameras 524, **530-533**
    3-D cameras 319, 533
    how to sell cameras 530
    miniature 23
Campbell Soup kids 413
can openers 30
Canada 295, 454 548, 549
    Mounties 380
candelabra, ceramic 59
candlesticks, black glass 64
candy containers 314
canes 27
    glass 69
    snake 331
cannibal ephemera 302
canning industry 407, 410, 433
canning jars 34, 378, 379
cannons 442, 444, 452
canoe ephemera 357
    Indian 297
cans 272-281, 340-376, 394,
    402-423, 434-435
Many people throughout this book want to buy cans because of what is printed on the can, what product it contained or who make the product. See advertising, tobacco, and liquor sections and in particular pp 402-425.
canteens, wooden 444
Cantor, Eddie 184
cap guns 115, 132, 133,
    135, 145 , 172
Capone, Al 327
Captain Action toys 132, 136
Captain Marvel 146
Captain Midnight 135, 151
card games 116

cards
- advertising 270-74, 385-86
- baseball 229, 230
- basketball 233
- **business** **384**
- Xmas & Holiday 314, 507, 513
- **cigarette** **270, 271**
- greetings 314, 513, 516
- gum 160
- non-sports 143, 160
- **playing** **254-257**
- tarot 312, 569
- tobacco advertising 271, 274
- trade 384, 386

Carl's Jr. collectibles **423**
Carnegie Hall ephemera 188
carnival glass **66**
carnival prizes 186
Carrie Nation 326
Carroll, Lewis, 156
cars (automobiles) **339**
cartoon glasses **158**
cartoons, 16mm film 177
carts, goat or dog 426
carvings 490
Case Tractor Co. 427
cash registers 389
casino chips 254-255, 257
cast iron 29, **36-37**, 407
- jewelry boxes 81
- toys 108
cat collectibles 333, 501
catalogs 272-281, 340-376, 385, 394, 402-435

Buyers throughout this book usually buy catalogs pertaining to what they collect. Use this index to look up the product advertised in the catalog. General buyers of catalogs are listed in italics above.

Catholic ephemera **310**
cave-related ephemera 432
celebrities
- advertising products 402
- clothing etc. 173, 222-23, 318
- vehicles 222, 318
- yearbooks 326
cellos **199**

celluloid items 18
Centennial 1876 178
ceramics 55-63
cereal boxes **134-136, 144, 145, 403, 405**
chairs **3-7, 436**
- folding 7
chalk carnival figures **186**
chandeliers 3, 9, 10, 398
Chandler, Jeff 175
Chapman, John, items 327
Charleston, SC, ephemera 538
Charlie McCarthy 151
Charlie's Angels 153
charm bracelets **78**
charms, silver 77, 80
chauffeur's badges 346
check protectors 23
check writers 388
checker boards, etc. 118
checks, illustrated 466, 468, 505
Chelsea ware 47
chemistry equipment 393
chess sets **118**
chewing gum items 411
Cheyenne Frontier Days 543
Chicago fire 559
children's books 576-78
children's china 51, 59
china, all **42-52,** 66

All types of china are bought by the buyers in this book. If you don't see your china listed in the index, look for it by reading pages 42-52.

china (con't)
- airline 358, 360
- Autumn Leaf 50
- chintz 48, 51
- **How to Sell China** **42**
- ocean liner 354-356
- railroad 364, 365
- souvenir 51, 536-37, 540, 544
- White House 291
Chinese, the, in America 285
Chinese items **455, 496, 550**
Chipette items 221
chiropractic memorabilia 373
Chris Craft boats, ephemera 357

Christmas collectibles 313-315
    Advent calendars 308
Church & Dwight ads 416
church pews 398
cigar bands **274, 275**
cigar box musical instrum 202
cigar boxes **274**
    things made from 202
cigar labels **274**
cigar store Indians 274, 275
cigarette items 267- 271
    holders 94
    lighters **268, 269, 274, 276**
    silks, items made from 271
    packs, slide type 267, 270
Cigarmaker's Union 274
Cinderella dolls 96
circus 186, 490
civil rights movement 285, 286, 292, 304
Civil War **444-448, 516, 538**
Civilian Conservation Corps 367
clocks **12-15**
    Art Deco 17
    blinking eye 12, 15
    cartoon character 84, 136
    dashboard 426
    electric unusual 12, 15, 401
    neon 404
    that play tunes 203
    time clocks 390
cloth scraps 75
clothing **70-75**
    coachman's 426
    concentration camp 311
    cowboy 299, 300
    designed by Peter Max 19
    fox hunt 249
    Indian 297, 298
    military jackets 451
    motorcycle 350, 351
    paisley shawls 492
    rock/movie star 222, 223, 318
clowns 186
coal company items 430
Coast Guard items 356
coasters 262, 505
Coca-Cola **403, 418-22**

cocktail shakers 260
coffee cans **404, 408, 414**
coffins 302
coin scales 464, 465
coin-operated mchns **215-219**
    kiddie rides 216
coins **460-464**
    Cuban 548
    elongated 464, 471, 473
    error 464
    How to Sell Coins **460**
Coleman products 416
collar boxes 18
collector's plates **503**
    Christmas 315
college plates 52
Collins, Floyd, rescue items 432
Colorado items 543
colorforms 111
coloring books **148**
Colt firearms Co. 441
Colt, Samuel, mblia 301
Coltrock products 441
Columbian expo 179
comic books 135, 138, **161-164**
    3-D 319
    Captain Marvel 146
    E.C. 143
    hardcover 148, 164
    hippie 286
    How to Sell Comics **161**
    monster 143
    sex 282
    Tarzan 147
comic character toys **131-139, 144, 148, 150**
comic strips 165
    original art for 135, 148
coming attraction slides 169
communal groups, religious 311
Communist Party USA 287
compacts **23, 70, 92, 94**
company seals 390
compasses 393
computers **391**
Concorde airplanes 359
condiment sets 35, 39, 40
condom machines 215, 284

condom tins 284
Coney Island ephemera 536
Confederate
    money 462
    stamps 475, 476
    uniform buttons 73
consular documents 508
contracts involving unions 287
cuckoo clocks 13
cookbooks **32, 563**
cookie jars **33**
    depicting Blacks 304
    cats 333
    plastic characters 144
Coon Chicken Inn 424
Coors pottery 50
corkscrews 258
corn shellers & planters 400
corsets 72
Cotton States Expo 178
counterfeit detectors 463-465
country music m'bilia **220**
court documents 380
Cowan flower frogs 59, 62
cowboy 'm'bilia 299-301, 542
cracker boxes 405
Cracker Jack prizes **412**
creamers 428
credit cards 435, 465
creels 231, 246, 247
cricket bats and balls 231
crime, organized, m'bilia 289
crocodiles, images of 331
croquet ephemera 231, 234
crossword puzzles 556, 570
crucifixes 308
crystal balls 312, 569
crystal stemware **44, 45, 68**
Cuban ephemera 274, 548
cuff links **78, 80, 565**
currency, ground up 464
Currier & Ives prints 485
cylinder recordings **203-4, 208**
cymbals 201
D
daggers **444-459**
Daguerreotypes 527
dairy items 428, 429

dairy, Isaly's items 424
Daisy BB guns 114
Dan Patch ephemera 243
dance, religious 309
date nails 366
DAV keychains 340, 346-348
Davis, Bette 172
Davis, Jefferson 290
Dean, James 172, 173
death paintings 492
Death Valley 543
Debs, Eugene 290
decals 22, 321
decanters 90, 258
decoys **249, 490**
Deere, John, anything **427**
Delorean, man & car 341
dental items 370, 371, 389
depression glass **67**
Detroit tobacco co. items 275
Devil's Island ephemera 455
DeVilbis items 91
Dewey, Tom, ephemera 294
diamonds 77
diaries 367, 505, 506, 514
Dick Tracy collectibles **149**
Dietrich, Marlene 172
dime novels 576
Dinky Toys 126
dinnerware, pottery 56
Dionne quints mblia 375
dishes **42-52**
    children's 51, 58, 59
    wooden by Nutting 489
Disney **132-139, 148, 165**
Disneyland **187**
display cases 389, 398
diving equipment 235, 356, 452
Dixie ice cream ephemera 425
dog 334-35
    carts 426
    collars 335
    collectibles 334-335
    fighting 235
    food packages 406
    licenses 335
    show medals 334
doilies 74

dolls 95-105, 110, 305, 490
  Barbie 96, 97, 100, 101, 138
  buggies, clothes, dishes 96, 97
  furniture 97, 103, 105
  houses 98, 103, 104, 105, 135
  How to Sell Dolls 95
  Indian 297
  nodding head 159, 160
  Schoenhut 110
  stoves 409
dolphins, images of 336
door handles and bells 399
doorknobs 37, 399
Doyle, Sir Arthur Conan 329
Dr. Pepper items 418-420
drafting instruments 398
dragsters & dragging 242, 339
draperies 70
drawings, architect's 398, 399
Drayton, Grace, art by 507
dresser sets 92, 565
drug store items 370, 376, 403
  Walgreens 415
drums & cymbals 201, 203, 222
duck calls 249
duck hunting stamps 476
Durante, Jimmy, items 184

E

ear trumpets 370, 371
earthenware 55-63
Easter collectibles 313, 316
Edison, Thos., items 204
egg beaters 31
egg cartons 428
egg cups 40
eggs, Russian 316
electric chairs 381
electric devices pre 1920 123
electric motors 123, 190
  toy motors 123, 124
  test equipment 401
electric trains 121, 122, 190
Elegant Heirs figures 155
elephant tusks 303, 494
Elks Club ephemera 288
Ellis Island memorabilia 285
Elsie the Cow 403, 413, 429
Elvis Presley 132, 138, 223-24

embalming kits 302
embossers 390
embroidery 8, 74, 453, 492
Emmett Kelly items 186
employee badges 386
encyclopedias 561, 571, 572
engine rebuilding equipment 345
Erector sets 111
Erphila figures and pots 502
Eskimo art 490, 491, 492
ESP 569
Esquire man figure 403
estates, entire 3
Eureka Springs, AR 538
evangelists 309-310
exercise equipment 324
execution devices 302, 381
Express Co. 364, 390
eye cups 374
eyeglasses & cases 371-374
eyes, glass 374

F

fabric 74
fabric sample books 493
faith healing 309
fans 26, 190, 401
  coin-operated 215
  hand 27, 405
farm equipment 426-427
farm toys (see toy tractor) 114
Farrah Fawcett items 153
fashion prints 487
fast food items 403, 422-424
  glasses 158
Fawcett, Farrah, items 153
FDR ephemera 294
feed sacks 75
Felix the Cat 148, 333
fences and gates, iron 398
Ferris wheel items 187
Fiestaware 45
figures related to tobacco 408
figurines 68, 497-503
  A few Trash or Treasure buyers want to buy figurines that depict what they collect. If you have a figurine, use this index to look up the subject of the figure (dog, horse,

clown, angel, etc.). Only a few of the most common types of figurines are listed below. Read pages 497-503.

figurines (con't)
John Rogers 498
Royal Doulton 498, 330
chess players 118
Bossons 503
Disney 132-139, 188
Hear no Evil 323
hula girls 547
Hummel 500
made in Italy 63
mermaids & mermen 323
Morton Studio 334
newsboys 289
nude 268, 252, 497, 498
Osborne Ivorex plaques 501
Pogo 150
psychoceramics 324
film, all 16mm 177
fingerprinting equipment 380
fire fighting items 368-369
alarms & extinguishers 369
fire insurance mblia 369, 417
firemarks 37, 417
fireplaces 398
Firestone tire ephemera 344
fireworks memorabilia 316-17
fiscal paper 466-468, 516
fish tanks and ephemera 336
fishing 246-49
inexpensive leftovers 231
licenses 477
Flaccus, items made by 377
flags 296
embroidered 453
military 444, 448
Nazi 406, 447, 456
flashlights 25
flea circus memorabilia 302
Flintstones 136
flip books 164
Florida ephemera 410, 538
flour sacks 75
flower frogs 59
fly traps 250
Flynn, Errol 172

fobs, watch 25
folk art 490-495
furniture 6
Christmas decorations 314
trench art by soldiers 450
Follies Bergere items 185
food advertising 402-406, 409-416, 422-423
pet food packages of 406
football cards 228
football ephemera 228-231, 236
Ford, Henry, ephemera 342
Ford cars & planes 342, 359
foreign service documents 508
fossils 302, 432
Fostoria glass 67
fountain pens 28, 29
Fourth of July items 316, 317
fox hunting 249
fraktur 491
frames, picture 17
Franciscan china 45
Franklin Mint items 470
Fraser-Art 503
fraternal order ephemera 288
French Foreign Legion 455
frogs, images of 331
fruit jars 34, 378, 379
fruit raising 433
frying pans 36
funeral ephemera 302, 303
furniture 2-6
Frank Lloyd Wright 5, 327
Wallace Nutting 489
from businesses 389
how to sell furniture 2
Oriental 496
Shaker 3, 311
unusual 6

G
G.A.R. ephemera 446, 470
G.I. Joe 132, 135-136, 140-41
gambling 254-257, 402
horse racing 243
games, all 116-120
Games based on radio, TV, or movies will often find buyers in the Pop Culture section 132-154.

games (con't)
    board   **116-119, 490, 570**
    card   254-255, 257
    fire related   128
    involving maps   510
    monster   136, 143
    occult or mystic   569
    w/sports theme   129, 228, 232
garden statuary   **398**
gargoyles   398, 490
garters   72
Garwood boats   357
gasoline co. items   339, 434-35
gasoline engines & ephem 426-7
gates, wrought iron   398
Gattling guns   438, 452
Gene Autry   151, 172
genealogy books   569
generators   401
Georgia ephemera   538
German military 448, 451, 455-6
giants, ephemera about   302
Gilmore Field ephemera   230
girdles   72
Girl Scout items   **306, 307, 325**
glass   **54, 64-69**
    art glass   69
    candy containers   313, 314
    depression   67
    how to sell glass   **54**
    knives   34
    milky blue or green   34
    paperweights   69
    pre 1500   461
    stained glass windows   **398**
glass eyes   374
glass maker's ephemera   379
glasses, characters   **158,** 266
    beer   158, 262-264
    etched   402
    horse racing   158, 243, 266
    ice cream   425
glassware, fine crystal   **44, 45**
gliders, military   447
globes of world   393, 510, 512
glove boxes   18, 80
Goebel figurines   **500**
gold coins   461-463

gold jewelry   77-78, 80
gold quartz, items made of   18
gold records   222
gold scrap   80
goldfish items   336
golf   **231, 238, 239, 553**
golliwogs   305, 323
Gompers, Samuel   327
Gone With the Wind   **176**
Grammy awards   222
Grateful Dead   225
Great Lakes ephemera   540
Great Smoky Mountains   538
Greek coins and relics   461
Greeley, Horace   327
Green Hornet   147
Greenland ephemera   549
greeting cards   **314**
grenades, hand   442
Grenfell mats/rugs   7
Greyhound bus ephemera   349
guitars   **197-199, 203, 222**
guitar amps & effects   203
gum cards   **160**
gum, chewing, items   411
gumball machines   219
gun seller's permits   477
guns   **437-442, 444**
    advertising for   408, 411
    airplane cannon   358
    alarm type   248
    BB   114-115
    Civil War   445
    Colt   299, 301
    flintlocks & muskets   444
    Gattling guns   438, 452
    How to Sell Guns   **437**
    machine guns   452
    military   444
    old West   299, 441
    shotguns   439, 442
    toy   114-115, 142
    USPO marked   367
    Winchester   299
gunsmiths' shops   389
gyro-copters   361
H
hair brushes, silver   92

hair jewelry & wreaths 78
half tracks 452
Hall, Samuel, anything 367
Hallmark ornaments 315
Halloween 313-316, 143
hand grenades 442
handbags 70
handcuffs 380-382
hands, palmistry 325
hands, wooden 325
Happy Meal items 422-423
Harlem Globetrotters 234
Harley-Davidson items 350, 351
Harlow, Jean 172
harmonicas 202
Harper's Weekly 558
harps 201
Hartland plastic figures 159
hat pins 565
hats 70, 72
    cowboy 300, 301
    riding, velveteen 231
Haviland china 36, 45, 46
Hawaiian items 547
Hawaiian shirts 71, 72
Hear No Evil figures 323
Hearn, Lafcadio, anything 327
hearse ephemera 349
heaters 20
Hebrew books 566
helicopter ephemera 361, 362
helmets (see military)
Herman, Pee Wee 154
hi-fi equipment 192, 193
high school yearbooks 326
highway souvenirs 534
hippie buttons 285-286, 292
Hires Root Beer ephemera 420
hitching post figures 426, 490
Hitler ephemera 327, 455
hobo nickels 471
hockey 229, 233
    home games 129
Holmes, Sherlock 329
Holocaust souvenirs 310
home movies 177
homeopathic medicine 371
hood ornaments 343

Hopalong Cassidy 132, 134-35, 145, 172
Hope, Bob 175
horns, hunting 249
horns, animal 303
    items made from 6, 301
horse bits & bridles 426
horse racing ephemera 243
horse, riding clothes 231, 249
horseshoeing 332, 234
hot rods 242,
    magazines 553
    speed equipment 339
Hot Wheels cars 128, 133
hotels, items from 389
Houdini 182, 183
Houston, Sam 301
How to Handle an Estate 251
Howdy Doody 96, 138, 151, 154
howitzers 452
Hubbard, Elbert 5
Hudson's Bay Company 549
hula girl figures 547
humidors 275
Hummel figurines 68, 500
    look-alikes 500
Humphrey, Maud, art by 507
hunting 248, 249
    licenses 477
hymnals 308-309, 311

I

I Dream of Jeannie 153
I Love Lucy 154
I.W.W. items 287
ice chests, soda pop 419
ice companies 427
ice cream ephemera 425
ice cream sticks, items from 490
ID badges 386
Idaho ephemera 544
Illinois items 295, 541
immigration material 285
incunabula (hand writ bks) 562
Indian items 297-99, 444, 492
    tomahawks 444
    jewelry 19, 444
    peace medals 470
    prints of American 487

Indian War items   446
Indians, cigar store   274, 275
Indy 500 ephemera   242
inkwells   29
insane asylum items   389
insects, mounted   302
instruments
    dental   370, 374
    medical   370, 371, 392
    navigation   354
    scientific   371, 392, 393
insulators   394, 395
insurance everything   368, 417
Iowa ephemera   540
irons   21
Isaly's dairy & deli items   424
Israeli items   310
Italian military   456
Iver Johnson gun co.   442
ivory carvings   491, 494, 496
                J
jackets
    car club   242
    military flight   72, 358, 451
    military tour   72
jacks, automobile   344
Jackson, Michael, items   223
jail items   382
James Bond   138, 146
Jamestown Expo   180
Japanese militaria   451, 456-457
jars, candy   411
jars, powder   19
jazz literature and misc   213
jeeps   444
Jehovah's Witness   312
Jersey Lily   328
jet-pack   361
Jewel Tea items   50
jeweler's shops   389
jewelry   76-81, 564-565
    ancient   461
    Arts & Crafts   17
    How to Sell Jewelry   76
    jewelry boxes   81
    Indian   297, 298
    Indian style   19
    Oriental   496

Jewish items   310, 311, 566
jigsaw puzzles   116, 117, 119
Jimmie Allen radio show   151
John Deere anything   427
Johnny Appleseed   327
Jolson, Al   184
Juarez, Benito   301
Judaica   310, 571
jugs   260, 498
juicers, advertising   433
jukeboxes   215, 217, 218
junk food characters   412
                K
Kachinas   297
kaleidoscopes   107
Keen Kutter items   409
Kelly, Walt, collectibles   150
Kentucky Derby   243
Kentucky Fried Chicken   424
kewpie, bisque   499
key chains   324
keyboards, musical   203
keys   85
    magician's   382
    railroad   366
kinetoscopes   215, 216
Kiss rock band   138, 223, 225
kitchen tools, juicers   433
kites   110
Klondike bar   424
Knights of Labor   287
knives, all type   86, 87, 325
    belt   444
    glass   35
    hunting   86, 87
    military 86, 445, 454-6, 458-9
    special purpose   23
Kodak ephemera   532
Koran   310
Krazy Kat & Ignatz   148
Kreiss figurines   155
Ku Klux Klan   305
                L
labels
    cigar   274
    firecracker   316, 317
    food   336, 410
    misc   487, 507

labor memorabilia   287, 320
lace   **70, 74**
lacrosse ephemera   231
lamps & parts   2, 8-12, 64, 398
    Art Deco   9, 10, 17, 64
    Arts & Crafts   3, 5, 9, 11
    carriage   426
    How to Sell Lamps   2
    Italian   63
    miner's   430
    oil   9, 10, 11
    revolving   12
    Roycroft   4, 5
    shades   8
    Tiffany   9, 10, 64
Langtry, Lillie, memorabilia   328
lanterns, railroad   364-366
Lapland items   550
Larkin Company items   415
Las Vegas everything   543
Laurel & Hardy items   174
law enforcement mblia   381
lawn sprinklers   37, 407
League Amer Wheelmen   352-3
Leary, Timothy   286
leather clothes
    flight jackets   72, 358, 451
    motorcycle jackets   350
leech jars   370, 371
legal documents   380
letters
    business   385
    obscene   508
    from prisoners   382
Levi's and similar denim   71, 72
Liberty   296
license plates   340, 346-349
license plates, DAV   346- 348
licenses, all types   477
    bicycle   354
    dog   335, 471, 541
    fishing & hunting   247, 248
    ships & boats   356
light bulbs   19
    Christmas   313, 315
lighters   23, 268-70, 276, 277
    airline   360
    cigar   274

lighthouses   354, 356
lighting fixtures   398, 399
limited edition plates   503
Lincoln, Abe   290, 291, 524-27, 484, 487
Lindberg, Charles   358
Lion's Club   288
lipsticks   94
lithography, commercial   407
Little Lulu, dolls   96
Little Orphan Annie   135, 151
Little Red Riding Hood items   156
lizards, images of   331
Lladro figures   501
lock boxes w/trick locks   390
lock picks   381
lockets   80
locks, all types   85, 119, 381
    door, ornate   399
    post office   367
locksmith ephemera   389
London, Jack, ephemera   328
Lone Ranger   132, 134-35, 145, 151
lottery tickets   256
Louis Vuitton luggage   29
love tokens   471
luggage, wicker   5
lunch boxes   132, 152, 157

M

M&Mj items   414
M.I.A. bracelets   453
MacArthur, Gen. Douglas   449
macerated money   462, 463
machine guns   452
machines   168
Mad magazine items   149, 150
Madame Alexander dolls   104
Mafia memorabilia   289
magazines   551-556

    One in every five people in Trash or Treasure wants to buy specialty magazines devoted to his or her hobby. If you have a specialty magazine, use this index to look up the subject (tobacco, auto racing, music, hi-fi, etc.). Only a few of the wanted magazines are listed below.

magazines (con't)
3-D	319
auto	242, 340, 341, 553
aviation	358, 362
crime	259, 289, 382, 555
farm	426, 433, 552
game playing	116
girlie	282, 283, 552
how to sell magazines	551
military	449
model building	121-22, 125
monster	142, 143
motorcycle	351, 552
movie	135, 171-172, 176, 206, 552
music	135, 206, 213-214, 309, 554
National Geographic	555
pulp	135, 552, 555, 556
Sci-Fi	556
TV Guide	554
volume 1, #1	552

magic lanterns, slides	169
magic show items	**182, 183, 381**
magician's keys	382
magic, black	302
mail boxes	399
majolica	**60, 62, 63**
mandolins	**197-199, 203**
mannequins	325
mantles, fireplace	398
map drawing tools	354
maps	**505, 510-513, 535-550**

Maps are popular with folks who collect a particular geographic region, but bus maps, sailing maps etc., also interest collectors. If you have a specialty map, use this index to look up the subject.

maps (con't)
signed by famous	516
trail	301
U.S. wall map	512
marbles	**120**
Mardi Gras	188
Marilyn Monroe	**138, 172, 175**
marine antiques	354-357
Marine Corps ephemera	450

Mary Marvel	146

masks
African	495
comic character	148
Halloween	143
Indian	297, 298
monster masks	136
Masonic items	288
Massachusetts souvenirs	535
massage devices	322
match boxes	280
box dispensers	281
match holders	37
match safes	281
Matchbox cars	**125, 126**
matchcovers	**280**
matches, items made from	490
material bolts & scraps	75
mats, Grenfell	7
Max, Peter	19
McDonald's items	**423**
McHenry, James, letters	516
medals, all	**470-473**

Medals are popular collectibles and some dealers will buy all kinds. Collectors buy medals associated with fields they collect, such as sports, Blacks, religion, and the like.If you have a medal, use the index to look up the subject of the medal to find other possible buyers

medals (con't)
awarded to Blacks	447
Indian War	446
military	444-459, 471-472
Olympic	234, 237
political	290-295
school attendance	473
shooting	443
medical items	**370-377**
quackery	190, 370-373, 401
instruments	370, 392
medicine show memorabilia	302
medicines, veterinary	375
medieval documents	515
meerschaum pipes	277
megalethescopes	107

menus
    Chicago hotels   425
    Southern Calif   541
Mercedes auto ephemera   343
mercenaries   455
Merchant Marines   302
mermaids and merman   323
meteorites   431
meters, electric   401
Mexican
    jewelry & silver   80
    tokens & smalls   549
    weavings   493
Mexican War items   445
Michigan ephemera   540
microphones   **192, 392**
microscopes   **371, 392, 393**
    toy   393
midgets ephemera   302
military   **444-459**
    Any good condition military item can be sold to people on pp 437-459. Buyers listed below may not be military specialists but BUT seek a few of the same things.
military (con't)
    airplane recognition model 362
    ancient   444
    Civil War   444-448, 516, 538
    German   448, 455, 456
    Japanese   456
    M.I.A.   453
    Russian   550
    shell casings   442
    uniform buttons   73
    US in Brazil   549
    vehicles   452
    Western forts   543
    Women's   449
milk company items   428-429
    milk bottles, colored   **379**
    milk bottle caps   429
milk glass vases   65
milk shakers   425
Miller, Glenn   **221**
mimeograph memorabilia   390
mineral specimens   **431**
mines, explosive   442

miniature anything   289
mining   287, 389, 430-1, 542-3
Minnesota ephemera   541
minstrel show items   184, 186
mirrors   19, 92, 471
missiles   366, 442
    models of   361, 362
Mission oak   **4**
missionaries, letters from   310
Missouri health buttons   320
Mix, Tom   132, 134, 135, 145
Mobil oil company   434
mobile homes   345
model kits   **125, 133, 143, 152, 242, 350, 354**
models
    aircraft identification   451
    airplane manufact'r   360, 361
    auto dealers   340
    ship   355
    space shot   366
    travel agent   361, 362
money   **460-465, 467,** 471
    fake, with advertising   404
    items made from   462, 464
    misprinted   464
    stage or prop   471
    wooden   **473**
money clips   80
Monkees   223, 225
monkey organs   203
Monroe, Marilyn   132, 138, 172, 175
monster toys   125, 133, 143
Montana ephemera   541, 544
mood rings   78
Moon Beings figurines   155
Mormonism   **310**
mortars & pestles   371
Morton Studio figurines   334
Moto Guzzi ephemera   350
motorcycle gang items   351
motorcycles & parts   350, 351
motors, open frame   401
Mounties memorabilia   380
mourning pictures   492
mouse traps   **249**
movies   **167-177,** 318
    animation   132, 137, 148, 165

coming attraction slides   168
costume/ props 173, 318, 326
How to Sell Movie Items 167
magazines   170, 172, 176,
    206, 552
posters   132, 135, 138, 142
theater sound equipment 193
16mm & 8mm   177
Farina from Our Gang   305
military training films   449
sex   282
Sherlock Holmes   329
Tarzan   147, 329
Westerns 132, 134, 135, 138,
    145, 162, 300
Moxie memorabilia   420
Mr. Peanut   413
mugs, beer   262, 265, 266
    wooden   535
mummies   302
music   196-225
How to Sell Music items 196
religious   309
musical instruments   196-203
    automatic   203
    African   495
    other cultures   197, 201
    used by rock stars   222
musk oxen ephemera   331
Mussolini ephemera   327
mustard sets   39

N

N.R.A.   443
nails, date   366
napkin rings   39
NASA items   366
Nation, Carrie   326
National Geographic   555
navigation tools   393
Navy, U.S., m'bilia   450
Nazi ephemera   455, 456
neckties   73
needlepoint   492
Negro collectibles   304, 305
neon signs   190, 401, 404-405
Ness, Elliott, ephemera   327
netsuke   496
Nevada memorabilia   543

New Guinea maps & prints 566
New Jersey souvenirs   536
New York World's Fair   181
newspapers, all   557-559
    hippie   286
How to Sell Newspapers 557
    NY Tribune   327
    prison   382
    Racing Form   243
    Sunday comics   165
newsreels   176
Newton Arms ephemera   441
nickelodeons   215
Night Before Xmas   171
Nike shoes   71
Nippon china   48
Nixon, Richard   286, 294
nodder dolls   159, 160
Noritake china   48
    figurines   499
North Dakota ephemera   541
Northwest Mounted Police 380
Norton, Emperor   545
not what they seem   318
Notre Dame sports   236
nude figurines   497, 498
nudist magazines   552
Nurnberg Trials   449
nuns, items related to   310
nursing items   371
Nutting, Wallace, art by   489

O

O'Niell, Rose, items by   499, 507
Oakley, Annie   186
obscene letters   508
occupied Germany   321
Odd Fellows items   288
office equipment   387-391
Ohio ephemera   540
oil company items   339, 351,
    434-435, 513
Old Ironsides   322
Olympics   234, 237-8, 320
opera glasses   27
opera programs   220
opthalmology & equipment   27
optician's signs   371
ore carts   430

Oregon items 544
Oriental items 484, 488, 491, **495-96, 550**
  letters from the Orient 476
Osborne Ivorex plaques 501
outboard motors 357
  toy 123, 124
owl decoys 249
oyster plates 51
oyster related items 336
Oz books 577

P

padlocks 85, 364, 366
paintings **479-485**

Paintings are bought because of who painted them or because of what they depict. In addition to the painting section (pp 479-485), other buyers will be found throughout the book who may buy paintings related to what they collect.

Palestine items 310
palmistry 312, 325
Pan Pacific Auditorium 230
Panama Canal ephemera 548
pantaloons 74
paper dolls 136, **508-509**
paper ephemera **383-386, 504-529,** 563

You'll find buyers of paper items throughout Trash or Treasure. Use the index to look up the subject of the paper to find a buyer.

How to Sell Paper **383, 504**
  toys 116, 136, 508-09
  medieval 515
paper fastening tools 388
paper plates, party stuff **513**
paperback books 576
  sexy stories 282
paperweights, art glass **69**
  cast iron 37, 407
  phone co 416
parasols 70
paratrooper items 444, 447
Parrish, Maxfield, art by 479-481
party paper 513
passports 285, 508

patent medicine 370-379, 402
  veterinary 375
patriotic ephemera 293
patterns, quilting 75
peace movement **285-86, 320**
peanut vending machines 219
peanuts ephemera 149
peanuts, Planters 413
pedal cars **126, 127, 130, 142**
Pee Wee Herman items 154
Pen Delfin rabbit figurines 502
pencil sharpeners 29
pencils 23
Pennsylvania Turnpike 534
penny arcade games 215, 217-19
pens, fountain **23, 28, 29**
Pentecostal church items 309
Pep Boys figures 403
Pepsi Cola items **419-422**
perfume bottles **90, 91**
Perry, Com'dore Matthew 327
pet food packages 406
Peter Max 19
PEZ dispensers 144
Philip Morris' Johnny 403
Philippine Islands 549, 566
phonograph records **208-214, 220-225**
  picture **208-210**
  TV related 152
phonographs **203-205**
  needle sharpeners 205
photographs **236, 505, 520, 521, 523-529, 533**

Pages 524-529 give you many photo buyers and dealers, but one quarter of all the people in Trash or Treasure also expressed interest in buying photographs of what they collect being made, sold, used or otherwise portrayed. Use this index to look up the subject matter of the photo, or where it was taken.

photographs (con't)
  albums 18
  autographed 173, 326, 514- 517, 524
  by listed artists 484

erotic 282, 284
How to Sell Photos **523**
in memorial mats 529
jewelry made from 81
phrenology 371, 373
piano, ephemera 220
piano, rolls 203
pianos, portable 203
pianos, rock star's 222
pickle castors 39
picture frames 17
pill rollers 376
pilot's handbooks 362
pin back buttons (see buttons)
pin-ups 282, 283
pinball games 216, 218
pins, Olympic 237
pipes, smoking **276-278**
Indian 297, 298, 490
meerschaum 276, 277
pipe racks 278
Pismo Beach photos 545
Pitcairn Island ephemera 549
pitchers, Art Deco 33
planetarium models 371, 392
planimeters 389
Planters Peanuts **402, 413**
plastic model kits 125, 143, 155
plates (see also china)
Christmas collector's 315
college 52
limited edition 503
oyster 50
redware 61
souvenir 483-497, 534, 544
tin 406
play suits 133
Playboy items 283
playing cards 254-255, 257, 360
Playmate ephemera 283
playsets 139
pocket knives 86, 87
pocket mirrors 471
poetry, amateur 506
Pogo & pals 150
poison bottles 377
poker chips **254-55, 257, 494**

police items 380-382, 389
political memorabilia **109, 286, 290-296,** 543
polo ephemera 332
pool tables, cues **245**
popcorn memorabilia 410
pop culture 131-166, throughout
How to Sell Pop Culture 131
porcelain figurines 497, 498
post office memorabilia 367
postcards, all **518-521**
Pages 520-521 give you many fine postcard buyers and dealers, but 20% of all the people in Trash or Treasure also expressed interest in buying postcards which depict what they collect being made, sold, used or otherwise portrayed. Use this index to look up the subject matter of the photo, or where the photo was taken.
How to Sell Postcards518-19
poster stamps 507
posters **181, 402, 522**
Posters sell because of what is advertised or pictured on them. Major poster dealers are in bold, but collectors and dealers throughout this book want posters. Use this index to look up the subject of the poster (e.g.: circus, boxing, rock and roll, etc.).
hippie 285, 286, 522
rock & roll 134, 222-225, 522
wanted criminals 301-02, 380
pottery **4, 5, 49, 52, 53-63**
19th century 490
how to sell pottery 53
Indian 297, 298, 490
pre 1500 461, 494, 495
powder jars 19
prayer books 309
pre-Columbian art 494, 495
Precious Moments figures 500
prescription files 376
Presley, Elvis 122, 132, 138, 224
printers' ephemera 407
printing presses 397

prints   480-484, 486-488
    Prints are purchased because of who created them or because of what they depict. In addition to the paintings and prints section (pp 479-489), other buyers will be found throughout the book who want prints depicting what they collect.
    How to Sell Prints   478
prison items   380, 382, 389
prisoner of war straw figures   491
prisoners, famous   382
programs, sports   228- 244
    classical music concerts   220
projectors, movie   168-169
    3-D   319
    magic lanterns   168-169
prom dresses   70
propellers   358
Protestant ephemera   308-312
Prudential insurance   417
psalters   309
psychic phenomenon   312
pulp magazines   555, 556
pulpits   398
punchboards   256
purses   70-71, 93-94
puzzles   116, 117, 119
    puzzle bottles   321
    rebus & pen and paper   507
pyramids   312
                Q
quack devices 190, 370-373, 401
quill cutters   28
quilting tools   74
quilts   74, 490, 493
    from cigarette silks   271
                R
race cars   , 339
racing, auto   242, 340
racing, horse   243
radical groups   285, 286, 287
radio(s)   189-194
    coin-operated   215
    how to sell radios   189
    manuals   192
    radio-phonographs   205, 218
    transistor   194

radio premiums 132, 134-37, 151
Raggedy Ann   99
Railroad Brotherhood Union   287
railroad items   364-365
    passes   467
    Canadian   548
    Colorado   542
    Eureka Springs   537
rain boots, rubber   73
ration tokens/coupons   453, 477
rattles, baby   111
ray guns   142
razors   88, 89
reamers, green   34
rebus puzzles   507
recognition models   362
recorders, wire, etc.   388
records, phonograph   208-214
    beat generation   285
    cylinder   203, 204
    harmonica music, old   202
    promo rock   223
    Sinatra   221
Red Cross nurses   371
Red Riding Hood dolls   96
Reddy Kilowatt   403, 413
redware pottery   61
refractometers   259
religious items   309-311
    books about   565, 572
    Russian   550
report cards   367
reptiles, images of   331
revival meetings   310
Revolutionary war   506
rewards of merit   367
rhinestone jewelry   78
ribbon pictures   493
ribbon, sewing   74
ribbons, award, all types   320
rides, coin-op animals   216
rifles   438-444
rings
    jewelry   77-81
    premium   132-136, 151
    sports   236
    toy   151
road maps   513

robes, chenille 75
robot toy 132, 134, 136-39, 142-3
rock and roll 221-225
    autographs 514, 517
rock collections **431**
rockets & rocketry 361, 366
Rockne, Knute 236
Rockwell, Norman, art 479-480
Rogers, Ginger, items 174
Rogers, John, statuary by 498
roller coaster items 187
Rolling Stones items 223
Rolls Royce ephemera 343
Roman relics 461
Ronson figures **497**
Rookwood **55, 56, 57**
Roosevelt (TR) photos of 527
root beer 266, 420
Roseville pottery **51, 55, 58, 59**
Roy Rogers restaurants 423
Royal Beyreuth, Devil&Cards 254
Royal Doulton **45-47, 52**
    animals 330
    whiskey bottles 259
Royal Worcester 46
royalty
    autographs 517
    British & European items 288
    Russian items 550
Roycroft 3-5, 571
RS Prussia 66
rugby memorabilia 232
rugs **2, 7, 8**
    animal skin 303
    chenille 75
    folk weavings 492
    hooked 8, 490, 492
    Indian 8, 297, 298, 490
    Mexican 494
    Oriental 7
Runaways, The, items 224
Russian antiques **316, 550**
    S
7-Up memorabilia 419
sacks, feed and flour 75, 321
saddle blankets 492
saddles **231, 249, 299, 300**
safes 390

saints, relics of 308
salesmen's samples 406
saloon memorabilia 259
saloons, entire contents 389
salt and pepper shakers **33-35, 40,144, 159, 360**
salt cellars 40
samovars 32
samplers 490, 492
Samurai items 457
San Diego 545
San Francisco 545
San Gabriel Valley 545
San Quentin 382
Santa Claus **137, 313-314, 499**
saxophones 200, 202
scales, all types **85**
    assay office 390
    coin 464, 465
    egg 428
    toy 85, 111
Schoenhut toys & dolls 110
school books & items **367, 577**
science fiction books 575
scissors 94
Scottish highlander relics 461
Scouting items **306, 307, 325**
scrapbooks **507**
scrimshaw 354, 355, 494
scrip 367, 382
scuba gear 235, 356
sculpture **491, 497-499**
sea rescue service 356
seal, sealing wax 322
Sears catalogs 385
Sebastian miniatures 503
self defense courses 234
serapes 494
sermons and sermon notes 309
Seven-Up 418-422
sewing machines **21, 23**
sewing tools 94
sextants 393
sexy stuff 282, 283
Shaker ephemera **311**
shark's teeth fossils 432
shaving mugs 88, 436
shaving, razors **88, 89**

shawls 8, 70
Shawnee pottery 58
sheet music 206, 207, 209, 214
    Black dancers 305
    comic character 133
    religious 309
shell casings 442
shells, carved 319
Sherlock Holmes 329
ships and boats 354-357
    military & maritime 449-50
    Old Ironsides 322
Shoenhut toys 105, 110
shoes 70
shooting competition 443
shooting gallery targets 37, 407
shot glasses 260, 266
shotguns 439, 442
shrunken heads 302
side show banners 490
signs 272-281, 340-376, 394, 402-423, 434-435

Most collectors want signs and other advertising picturing products they collect. Advertising dealers are featured on the pages set in bold, but buyers of signs are almost everywhere in this book. Use this index to look up both the type of product advertised on your sign, and/or what is pictured on it.

signs (con't)
    3-D outside 403
    animated 404
    hand made 490
    neon 401, 404, 405
silver
    tableware 38-40
    Mexican 80
    souvenir spoons 41
    wine labels 258
silverplate 38, 39, 40
silverware 38-39, 41, 44, 50, 80
Simmons Hardware Co. 409
Sinatra memorabilia 221
Sing Sing Prison 382
skeletons 303
skins, animals 303

skis, wooden 231
Skookum dolls 105
skulls 302, 331
slavery 286, 304, 470, 538
sleds, Flexible Flyer 235
slide projectors 169
slide rules 389, 392, 398
slides, magic lantern 169
slot machines 215-218, 256-57
smile faces 320
Smith, Oberlin, items 433
Smokey Bear 155
smoking stands 275
Smoky Mountains mblia 538
Smurf items 154
snake handling boxes 309
snake skulls 331
snakes, images of 331
Snoopy items 149
snow babies 97, 231, 499
snow shoes 231
snowmobile everything 322
snuff boxes 279
soccer memorabilia 232
Socialists in US pre-1940 287
soda fountain items 425
soft drinks 404, 418-422
solar system models 512
soldiers of fortune 455
soldiers, toy 114, 450
song books 207
Sousa, John Philip 450
South Dakota ephemera 541
South Pacific ephemera 547
souvenir spoons 41
souvenirs 534-550
    buildings, metal 289
    How to Sell Souvenirs 534
space shot memorabilia 366
space toys 132-34, 136-39, 142
spark plugs 340, 343
speakeasy ephemera 259
speedboats 357
spiritualism 312
spongeware 61
spoons, souvenir 41, 169
sports 226-250
    dolls 159

How to Sell Sports   **226**
  prints of   487
sprigware china   47
spurs   299-301
St. Louis World's Fair   180
stagecoach boxes   390
stained glass windows   **398**
Stalin ephemera   327
stamps, trading stamps   324
stamps, US & foreign   **474-476**
  first flight   360
  poster   507
  revenue   370, 468, 475, 477
  zeppelin   362
staplers   388
Star Wars toys   **132,** 141, **142**
State Farm Insurance   417
statuary   398, 497-499
Statue of Liberty   296
steam engines, toy   122, 123
steer horn furniture   6
steer horns   301
Steinbeck, John   574
steins   **265, 266**
  modern beer mugs   158, 262
stereoviews   **172, 524- 528**
sterling silver   **38, 39, 77**
  accessories & jewelry   19,
    77, 78
stethoscopes   370-372
Steuben glass   **64, 67**
Stickley items   3, 4
stock market tickers   390, 392
stocks and bonds 340, 348, 356
    358, 364-65, 431, 433,
    466-468, 505, 516, 544, 548
stoneware   61, 377
stopwatches   **84**
stoves   20
  toy or salesmen's   409
straight jackets   381
straw figures   491
street lamps   9
string holders, cast iron   37
strippers & burlesque   284
strongmen   244
student movement of 60's   286
stuffed animals   303

suffragettes   293
sugar shakers   65
sunglasses on cards   406
Sunkist products   410
Sunshine Biscuit Co.   414
Super Bowl items   236
Superman   132-136, 146, 151
surfboards   235
surgical tools   371
surveying instruments   393
Swarovski crystal   502
Switzerland, items from   550
swords   438, 444-45, 454,
    456- 459, 461, 496
T
t-shirts, rock concert   221
tack (horse stuff)   300
tanks, Army   444, 452
tapestries   8
tarot cards   312, 569
Tarzan   147, 329
tattoo memorabilia   186, 302
tax stamps   370, 468, 475, 477
taxi memorabilia   348-349
tea caddies   32, 40
teaching ephemera   367
teapots   **33**
Teddy bears   **98**
telegraph instruments   396
telephone books   **394, 537**
telephone company   394
telephones   **394**
telescopes   354, 393
television sets   **191, 195**
Tennessee Centennial Expo 179
tennis memorabilia   **231, 241**
Texas   542-544
textiles   **3, 8, 74-75, 495**
theatrical ephemera   184, 185
thermometers   24 , 405
Thermos bottles   157
thermostats, Victorian   24
thimbles   21, 94
3-D items   319
Three Stooges   174
Tibbs, Casey   300
tickets, sports events   **232**
  (see also: individual sports)

lottery 256
rock concert tickets 222
tie bars 80
Tiffany glass 9-11, 29, 64
timetables 364
tin cans 272-281, 340-376, 394,
402-423, 434-435
  blasting caps 430
  typewriter ribbon 387
  cigars 274
  condom 284, 404
tire company giveaways 344
tire repair kits 344
toast racks 40
toasters 31, 40
tobacco collectibles 272-279
toilets 398
tokens, all 470-473
Tom Mix 132-35, 138, 145, 172
tomahawks 444
tombstones 302
tools, all types 87, 400, 401
  boatwright 389
  bookbinder's 573
  cutting 87
  gunsmiths 389, 441
  ice harvesting 427
  piano tuners 220
  pre 1500 a.d. 461
  quilting 74
  undertakers 389
  veterinary 426
toothpick holders 68
Tootsietoys 105, 126
torture devices 302, 381
toys 106-156, 159-164
  action figures 132-134, 141
  airplanes 126-27, 358-59, 362
  animals on wheels 98, 108
  bell, that ring a 108, 109
  blimps 362
  blocks 109, 116
  boats 109-110, 126, 127, 355
  cast iron 108, 110, 126
  comic character 132-9, 148-51
  electric 124, 129
  Erector sets 111
  farm animals & vehicles 113

gasoline engine 126
guns 115, 133
hand made, old 490
helicopters 361
How to Sell Toys 106
magic sets 182
marble driven 120
model kits 125, 350
monster 143
motorcycle 126, 350
outboard motors 123, 124
paper, made of 116, 509
phonographs 204, 225
play sets of figures 139
play suits 133
robot & space 132, 134-137
rubber 127
scales 85, 111
Schoenhut 110
soldiers 113, 114, 127
steam 122, 123
stoves 409
tractors 114, 127, 128, 427
trains 109, 121-123, 127
vehicle models 125
vehicles 108, 110, 113, 122,
  125-130, 135, , 342, 349
Victorian 108
wind-up & battery 109-110,
  132, 134, 136, 137, 139
zeppelin 362
tractors & ephemera 426, 427
trade cards 384, 386, 402, 507
  banks, toy 112, 113
  ice cream 425
  medical 370, 376
  tobacco 274
trade stimulators 218, 219
trailers and motorcoaches 345
trailer park ephemera 534
trains, toy 121-123
trains, railroad 364-366
tramp art 491
Transformers 142, 143
transistor radios 194
transportation items 339-366
  How to Sell 338

traps, all type 248-250
travel agent plane models 451
trees, cuttings from 433
trench art 450
trick devices 23
trophies
    sports 234, 240-44, 351, 443
    chess 118
    loving cup style 235
tropical fish ephemera 336
tubes, radio & hi-fi 190-192, 401
tubes, x-ray 371
Tucker, Sophie, items 184
Turnbridge ware 32
turtle shells & images 331
Tuskegee Airmen 447
tusks **302, 494**
tuxedos 70
TV sets **191, 195**
TV show collectibles 132-138,
    141-143, 318
TV dinner boxes **405**
Twain, Mark, ephemera 328
twins, triplets, etc. mblia 375
type, printer's 397
typewriter ribbon tins 404, 406
typewriters **387, 388, 392**
U
UFO items 312
ukuleles **197, 198, 203, 547**
umbrellas 70
Uncle Wiggily 156, 577
underwear, rubber 72
Unger Bros. items 19
uniforms
    beer deliverymen 263
    airline 358, 361
    British Army 454
    C.C.C. 367
    Canadian police 380
    Chicago police 382
    Civil War 445
    Coca-Cola delivery 418, 422
    concentration camp 311
    Harlem Globetrotter 233
    McDonalds 423
    Merchant Marine 449
    military 438, 444, 448, 450-51

    Nazi 455
    ocean liners 355
    Olympic 237
    post office 367
    prison 381, 382
    railroad 364, 366
    roller derby 232
    Scouting 306, 307
    sports 228-230, 232
    women's military 449, 452
    zeppelin 362
union items 274, 287, 320, 430
Utah ephemera 544
V
vacuum cleaners 24
valentines 317, 508, 513
vanity cases 94
Vargas, art by 283, 480
vases **55-63**
    cameo glass 66
    Nippon 48, 66
    patriotic 52
    silver overlay 90
vaudeville items 183, 184
vegetable growing 433
vehicles, military 452
vending machines **215-219**
ventriloquism items 184
veterinary items **375, 426**
vibrators, electric 322, 436
Vietnam War 444, 447-448
View Master **319, 533**
Viking relics 461
violins & violas **198, 199, 203**
Volkswagens 342, 345
Von Braun, Wernher 366
voodoo memorabilia 302
Vuitton luggage 29
W
Wacky Packs 138
wagons and wagon parts 426
Walgreens ephemera 415
walking sticks 27
wall plaques 501
Wallace Nutting ephemera 489
wallpaper **22**
wanted posters 301, 380
war crimes trials 449

Warwick china 49
washing machines 20
Washington state items 544, 545
watch chains & fobs 25, 72, 78
watches **81, 83-84**
   How to Sell Watches **82**
   advertising 412
   cartoon character 84, 136
   railroad 83, 364
   that play tunes 83, 203
watchmakers' tools 392
watchmakers, entire shop 389
Watchtower Society 311, 312
watercolor boxes 398
waterpipes 278
Waugh, Ida, art by 507
wax sealers 322
weapons **438-442, 452, 457-59**
   ancient 444, 461
   primitive 445, 495
weathervanes 490
weavings (see textiles)
wedding cake figures 325
wedding invitations 325
wedding announcements 513
Wedgwood **46, 64,334**
weight lifting ephemera 244
Western memorabilia **297-301,**
   542-546
whales, images of 336
whaling industry 354, 355, 547
whips, riding 231, 249
whiskey collectibles **259-261,**
   266, 377, 402, 404
White House ephemera 291
Whizzers 353
whorehouse ephemera 389
wicker furniture & luggage **5**
Wild West shows 186
Willy's auto ephemera 342
windmill items 37, 428, 490
windows, fancy 398
wine accessories 258
   books about wine 568
wine, Langtry farms 328
wire recorders **388**
Wisconsin ephemera 540

Wizard of Oz **136, 176**
women's suffrage 285, 293
wood carvings 21, 490
woodblock prints 487, 488
woodburned boxes 81
woodcuts 486
wooden money 473
wooden ware 21, 32
Woodstock items **286**
woodworking tools 400
World Cup relics 232
World's Fair **178-180, 470**
WPA art 483
wrestling ephemera 244
Wright, Frank Lloyd 5, 327
Wrigley's chewing gum 411
wrought iron 398
Wyoming items 541, 543, 544

Y

yachting 354, 357
yearbooks, high school **326**
Yellow Kid 148
Yoga items 312
youth hostels 425
Yukon memorabilia 546

Z

zebra ephemera 330
zeppelin ephemera 361
Zippo 268-270

SELL-A-GRAM from one of Tony Hyman's readers

TO:

FROM:

Phone: (   )

I have the following item:

Remember to include the (1) shape, (2) colors, (3) dimensions, and (4) all names, dates, and marks.

It's condition is:

List all chips, creases, cracks, dents, scratches, rips, tears, holes, stains, fading, and foxing. Note any missing pages, parts, or paint. Describe any repairs that have been done.

CHECK ONE

☐ The item is for sale for $_____ plus shipping.

☐ The item is for sale. I am an amateur seller and would like you to make an offer.

☐ The item may be for sale if the price is sufficient. Would you like to make an offer?

☐ The item is not for sale, but I am willing to pay a fee to learn its value.

To assist you to evaluate the item, I am enclosing a:

☐ Sample ☐ Photocopy ☐ Photo ☐ Tracing ☐ Sketch ☐ Rubbing ☐ Nothing

This is to certify that, to the best of my knowledge, the item is genuine and as described. Buyer has a 5 day examination period during which the item may be returned for any reason.

Signature: **Date:**

☐ Answer Requested (SASE enclosed).   ☐ No answer needed.

BUYER'S RESPONSE:

These two pages list all changes reported by readers and buyers as of January 2005.

Anderson, Robert: area code now (260)

Baltrusaitis, Tom: Retired. Contact Todd Bridgeman, Main St. Eye Clinic, 3201 Highway 61 North, Hannibal, MO 64301 (573) 248-3937

Baum, Rod: <phil@rarerecords.com>

Billard, Gerry: has died.

Buonaguidi, Debra & **John:** 883 Lighthouse Ave., Monterey, CA 93940 (831) 655-2363 day (831) 375-7345 eve <hawkrise@redshift.com>

Burke, Mike <hardhatdiverman@aol.com>

Chartrand, George: (204) 783-2024 **now buys Garfield**

Clee, Ken: 8 Angus Drive, Stevens, PA 17578 (717) 336-2355 <waxntoys@aol.com>

Council, Michael: area code is (614) not (616)

Cuningham, Steve: 803 Byrne St., Houston, TX 77009 (713) 868-1476 <tcunningham5@houston.rr.com>

Dipboye, Marilyn: has quit collecting.

Dolin, Harvey: died, never recovering from 9-11 wiping out his store

Edmisten, Rick: <tacklechaser@aol.com>

Eisenstadt, Robert: correct zip is 11201

Engelke, Paul: has died.

Fitzpatrick, Reed: (206) 567-0555

Friedman, Barry: 4143 East Alan Lane, Phoenix, AZ 85028 (602) 595-1157 <blanket boy@cox.net>

Gawchick, Bill: <mrpanam@yahoo.com>

Gibbs, Linda: <heirloomkeepsakes2002@yahoo.com>

Hake, Ted: 1966 Greenspring Drive #400, Timonium, MD 21093 (866) 404-9800 toll free <hakes@hakes.com>

Hammelbacher, Frank: Fax no longer on. <www.norrico.com>

Herz, Mike: new phone: (407) 342-2849

Jacobsen, Pat: <pjacobsen@fruitcratelabels.com>

Kaplan, Mike: <coololdbikes@aol.com>

Kidder, Clark: 2805 N. Wuthering Hills Dr., Janesville, WI 53546 (608) 743-0923 <cokidder@charter.net>

Konet, Ken: 4441 McPherson Ave., St. Louis, MO 63108 (314) 486-3085 <konet@mindspring.com>

Ledford, Gordon: is no longer buying clocks.

Mahfuz, Geof: has moved. Wants contact only by email.

Maymudes, August: <amaym@comcast.net>

McGonagle, Hank has sadly died of cancer.

Nauck, Kurt: 22004 Sherrod Ln, same town (281) 288-7826 <www.78rpm.com>

Palm, Phyllis: Elim Park, 150 Cook Hill Rd., Cheshire, CT 06410

Pattison, Lee: moved to 5025 St. Rte 19A, Silver Springs, NY 14550

Reamer, Arnold: a very helpful man, has sadly passed away.

Rehr, Darryl: email has changed   <rehrdc@earthlink.net>

Reincke, Chuck: 391 Arroyo Vista, Fallbrook, CA 92028   (760) 728-8873   <iam3dking@adelphia.net>

Rendell, Kenneth: 46 Eliot St., Natick, MA 01760

Roenigk, Martin: phone misprinted in Price Guide.   (479) 253-0405

Rosenhoover, John: no longer buys books.

Rowe, Edie: <edbdbobd@proaxis.com>

Savitt, Claire: <savitt@bellsouth.net>

Senerchia, Steve: <musicman5@cox.net>

Shannon, Tom: <shannonkissbook@hotmail.com>

Smiley, Bill: <wsmiley@chorus.net>

Speck, David: <dave@davidspeckmd.org>

Speezak, Judy: email is misprinted <speezakquilt@earthlink.net>

Sutton, Mark: <mdsutton2@comcast.net>

Swindall, Fred: has either died or moved with no forwarding address.

Swisher, Doug: Box 11766, Jacksonville, FL, 32239   (904) 744-5493   <doug7777@comcast.net>

Tamaru, Stuart: Box 1650, Sunset Beach, CA 90742   (800) 511-0583

Thalberg, Bruce: has died and his wife

Thalberg, Jan: has quit collecting.

Van Trump, George: Box 1537, Wheat Ridge, CO 80034

Voigt, Gary: area code changed to (952)

Weltman, Sandy: 2 Roxbury Lane, Pittsford, NY 14534 (585) 249-9417

West, Richard: buys pre 1950 magazines ONLY. No more detective fiction.

Wilson, Chris: is no longer responding.

Zecker, Barry: <collexch@hotmail.com>

Zeckley, Mickie: <mickie@larkcamp.com>

The email addresses of other buyers have changed recently and neither they nor readers have notified us. If you are an email user you know how many servers have shut down, merged or otherwise altered service and addresses recently. If your email to a buyer is returned, try telephoning or writing the buyer in question.

If you are able to get a new useable email or snail mail address for any of our buyers, please email us with the new email address so we can report it.

Send changes to Tony Hyman <thyman@charter.net>. Thank you.

Special money-saving bonus
Send Trash or Treasure as a gift

You get a very special offer. To help you share this valuable book with friends, **we have lowered the price**:

You get one for $29.95 postpaid (save $5) and two for $49.90 (save $20). The best deal of all is three for only $69.85. That's like getting one free.

Your friends and relatives will also get the free Price Guide and Sell-A-Grams included with each Trash or Treasure Guide ordered. **Neither of these two valuable bonuses are available in stores.**

Yes, I'd like to order more Trash or Treasure and SAVE with this Coupon. Regularly $34.95

* One for $29.95 postpaid (save $5)
* Two for $49.90 postpaid (save $20)
* Three for $69.85 postpaid (save $35...like getting one free)

California residents add 8.25% sales tax
Offer includes The World's Most Accurate Price Guide
and Sell-A-Grams

Send to_____

_____

_____

Treasure Hunt Offer
Box 3000, Pismo Beach, CA 93448